SHELL-MODEL APPLICATIONS IN NUCLEAR SPECTROSCOPY

SHELL - MODEL APPLICATIONS IN NUCLEAR SPECTROSCOPY

P. J. BRUSSAARD and P. W. M. GLAUDEMANS

Department of Physics, University of Utrecht

1977

NORTH-HOLLAND PUBLISHING COMPANY
AMSTERDAM · NEW YORK · OXFORD

North-Holland ISBN 0 7204 0336 7

Publishers:

NORTH-HOLLAND PUBLISHING COMPANY
AMSTERDAM – NEW YORK – OXFORD

Sole distributors for the USA and Canada:

ELSEVIER/NORTH-HOLLAND, INC.
52 VANDERBILT AVENUE
NEW YORK, N.Y. 10017

Library of Congress Cataloging in Publication Data

Brussaard, P J
Shell-model applications in nuclear spectroscopy.

Bibliography: p.
Includes index.
1. Nuclear spectroscopy. 2. Nuclear shell theory.
I. Glaudemans, P. W. M., joint author. II. Title.
QC454.N8B78 539.7'44 77-7915
ISBN 0-7204-0336-7

PRINTED IN THE NETHERLANDS

PREFACE

The topics discussed in this book have been chosen to enable the reader to interpret experimental data in terms of the nuclear shell model. The treatment is intended to be comprehensive enough to provide experimental nuclear physicists with the techniques of current shell-model calculations and an understanding of how such calculations should actually be carried out. Attention is concentrated upon applications of the many-particle shell model rather than upon its foundations. We feel there is a need for such a treatment. Modern experiments in nuclear-structure physics are characterized by large amounts of data of increasing precision. Concurrently the accessibility of third-generation computers has increased and highly developed coding techniques have become available. This presents us with the opportunity of comparing the experimental data with advanced shell-model calculations in the hope of deepening our theoretical understanding.

The formulas needed to perform a shell-model calculation are derived in detail. The presentation of the formal theory is complemented with illustrations of explicit calculations of observable quantities such as energies, electromagnetic transition rates and moments, beta-decay rates and spectroscopic factors. The results of many of these calculations are compared with recent experimental data.

The level of presentation is that of a first-year graduate-level course in nuclear physics, with only the knowledge of an introductory one-year course in quantum mechanics being assumed. Since the treatment is essentially selfcontained the book is suitable as a textbook for such a course. The material has been arranged so that different subjects can be studied independently. This, and the examples which enable the reader to explicitly confirm his own grasp of the formalism, also make the book suitable as a textbook for selfstudy and as a convenient reference manual for the practising nuclear spectroscopist.

A suitable selection of the material presented in this book can provide the material for a shorter introduction to nuclear shell-model theory which should require approximately 10 to 20 lecture hours. The summaries preceding each chapter will be helpful in making this selection for such a course, and should provide a guide to an individual seeking information on a specific topic.

To make the material more accessible to those interested in a survey of the essentials of the shell-model approach we add the following suggestions, based on our experience in presenting these ideas to a variety of audiences. The general introduction and outline of the basic principles given in chapters 1 to 4 are essential and should be discussed, and understood, in full in all instances (possibly with the exceptions of sections 3.4 and 4.4). The calculations for ^{50}Ti and ^{51}V discussed at the end of chapter 4 serve to illustrate the theory developed in the first four chapters.

Chapter 5 deals with the more technical aspects of shell-model calculations. The methods presented are applicable to nuclei described with a model space in which several particles move in more than one active orbit. This material may be omitted from a condensed presentation of the main ideas of the book, although the methods discussed are quite general and quite useful in calculations on more complex nuclei. Chapter 6 is concerned with the evaluation of the two-body matrix elements of the effective interaction. Most of this chapter needs to be discussed. The Surface Delta Interaction should be treated in some detail, since this schematic interaction has proven to be very successful in correlating data with the shell model and is, moreover, mathematically very simple. The explicit derivation of the two-body matrix elements in section 6.3 may be omitted. The semiclassical interpretation of the effective interaction, discussed in section 6.6, is worth special attention and should certainly be mentioned even in a short course.

Determination of the effective model Hamiltonian from experimental data is discussed in chapter 7. Although the developments in this chapter are simple, the specialized nature of the topic might justify its omission from the syllabus of a short or introductory course.

Single-nucleon transfer spectroscopic factors are treated in chapter 8. Since the correct reproduction of stripping and pick-up data constitutes a basic test of calculated wave functions, most of sections 8.1–8.6 (with the exception of those parts dealing with two active orbits) should be included even in a condensed presentation. The application of the theory to a one-orbit case is illustrated again with ^{51}V in section 8.3. The discussion of two-particle transfer cross sections in sections 8.7 and 8.8 could be omitted if time required.

The operators associated with electromagnetic transitions are discussed in chapter 9. Gamma-decay measurements constitute a large fraction of the experimental data on nuclear states and are correspondingly essential to nuclear-structure theories that deal with these phenomena. Hence, sections 9.4–9.7, which deal with selection rules, transition probabilities, single-particle estimates and the role of the isospin quantum numbers, should be discussed in some detail. Sections 9.1–9.3, which deal with the derivation of the operators, might be omitted from a short presentation.

The calculation and interpretation of electromagnetic transition rates are the topic of chapter 10. We suggest that at least sections 10.1 and 10.2 be treated in a condensed presentation and, if possible, section 10.5, which describes the calculation of electric quadrupole strengths in ^{51}V. Chapter 11 deals with electric and magnetic multipole moments. The first two sections show that the corresponding operators are very similar to those for electromagnetic transitions and are not essential for a condensed presentation. Most of the material presented in sections 11.3 to 11.6, which relates to selection rules, intrinsic and spectroscopic quadrupole moments and single-particle moments, should be covered in some detail, as should the results treated in sections 11.8 and 11.9.

The calculation of log *ft* values in beta decay is treated in chapter 12. Most of the contents of sections 12.1–12.5 should be either discussed or given as a reading assignment. The approximate relations between magnetic dipole strengths and *ft*-values, discussed in section 12.6, may also be mentioned.

Chapters 13–17 are less directly connected to experimental results than are the preceding portions of the book and hence can logically be omitted from a condensed course. In chapters 13–15 the formalisms of first and second quantization are employed in the discussion, and evaluation, of the various methods used for the treatment of many-particle systems. While this material is more abstract than that of the earlier chapters it is not intrinsically difficult to understand. The introductory material given in sections 13.1 and 13.2 should provide a useful, albeit rudimentary, grasp of the widely employed second-quantization formalism. In chapters 16 and 17 the principles underlying the derivation of an effective interaction are discussed and fundamental concepts such as perturbation theory, Feynman diagrams and the G matrix are related to the operational aspects of shell-model calculations. A derivation of the well-known relation between particle-hole and particle-particle two-body matrix elements is presented in chapter 17.

In chapter 18 we have brought together a variety of subjects which are closely connected to the main themes of the book but which did not fit naturally into the logical sequence of development.

Mathematical formulas and their derivations which are frequently referred to in the text are collected in appendix A. Various numerical tables and results which should be useful in testing shell-model computer programs, are included in appendix B.

We should like to thank J.B. French for his inspiring lectures at Utrecht, E.C. Halbert and J.B. McGrory for supplying us with shell-model computer programs, and P.M. Endt for suggesting that we write this book. We are grateful to A.E.L. Dieperink, K. Heyde and B.H. Wildenthal for reading and critizing parts of the manuscript. Many thanks are also due to our colleagues J.E. Koops, F. Meurders, G.A. Timmer, J. Van Hienen and P.C. Zalm for scrutinizing many of the formulas and helping to prepare the numerical tables. Finally we express our appreciation to Miss Hilde Elberse for her skilful preparation of the drawings and to the secretaries for their efficient typing of the manuscript.

CONTENTS

Preface v

Contents viii

1. *Introduction* 1

2. *One- and two-particle systems* 10
   2.1. Angular momentum 10
   2.2. Single-particle states 13
   2.3. Isospin 22
   2.4. Antisymmetric two-particle wave functions 30
   2.5. Applications of the two-particle model 32

3. *Perturbation theory and configuration mixing* 34
   3.1. Perturbation theory 34
   3.2. Binding energies and excitation energies 37
   3.3. Applications 42
   3.4. Protons and neutrons filling different orbits 47
   3.5. States of mixed configuration 52
   3.6. Application of configuration mixing 56
   3.7. Examples 59

4. *Interacting particles in one orbit* 62
   4.1. Notation 62
   4.2. Coefficients of fractional parentage 64
   4.3. The interaction energy for n particles 68
   4.4. Double-parentage coefficients 71
   4.5. Allowed J, T combinations for n particles 73
   4.6. Examples 75

5. *Particles in two active orbits* 79
   5.1. Coupling rules and antisymmetry 79
   5.2. Several particles in two active orbits 85
   5.3. Matrix elements of categories I and II 85
   5.4. Sum rules for diagonal matrix elements 90
   5.5. Applications 91
   5.6. Matrix elements of category III 93
   5.7. Matrix elements of category IV 97

6. *Effective interactions* 100
6.1. Evaluation of two-body matrix elements 100
6.2. Exchange potentials 103
6.3. Matrix elements of the surface delta interaction 106
6.4. The modified surface delta interaction 113
6.5. Applications 118
6.6. Comparison of various two-body matrix elements 120
6.7. Spectra from different interactions 127
6.8. Effects of the configuration space 129

7. *Determination of empirical effective interactions* 132
7.1. Construction of linear equations 133
7.2. The least-squares fitting procedure 136
7.3. The iteration procedure 137
7.4. Selection of experimental data 141
7.5. Phase ambiguities 142

8. *One- and two-nucleon transfer reactions* 144
8.1. Single-particle transfer reactions 144
8.2. Spectroscopic factors for stripping reactions 148
8.3. Examples 155
8.4. Spectroscopic factors for pick-up reactions 157
8.5. Effects of the configuration space 160
8.6. Sum rules for single-particle transfer reactions 162
8.7. Two-particle transfer reactions 168
8.8. Spectroscopic amplitudes 171

9. *Electromagnetic transition operators* 176
9.1. Basic formulas 176
9.2. Electric and magnetic transition operators 179
9.3. Centre-of-mass corrections 184
9.4. Selection rules 187
9.5. Transition probabilities and mixing ratios 188
9.6. Single-particle estimates 191
9.7. Transition operators and isospin 196

10. *Electromagnetic transition rates* 199
10.1. Weisskopf estimates 199
10.2. Isoscalar and isovector contributions 204
10.3. Single-particle matrix elements for $\mathcal{E}\,L$ transitions 213
10.4. Single-particle matrix elements for $\mathcal{M}\,L$ transitions 216
10.5. Transitions within a single-orbit configuration 221
10.6. Particles in two orbits 226

10.7. Configuration mixing 231
10.8. Effective matrix elements from experimental data 233

11. *Electric and magnetic multipole moments* 237
11.1. Electric multipole moments 237
11.2. Magnetic multipole moments 241
11.3. Selection rules 246
11.4. Intrinsic and spectroscopic quadrupole moments 247
11.5. Single-particle electric quadrupole moments 249
11.6. Single-particle magnetic dipole moments 250
11.7. Moments in a multiorbit configuration space 251
11.8. Illustrations 253
11.9. The additivity relation 256

12. *Allowed beta decay* 259
12.1. Beta transition rates 259
12.2. Selection rules 262
12.3. Fermi matrix elements 264
12.4. Gamow-Teller matrix elements 264
12.5. Log *ft* values 266
12.6. Beta decay and the magnetic dipole interaction 268

13. *The second-quantization formalism* 275
13.1. Creation and annihilation operators 275
13.2. Operators in second-quantized form 280
13.3. Angular-momentum coupled states 283
13.4. Particle-hole conjugation 286
13.5. Many-particle state operators 289
13.6. Multishell operators 291

14. *Matrix elements in second quantization* 294
14.1. General reduction formula 294
14.2. Relation between c.f.p. in first and second quantization 299
14.3. The evaluation of single-shell matrix elements 301
14.4. Operators of the nuclear Hamiltonian 305
14.5. The single-particle energy contribution 306
14.6. The residual two-body interaction 308

15. *Further applications of second quantization* 312
15.1. Comparison between first and second quantization 312
15.2. Single-particle operators 318
15.3. Spectroscopic factors 321
15.4. Double-parentage coefficients and spectroscopic amplitudes 324

16. *Realistic and effective operators* 327
16.1. Effective interaction operators 327
16.2. General principles 328
16.3. Diagrammatic representation 333
16.4. Single-particle basis 337
16.5. The *G* matrix 339
16.6. Effective transition operators 346
16.7. Effective charges 348
16.8. Magnetic dipole transitions 352
16.9. Terms of higher order in *G* 355
16.10. Many-particle systems 356

17. *Applications of Wick's theorem* 357
17.1. Wick's theorem 357
17.2. Hartree-Fock equations 360
17.3. Evaluation of Feynman diagrams 362
17.4. Particle-hole configurations 366

18. *Miscellaneous subjects* 371
18.1. The Lanczos method 371
18.2. Some truncation methods 376
18.3. Coulomb energies 381
18.4. Spurious states 384
18.5. The particle-vibrator model 387

Appendix A 399

A.1. *Coupling coefficients* 399
(a) Clebsch-Gordan coefficients and 3-*j* symbols 399
(b) Normalized Racah coefficients and 6-*j* symbols 401
(c) The 9-*j* symbols 404

A.2. *Spherical harmonics and spherical components* 405

A.3. *Reduced matrix elements* 409
(a) The Wigner-Eckart theorem 409
(b) A symmetry property of the reduced matrix elements 413
(c) Elementary reduced matrix elements 414
(d) Reduced matrix elements of tensor products 415
(e) Reduced matrix elements of spherical harmonics 419

A.4. *The Landé formula* 420

A.5. *Some relations for vector operators* 421

A.6. *Antisymmetry of many-particle wave functions* 424

Appendix B 425

B.1. *Numerical values of 3-j and 6-j symbols* 425
B.2. *Quantum numbers of single-shell states* 432
B.3. *Coefficients of fractional parentage* 433
B.4. *Values of MSDI two-body matrix elements* 434
B.5. *Harmonic-oscillator radial matrix elements* 435
B.6. *Reduced single-particle matrix elements* 436
B.7. *Numerical results of the* $A = 57$–59 *isotopes of Ni and Cu* 438

References 444

Subject index 448

CHAPTER 1

INTRODUCTION

The basic assumption of the nuclear shell model is that to a first approximation each nucleon (proton or neutron) moves independently in a potential that represents the average interaction with the other nucleons in the nucleus. This independent motion of the nucleons can be understood qualitatively from a combination of the weakness of the nuclear long-range attraction and the Pauli exclusion principle. The latter prevents the presence of more than one particle occupying a given state. Thus, in spite of the presence of a strongly fluctuating potential, the motion of a nucleon will often be fairly smooth, since there are not many empty states available into which it can scatter. For more details on this subject the reader is referred to e.g. [DeShalit and Feshbach (1974) ch. 3].

Before 1945 progress in the development of the nuclear shell model was rather slow. This was mainly due to the failure of the model to reproduce binding energies, which were the most extensively investigated data at that time. After the addition of a strong spin-orbit term to the single-particle potential [Mayer (1949); Haxel, Jensen and Suess (1949)] the usefulness of the shell model in correlating many experimental data began to be widely accepted. Since then with improvements in experimental techniques, a much larger amount of experimental nuclear data has been accumulated. At the same time the shell-model methods used to systematize these data have been developed much further.

In the study and description of nuclei, which are systems of many protons and neutrons held together by the nucleon-nucleon interaction, one has to cope with two major problems. In the first place it is a many-body system one wishes to describe, but it is known that even the classical three-body problem is not exactly soluble. Therefore one has to employ an approach in terms of perturbation theory with its accompanying problems of convergence. Secondly, the exact nature of the nucleon-nucleon interaction is not known.

A theory that explains the magic numbers in atoms was given by N. Bohr [Bohr (1913)] with the introduction of the atomic shell model. For electrons the relevant interaction is given by the well-known Coulomb force. The heavy nucleus provides a centre that fixes the Coulomb field in which the light electrons move independently in first approximation. The spherical Coulomb potential is given by $V = Ze^2/r$, with Z the atomic number, e the electron charge and r the distance between the electron and the nucleus. Solving the Schrödinger equation for this particular potential, one obtains electron orbits characterized by various quantum numbers. A complication arises from screening effects; electrons moving mainly at the periphery of the atom do not experience the full Coulomb force from the nucleus due to the presence of the other electrons in the interior.

According to the Pauli exclusion principle no more than two spin-$\frac{1}{2}$ particles can occupy a quantum state and thus the fundamental rules are laid down for the building up of the atomic electron configuration. The electronic states of given principal quantum number, orbital angular momentum l and total spin j (the latter obtained from coupling $\boldsymbol{j} = \boldsymbol{l} + \boldsymbol{s}$ with s denoting the intrinsic spin) may still differ in the projection $m = -j, -j+1, ..., j-1, j$ of the total spin $\boldsymbol{j}$ onto the quantization axis, but they all possess the same energy. These $2j + 1$ states are said to form an electronic subshell. In general several subshells are almost degenerate in energy. Taken together these form shells (sometimes referred to as major shells). Atoms with closed (major) shells, i.e. with all states of the (major) shells occupied, show relatively high stability against addition or removal of an electron; these are the inert gases.

A similar shell-model approach is found to be very useful in describing nuclei. There are, however, several essential differences with the atomic case.

(i) Besides being attractive, the nuclear interaction is quite different from the Coulomb interaction and it contains, moreover, a strong spin-orbit interaction term.

(ii) There are two kinds of nucleons (protons and neutrons) giving rise to a new additional quantum number, the isospin.

(iii) In the nuclear system there is no heavy centre of force similar to that of the atom.

For these reasons the maximum number of particles in successive shells differs for nuclei and atoms. Thus the shell closures occur at different particle numbers in the two systems.

The discrete and generally degenerate nuclear energy levels of the single-particle states in a central field are clustered in groups, i.e. they show a shell structure as in the atomic case. Due to the Pauli principle each state or orbit of given j can be occupied only by a restricted number of identical fermions, thus forming a subshell. A group of orbits lying close in energy is referred to as a shell, or rather a major shell. Each orbit is characterized by a particular value of the radial quantum number, the orbital angular momentum and total angular momentum, denoted by n, l and j, respectively. Nuclei with closed shells, i.e. with a number of orbits completely filled and no partly filled orbits, play a particular role. Closed-shell states are coupled to total spin $J = 0$. *

The only way to excite closed-shell nuclei is by promoting at least one nucleon

* The total angular momentum $J = 0$ for a closed-shell configuration can be derived as follows. Defining the projection raising and lowering operators $J_\pm = J_x \pm iJ_y$ (see chapter 2), one has the identity $\boldsymbol{J}^2 = J_+J_- + J_z^2 - J_z$, where $\boldsymbol{J} = \Sigma_{k=1}^{2j+1} \boldsymbol{j}(k)$ denotes the total angular-momentum operator for the $2j + 1$ particles filling the states $m = -j, -j+1, ..., j-1, j$ of the shell. For the projection one finds immediately $M = \Sigma_{-j}^{+j} m = 0$. The lowering operator J_- (and similarly the raising operator J_+) also yields zero when acting on the $(2j + 1)$ particle state. Each term $j_-(k)$ (and similarly $j_+(k)$) produces either a state with two particles in the same single-particle orbit, which vanishes because of the Pauli exclusion principle, or a state that contains a single-particle orbit of projection $m = -j - 1$ (or $m = j + 1$), which also vanishes, of course. As a result one obtains for closed orbits vanishing eigenvalues for the operator $\boldsymbol{J}^2$. Similarly, when the isospin T is introduced, a closed-shell nucleus is characterized by $J = 0$ and $T = 0$.

EXPERIMENTAL EVIDENCE FOR MAGIC NUMBERS

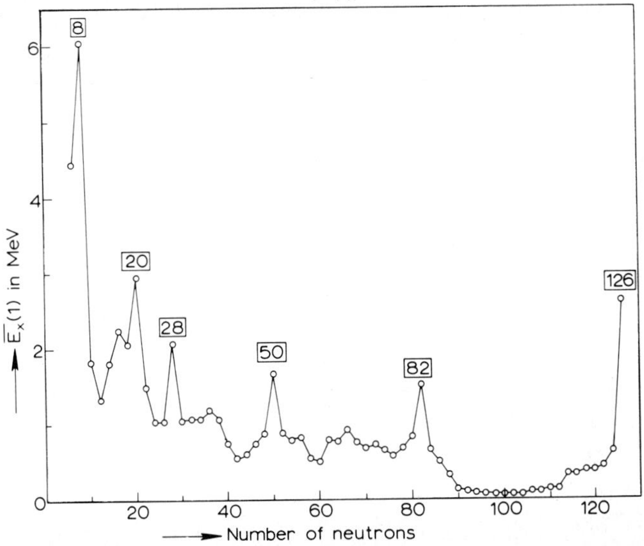

Fig. 1.1. The occurrence of the magic numbers is demonstrated by the average excitation energy of the first excited states in doubly even nuclei plotted as a function of the neutron number N. The experimental data are obtained from the compilations [Lederer, Hollander and Perlman (1968); Endt and Van der Leun (1973) and Nuclear Data Sheets].

to a higher-lying shell. This agrees with the observation that excited states of such nuclei are usually found at relatively high excitation energies. Other nuclei, i.e. those with partly filled shells, may have excited states that result from a recoupling of the angular momenta only. This usually leads to appreciably smaller excitation energies for these states. For example, one finds the excitation energy of the first excited state in even-N, even-Z nuclei at an anomalously high energy when Z or N equals one of the numbers 2, 8, 20, 28, 50, 82 or 126. This is illustrated in fig. 1.1 for some stable nuclei.

The nucleon number at a shell closure is called a *magic number*. The closed-shell nuclei exhibit extra stability compared to neighbouring nuclei. It is only after the introduction of a strong spin-orbit coupling term into the independent-particle Hamiltonian that the magic numbers as they are observed in nature can be reproduced.

Let the single-particle wave functions $\phi_a(\boldsymbol{r})$, with a denoting the quantum numbers that label a particular state and $\boldsymbol{r}$ the particle coordinate, be the solutions of the Schrödinger equation

$$[T + U(\boldsymbol{r})]\ \phi_a(\boldsymbol{r}) = e_a\phi_a(\boldsymbol{r})\,. \tag{1.1}$$

In this equation T denotes the kinetic-energy operator, $U(\boldsymbol{r})$ is some potential and the quantities e_a represent the single-particle energies. For brevity the spin variables are suppressed here and we write only the coordinate vector $\boldsymbol{r}$. From standard quantum mechanics it is known that the functions $\phi_a(\boldsymbol{r})$ can be made to form a complete set of orthonormal states

$$\int \phi_a^*(\boldsymbol{r})\phi_b(\boldsymbol{r})\, \mathrm{d}\boldsymbol{r} = \delta_{ab} \,. \tag{1.2}$$

The Kronecker delta symbol δ_{ab} with $\delta_{ab} = 1$ for $a = b$, $\delta_{ab} = 0$ for $a \neq b$ in eq. (1.2) refers to the case of bound states with discrete energies.

The model Hamiltonian for independent-particle motion is given by

$$H^{(0)} = \sum_{k=1}^{A} [T(k) + U(\boldsymbol{r}(k))] \tag{1.3}$$

with A denoting the total number of nucleons in the nucleus. Eigenfunctions of this Hamiltonian are obtained as a product of single-particle wave functions

$$\Phi_{a_1 a_2 \dots a_A}(1,2,\dots,A) = \prod_{k=1}^{A} \phi_{a_k}(\boldsymbol{r}(k)) \tag{1.4}$$

with eigenenergies

$$E^{(0)} = \sum_{k=1}^{A} e_{a_k} \,, \tag{1.5}$$

as follows directly from eqs. (1.1) and (1.3).

For identical nucleons, i.e. either neutrons or protons, the simple product wave function given by eq. (1.4) is not appropriate, since one still has to take into account the fact that it must describe indistinguishable particles. For nucleons, which are fermions, this implies according to the Pauli exclusion principle that the wave functions should be antisymmetric. For two particles the normalized, antisymmetric wave function is written as

$$\Phi_{ab}(1,2) = \sqrt{\tfrac{1}{2}}\,[\phi_a(1)\,\phi_b(2) - \phi_a(2)\,\phi_b(1)] \,, \tag{1.6}$$

or, equivalently, as a Slater determinant

$$\Phi_{ab}(1,2) = \sqrt{\tfrac{1}{2}} \begin{vmatrix} \phi_a(1) & \phi_a(2) \\ \phi_b(1) & \phi_b(2) \end{vmatrix} \,. \tag{1.7}$$

Here the position coordinate $\boldsymbol{r}\,(k)$ has been replaced by the label k for brevity. The wave function $\Phi_{ab}(1,2)$ is antisymmetric, since the operator P_{12} that interchanges particles 1 and 2 yields $P_{12}\Phi_{ab}(1,2) = \Phi_{ab}(2,1) = -\Phi_{ab}(1,2)$. The normalization of $\Phi_{ab}(1,2)$ is guaranteed by the orthonormality of the single-particle wave functions ϕ_a and ϕ_b.

Similarly a normalized, antisymmetric A-particle wave function is defined by the

Slater determinant

$$\Phi_{a_1a_2...a_A}(1,2,...,A)=\frac{1}{\sqrt{A!}}\begin{vmatrix}\phi_{a_1}(1) & \phi_{a_1}(2) \ldots \phi_{a_1}(A)\\ \phi_{a_2}(1) & \phi_{a_2}(2) \ldots \phi_{a_2}(A)\\ \cdot & \cdot\\ \cdot & \cdot\\ \cdot & \cdot\\ \phi_{a_A}(1) \ldots\ldots & \phi_{a_A}(A)\end{vmatrix} . \tag{1.8}$$

Explicit use of these determinantal wave functions soon leads to complicated expressions for matrix elements. In chapter 13 it will be shown how the introduction of the occupation number formalism simplifies the explicit expressions and calculations for many-nucleon states.

The potential introduced in eqs. (1.1) and (1.3) is not given *a priori* for a many-nucleon system. In fact there is no single-particle potential at all, but the actual Hamiltonian consists of the kinetic-energy terms $\Sigma_k T(k)$ and the two-particle interaction $\Sigma_{k<l} W(k, l)$. The complete Schrödinger equation reads

$$H\Psi(1,2,...,A)=\left[\sum_{k=1}^{A} T(k)+\sum_{1=k<l}^{A} W(k,l)\right]\Psi(1,2,...,A)=E\Psi(1,2,...,A)\,. \tag{1.9}$$

In principle one can introduce any single-particle potential $U(r)$ that leads to a complete set of proper eigenfunctions $\phi_a(\boldsymbol{r})$ and write the Hamiltonian given in eq. (1.9) as

$$H=\sum_{k=1}^{A}[T(k)+U(k)]+\left[\sum_{1=k<l}^{A} W(k,l)-\sum_{k=1}^{A} U(k)\right]=H^{(0)}+H^{(1)}\,. \tag{1.10}$$

Here $H^{(0)}$ defines the independent-particle motion and $H^{(1)}$ represents a *residual interaction* reflecting the fact that the particles do not move completely independently. The smaller the residual interaction, the better the true wave function $\Psi(1,2, ..., A)$ is represented by the independent-particle Slater determinant $\Phi(1,2, ..., A)$ given in eq. (1.8).

The Hartree-Fock theory provides us with a method to derive a single-particle potential U from the two-particle interaction W, such that the Slater determinant wave function $\Phi(1,2, ..., A)$ is a good approximation for the description of the A-particle system. The criterion in the Hartree-Fock theory for the "best" A-particle Slater determinant wave function is that the expectation value of the Hamiltonian H for this state should be a minimum. The condition for a stationary expectation value of the Hamiltonian is given by

$$\delta\langle\Phi|H|\Phi\rangle=0 \tag{1.11}$$

for small variations $\delta\Phi$ that preserve the normalization condition $\langle\Phi|\Phi\rangle = 1$. It can be shown that, if δ is taken to denote arbitrary variations of an arbitrary wave function Φ, eq. (1.11) leads to the Schrödinger equation and therefore to the exact wave function [Pauli (1958) p. 50]. Since this problem is intractable in its full generality, one sets oneself more modest aims in Hartree-Fock theory and one restricts Φ to be a Slater determinant. Thus eq. (1.11) defines an A-particle wave function with an energy that in general will be higher than the true ground-state energy. For the variational procedure one varies the single-particle wave functions $\phi(\boldsymbol{r})$ in the A-particle Slater determinant independently. Then one can show that the condition (1.11) with wave functions (1.8) and Hamiltonian (1.9) leads to a set of A coupled equations for the single-particle wave functions, see e.g. [Rowe (1970) ch. 9; Eisenberg and Greiner (1972) ch. 6]. These are known as the Hartree-Fock equations.

As the calculation of a Hartree-Fock basis of wave functions is very involved, one does not usually follow this line of approach for detailed spectroscopic calculations, but rather starts from a simple single-particle potential. Numerical results of Hartree-Fock calculations indicate that the harmonic-oscillator wave functions are a good approximation to the self-consistent wave functions. The harmonic-oscillator potential

$$U(r) = \tfrac{1}{2} M\omega^2 r^2 \,, \tag{1.12}$$

with M denoting the particle mass and ω the angular frequency, has the advantage that many mathematical operations can be performed analytically. An unrealistic feature is the fact that the harmonic-oscillator potential goes to infinity when the distance to the origin, r, increases (see fig. 1.2). This leads to a discrete spectrum for all energies, but for the spectroscopy of bound states such a defect should not be too important. Another choice is the Saxon-Woods potential, which vanishes for large distances to the origin (see fig. 1.2), but it necessitates the use of numerical methods of solution. Since the latter potential is of finite range, its spectrum

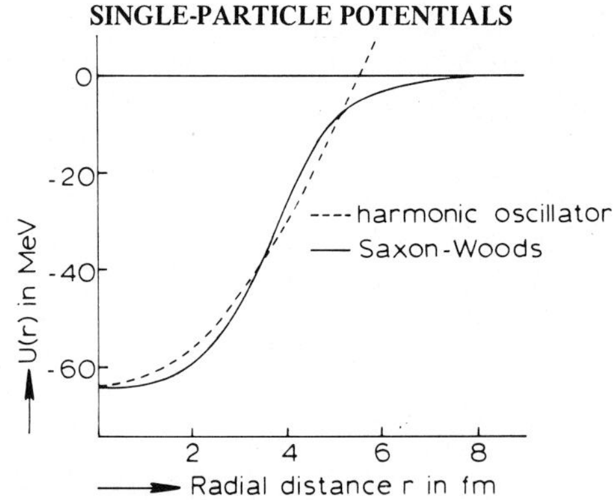

Fig. 1.2. Two frequently used single-particle potentials $U(r)$ calculated for mass A = 29. The harmonic-oscillator potential is such that for r = 0 the two potentials possess the same depth.

consists of two parts: (i) a discrete spectrum for negative energies (bound states) and (ii) a continuous spectrum for positive energies.

Although a selfconsistent potential should represent, as well as possible, the combined action of all other nucleons in the system, one cannot ignore the residual interaction (given by $H^{(1)}$ in eq. (1.10)), which in fact is treated as a perturbation in the system of independent-particle motion. In the discussion so far, antisymmetrized product wave functions (Slater determinants) have been employed for the description of many-particle states. However, as nuclear states are independent of their orientation in space, the total angular momentum J is conserved and thus is a good quantum number. It is quite common, therefore, to construct many-particle states of definite angular momentum. In this approach Slater determinant wave functions are not suitable as basis states, since they contain states of different total angular momenta. The coupling of single-particle wave functions to a many-particle wave function of well-defined spin, can be realized with the aid of *Clebsch-Gordan coefficients.* The Pauli principle requires that these states are antisymmetric in the coordinates of identical particles. This combination of rotational and permutational (anti-) symmetry introduces the *coefficients of fractional parentage* into the theory. With these coefficients it is possible to construct antisymmetric many-particle wave functions of definite angular momentum.

It should be remarked here that another method of generating the basis states for the configuration space is in use. In this approach all the rotational symmetry is disregarded and the many-particle wave functions are not coupled to a well-defined angular momentum J. In fact one specifies only whether a single-particle state $|nljm\rangle$ is occupied or not, i.e. one works in the *m-scheme* to construct determinantal wave functions. Due to the many different m-values this results in large dimensions of the configuration space. These can be handled efficiently, however, when the Lanczos tri-diagonalization procedure is used to obtain the lowest eigenenergies and the corresponding wave functions. This method will be discussed only briefly in this book.

The dimension of a configuration space increases very rapidly with the number of (sub) shells one wishes to take into account explicitly. This is demonstrated in table 1.1. The dimension also depends strongly on the number of particles. This is

Table 1.1
Dimensions of the configuration space for ten particles in the orbits nlj with $j = \frac{1}{2}, \frac{3}{2}, \frac{5}{2}$ and $\frac{7}{2}$, coupled to a total spin $J = 2$ and total isospin $T = 1$

j-values of active orbits	dimension [a]
$\frac{1}{2}, \frac{3}{2}$	2
$\frac{1}{2}, \frac{3}{2}, \frac{5}{2}$	4 500
$\frac{1}{2}, \frac{3}{2}, \frac{5}{2}, \frac{7}{2}$	604 907

[a] Sebe and Harvey (1968).

DIMENSIONS OF CONFIGURATIONS

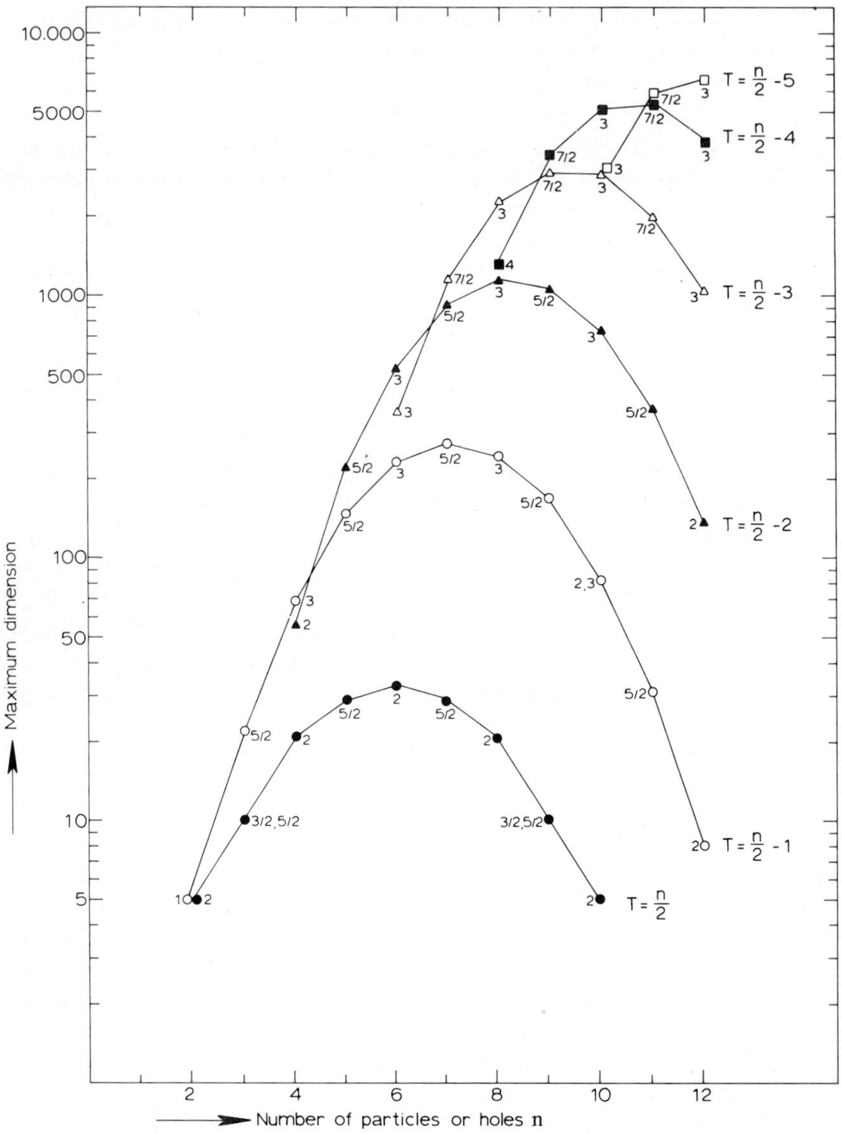

Fig. 1.3. Dimension of the configuration space as a function of the number n of active particles or holes, which are distributed over three orbits with $j = \frac{1}{2}, \frac{3}{2}$ and $\frac{5}{2}$. Each curve is labelled by the total isospin T of the n active particles. The numbers on each curve refer to the value of the total spin J that corresponds to the maximum dimension for a given n and T. For example, for nine active particles ($n = 9$) coupled to isospin $T = \frac{7}{2}$, one finds the maximum dimension of 167 for $J = \frac{5}{2}$.

illustrated in fig. 1.3 for active particles or holes occupying the single-particle states $|nlj\rangle$ with $j = \frac{1}{2}, \frac{3}{2}$ and $\frac{5}{2}$.

After choosing a configuration space, i.e. a restricted set of single-particle states that are taken into account explicitly, one can set up a system of basis wave functions and subsequently determine energies and wave functions, i.e. diagonalize the residual interaction. The diagonalization implies that one can never perform such calculations in a complete configuration space, since this would lead in principle to matrices of infinite size. In order for the computations to be feasible, a *truncation* of the configuration space has to be made. Usually this truncation is dictated by the capacity of the computer available for the matrix diagonalization. The truncation of the configuration space will affect the results, of course. Only if unimportant parts of the complete configuration space have been left out for the processes under consideration, can one expect to obtain realistic results.

An important consequence of the truncation is the distinction one has to make between true and *effective operators* for physical quantities. Effective operators are defined to yield the same results in the truncated configuration space as the true operators in the complete configuration space. For instance, consider the case that one wishes to determine an observable O for a particular state ψ. The expectation value is given by

$$O = \langle\psi|O^{\mathrm{op}}|\psi\rangle\,, \tag{1.13}$$

where ψ is the true wave function and O^{op} is the operator representing the observable O. In a model calculation one has to work with approximate wave functions ψ'. In order to obtain true results from the model wave functions, one imposes the condition

$$O = \langle\psi|O^{\mathrm{op}}|\psi\rangle = \langle\psi'|O^{\mathrm{op}'}|\psi'\rangle\,, \tag{1.14}$$

where an effective operator $O^{\mathrm{op}'}$ is introduced. For example, one has to make use of an effective nucleon-nucleon interaction and effective electromagnetic transition operators.

There are two completely different approaches to obtain effective operators. One is to construct them from the true (realistic) or bare-nucleon operators with the aid of perturbation theory. This means that the contribution of the processes that take place outside the chosen configuration space is considered as a perturbation.

Another approach is the assumption of a parametrized operator. In this case one expresses the matrix elements one wishes to evaluate in terms of free parameters. The parameter values are then fitted to reproduce a large amount of spectroscopic data. Such an effective operator may bear little resemblance to the true nucleon-nucleon operator. With the latter procedure, however, it may be possible to correlate many experimental data in the framework of the shell model with a rather small number of parameters. Both methods, i.e. the perturbational approach and the parameter adjustment, will be discussed in this book.

CHAPTER 2

ONE- AND TWO- PARTICLE SYSTEMS

In this chapter some simple properties are discussed for nuclei, which are assumed to be described by an inert closed-shell core plus one or two active nucleons.

In sect. 2.1 a very brief summary of angular-momentum algebra is given. In sect. 2.2 we discuss some properties of the nuclear single-particle potential, restricting ourselves mainly to the harmonic-oscillator potential. The isospin quantum number is introduced in sect. 2.3. In sect. 2.4 allowed values of the spin and isospin of an antisymmetric two-particle system are derived, and in sect. 2.5 these results are illustrated with some examples.

2.1. Angular momentum

Properties of a free nucleus do not depend on the orientation of the nucleus in space. The rotational invariance of the nuclear Hamiltonian implies that the total angular momentum J of the nucleus is conserved, i.e. J is a good quantum number. For the construction of the independent-particle states in the shell model one employs for convenience the isotropic harmonic-oscillator potential (see sect. 2.2).

The theory of angular momentum in quantum mechanics has been discussed thoroughly in many books and articles, and this subject will not be redeveloped here. Because of its central importance in shell-model theory, however, we present (without proofs) a resumé of the key elements of the quantum mechanical angular-momentum algebra, so as to provide a convenient and concise reference for the remainder of the book.

Classically (orbital) angular momentum $\boldsymbol{l}$ is defined with respect to the origin of the coordinate frame as the vector product of the position coordinate $\boldsymbol{r}$ and the linear momentum $\boldsymbol{p}$

$$\boldsymbol{l}_{\text{cl}} = \boldsymbol{r} \times \boldsymbol{p} \,. \tag{2.1}$$

For a central potential, i.e. for forces which act along the radius vector, it can be deduced that $\boldsymbol{l}$ is a constant of motion. The quantum mechanical definition of the orbital angular momentum operator is very similar to eq. (2.1),

$$\hbar \boldsymbol{l} = \boldsymbol{r} \times \boldsymbol{p} \,, \tag{2.2}$$

or, after substitution of $\boldsymbol{p} = -\mathrm{i}\,\hbar\,\boldsymbol{\nabla}$, one can write

$$\boldsymbol{l} = -\mathrm{i}\,\boldsymbol{r} \times \boldsymbol{\nabla} \,. \tag{2.3}$$

According to this definition the operator $\boldsymbol{l}$ is made dimensionless. From the commutation properties of the position coordinate $\boldsymbol{r}$ and linear momentum $\boldsymbol{p}$, the commutation relation

$$[l_x, l_y] \equiv l_x l_y - l_y l_x = \mathrm{i} l_z \,, \tag{2.4}$$

and its cyclic permutations are derived immediately.

These relations are taken to define angular momentum in general, i.e. also for those cases in which no classical analogue is available, such as for the spin (or intrinsic angular momentum) of elementary particles. Thus this internal degree of freedom of particles is also described by a vector operator satisfying the commutation relations

$$[s_x, s_y] = \mathrm{i}\, s_z \,, \tag{2.5}$$

and cyclic permutations. Eqs. (2.4) and (2.5) imply that not all three vector components can be sharply determined. One can derive, however, the commutators

$$[\boldsymbol{l}^2, l_k] = 0 \qquad \text{for} \quad k = x,y,z \tag{2.6}$$

and

$$[\boldsymbol{s}^2, s_k] = 0 \qquad \text{for} \quad k = x,y,z \,. \tag{2.7}$$

Hence one can construct a simultaneous eigenfunction for only one component (conventionally chosen to be l_z or s_z) and for the square length given by

$$\boldsymbol{l}^2 = l_x^2 + l_y^2 + l_z^2 \quad \text{or} \qquad \boldsymbol{s}^2 = s_x^2 + s_y^2 + s_z^2 \,. \tag{2.8}$$

The orbital angular momentum and the spin refer to independent degrees of freedom and therefore commute with each other

$$[\boldsymbol{l}, \boldsymbol{s}] = 0 \,. \tag{2.9}$$

Thus one can also define the sum vector

$$\boldsymbol{j} = \boldsymbol{l} + \boldsymbol{s} \tag{2.10}$$

and verify with eqs. (2.4), (2.5) and (2.9) that its components satisfy the commutation relations of an angular-momentum vector

$$[j_x, j_y] = \mathrm{i}\, j_z \tag{2.11}$$

and cyclic permutations.

It has been mentioned in chapter 1 that a strong spin-orbit coupling term in the single-particle Hamiltonian is required to reproduce the appropriate ordering of single-particle states. Due to the coupling of the orbital angular momentum $\boldsymbol{l}$ and the spin $\boldsymbol{s}$ through the term $f(r)\boldsymbol{l} \cdot \boldsymbol{s}$, the orbital angular momentum $\boldsymbol{l}$ of a nucleon and its spin $\boldsymbol{s}$ are not individually constants of motion, but their sum $\boldsymbol{j}$ still is. It is left to the reader as an exercise to prove that the term $f(r)\, \boldsymbol{l} \cdot \boldsymbol{s}$ commutes with all components of the angular momentum $\boldsymbol{j}$. [Hint: the orbital angular momentum operator $\boldsymbol{l}$ commutes with the radial coordinate r and hence with the function $f(r)$.]

The quantities $\boldsymbol{l}^2, \boldsymbol{s}^2, \boldsymbol{j}^2$ and j_z form a set of commuting operators and therefore wave functions ψ_{lsjm} that are simultaneous eigenstates of these four operators, can be constructed.

The commutation relations imply integral or half-integral eigenvalues for angular momentum. It can be shown that the eigenfunctions of the orbital angular-momentum operator $\boldsymbol{l}$ possess physical significance only for integral eigenvalues [Pauli (1958) p. 45]. The nucleon intrinsic spin assumes the half-integral value $s = \frac{1}{2}$. Thus one has for the eigenfunctions $\psi_{l\frac{1}{2}jm}$

$$\boldsymbol{l}^2 \psi_{l\frac{1}{2}jm} = l(l+1)\, \psi_{l\frac{1}{2}jm} , \tag{2.12a}$$

$$\boldsymbol{s}^2 \psi_{l\frac{1}{2}jm} = \tfrac{1}{2}(\tfrac{1}{2}+1)\, \psi_{l\frac{1}{2}jm} = \tfrac{3}{4} \psi_{l\frac{1}{2}jm} , \tag{2.12b}$$

$$\boldsymbol{j}^2 \psi_{l\frac{1}{2}jm} = j(j+1)\, \psi_{l\frac{1}{2}jm} \tag{2.12c}$$

and

$$j_z \psi_{l\frac{1}{2}jm} = m \psi_{l\frac{1}{2}jm} \tag{2.12d}$$

with $m = -j, -j+1, ..., j-1, j$. Here j can assume the half-integral values $j = |l \pm \frac{1}{2}|$ only. This follows from the rule that for $\boldsymbol{J} = \boldsymbol{J}_a + \boldsymbol{J}_b$ one has for the eigenvalues the range

$$J = J_a + J_b, J_a + J_b - 1, ..., |J_a - J_b| . \tag{2.13}$$

The functions $\psi_{l\frac{1}{2}jm}$ can be constructed from eigenstates of the orbital angular momentum, φ_{lm_l}, and eigenstates of the intrinsic spin, the spinors $\chi_{\frac{1}{2}m_s}$. Summing over different eigenvalues m_l and m_s of l_z and s_z, respectively, one obtains

$$\psi_{l\frac{1}{2}jm} = \sum_{m_l m_s} \langle l m_l \tfrac{1}{2} m_s | jm \rangle\, \varphi_{lm_l} \chi_{\frac{1}{2}m_s} . \tag{2.14}$$

The expansion coefficients $\langle l m_l \frac{1}{2} m_s | jm \rangle$ are known as Clebsch-Gordan coefficients.

The square of a Clebsch-Gordan coefficient $\langle j_a m_a j_b m_b | JM \rangle$ represents the probability of finding the product state $\phi_{j_a m_a}(1)\, \phi_{j_b m_b}(2)$ in the coupled state $\Phi_{j_a j_b JM}(1,2)$ or, which is equivalent, the probability of finding the coupled state $\Phi_{j_a j_b JM}(1,2)$ in the product state $\phi_{j_a m_a}(1)\, \phi_{j_b m_b}(2)$.

The presence of the Clebsch-Gordan coefficient in eq. (2.14) restricts the summation in fact to run only over the pairs m_l and m_s such that the condition $m_l + m_s = m$ is satisfied.

The Clebsch-Gordan coefficients have been widely tabulated for the most common values of the arguments, see e.g. [Rotenberg, Bivins, Metropolis and Wooten (1959)]. Moreover, small computers can be programmed easily to calculate their values. Some of the symmetry relations governing their behaviour under permutation of indices are given in appendix A.1. The numerical values of Clebsch-Gordan coefficients $\langle j_a m_a j_b m_b | j_c m_c \rangle$ with $j \leqslant \frac{5}{2}$ are tabulated in appendix B.1.

In a nucleus the angular momenta $\boldsymbol{j}(k)$ of the individual nucleons are no longer constants of motion due to the nucleon-nucleon interaction. The total angular momentum $\boldsymbol{J} = \Sigma_{k=1}^{A} \boldsymbol{j}(k)$, however, still is such a constant. The total angular momentum $\boldsymbol{J}$ for a system of nucleons can be obtained from the orbital angular momenta and spins of the individual nucleons along two coupling schemes.

In the *L-S* coupling scheme one combines the orbital angular momenta $\boldsymbol{l}(k)$, with k labelling the particles, into a total orbital angular momentum $\boldsymbol{L} = \Sigma_{k=1}^{A} \boldsymbol{l}(k)$ and the spins $\boldsymbol{s}(k)$ into a total spin $\boldsymbol{S} = \Sigma_{k=1}^{A} \boldsymbol{s}(k)$. Then these are coupled to a total angular momentum $\boldsymbol{J} = \boldsymbol{L} + \boldsymbol{S}$. This *L-S* coupling scheme is in general not convenient, however, as neither $\boldsymbol{L}$ nor $\boldsymbol{S}$ is conserved under the spin-orbit interaction.

In the *j-j* coupling scheme one combines first for each particle its orbital angular momentum and spin to obtain $\boldsymbol{j}(k) = \boldsymbol{l}(k) + \boldsymbol{s}(k)$ and then constructs the total angular momentum as $\boldsymbol{J} = \Sigma_{k=1}^{A} \boldsymbol{j}(k)$. It was mentioned earlier that the angular momenta $\boldsymbol{j}(k)$ commute with the spin-orbit term, $\Sigma_{k=1}^{A} f(r(k))\, \boldsymbol{l}(k) \cdot \boldsymbol{s}(k)$. The *j-j* coupling scheme thus leads to commuting operators $\boldsymbol{l}^2, \boldsymbol{s}^2, \boldsymbol{j}^2, \boldsymbol{J}^2$ and J_z, that all commute with the spin-orbit term, and therefore can be used to label the many-particle states. The addition of the angular momenta $\boldsymbol{j}(k)$ to a total angular momentum $\boldsymbol{J}$ can again be performed with the aid of Clebsch-Gordan coefficients. The requirement that the total wave function must be antisymmetric causes an additional complication. The angular-momentum coupling and antisymmetrization operations are combined in the coefficients of fractional parentage (c.f.p.). This topic is discussed in some detail in chapter 4.

2.2. Single-particle states

In the independent-particle model it is assumed that the interaction between one particle and all other particles in the nucleus can be approximated by a central potential. One of the simplest choices for the central potential is the isotropic harmonic-oscillator potential, which can be written as

$$U(r) = \tfrac{1}{2} M_{\mathrm{p}} \omega^2 r^2 \,, \tag{2.15}$$

where M_{p} denotes the proton mass, $\hbar\omega$ the energy quantum of the harmonic oscillator and r the distance between the nucleon and the origin of the coordinate frame.

The Schrödinger equation for a nucleon in the harmonic-oscillator potential,

$$H^{(0)} \phi(\boldsymbol{r}) = E^{(0)} \phi(\boldsymbol{r}) \tag{2.16a}$$

with

$$H^{(0)} = T + U = \frac{\boldsymbol{p}^2}{2M_{\mathrm{p}}} + \tfrac{1}{2} M_{\mathrm{p}} \omega^2 r^2 \tag{2.16b}$$

is separable in radial and angular coordinates. Thus the eigenfunctions can be given as the product function

$$\phi_{nlm}(\boldsymbol{r}) = R_{nl}(r)\, Y_{lm}(\theta, \phi) \,. \tag{2.17}$$

Here l and m are the quantum numbers of angular momentum and its projection, respectively, whereas n is the radial quantum number that will be discussed below. After substitution of $\boldsymbol{p} = -i\hbar\boldsymbol{\nabla}$ into eq. (2.16) a second-order differential equation is obtained

$$H^{(0)}\phi(\boldsymbol{r}) = \tfrac{1}{2}\hbar\omega\left\{\frac{\hbar}{M_\mathrm{p}\omega}\boldsymbol{\nabla}^2 + \frac{M_\mathrm{p}\omega}{\hbar}r^2\right\}\phi(\boldsymbol{r}) = E^{(0)}\phi(\boldsymbol{r})\,. \tag{2.18}$$

With $\boldsymbol{r}' = \boldsymbol{r}/\sqrt{\hbar/M_\mathrm{p}\omega}$ and $\boldsymbol{\nabla}' = \boldsymbol{\nabla}\sqrt{\hbar/M_\mathrm{p}\omega}$ the Hamiltonian in eq. (2.18) assumes the form

$$H^{(0)} = \tfrac{1}{2}\hbar\omega\,\{\boldsymbol{\nabla}'^2 + r'^2\}\,, \tag{2.19}$$

where the first factor possesses the dimension of an energy and the second factor is dimensionless. Hence the harmonic-oscillator wave functions can be given as functions of the dimensionless coordinates $\boldsymbol{r}' = \boldsymbol{r}/b$, where the size parameter

$$b \equiv \sqrt{\frac{\hbar}{M_\mathrm{p}\omega}} \tag{2.20}$$

plays the role of a characteristic length of the harmonic-oscillator potential.

The size parameter b determines the "scale" of the harmonic-oscillator well. For a potential well of finite depth, such as a square well, the size is an obvious quantity. For the harmonic-oscillator well, which extends to infinity for large distance, the size is not so self-evident. Later a numerical estimate of the size parameter b will be made.

Substitution of the factorized wave function (2.17) into eq. (2.18) leads to a second-order differential equation for the radial eigenfunction with the solutions ($n = 1,2,3,\ldots$)

$$R_{nl}(r) = \frac{1}{(2l+1)!!}\left\{\frac{2^{l-n+3}(2n+2l-1)!!}{b^3\,\pi^{1/2}(n-1)!}\right\}^{1/2}\left(\frac{r}{b}\right)^l \mathrm{e}^{-r^2/2b^2}\;{}_1F_1\!\left(1-n,\, l+\tfrac{3}{2};\frac{r^2}{b^2}\right). \tag{2.21}$$

Here the double factorial is defined by

$$n!! = n(n-2)\,(n-4)\,\ldots\,(2 \text{ or } 1) \tag{2.22}$$

and the confluent hypergeometric series is given by [Magnus, Oberhettinger and Soni (1966); Morse and Feshbach (1953)]

$${}_1F_1\!\left(1-n,\, l+\tfrac{3}{2};\frac{r^2}{b^2}\right) = \sum_{k=0}^{n-1}(-1)^k\,\frac{(n-1)!\,2^k}{(n-k-1)!k!}\,\frac{(2l+1)!!}{(2l+2k+1)!!}\left(\frac{r}{b}\right)^{2k}. \tag{2.23}$$

The corresponding eigenvalues of eq. (2.18) are given by

$$E^{(0)}_{nl} = (2n+l-\tfrac{1}{2})\,\hbar\omega = (N+\tfrac{3}{2})\,\hbar\omega\,. \tag{2.24}$$

Here $N = 2(n-1)+l$ represents the total number of oscillator quanta excited. From eq. (2.21) it is seen that the radial part of the eigenfunctions for small values of r behaves as r^l, i.e. it vanishes at the origin except for s-waves ($l = 0$); for large values of r it vanishes exponentially. Since the confluent hypergeometric series in eq. (2.23) is a polynomial of degree $n-1$ in r^2, the number of radial nodes between $r = 0$ and $r = \infty$ is given by $n-1$. As is clear from eq. (2.24) the value of n occurring in the set of single-particle quantum numbers nlj (such as $1s_{1/2}$, $2s_{1/2}$, $3s_{1/2}$) can be looked at also as giving the order in which the various states of given angular momentum l appear with increasing energy. The notation s,p,d,f,g, ... (and alphabetically thereafter) for the orbital angular momentum $l = 0, 1, 2, 3, 4, \ldots$ stems from atomic spectroscopy.

The spherical harmonics $Y_{lm}(\theta, \phi)$ describing the angular dependence of the harmonic-oscillator eigenfunctions (see eq. (2.17)) are normalized eigenfunctions of the orbital angular momentum operator, or more precisely

$$l^2\, Y_{lm}(\theta,\phi) = l(l+1)\, Y_{lm}(\theta,\phi) \tag{2.25}$$

and

$$l_z Y_{lm}(\theta,\phi) = m Y_{lm}(\theta,\phi)\,. \tag{2.26}$$

They constitute a complete system of orthonormal functions,

$$\int_0^{2\pi} \mathrm{d}\phi \int_0^{\pi} \mathrm{d}\theta \sin\theta\, Y^*_{l_a m_a}(\theta,\phi)\, Y_{l_b m_b}(\theta,\phi) = \delta_{l_a l_b}\delta_{m_a m_b}\,, \tag{2.27}$$

that can be used for the expansion of angular functions. Some of the spherical harmonics for low values of l are given explicitly in appendix A.2.

The parity Π of a function describes the behaviour under the coordinate transformation $\boldsymbol{r} \to -\boldsymbol{r}$, or in polar coordinates $r \to r$, $\theta \to \pi - \theta$, $\phi \to \pi + \phi$, i.e.

$$\Pi^{\mathrm{op}} f(\boldsymbol{r}) = f(-\boldsymbol{r}) = \Pi f(\boldsymbol{r})\,. \tag{2.28}$$

Since obviously one has $\Pi^2 = 1$, the parity operator Π^{op} can possess the eigenvalues $+1$ (positive or even parity) or -1 (negative or odd parity) only. The notion of parity will lead to important selection rules, in particular for electromagnetic transitions. The spherical harmonics all possess definite parity

$$\Pi^{\mathrm{op}} Y_{lm}(\theta,\phi) = Y_{lm}(\pi-\theta, \pi+\phi) = (-1)^l Y_{lm}(\theta,\phi)\,. \tag{2.29}$$

The parity is seen to be even or odd for l even or odd, respectively.

It is clear from eq. (2.24) that different combinations of n and l can belong to the same value of $N = 2(n-1)+l$, thus yielding degenerate states as illustrated in table 2.1.

It may be stressed here, in order to preclude any possible confusion, that in atomic spectroscopy the independent-particle orbits are derived from the Coulomb potential with a $1/r$ radial dependence. The corresponding eigenfunctions therefore

Table 2.1
Quantum numbers for the lower single-particle states of a nucleon in the harmonic-oscillator potential

Energy	N	n	l	$\|nl\rangle$	parity
$\frac{3}{2}\hbar\omega$	0	1	0	1s	+
$\frac{5}{2}\hbar\omega$	1	1	1	1p	−
$\frac{7}{2}\hbar\omega$	2	1	2	1d	+
		2	0	2s	+
$\frac{9}{2}\hbar\omega$	3	1	3	1f	−
		2	1	2p	−
$\frac{11}{2}\hbar\omega$	4	1	4	1g	+
		2	2	2d	+
		3	0	3s	+

The symbol N denotes the number of oscillator quanta excited, the value $n - 1$ gives the number of nodes in the radial wave function between $r = 0$ and $r = \infty$, and l represents the orbital angular momentum.

possess radial wave functions quite different from those in the nuclear case. They also belong to quite different eigenenergies, but the spectroscopic notation of the states is very similar.

Let us now find an estimate of the energy quantum $\hbar\omega$ for the harmonic oscillator. For each value of the orbital angular momentum l there are $2(2l + 1)$ states that correspond to the $2l + 1$ values $m_l = -l, -l + 1, ..., l - 1, l$, where a factor 2 has been added for the two possible intrinsic spin orientations. Since l takes the values $l = N, N-2, ..., 1$ or 0, the total number of nucleons in a shell with oscillator quantum number N is given by

$$2 \sum_{l=0 \text{ or } 1}^{N} 2(2l + 1) = 2(N + 1)(N + 2)\,, \tag{2.30}$$

where the additional factor 2 takes into account the presence of protons and neutrons, which may occupy the same state. Thus the total number of nucleons with all shells from $N = 0$ to a given $N = N_{\max}$ being filled, is given by

$$A = \sum_{N=0}^{N_{\max}} 2(N + 1)(N + 2) = \tfrac{2}{3}(N_{\max} + 1)(N_{\max} + 2)(N_{\max} + 3) \approx \tfrac{2}{3}(N_{\max} + 2)^3\,. \tag{2.31}$$

The mean square radius of a single-particle orbit can be calculated with the aid of the radial wave function given in eq. (2.21). It can be shown that it is given by

$$\langle r^2\rangle_{nl} = \langle\psi_{nlm}|r^2|\psi_{nlm}\rangle = \int_0^\infty R_{nl}(r)\, r^2 R_{nl}(r)\, r^2\, \mathrm{d}r = b^2(N + \tfrac{3}{2})\,. \tag{2.32}$$

The mean square radius $\overline{r^2}$ of a nucleus A is obtained by combining eqs. (2.30) and (2.32)

$$\overline{r^2} = \frac{1}{A}\sum_{k=1}^{A} \langle r^2(k)\rangle_{nl} = \frac{2b^2}{A}\sum_{N=0}^{N_{\max}} (N+\tfrac{3}{2})(N+1)(N+2) \approx \frac{b^2}{2A}(N_{\max}+2)^4 \,. \tag{2.33}$$

An alternative formulation of the mean square radius of the nucleus is obtained by assuming that it can be represented by a homogeneous sphere of nuclear matter with radius $R = r_0 A^{1/3}$. This yields the expression

$$\overline{r^2} = \int_0^R r^2 r^2 \,\mathrm{d}r \Big/ \int_0^R r^2 \,\mathrm{d}r = \tfrac{3}{5}R^2 = \tfrac{3}{5}A^{2/3} r_0^2 \,. \tag{2.34}$$

Usually the energy quantum $\hbar\omega$ of the harmonic oscillator is chosen such that eqs. (2.33) and (2.34) yield the same numerical value. With the aid of eqs. (2.20) and (2.31) it follows that this requirement is equivalent to

$$\hbar\omega = \frac{\hbar^2}{M_\mathrm{p} r_0^2}\,\frac{5}{4}\left(\frac{3}{2}\right)^{1/3} A^{-1/3} = 41 A^{-1/3}\ \mathrm{MeV}\,, \tag{2.35}$$

where the numerical values $r_0 = 1.2$ fm, $\hbar c = 197$ MeV · fm and $M_\mathrm{p}c^2 = 938$ MeV have been used (1 fm = 10^{-15}m). From eqs. (2.31), (2.33) and (2.34) it follows that the size parameter, defined in eq. (2.20), is expressed as

$$b = 2^{7/6} 3^{-1/6} 5^{-1/2} r_0 A^{1/6} = 1.00\, A^{1/6}\ \mathrm{fm}\,. \tag{2.36}$$

It is seen that the size parameter b for the harmonic-oscillator well shows a dependence on the nuclear mass number A, which differs from that for the rms radius of the corresponding density distribution $(\overline{r^2})^{1/2} \propto A^{1/3}$. The origin of this difference is to be found in eq. (2.32), since N also depends on A.

A form for the nuclear potential which is more realistic than the harmonic-oscillator potential, but which is mathematically less tractable, is the Saxon-Woods potential defined by

$$U(r) = \frac{U_0}{1+\mathrm{e}^{(r-R_0)/a}}\,. \tag{2.37}$$

Typical values of the parameters are a depth $U_0 \approx -50$ MeV, a radius $R_0 = r_0 A^{1/3}$ with $r_0 = 1.2$ fm and a diffuseness $a \approx 0.7$ fm. This potential and the radial parts of some single-particle wave functions are shown in fig. 2.1.

The single-particle eigenvalues that follow from the harmonic-oscillator and Saxon-Woods potential are given in fig. 2.2, cases (a) and (b), respectively. Note that the degeneracies of the harmonic-oscillator energy levels do not occur for the Saxon-Woods potential. A qualitative explanation of this different behaviour can

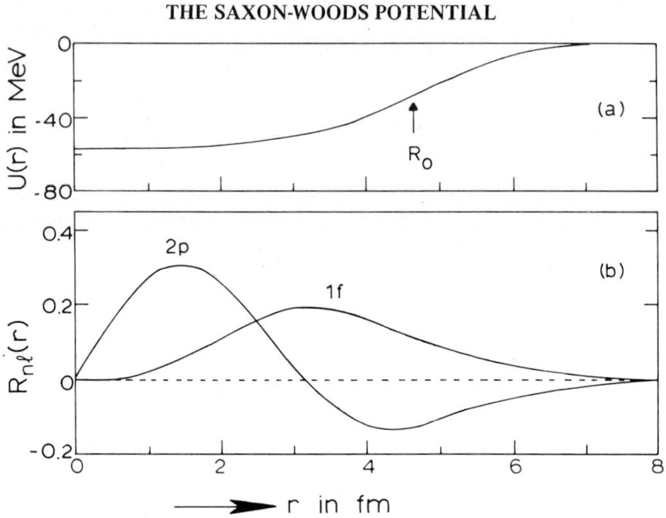

Fig. 2.1. (a) The Saxon-Woods single-particle potential $U(r)$ calculated for $A = 57$ as a function of the distance r to the origin. (b) The radial parts $R_{nl}(r)$ of the 2p and 1f single-particle wave functions.

be given as follows. The particles with the higher l-values have on the average a larger distance to the centre of the well than particles with a lower l-value. Comparing the two wells (see fig. 1.2) one notices that, at least for low-lying states, the states of higher orbital-angular momentum in the Saxon-Woods potential are more strongly bound (due to the flat bottom of this potential) than those in the harmonic-oscillator potential. As a result one finds for the Saxon-Woods potential that for a given n the state of higher l-value lies below that of lower l-value.

The numbers of particles at shell closures for the pure harmonic oscillator do not agree with the observed magic numbers, anyway not beyond the 2s1d shell.

One can reproduce the magic numbers, however, by introducing a strong spin-orbit coupling term into the single-particle Hamiltonian. This term is given by

$$U_{\text{s.o.}}(r) = f(r)\, \boldsymbol{l} \cdot \boldsymbol{s}\,. \tag{2.38}$$

Here the function $f(r)$, that defines the dependence on the radial coordinate r, can be related to the central potential in which the nucleons move.

In eq. (2.14) wave functions were introduced to describe the angular dependence for spin-$\frac{1}{2}$ particles. Multiplication with the radial wave function $R_{nl}(r)$ (cf. eq. (2.17)) then yields the complete wave function $\phi_{nljm}(\boldsymbol{r})$. Here the quantum number $\frac{1}{2}$ for the intrinsic spin of the particle is suppressed for convenience of notation.

The contribution of the spin-orbit term to the energy of the single-particle state

APPROXIMATE SEQUENCE OF SINGLE-PARTICLE STATES

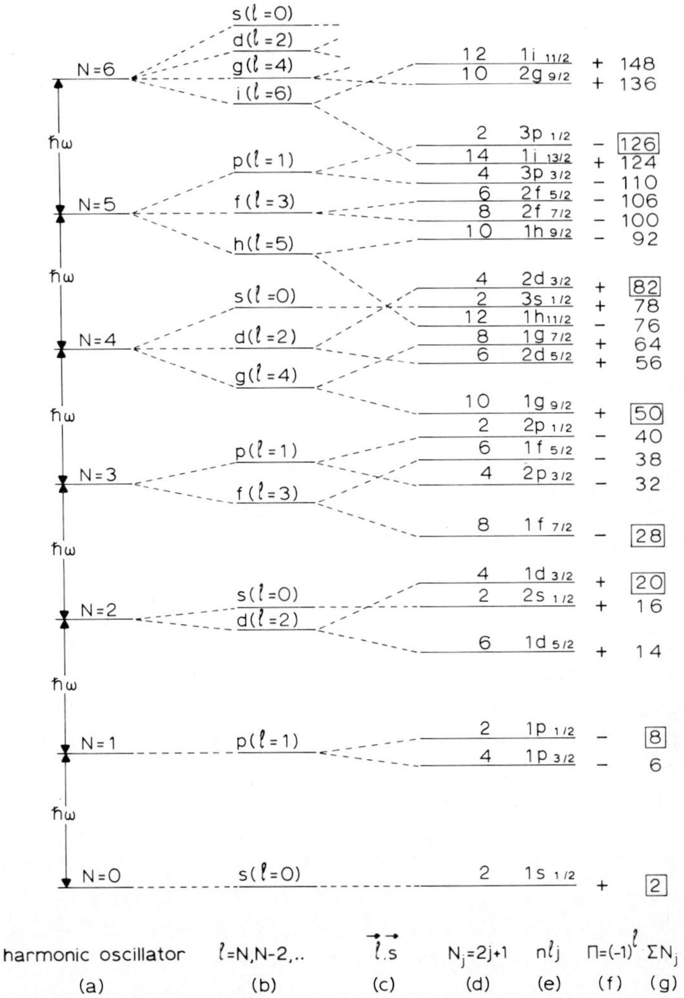

Fig. 2.2. (a) The single-particle energies of a harmonic-oscillator potential as a function of the oscillator quantum number N. (b) A schematic representation of the single-particle energies of a Saxon-Woods potential. (c) A schematic illustration of the level splitting due to the spin-orbit coupling term. (d) The number $N_j = 2j + 1$ of identical particles that can occupy each state. (e) The spectroscopic notation of the single-particle quantum numbers n,l and j. (f) The parity of each state, (g) The magic numbers are seen to appear at the energy gaps as the subtotals of the number of particles.

The level pattern given above represents qualitative features only. This holds especially for states with $N \geqslant 4$, where the single-particle level order differs for protons and neutrons and depends also on the number of nucleons occupying lower states.

$\phi_{nljm}(\boldsymbol{r})$ is given by the expectation value

$$\langle\phi_{nljm}|U_{\text{s.o.}}|\phi_{nljm}\rangle = \langle\phi_{nljm}|\tfrac{1}{2}f(r)\,[(\boldsymbol{l}+\boldsymbol{s})^2 - \boldsymbol{l}^2 - \boldsymbol{s}^2]\,|\phi_{nljm}\rangle$$
$$= \tfrac{1}{2}\langle f(r)\rangle_{nl}[j(j+1) - l(l+1) - s(s+1)]$$
$$= \begin{cases} -\tfrac{1}{2}(l+1)\,\langle f(r)\rangle_{nl} & \text{for} \quad j = l - \tfrac{1}{2} \\ +\tfrac{1}{2}l\,\langle f(r)\rangle_{nl} & \text{for} \quad j = l + \tfrac{1}{2} \end{cases} . \tag{2.39}$$

This shows that the originally degenerate single-particle levels $j = l \pm \frac{1}{2}$ are split up. It is found empirically [Bohr and Mottelson (1969) p. 210] that the radial integrals $\langle f(r)\rangle_{nl}$ can be represented approximately by the relation

$$\langle f(r)\rangle_{nl} \approx -20A^{-2/3}\ \text{MeV}\ , \tag{2.40}$$

which implies according to eq. (2.39) that the spin-orbit splitting increases with orbital angular momentum l. The negative value of the radial integrals $\langle f(r)\rangle_{nl}$ reflects the experimental fact that the $j = l + \frac{1}{2}$ level is lowered with respect to the $j = l - \frac{1}{2}$ level. The effect of the inclusion of the spin-orbit coupling term is shown in fig. 2.2c.

As a specific example, consider the eight degenerate states of the $1f_{7/2}$ level ($m = -\frac{7}{2}, -\frac{5}{2}, ..., +\frac{7}{2}$) above the 2s 1d shell. Since the spin-orbit interaction is strong this $1f_{7/2}$ level is depressed such that a gap results at the nucleon number 28. Similarly one can obtain the higher magic numbers at energy gaps between (sub) shell closures. Such gaps in the single-particle energy spectrum are observed at the magic numbers 8, 20, 28, 50, 82, 126, ... In spite of the strong empirical evidence for the spin-orbit term in the independent-particle model, a satisfactory theoretical explanation of the presence of the spin-orbit term has not yet been provided.

Empirically the nuclear binding energies show a systematic and large variation depending on Z or N being even or odd. This can be explained in terms of pairwise correlation of the protons and the neutrons, such that each pair is preferentially coupled to a total angular momentum $J_{\text{pair}} = 0$. This pairing effect is responsible for the experimental observation that the ground states of doubly even nuclei without exception all possess a spin $J = 0$ with $\boldsymbol{J} = \Sigma_{k=1}^{A}\boldsymbol{j}(k)$. Odd-mass nuclei should then have a spin J equal to the j-value of the last unpaired particle. From the shell model one can deduce the spin j of the last particle, if one assumes that it occupies the lowest available orbit. A nice example is shown in fig. 2.3 for the ground-state spins of odd-mass light nuclei. In this case it is assumed that the nuclear spin is that of the unpaired proton. Those nuclei were selected that satisfy the condition $N = Z + 3$, where N and Z denote the total number of neutrons and protons, respectively. One finds that the single-particle ordering, as obtained from fig. 2.2, agrees with the presently available experimental data on these nuclei.

One can try also to reproduce the spins of some low-lying excited states with this simple

SINGLE-PARTICLE STATES OF ODD-PROTON NUCLEI

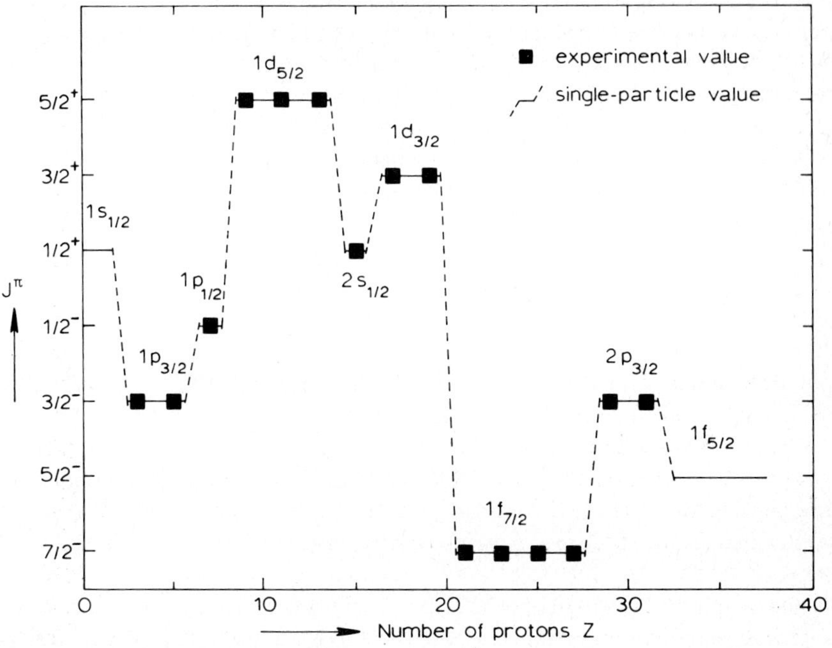

Fig. 2.3. Ground-state spins and parities, J^π, of odd-proton nuclei ($\hat{N} = Z + 3$) provide empirical evidence for the ordering of the single-particle states given in fig. 2.2.

Table 2.2
A comparison between theory and experiment for the spins and parities $J^\pi(i)$ of the ground states ($i = 0$) and first excited states ($i = 1$) of odd-mass sd-shell nuclei.

	$J^\pi(0)$	$J^\pi(1)$		$J^\pi(0)$	$J^\pi(1)$		$J^\pi(0)$	$J^\pi(1)$
Single-particle estimate	$\frac{5}{2}^+$ a)	$\frac{1}{2}^+$a)		$\frac{1}{2}^+$	$\frac{3}{2}^+$		$\frac{3}{2}^+$	$\frac{7}{2}^-$
^{17}O/F	*	*	^{27}Mg	*	*	^{31}Si	*	$\frac{1}{2}^+$
^{19}F/Ne	$\frac{1}{2}^+$	$\frac{1}{2}^-$	^{29}Si/P	*	*	^{33}Cl/S	*	$\frac{1}{2}^+$
^{19}O	*	$\frac{3}{2}^+$	^{31}P/S	*	*	^{35}S	*	$\frac{1}{2}^+$
^{21}Ne/Na	$\frac{3}{2}^+$	$\frac{5}{2}^+$	^{33}P	*	*	^{35}Ar/Cl	*	$\frac{1}{2}^+$
^{21}F/Mg	*	*				^{35}Ar/K	*	$\frac{1}{2}^+$
^{23}Ne	*	*				^{37}Cl	*	$\frac{1}{2}^+$
^{23}Na/Mg	$\frac{3}{2}^+$	$\frac{5}{2}^+$				^{39}K/Ca	*	$\frac{1}{2}^+$
^{25}Mg/Al	*	*						
^{25}Na	*	$(\frac{3}{2}, \frac{5}{2})^+$						
^{27}Al	*	*						
^{29}Al	*	*						

a) An asterisk indicates that the single-particle value agrees with experiment.

single-particle model by assuming that only the last unpaired particle moves to higher-lying orbits. We test this simple picture with nuclei having particles in the $1d_{5/2}$, $2s_{1/2}$ and $1d_{3/2}$ orbits, assuming that the low-lying 1s and 1p shells are filled completely. The result is shown in table 2.2. It is seen that this very simple model works reasonably well for ground-state spins in the $A = 17$–40 mass region and for some first excited states in the $A = 17$–32 mass region. Most discrepancies can be explained in terms of a more complicated model, to be discussed later, in which it is no longer assumed that an even number of protons or neutrons is always coupled to a total angular momentum $J = 0$.

2.3. Isospin

Protons and neutrons not only possess almost the same mass ($M_n/M_p = 1.0014$), but they also show a far reaching symmetry with regard to the nuclear interaction. In 1932, soon after the discovery of the neutron, W. Heisenberg proposed that the neutron and proton could be considered as two different charge states of one and the same particle, the nucleon [Heisenberg (1932)]. In order to distinguish these two states, Heisenberg introduced an isospin variable, here denoted by t_z, that can assume two values: $t_z = -\frac{1}{2}$ to label a proton and $t_z = +\frac{1}{2}$ to label a neutron ★. The ensuing isospin formalism can be developed in complete analogy with the description of intrinsic spin in terms of Pauli spinors with the two possibilities of spin up and spin down. Before discussing the isospin formalism, however, we first turn to the experimental evidence of the symmetry between protons and neutrons.

Analysis of the results obtained experimentally from scattering protons by protons and neutrons by protons show that the nuclear forces for the p-p and the n-p system are equal to within a few percent. Results on direct measurements of n-n scattering cross sections are still not available, but consideration of mirror nuclei and other sets of isobars provides further pertinent information.

It is observed that the energy spectra of mirror nuclei (i.e. nuclei which transform into each other by an interchange of protons and neutrons) are very much alike. An example is given in fig. 2.4 for the odd-mass mirror pair $^{25}_{12}Mg_{13} - ^{25}_{13}Al_{12}$. The differences in excitation energies are very small and are probably due to Coulomb forces only. The ground-state binding energies 205.58 and 200.54 MeV for ^{25}Mg and ^{25}Al, respectively, are different but can be well explained as a difference in the pure Coulomb energy part of the p-p interaction (see also sect. 18.3).

From the level schemes of the mirror nuclei, such as given in fig. 2.4, it thus follows that apart from a pure Coulomb contribution a substitution of all protons by neutrons and *vice versa* does not affect the binding energy of the many-nucleon

★ The opposite sign convention is used in high-energy physics as well as in some texts on low-energy nuclear physics. The present convention leads to positive values of the total isospin component T_z for most nuclei, which in general possess a neutron excess [cf. eq. (2.59)].

THE A = 25 MIRROR NUCLEI

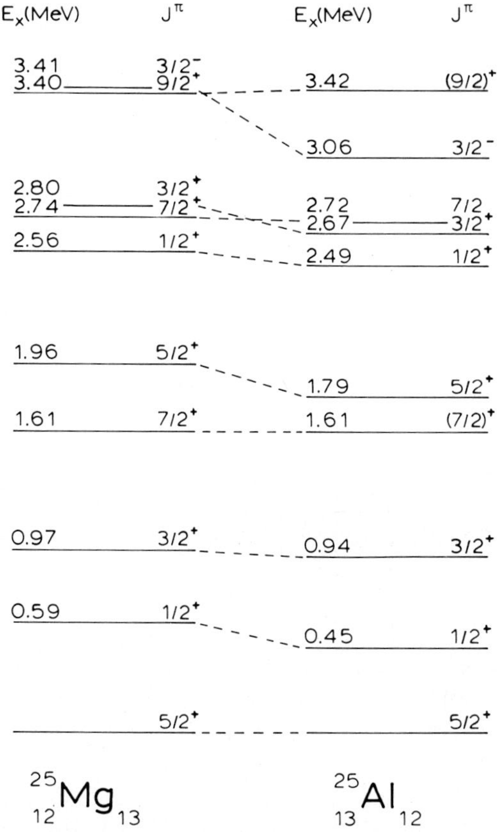

Fig. 2.4. A comparison of the level schemes of the A = 25 mirror nuclei shows the close similarity of the excitation energies of the states with the same J^{π} values.

system. This means that a replacement of the nucleon-nucleon bonds n-n by p-p, n-p by p-n and p-p by n-n leaves the total energy unchanged. It can be concluded therefore that the n-n force is the same as the p-p force. This property of nuclear forces is called *charge symmetry.*

Nothing can be concluded from mirror nuclei about the relation between the p-p or n-n force on the one-hand and the n-p force on the other hand. More information is obtained from experimental data on isobaric mass triplets such as given in fig. 2.5 for $^{30}_{14}Si_{16}$, $^{30}_{15}P_{15}$ and $^{30}_{16}S_{14}$. From the similarity of the ^{30}Si and ^{30}S spectra only charge symmetry follows as was the case for the nuclei discussed above. From a comparison of the spectrum of ^{30}P with those of ^{30}Si and ^{30}S another property of the nuclear forces emerges, however.

Consider the $J^{\pi} = 0^{+}$ ground state of ^{30}Si or ^{30}S. A $J^{\pi} = 0^{+}$ level occurs also in

THE A = 30 ISOSPIN TRIPLET

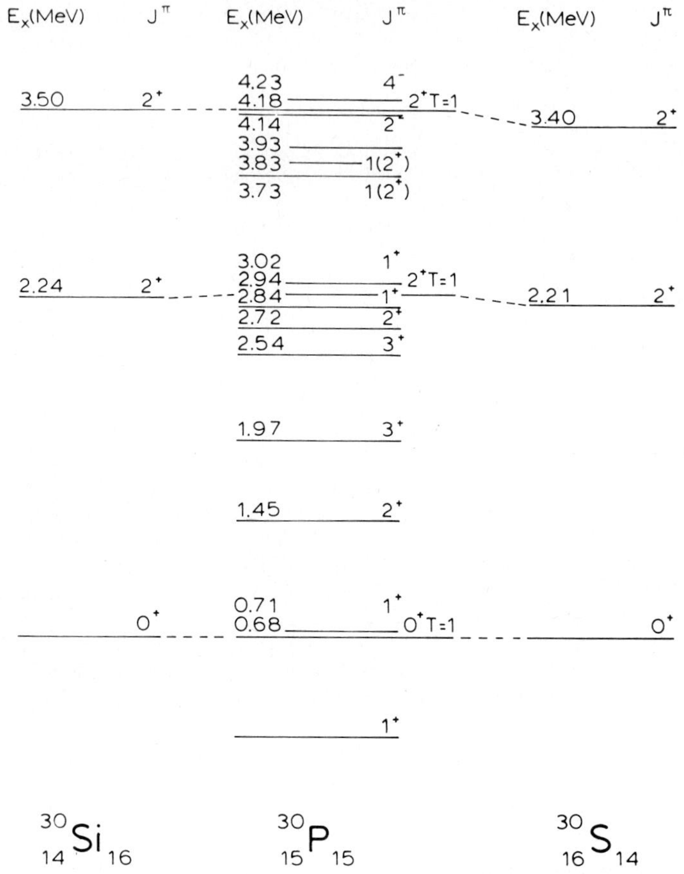

Fig. 2.5. The level spacings between the T = 1 states in ^{30}P are very similar to those between the corresponding states in ^{30}Si and ^{30}S. The states in ^{30}P of which the isospin is not indicated are characterized by T = 0.

^{30}P as first excited state (see fig. 2.5). The absolute binding energies of these corresponding states are identical once they are corrected for Coulomb energies and the n-p mass difference. The analogue of the first $J^\pi = 2^+$ level in ^{30}Si or ^{30}S is also observed in ^{30}P at an energy above the $J^\pi = 0^+$ first excited state that agrees well with the excitation energy of the lowest $J^\pi = 2^+$ state in ^{30}Si or ^{30}S. Also for higher excited states in ^{30}Si and ^{30}S corresponding states can be found in ^{30}P.

The states in ^{30}P corresponding to ^{30}Si or ^{30}S states are called *isobaric analogue states.* Not only their excitation energy but also other properties such as spectroscopic factors (chapter 8) and electromagnetic transition strengths (chapter 10) point towards a close similarity. One may conclude that when one neutron in $^{30}_{14}Si_{16}$ is replaced by a proton (which thus yields ${}^{30}_{15}P_{15}$) the total interaction energy of the many-nucleon system is not changed, apart from the Coulomb energy. In ${}^{30}Si$ this single neutron interacts with all other nucleons by n-n and n-p forces, while in ${}^{30}P$ these bonds are replaced by p-n and p-p forces, respectively. Thus one is led to the assumption of *charge independence* of the nuclear forces, i.e. the equality of n-n, p-p and n-p interactions.

It is seen in fig. 2.5 that ${}^{30}P$ has also levels not found in ${}^{30}Si$ or ${}^{30}S$. This feature can be qualitatively understood as follows. A neutron and proton can occupy the same state without violating the Pauli principle. This is not possible for identical nucleons, i.e. when both nucleons are protons or neutrons. The nucleons in ${}^{30}_{15}P_{15}$ can be grouped in 15 n-p pairs, whereas in ${}^{30}_{14}Si_{16}$ and ${}^{30}_{16}S_{14}$ one has only 14 n-p pairs together with two identical nucleons. Thus the last pair in ${}^{30}P$ can produce states not allowed, due to the Pauli principle, for the last pair in ${}^{30}Si$ or ${}^{30}S$. In particular the nuclei ${}^{30}Si$ and ${}^{30}S$ do not possess the low-lying state which corresponds to the ${}^{30}P$ ground state. This state by itself constitutes therefore a so-called isobaric mass singlet. In other words, such a state exists in only one nucleus of a given mass number.

The general symmetry that follows from the charge independence of nuclear forces and its consequences can be described most conveniently in terms of the *isospin formalism.* Before charge independence of the nuclear forces was suggested in 1936 (see [Wilkinson (1969)]) the variable t_z was introduced only as a mathematical tool to describe a system made up of two kinds of particles. However, the complete formalism of ordinary (intrinsic) spin can be used for a concise formulation of charge independence. The nucleon is considered as a particle of isospin $\frac{1}{2}$, with projection either $t_z = +\frac{1}{2}$ or $t_z = -\frac{1}{2}$ along one of the coordinate axes in a newly introduced isospin space. A neutron wave function ($t_z = +\frac{1}{2}$ or isospin "up") then is represented by the isospinor

$$\phi_n(\boldsymbol{r}) = \begin{pmatrix} \phi(\boldsymbol{r}) \\ 0 \end{pmatrix} = \phi(\boldsymbol{r}) \begin{pmatrix} 1 \\ 0 \end{pmatrix} \tag{2.41}$$

and a proton function ($t_z = -\frac{1}{2}$ or isospin "down") by the isospinor

$$\phi_p(\boldsymbol{r}) = \begin{pmatrix} 0 \\ \phi(\boldsymbol{r}) \end{pmatrix} = \phi(\boldsymbol{r}) \begin{pmatrix} 0 \\ 1 \end{pmatrix} . \tag{2.42}$$

Introducing the analogues of the Pauli matrices into isospin space

$$\tau_x = \begin{pmatrix} 0 & 1 \\ 1 & 0 \end{pmatrix}, \quad \tau_y = \begin{pmatrix} 0 & -\mathrm{i} \\ \mathrm{i} & 0 \end{pmatrix}, \quad \tau_z = \begin{pmatrix} 1 & 0 \\ 0 & -1 \end{pmatrix}, \tag{2.43}$$

one defines the isospin vector operator as

$$\boldsymbol{t} = \tfrac{1}{2}\,\boldsymbol{\tau} . \tag{2.44}$$

From eqs. (2.43) it follows that the components t_x, t_y and t_z obey the commutation relations of an angular momentum

$$[t_x, t_y] = \mathrm{i}\, t_z \tag{2.45}$$

and cyclic permutations.

The commutation relations (2.45) imply that the transformation proton ⇋ neutron can be regarded as a rotation in some abstract space, the isospace. It should be stressed that, although we label the three components of the isospin operator with x, y and z, the isospin bears no relation to ordinary space. Instead of x,y,z one also uses the labels 1,2,3 or ξ, η, ζ to emphasize the distinction.

One now verifies immediately from eqs. (2.41), (2.42) (2.43) and (2.44) that in fact one has for the isospin variable t_z the eigenvalues

$$t_z \phi_\mathrm{n}(\boldsymbol{r}) = +\tfrac{1}{2}\phi_\mathrm{n}(\boldsymbol{r})\,, \tag{2.46}$$

$$t_z \phi_\mathrm{p}(\boldsymbol{r}) = -\tfrac{1}{2}\phi_\mathrm{p}(\boldsymbol{r})\,. \tag{2.47}$$

The commutation relations (2.45) also imply, as in the case of angular momentum, that $\boldsymbol{t}^2$ and t_z are commuting operators

$$[\boldsymbol{t}^2, t_z] = 0 \tag{2.48}$$

and that the eigenvalues of $\boldsymbol{t}^2$ are given by

$$\boldsymbol{t}^2 \Rightarrow t(t+1)\,. \tag{2.49}$$

From eqs. (2.44), (2.46) and (2.47) one immediately finds the relations

$$\tfrac{1}{2}(1-\tau_z)\,\phi_\mathrm{p} = \phi_\mathrm{p}\,, \quad \tfrac{1}{2}(1-\tau_z)\,\phi_\mathrm{n} = 0\,,$$

$$\tfrac{1}{2}(1+\tau_z)\,\phi_\mathrm{p} = 0\,, \quad \tfrac{1}{2}(1+\tau_z)\,\phi_\mathrm{n} = \phi_\mathrm{n}\,. \tag{2.50}$$

These equations are necessary for a description of electromagnetic nuclear properties in the isospin formalism when a distinction between protons and neutrons is needed. For instance, the electric-charge operator for the nucleons can be given as

$$\frac{Q}{e} = \tfrac{1}{2}(1-\tau_z)\,, \tag{2.51}$$

or, in matrix representation, as

$$\frac{Q}{e} = \begin{pmatrix} 0 & 0 \\ 0 & 1 \end{pmatrix}. \tag{2.52}$$

In analogy with angular momentum one can define raising and lowering operators as

$$t_+ = \tfrac{1}{2}\tau_+ = \tfrac{1}{2}(\tau_x + \mathrm{i}\tau_y) = \begin{pmatrix} 0 & 1 \\ 0 & 0 \end{pmatrix}, \tag{2.53}$$

$$t_- = \tfrac{1}{2}\tau_- = \tfrac{1}{2}(\tau_x - \mathrm{i}\tau_y) = \begin{pmatrix} 0 & 0 \\ 1 & 0 \end{pmatrix} . \tag{2.54}$$

Direct application of the explicit matrix representations (2.43) to the isospinors (2.41) and (2.42) yields the relations

$$t_+\phi_\mathrm{p} = \phi_\mathrm{n} , \qquad t_+\phi_\mathrm{n} = 0 , \qquad t_-\phi_\mathrm{p} = 0 , \qquad t_-\phi_\mathrm{n} = \phi_\mathrm{p} . \tag{2.55}$$

The operators $\tau_\pm$ that transform a proton state into a neutron state and *vice versa* are required, for example, to describe beta-decay processes.

For the isospin one can now employ the techniques that have been developed for the description of angular momentum, in particular for many-nucleon systems. For instance, for the reduction of matrix elements use will be made of Clebsch-Gordan coefficients in isospace. In a composite system of two or more nucleons the (commuting) individual isospins may be coupled to a total isospin

$$\boldsymbol{T} = \sum_{k=1}^{A} \boldsymbol{t}(k) , \tag{2.56}$$

where A denotes the number of nucleons in a nucleus. Again in analogy with the composition of ordinary spins, one finds that the vector operator $\boldsymbol{T}$ obeys the angular-momentum commutation relations and hence the following eigenvalues are possible:

$$\boldsymbol{T}^2 \Rightarrow T(T+1) , \tag{2.57}$$

$$T_z \Rightarrow -T, -T+1, \ldots, T-1, T . \tag{2.58}$$

The total isospin quantum number T is integral or half-integral depending on whether A is even or odd. For a given eigenvalue T the state is seen to be $(2T+1)$-fold degenerate, i.e. an isomultiplet is formed that consists of $2T+1$ states characterized by different values of the z-component

$$T_z = \tfrac{1}{2}(N - Z) , \tag{2.59}$$

where N and Z denote the number of neutrons and protons, respectively. On the other hand in a particular nucleus, i.e. an A-nucleon system with given value of $T_z = \frac{1}{2}(N-Z)$, levels of total isospin

$$T = |T_z|, |T_z|+1, |T_z|+2, \ldots, \tfrac{1}{2}A \tag{2.60}$$

are possible. It is found experimentally that for virtually all nuclei the ground state possesses an isospin $T = |T_z|$.

The members of an isomultiplet of many-particle states are connected by the raising and lowering operators defined by

$$T_\pm \equiv T_x^\mathrm{op} \pm \mathrm{i}T_y^\mathrm{op} = \sum_{k=1}^{A} \{t_x^\mathrm{op}(k) \pm \mathrm{i}t_y^\mathrm{op}(k)\} . \tag{2.61}$$

From eq. (2.45) it follows that the operators defined in eq. (2.61) satisfy the commutation relation

$$[T_z^{\mathrm{op}}, T_\pm] = \pm T_\pm \,. \tag{2.62}$$

Application of eq. (2.62) leads to

$$T_z^{\mathrm{op}} T_\pm |T, T_z\rangle = T_\pm (T_z^{\mathrm{op}} \pm 1) |T, T_z\rangle = (T_z \pm 1) T_\pm |T, T_z\rangle \,. \tag{2.63}$$

The latter equation implies that the projection quantum number T_z is raised and lowered by one unit by the operators T_+ and T_-, respectively.

Since rotations never change the angular momentum, the states $T_\pm |T, T_z\rangle$ still possess the original isospin T, i.e.

$$T_\pm |T, T_z\rangle = N_\pm |T, T_z \pm 1\rangle \,. \tag{2.64}$$

The numerical factor $N_\pm$ is introduced to maintain normalized wave functions. The value of $N_\pm$ can be determined from the normalization condition

$$1 = \langle T, T_z \pm 1 | T, T_z \pm 1\rangle = N_\pm^{-2} \langle T, T_z | T_\mp T_\pm | T, T_z\rangle \,, \tag{2.65}$$

where the relation

$$(T_\pm)^\dagger = T_\mp \tag{2.66}$$

for the hermitian conjugate follows from the definition (2.61). The operator in eq. (2.65) can be written as

$$T_\mp T_\pm = (T_x^{\mathrm{op}})^2 + (T_y^{\mathrm{op}})^2 \pm \mathrm{i}\,[T_x^{\mathrm{op}}, T_y^{\mathrm{op}}] = (\boldsymbol{T}^{\mathrm{op}})^2 - (T_z^{\mathrm{op}})^2 \mp T_z^{\mathrm{op}} \,. \tag{2.67}$$

Inserting the eigenvalues of the operators into eq. (2.65) one obtains

$$N_\pm^2 = [T(T+1) - T_z(T_z \pm 1)]\ \langle T, T_z | T, T_z\rangle = (T \mp T_z)(T \pm T_z + 1) \,, \tag{2.68}$$

from which follows

$$T_\pm |T, T_z\rangle = \sqrt{(T \mp T_z)(T \pm T_z + 1)}\,|T, T_z \pm 1\rangle = \sqrt{T(T+1) - T_z(T_z \pm 1)}\,|T, T_z \pm 1\rangle \,. \tag{2.69}$$

This relation will be useful, e.g. for the discussion of the beta-decay process given in chapter 12.

By repeated application of $T_\pm$ one can generate states differing from the original value T_z by more than one unit, but one remains always within the same isomultiplet characterized by T. From eq. (2.64) it is clear that the operators T_+ and T_-, each time they are applied, change a proton into a neutron or a neutron into a proton, respectively. For $T_+|T, T_z\rangle = 0$ or $T_-|T, T_z\rangle = 0$ the extreme values of T_z are reached, i.e. $T_z = T$(only neutrons) or $T_z = -T$ (only protons), respectively. It should be pointed out that states of different isospin T bear no resemblance, whereas the wave functions of all analogue states in one isomultiplet (T fixed, A fixed and $T_z = -T, -T+1, \ldots, T-1, T$) are similar if isospin really is a good quantum number.

It is an empirical fact that electric charge is absolutely conserved, that is, there are no exceptions whatsoever to the rule that electric charge cannot be destroyed or created. The connection

$$Z = \tfrac{1}{2}A - T_z \tag{2.70}$$

between charge Ze and the isospin projection T_z implies that charge conservation is equivalent to the commutation relation

$$[T_z^{\mathrm{op}}, H] = 0\,. \tag{2.71}$$

Charge independence of the nuclear forces was defined for a two-nucleon system that can exist in the states $T_z = 1$ (n-n), $T_z = 0$ (n-p) or $T_z = -1$ (p-p). For given isospin T, the nuclear interaction for a two-nucleon system should not depend on T_z, i.e.

$$[T_\pm, H] = 0\,. \tag{2.72}$$

The condition that guarantees charge independence for any many-nucleon system can be summarized as

$$[\boldsymbol{T}^{\mathrm{op}}, H] = 0\,. \tag{2.73}$$

This condition can be interpreted in analogy with angular momentum as to mean invariance of the total Hamiltonian under rotation in isospace. It is a more general definition of charge independence of the strong interaction than the condition that the nuclear forces are the same for any two-nucleon system, since eq. (2.73) applies to other particles as well (e.g. mesons) for which isospin can also be introduced.

With the charge operator (2.51) one can write the Coulomb interaction as

$$V_{\mathrm{C}} = \sum_{\substack{j<k \\ \text{protons}}}^{Z} \frac{e^2}{|\boldsymbol{r}(j) - \boldsymbol{r}(k)|} = \sum_{j<k}^{A} \frac{e^2\{1 - \tau_z(j)\}\{1 - \tau_z(k)\}}{4|\boldsymbol{r}(j) - \boldsymbol{r}(k)|}$$

$$= \sum_{j<k}^{A} \frac{e^2\{1 - [\tau_z(j) + \tau_z(k)] + \tau_z(j)\,\tau_z(k)\}}{4|\boldsymbol{r}(j) - \boldsymbol{r}(k)|}\,. \tag{2.74}$$

One can now verify that the components T_x and T_y of the total isospin do not commute with the Coulomb interaction V_{C}. Thus isospin can no longer be a conserved quantity if the Coulomb interaction V_{C} is taken into account, i.e.

$$[\boldsymbol{T}^{\mathrm{op}}, H + V_{\mathrm{C}}] \neq 0\,. \tag{2.75}$$

However, it turns out that the influence of the Coulomb field can still be treated in many cases as a perturbation in the energy, leaving the total isospin quantum number T virtually unimpaired as a state label. At present one has obtained a large body of data on isomultiplets corroborating the assumption of charge independence of the nuclear forces.

2.4. Antisymmetric two-particle wave functions

For identical nucleons, i.e. either protons or neutrons, the Pauli exclusion principle requires that a many-nucleon wave function be antisymmetric in all particle coordinates. Thus if the space and spin variables of any two protons or any two neutrons are interchanged, the wave function must reverse its sign.

In the isospin formalism neutrons and protons are considered as different charge states of one particle, the nucleon. Now it is not directly clear which symmetry requirements should be imposed upon the complete wave function in isospin formalism. It can be shown, however, that a one-to-one correspondence between the proton-neutron formalism and the isospin formalism results if one allows in the latter formalism completely antisymmetrized wave functions only [Klein (1938)]. This *generalized Pauli exclusion principle* requires that the wave function reverse its sign upon an odd permutation of all coordinates (i.e. space, spin and isospin) of any two nucleons. It should be noted that, in spite of its name, the generalized Pauli exclusion principle does not involve any new physical facts or assumptions. In this section the consequences of the generalized Pauli principle on two-particle wave functions are investigated. It is shown that this principle can restrict the number of spin-isospin values for a two-particle state. First we discuss the situation with both particles in the same orbit. Thereafter systems with two particles in different orbits are treated.

Two particles in the same orbit. Suppose we have two particles in the same $s_{1/2}$ orbit, and thus each particle is characterized by $j = \frac{1}{2}$ and $t = \frac{1}{2}$. The total J and T of the two-particle wave function denoted as $|(s_{1/2})^2\rangle_{JT}$ can be obtained from the vector additions $\boldsymbol{J} = \boldsymbol{j} + \boldsymbol{j}$ and $\boldsymbol{T} = \boldsymbol{t} + \boldsymbol{t}$, and one finds $J = 0$ or 1 and $T = 0$ or 1. Thus for the two-particle system under consideration there are four possible (J, T) combinations given by (0, 0), (0, 1), (1, 0) and (1,1). We shall show, however, that only the (J,T) combinations (0, 1) and (1,0) are allowed.

As a consequence of the generalized Pauli principle a symmetric space-spin wave function must be combined with an antisymmetric isospin function or *vice versa.* In both cases the complete wave function is antisymmetric under the interchange of all coordinates of the two particles. This leads to the general statement that one obtains allowed two-particle states $|(lj)^2\rangle_{JT}$ only for

$$J + T = \text{odd}\ , \tag{2.76}$$

as can be proved as follows.

Let us first construct the two-particle function

$$\Phi_{JM}(j_a(1)\, j_b(2)) = \sum_{m_a m_b} \langle j_a m_a j_b m_b | JM\rangle\, \phi_{j_a m_a}(1)\, \phi_{j_b m_b}(2)\ , \tag{2.77}$$

where $\langle j_a m_a j_b m_b | JM\rangle$ is a Clebsch-Gordan coefficient and $\phi_{j_a m_a}(1)$ and $\phi_{j_b m_b}(2)$ denote the single-particle wave functions for particle 1 in orbit j_a and particle 2 in orbit j_b, respectively. When P_{12} denotes the operator that interchanges particles 1 and 2, one obtains

$$P_{12}\Phi_{JM}(j_a(1)\,j_b(2)) = P_{12} \sum_{m_a m_b} \langle j_a m_a j_b m_b | JM\rangle\, \phi_{j_a m_a}(1)\, \phi_{j_b m_b}(2)$$

$$= \sum_{m_a m_b} \langle j_a m_a j_b m_b | JM\rangle\, \phi_{j_a m_a}(2)\, \phi_{j_b m_b}(1)\,. \tag{2.78}$$

From the symmetry property of Clebsch-Gordan coefficients,

$$\langle j_a m_a j_b m_b | JM\rangle = (-1)^{J-j_a-j_b} \langle j_b m_b j_a m_a | JM\rangle\,, \tag{2.79}$$

one finds

$$P_{12}\Phi_{JM}(j_a(1) j_b(2)) = \sum_{m_a m_b} (-1)^{J-j_a-j_b} \langle j_b m_b j_a m_a | JM\rangle\, \phi_{j_a m_a}(2)\, \phi_{j_b m_b}(1)$$

$$= (-1)^{J-j_a-j_b} \Phi_{JM}(j_b(1)\, j_a(2))\,. \tag{2.80}$$

For identical orbits, i.e. $n_a = n_b$, $l_a = l_b$ and $j_a = j_b = j$, this leads to

$$P_{12}\Phi_{JM}(j(1)\,j(2)) = (-1)^{J-2j}\Phi_{JM}(j(1)\,j(2)) = -(-1)^J\Phi_{JM}(j(1)j(2))\,, \tag{2.81}$$

since $2j$ is always odd (j is half-integral). Thus Φ_{JM} is antisymmetric for J even and symmetric for J odd. Similarly one finds that the isospin part of the two-particle wave function is antisymmetric for an even value of T and symmetric for an odd value of T.

Writing now the complete two-particle wave function as a product of a space-spin and isospin function, $\Phi_{JMTT_z} = \Phi_{JM} \times \Theta_{TT_z}$, one only obtains antisymmetry for $J + T =$ odd. The allowed (J,T) combinations for $|(s_{1/2})^2\rangle_{JT}$ are thus given by $(J,T) = (0, 1)$ or $(1, 0)$. It is easily seen that for two particles in the $d_{5/2}$ orbit, only the combinations $(J, T) = (0, 1), (1, 0), (2,1), (3,0), (4,1)$ and $(5,0)$ are allowed.

Two particles in different orbits. A two-particle wave function, with the two particles in different orbits, can always be antisymmetrized for any combination of the total J and T values. Consider again the function $\Phi_{JM}(j_a(1)\,j_b(2))$, given in eq. (2.77), but now for $n_a, l_a, j_a \neq n_b, l_b, j_b$. Define the normalized wave functions

$$\Phi^{\pm}_{JM} = \sqrt{\tfrac{1}{2}}\,(1 \pm P_{12})\,\Phi_{JM}(j_a(1)\,j_b(2))$$

$$= \sqrt{\tfrac{1}{2}}\,\{\Phi_{JM}(j_a(1)\,j_b(2)) \pm (-1)^{J-j_a-j_b}\Phi_{JM}(j_b(1)\,j_a(2))\}\,. \tag{2.82}$$

Application of the permutation operator P_{12} yields

$$P_{12}\Phi^{\pm}_{JM} = \sqrt{\tfrac{1}{2}}\,P_{12}(1 \pm P_{12})\,\Phi_{JM} = \sqrt{\tfrac{1}{2}}(P_{12} \pm P^2_{12})\,\Phi_{JM} = \sqrt{\tfrac{1}{2}}(P_{12} \pm 1)\,\Phi_{JM}$$

$$= \pm\sqrt{\tfrac{1}{2}}(1 \pm P_{12})\,\Phi_{JM} = \pm\,\Phi^{\pm}_{JM}\,. \tag{2.83}$$

Hence Φ^{+}_{JM} is symmetric, while Φ^{-}_{JM} is antisymmetric. In order to make the wave functions totally antisymmetric in space-spin and isospin coordinates, we must combine the $T = 1$ (symmetric) isospin part with the antisymmetric space-spin part Φ^- and the $T = 0$ (antisymmetric) isospin part with the symmetric space-spin part Φ^+.

2.5. Applications of the two-particle model

Consider the nucleus ${}^{30}_{14}\mathrm{Si}_{16}$. Let us assume that the lower states in this nucleus can be represented by configurations in which 14 protons and 14 neutrons form a system of closed orbits (the ${}^{28}_{14}\mathrm{Si}_{14}$ core), which therefore couple to total angular momentum $J = 0$ and total isospin $T = 0$. Let us also assume that the remaining two neutrons occupy the next two orbits only, i.e. the $2s_{1/2}$ and $1d_{3/2}$ orbits (see fig. 2.6).

When the two neutrons are in a configuration $|(2s_{1/2})^2\rangle_{J,T=1}$ only the value $J = 0$ is allowed, due to the requirement of total antisymmetry. The configuration space can be extended by permitting the extra neutrons to occupy the $1d_{3/2}$ orbit also. All possible J values that can be obtained this way are also indicated in fig. 2.6. It is seen that the experimentally determined spins of the lowest five states do agree with this model.

An example in another mass region is the nucleus ${}^{90}_{40}\mathrm{Zr}_{50}$. This nucleus can be considered as a core of 38 protons and 50 neutrons plus two extra protons. Assuming that the lower states have a configuration with two protons in the $2p_{1/2}$ and $1g_{9/2}$ orbits, one finds the situation given in fig. 2.7. It can be seen that the spins obtained in this simple shell-model picture do agree with those observed experimentally. The further states $J^\pi = 3^-$ and 2^+ found experimentally can only

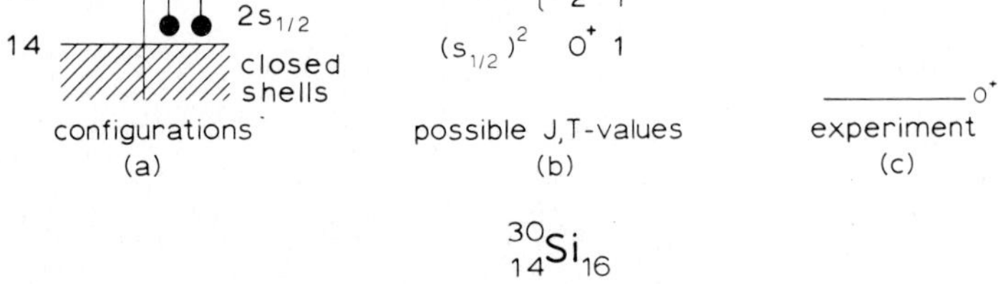

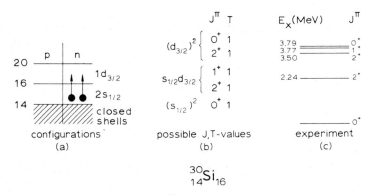

Fig. 2.6. The two-particle model applied to ${}^{30}\mathrm{Si}$. (a) The configurations taken into account. (b) The possible J^π, T values for two neutrons in the $2s_{1/2}$ and $1d_{3/2}$ orbits. (c) The experimentally determined low-lying states in ${}^{30}\mathrm{Si}$.

THE TWO-PARTICLE MODEL FOR ^{90}Zr

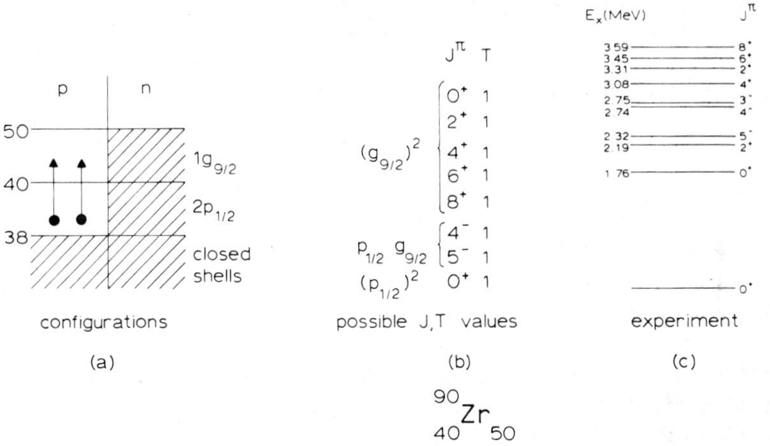

Fig. 2.7. The two-particle model applied to ^{90}Zr. (a) The configurations taken into account. The hatching indicates completely filled orbits. (b) The possible J^π, T values for two protons in the $2p_{1/2}\ 1g_{9/2}$ orbits. (c) The experimentally determined low-lying states in ^{90}Zr. The $J^\pi = 3^-$ state and one of the $J^\pi = 2^+$ states are not reproduced within this simple model space.

be explained in a more complex shell-model space in which higher-lying orbits and/or holes in the closed-shell core are taken into account.

The procedure illustrated above for two nuclei is a first step in setting up a shell-model calculation. Once it has been checked that most of the experimentally determined spins can be reproduced within the assumed model space, one can proceed with a calculation of the energies of these states.

CHAPTER 3

PERTURBATION THEORY AND CONFIGURATION MIXING

In sect. 3.1 of this chapter a brief review of first-order perturbation theory is given. A discussion of the various contributions, which must be taken into account in the calculation of binding and excitation energies is given in sect. 3.2. In sect. 3.3 these procedures are illustrated with some examples. Section 3.4 contains a discussion of some complications that arise when the inert core does not have equal numbers of protons and neutrons. In sect. 3.5 it is shown that in general a nuclear state is described by a mixed-configuration wave function. Such a wave function can be obtained from a diagonalization of the interaction matrix. This procedure is discussed in detail for a 2 × 2 matrix in sect. 3.6. In sect. 3.7 some applications are given.

3.1. Perturbation theory

In order to calculate the various properties of nuclear ground states and excited states one must have available the wave functions of these states. The wave functions can be obtained by solving the many-body Schrödinger equation

$$H\Phi(\boldsymbol{r}(1), ..., \boldsymbol{r}(A)) = E\Phi(\boldsymbol{r}(1), ..., \boldsymbol{r}(A)) . \tag{3.1}$$

The Hamiltonian H is given by

$$H = \sum_{k=1}^{A} T(k) + \sum_{1=k<l}^{A} W(k, l) . \tag{3.2}$$

This Hamiltonian consists of a sum over the kinetic-energy terms $T(k)$ and over the nucleon-nucleon interaction $W(k, l)$ for all pairs of nucleons in the nucleus. An exact solution of this many-body problem, even with the internucleon interaction being the sum of two-body terms only, does not exist. The first step towards an approximate solution is the introduction of a single-particle potential $U(k)$, in order to rewrite the Schrödinger equation as

$$H = \sum_{k=1}^{A} \{T(k) + U(k)\} + \{\sum_{1=k<l}^{A} W(k, l) - \sum_{k=1}^{A} U(k)\} = H^{(0)} + H^{(1)} . \tag{3.3}$$

This equation is correct for any choice of the potential $U(k)$, of course, but for the application of perturbation theory it is advantageous to make the influence of the *residual interaction*

$$H^{(1)} = \sum_{1=k<l}^{A} W(k, l) - \sum_{k=1}^{A} U(k) \tag{3.4}$$

as small as possible.

It has been mentioned in chapter 1 that in the practice of spectroscopic shell-model calculations one avoids the very complicated numerical derivation of a selfconsistent Hartree-Fock potential. One usually employs either the harmonic-oscillator potential or the Saxon-Woods potential as an approximation for U. The basis of single-particle states $\phi_a(\boldsymbol{r})$ is determined by the single-particle Schrödinger equation

$$T\phi_a(\boldsymbol{r}) + U\phi_a(\boldsymbol{r}) = e_a\phi_a(\boldsymbol{r}) \,. \tag{3.5}$$

Here the eigenvalue e_a represents the single-particle energy with a labelling the single-particle state $|nljm\rangle$. Any product of A single-particle functions $\Phi_{\boldsymbol{a}}^{(0)} \equiv \phi_{a_1}(\boldsymbol{r}(1))$ ... ... $\phi_{a_A}(\boldsymbol{r}(A))$ satisfies the Schrödinger equation

$$H^{(0)}\Phi_{\boldsymbol{a}}^{(0)} = E_{\boldsymbol{a}}^{(0)}\,\Phi_{\boldsymbol{a}}^{(0)} \tag{3.6}$$

with the unperturbed Hamiltonian

$$H^{(0)} \equiv \sum_{k=1}^{A} (T(k) + U(k)) \tag{3.7}$$

and the unperturbed energy

$$E_{\boldsymbol{a}}^{(0)} = \sum_{k=1}^{A} e_{a_k} \,. \tag{3.8}$$

The index $\boldsymbol{a}$ represents the labels of all single-particle states involved.

The product function $\Phi_{\boldsymbol{a}}^{(0)}(\boldsymbol{r}(1), ..., \boldsymbol{r}(A))$, however, is not yet a many-particle wave function since the Pauli exclusion principle requires complete antisymmetry. Antisymmetrized A-particle wave functions at the energy $E_{\boldsymbol{a}}^{(0)}$ can be constructed by taking appropriate linear combinations of functions $\Phi_{\boldsymbol{a}}^{(0)}(\boldsymbol{r}(1), ..., \boldsymbol{r}(A))$. For instance, in eq. (1.8) a Slater determinant wave function was constructed. For the description of a nuclear state, however, the wave function should possess a well-defined total angular momentum and isospin. Therefore, more complicated linear combinations of the product functions $\Phi_{\boldsymbol{a}}^{(0)}(\boldsymbol{r}(1), ..., \boldsymbol{r}(A))$ are required in order to satisfy the conditions of both antisymmetry and well-defined total angular momentum and isospin. For the time being we assume that we have succeeded in constructing the proper wave functions that are denoted by $\Phi_\Gamma(\boldsymbol{r}(1), ..., \boldsymbol{r}(A))$, where from now on a set of quantum numbers necessary to specify a given state will be denoted by one Greek symbol. Thus the letter Γ given above includes the total spin J and isospin T.

The true wave functions ψ_Γ and energies E_Γ, i.e. the solutions of the Schrödinger equation (3.1), can now be approximated when the residual interaction given by $H^{(1)}$ in eq. (3.4) is considered as a perturbation. The assumption that $H^{(1)}$ is small suggests that an expansion of the true eigenfunction Ψ_Γ and the true eigenenergy E_Γ can be made such that we have in first-order perturbation theory

$$|\Phi_\Gamma\rangle = |\Phi_\Gamma^{(0)}\rangle + |\Phi_\Gamma^{(1)}\rangle\,, \tag{3.9}$$

$$E_\Gamma = E_\Gamma^{(0)} + E_\Gamma^{(1)}\,, \tag{3.10}$$

where $|\Phi_\Gamma^{(1)}\rangle$ and $E_\Gamma^{(1)}$ represent the supposedly small changes in the wave function and the energy of the unperturbed state. Substitution of eqs. (3.3), (3.9) and (3.10) into eq. (3.1) then yields

$$(H^{(0)} + H^{(1)})(|\Phi_\Gamma^{(0)}\rangle + |\Phi_\Gamma^{(1)}\rangle) = (E_\Gamma^{(0)} + E_\Gamma^{(1)})(|\Phi_\Gamma^{(0)}\rangle + |\Phi_\Gamma^{(1)}\rangle)\,. \tag{3.11}$$

After separation of zeroth- and first-order quantities one obtains

$$H^{(0)}|\Phi_\Gamma^{(0)}\rangle = E_\Gamma^{(0)}|\Phi_\Gamma^{(0)}\rangle\,, \tag{3.12}$$

$$H^{(0)}|\Phi_\Gamma^{(1)}\rangle + H^{(1)}|\Phi_\Gamma^{(0)}\rangle = E_\Gamma^{(0)}|\Phi_\Gamma^{(1)}\rangle + E_\Gamma^{(1)}|\Phi_\Gamma^{(0)}\rangle\,, \tag{3.13}$$

where second-order quantities, i.e. products of two first-order quantities have been disregarded. Multiplying eq. (3.13) by $\langle\Phi_\Gamma^{(0)}|$ on the left, one obtains

$$E_\Gamma^{(1)}\langle\Phi_\Gamma^{(0)}|\Phi_\Gamma^{(0)}\rangle = \langle\Phi_\Gamma^{(0)}|H^{(1)}|\Phi_\Gamma^{(0)}\rangle + \langle\Phi_\Gamma^{(0)}|H^{(0)} - E_\Gamma^{(0)}|\Phi_\Gamma^{(1)}\rangle\,. \tag{3.14}$$

Due to eq. (3.12) the second term on the right-hand side of eq. (3.14) vanishes, since $H^{(0)}$ is a hermitian operator. For normalized functions $\Phi_\Gamma^{(0)}$ one obtains

$$E_\Gamma^{(1)} = \langle\Phi_\Gamma^{(0)}|H^{(1)}|\Phi_\Gamma^{(0)}\rangle\,. \tag{3.15}$$

This shows that the energy shift due to the residual interaction $H^{(1)}$ can be calculated as the expectation value of the residual interaction in the *unperturbed state.* The energy of the state $\Phi_\Gamma^{(0)}$ is then according to eqs. (3.8), (3.10) and (3.15) given by

$$E_\Gamma = E_\Gamma^{(0)} + E_\Gamma^{(1)} = \langle\Phi_\Gamma^{(0)}|H^{(0)} + H^{(1)}|\Phi_\Gamma^{(0)}\rangle = \sum_{k=1}^{A} e_{a_k} + \langle\Phi_\Gamma^{(0)}|H^{(1)}|\Phi_\Gamma^{(0)}\rangle\,, \tag{3.16}$$

where the first term gives the contribution from the single-particle energies and the second term that from the residual interaction. This is a very important result, since it shows that for a calculation of the first-order change in energy one only needs the zeroth-order wave functions obtained from the unperturbed Hamiltonian $H^{(0)}$.

3.2. Binding energies and excitation energies

Let us apply the procedures outlined in the preceding section to find expressions for the binding energy and excitation energies of a nucleus. The binding energy E^{b} of a nucleus is defined as the negative value of the total energy needed to decompose the nucleus into free protons and neutrons. Often the binding energy is given with the opposite, positive sign. With the negative sign used here, however, there is a more direct connection with the expectation value of the Hamiltonian of the nuclear system. The absolute value of the binding energy is largest for the nucleus in its ground state. The excitation energy $E_{\mathrm{x}}(n)$ of the nth excited state follows from the binding energy $E^{\mathrm{b}}(n)$ of the nucleus in that state taken with respect to the ground-state binding energy $E^{\mathrm{b}}(0)$, i.e.

$$E_{\mathrm{x}}(n) = E^{\mathrm{b}}(n) - E^{\mathrm{b}}(0) . \tag{3.17}$$

Let us assume that a meaningful description of a nucleus can be made in terms of an inert core of closed shells and two extra nucleons in the orbit ρ not occupied by core nucleons (see fig. 3.1). The various terms contributing to the total binding energy of this nucleus can be written down at once from the definition of the binding energy given above as

$$E^{\mathrm{b}}_{\Gamma}(\mathrm{core} + \rho^2) = 2e_\rho + E^{(1)}_{\Gamma}(\rho^2) + E^{\mathrm{b}}(\mathrm{core}) , \tag{3.18}$$

where each term has a simple physical interpretation. Here the term $2e_\rho$ represents the negative value of the energy needed to remove the two particles from the potential well in which they are assumed to move independently in the orbit ρ. It is usually assumed that this potential well does not depend on the number of particles outside the core. The contribution to the binding energy from the mutual nuclear interaction of the two outer-core particles is given by $E^{(1)}_{\Gamma}(\rho^2)$. Note that this term depends not only on the orbit ρ, but also on the spin J_Γ and isospin T_Γ of the two-particle system. The last term, E^{b}(core), represents the binding energy of the par-

THE TWO-PARTICLE SINGLE-ORBIT MODEL

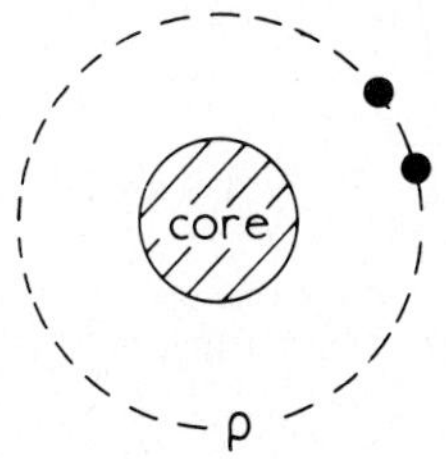

Fig. 3.1. Schematic illustration of a nucleus described by an inert core and two particles in the orbit ρ.

ticles in the core. When it is assumed that the closed-shell core is inert (i.e. it will maintain its closed-shell configuration and thus cannot be excited), it follows that the term $E^{\mathrm{b}}(\mathrm{core})$ is a constant.

The ground state of the core-plus-two-nucleon system is characterized by a minimum of the total energy. Generally, the two extra nucleons are then in the lowest available single-particle orbits ρ and are coupled to that value of the total spin and isospin Γ for which $E_{\Gamma}^{(1)}(\rho^2)$ assumes its minimum value. All other states, in which the two particles are coupled to different values of Γ or when one or both of the extra nucleons are excited into a different single-particle orbit, represent excited states.

Let us discuss each term of eq. (3.18) more precisely in the spirit of sect. 3.1. The Hamiltonian of the core-plus-two-nucleon system can be split into two terms (cf. eq. (3.3))

$$H = H_{\mathrm{core}} + H_{12} \tag{3.19}$$

with

$$H_{\mathrm{core}} = \sum_{k=3}^{A} [T(k) + U(k)] + [\sum_{3=k<l}^{A} W(k, l) - \sum_{k=3}^{A} U(k)] \,, \tag{3.20}$$

$$H_{12} = \sum_{k=1}^{2} [T(k) + U(k)] + [\sum_{k=1}^{2} \sum_{l=3}^{A} W(k, l) + W(1,2) - \sum_{k=1}^{2} U(k)] \,. \tag{3.21}$$

Here H_{core} refers to the interaction between the core particles (numbered $k = 3, ..., A$). If it is assumed that the closed-shell core is inert, it follows that the contribution of H_{core} to the total energy is a constant. The term H_{12} describes the contribution from the two extra-core particles. It can be written more specifically as

$$H_{12} = H_{12}^{(0)} + H_{12}^{(1)} \,. \tag{3.22}$$

In this expression

$$H_{12}^{(0)} = [T(1) + U(1)] + [T(2) + U(2)] = H_{\mathrm{s.p.}}(1) + H_{\mathrm{s.p.}}(2) \tag{3.23}$$

denotes the single-particle Hamiltonian and

$$H_{12}^{(1)} = [\sum_{l=3}^{A} W(1,l) - U(1)] + [\sum_{l=3}^{A} W(2,l) - U(2)] + W(1,2) \tag{3.24}$$

specifies the residual interaction. The choice of the single-particle potential U is still free. If we now take

$$U(k) = \sum_{l=3}^{A} W(k, l) \qquad \text{for } k = 1, 2 \,, \tag{3.25}$$

then the single-particle terms in the residual interaction $H_{12}^{(1)}$ exactly cancel and only the two-particle term $W(1,2)$ survives. In other words, the residual interaction is given by $H_{12}^{(1)} = W(1,2)$, where $W(1,2)$ does not contain any single-particle terms.

The definition in eq. (3.25) with the summation over all particles of the core implies that the single-particle states are defined with respect to the core nucleus. The general derivation of a self-consistent single-particle potential U is given in the Hartree-Fock theory. The latter approach, being quite complex, will not be discussed here, however. In most shell-model calculations one makes the approximation that the single-particle potential can be represented by the mathematically simple harmonic-oscillator or the Saxon-Woods potential. In that case $H_{12}^{(1)}$ is no longer equal to $W(1,2)$. It is assumed now that for such a simplified single-particle potential U, the residual interaction, as given e.g. in eq. (3.24), still can be represented by a two-body interaction. The residual two-body interaction will from now on be denoted by $\Sigma_{i<j} V(i,j)$. Thus, in the case of two active particles outside a core one has

$$H_{12}^{(1)} = V(1,2)\,. \tag{3.26}$$

With eqs. (3.19), (3.22), (3.23) and (3.26) one can write for the total Hamiltonian

$$H = H_{\text{core}} + H_{\text{s.p.}}(1) + H_{\text{s.p.}}(2) + V(1,2)\,. \tag{3.27}$$

The binding energy of the nucleus with two particles outside the core in the orbit ρ and coupled to spin and isospin Γ is given by the expectation value

$$E_\Gamma^{\text{b}}(A) = \langle \Phi_\Gamma^{(0)}(1, ..., A)|H|\Phi_\Gamma^{(0)}(1, ..., A)\rangle \tag{3.28}$$

of the total Hamiltonian in the state $\Phi_\Gamma^{(0)}(1, ..., A)$ of the complete nucleus. The wave function $\Phi_\Gamma^{(0)}(1, ..., A)$ can be written as the antisymmetrized product of the core wave function, $\Phi_{00}(\text{core})$, and the wave function $\Phi_\Gamma^{(0)}(1,2)$ describing the extra two nucleons, i.e.

$$\Phi_\Gamma^{(0)}(1, ..., A) = \mathcal{A}\,\{\Phi_{00}(\text{core})\,\Phi_\Gamma^{(0)}(1,2)\}\,. \tag{3.29}$$

The functions $\Phi_{00}(\text{core})$ and $\Phi_\Gamma^{(0)}(1,2)$ are taken to be antisymmetric in the particles $3, ..., A$ and $1, 2$, respectively. The antisymmetrizer $\mathcal{A}$ must complete the antisymmetrization in *all* particles by permuting particle coordinates and taking appropriate linear combinations. It can be shown with the aid of the techniques that will be discussed in chapter 5, however, that for the evaluation of the matrix element in eq. (3.28), the correct results are also obtained with the simpler product function $\Phi_{00}(\text{core})\,\Phi_\Gamma^{(0)}(1,2)$. Since in eq. (3.27) the total Hamiltonian has been decomposed into terms that operate on either particles 1, 2 or particles $3, ..., A$, one obtains from the orthonormality of the wave functions $\Phi_{00}(\text{core})$ and $\Phi_\Gamma^{(0)}(1,2)$

$$\begin{aligned}\langle \Phi_{00}(\text{core})\,\Phi_\Gamma^{(0)}(1,2)|H|\Phi_{00}(\text{core})\,\Phi_\Gamma^{(0)}(1,2)\rangle \\ = \langle \Phi_{00}(\text{core})|H_{\text{core}}|\Phi_{00}(\text{core})\rangle + \langle \Phi_\Gamma^{(0)}(1,2)|H_{\text{s.p.}}(1) + H_{\text{s.p.}}(2)|\Phi_\Gamma^{(0)}(1,2)\rangle \\ + \langle \Phi_\Gamma^{(0)}(1,2)|V(1,2)|\Phi_\Gamma^{(0)}(1,2)\rangle\,.\end{aligned} \tag{3.30}$$

The coupled two-particle wave function $\Phi_\Gamma(1, 2)$ is defined in eqs. (2.77) and (2.82).

For the evaluation of the matrix element of $H_{\text{s.p.}}(1)$ in eq. (3.30) one can integrate out the coordinates of particle 2, and similarly for $H_{\text{s.p.}}(2)$ the coordinates of particle 1. Because of the orthonormality of Clebsch-Gordan coefficients the matrix elements each reduce to expectation values of $H_{\text{s.p.}}$ for single-particle eigenstates, i.e. e_ρ. Eq. (3.30) is seen to be identical to eq. (3.18) with the single-particle energies given by

$$2e_\rho = \langle\Phi_\Gamma^{(0)}(1, 2)|H_{\text{s.p.}}(1) + H_{\text{s.p.}}(2)|\Phi_\Gamma^{(0)}(1, 2)\rangle = \langle\rho^2|H_{12}^{(0)}|\rho^2\rangle_\Gamma \,, \tag{3.31}$$

the residual interaction by

$$E_\Gamma^{(1)}(\rho^2) = \langle\Phi_\Gamma^{(0)}(1, 2)|V(1, 2)|\Phi_\Gamma^{(0)}(1, 2)\rangle = \langle\rho^2|V(1, 2)|\rho^2\rangle_\Gamma \tag{3.32}$$

and the binding energy of the core given by

$$E^{\text{b}}(\text{core}) = \langle\Phi_{00}(\text{core})\,|H_{\text{core}}|\,\Phi_{00}(\text{core})\rangle \,. \tag{3.33}$$

Note that in order to abbreviate the notation the two-particle wave function $\Phi_\Gamma^{(0)}(1, 2)$ is denoted by ρ^2, while the values Γ of bra and ket states are given as a subscript to the matrix element. This shorter notation will be used from now on.

Up till here the Coulomb energy has been ignored completely. However, its contribution to the total binding energy can be accounted for rather easily since, due to the long-range character of the Coulomb forces, it does not significantly depend on the detailed nuclear structure. For the calculation of the Coulomb energy, E_{C}, various approximate expressions exist (see also sect. 18.3).

For the term $E^{\text{b}}(\text{core})$ in eq. (3.18), being the contribution from the inert core, one can take the experimental value for the binding energy. The single-particle energy e_ρ can also be extracted directly from experiment by comparing the binding energy of the core nucleus with that of the core-plus-neutron nucleus. For example, when the $J^\pi = \frac{5}{2}^+$ ground state in ^{17}O is assumed to be described by a $1d_{5/2}$ neutron coupled to a ^{16}O core, one obtains (see fig. 3.2)

$$e_{1d_{5/2}} = E^{\text{b}}(^{17}\text{O}) - E^{\text{b}}(^{16}\text{O}) = (-131.77 + 127.62)\text{MeV} = -4.15 \text{ MeV} \,.$$

For an evaluation of the term $E_\Gamma^{(1)}(\rho^2)$ in eq. (3.18), in principle one must know the nucleon-nucleon interaction. There are different approaches to this problem as was mentioned before in chapter 1. One can either determine these matrix elements after parametrization in some form from a fit to experimental spectroscopic data or one can extract the behaviour of the nucleon-nucleon interaction from a study of free-nucleon scattering data and then calculate the matrix elements. Both procedures will be discussed later.

When there are more than two particles outside a core, say n particles in shell ρ and m particles in shell λ, one derives analogously that the binding energy is given by

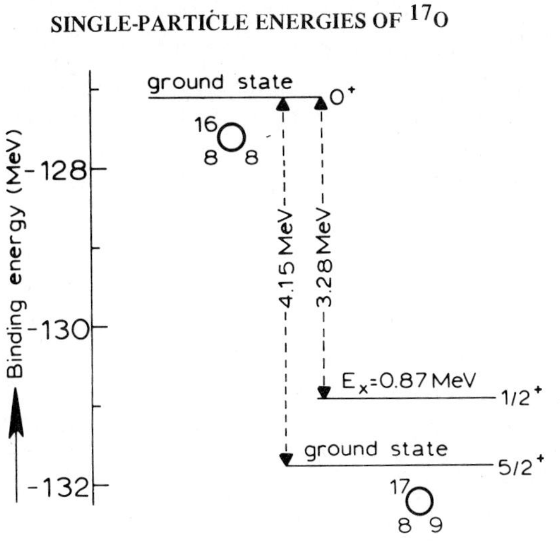

Fig. 3.2. The relation between the ground-state binding energies of ^{16}O and ^{17}O and the single-particle energies of the $1d_{5/2}$ and $2s_{1/2}$ neutron with respect to the ^{16}O core.

the expression

$$E^{\mathrm{b}}_{\Gamma}(\mathrm{core} + \rho^n + \lambda^m) = E_{\mathrm{C}} + E^{\mathrm{b}}(\mathrm{core}) + ne_{\rho} + me_{\lambda} + E^{(1)}_{\Gamma}(\rho^n\lambda^m) \,. \tag{3.34}$$

The first four terms have been explained above. The last term, describing the interaction between more than two active particles outside the core, can be expressed in terms of two-body matrix elements as

$$E^{(1)}_{\Gamma}(\rho^n\lambda^m) \equiv \langle \rho^n\lambda^m | \sum_{1=k<l}^{n+m} V(k,l) | \rho^n\lambda^m\rangle_{\Gamma} = \sum_{\Gamma'} c_{\Gamma'} E^{(1)}_{\Gamma'}(\rho\lambda) \,, \tag{3.35}$$

where the two-body matrix elements are defined by (cf. eq. (3.32))

$$E^{(1)}_{\Gamma'}(\rho\lambda) = \langle \rho\lambda | V(1,2) | \rho\lambda\rangle_{\Gamma'} \,. \tag{3.36}$$

The coefficients $c_{\Gamma'}$ bear no relation to the interaction, but are of pure geometrical nature. This essential step, which allows us to express the interaction between many active particles in terms of a restricted number of two-body matrix elements, will be discussed in detail in chapters 4 and 5.

It should be remarked that eq. (3.35), giving an expression for the binding energy, is only meaningful when it is assumed that the state $|\rho^n\lambda^m\rangle_{\Gamma}$ is described uniquely by one unperturbed wave function, i.e. a configuration with a given particle distribution and a given coupling of single-particle quantum numbers. The complications that arise if this condition is not met will be discussed in sect. 3.5.

3.3. Applications

In this section the theory developed so far will be applied to calculate the binding energy and excitation energies of some nuclei that we assume to be described by an inert closed-shell core and two nucleons.

In the first example, ${}^{18}_{8}\mathrm{O}_{10}$, we take as a core the closed-shell nucleus ${}^{16}_{8}\mathrm{O}_{8}$, and assume that the remaining two neutrons occupy the $1d_{5/2}$ orbit. With these severe restrictions on the model space only a few states in ${}^{18}\mathrm{O}$ can be described. This is because only the Γ values representing the (J^π, T) combinations $(0^+, 1), (2^+, 1)$ and $(4^+, 1)$ are allowed for the two extra neutrons (see sect. 2.4) thus leading to three states in ${}^{18}\mathrm{O}$ (see fig. 3.3). The binding energy of the nucleus for each of these Γ-values can be calculated with eq. (3.18). The terms e_ρ and $E^{\mathrm{b}}(\mathrm{core})$ of this expression are independent of Γ. Therefore the excitation energies follow directly from the different values of the term $E^{(1)}_\Gamma(\rho^2)$. Here we must anticipate the results of chapter 6, where numerical values of the two-body matrix elements of the residual interaction are obtained. In particular the evaluation of the modified surface delta interaction

THE TWO-PARTICLE MODEL FOR ${}^{18}\mathrm{O}$

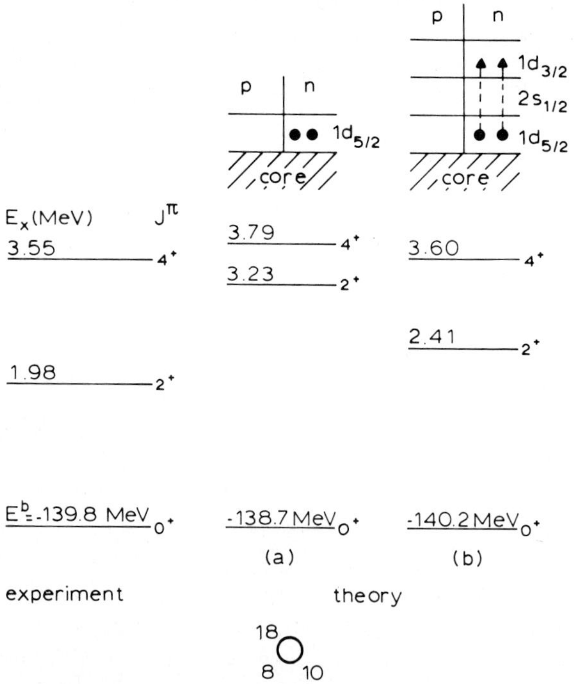

Fig. 3.3. A comparison between theory and experiment for the binding energy and the excitation energies of the low-lying states in ${}^{18}\mathrm{O}$. (a) The spectrum calculated for two neutrons in the $(1d_{5/2})^2$ configuration. (b) The spectrum for two neutrons in the $1d_{5/2}2s_{1/2}1d_{3/2}$ configuration space. In both cases the MSDI is used to describe the two-body interaction.

(MSDI) is used here. This interaction allows a very simple calculation of the two-body matrix elements. For $T = 1$ coupled pairs it contains parameters A_1, B and C that must be determined such that optimum agreement with the experimental data is obtained. A list of two-body matrix elements calculated with the MSDI is given in appendix B.4. One finds

$$\langle (d_{5/2})^2 | V | (d_{5/2})^2 \rangle_{01} = -3A_1 + B + C\,,$$

$$\langle (d_{5/2})^2 | V | (d_{5/2})^2 \rangle_{21} = -0.69A_1 + B + C\,,$$

$$\langle (d_{5/2})^2 | V | (d_{5/2})^2 \rangle_{41} = -0.29A_1 + B + C\,. \tag{3.37}$$

The parameter A_1 is related to the strength of the nuclear interaction for $T = 1$ coupled nucleon pairs. It enters as a multiplicative factor of the calculated matrix elements. A very crude estimate of its value, found empirically, is given by $A_1 \approx 25\,\text{MeV}/A$, where A denotes the nuclear mass number. The parameters B and C, however, shift only the energies of $T = 1$ states. A first estimate of these parameters is given by $B \approx 25\ \text{MeV}/A$ and $C \approx 0$ (see chapter 6). More accurate values of the parameters are obtained from a fit to many experimentally determined binding and excitation energies. For such a fit one assumes that the parameters of the effective two-body interaction are constant in a certain mass region.

The binding energies of the various states of ^{18}O in a $(1d_{5/2})^2$ configuration space are given by

$$E^b_\Gamma(^{18}\text{O}) = E^b(^{16}\text{O}) + 2e_{1d_{5/2}} + \langle (1d_{5/2})^2 | V | (1d_{5/2})^2 \rangle_\Gamma\,. \tag{3.38}$$

The Coulomb energy can be ignored in this approximation, since the protons that are responsible for the Coulomb interaction are all contained in the ^{16}O core. We have assumed that the two extra neutrons do not disturb the inert core.

Let us first restrict ourselves to the excitation energies of the $J^\pi = 2^+$ and 4^+ states with respect to the $J^\pi = 0^+$ ground state. Eqs. (3.17), (3.37) and (3.38) directly lead to the relations $E_x(2^+) = 2.31\,A_1$ and $E_x(4^+) = 2.71\,A_1$, which depend only on the value of the parameter A_1. The result obtained by taking $A_1 = 25\ \text{MeV}/A = 1.4$ MeV is given in fig. 3.3a. It is seen that only the level sequence for the lowest three levels is correctly reproduced. The simple description cannot give the correct level spacing since the ratio of the theoretical excitation energies $E_x(4^+)/E_x(2^+) = 2.71A_1/2.31A_1 = 1.2$ has to be compared with the experimental ratio 3.5 MeV/1.9 MeV = 1.8.

The binding energy of the ^{18}O ground state follows from eq. (3.18) after substitution of the experimental values $E^b(^{16}\text{O})_{\text{g.s.}} = -127.62$ MeV and $e_{1d_{5/2}} = E^b(^{17}\text{O})_{\text{g.s.}} - E^b(^{16}\text{O})_{\text{g.s.}} = (-131.77 + 127.62)\,\text{MeV} = -4.15$ MeV. This yields $E^b(^{18}\text{O})_{\text{g.s.}} = (-127.62 - 2 \times 4.15)\,\text{MeV} - 3A_1 + B = -138.7$ MeV, where the values $A_1 = B = 25\ \text{MeV}/A$ and $C = 0$, given before, are used. The experimental value of the binding energy of ^{18}O is $E^b(^{18}O) = -139.8$ MeV and thus is reproduced reasonably well by the simple model.

It can be shown that when the neutrons are allowed to occupy also higher orbits (i.e. when the configuration space is enlarged and configuration mixing – see sect. 3.5 – is taken into account) a much better agreement with experiment can be obtained. See, for comparison, the results obtained [Halbert, McGrory, Wildenthal and Pandya (1971)] in a $1d_{5/2}2s_{1/2}1d_{3/2}$ configuration space with the same effective interaction (MSDI) given in fig. 3.3b.

Another example is the nucleus $^{30}_{14}Si_{16}$. It has been demonstrated in sect. 2.5 that the J-values of the lower states of this nucleus can be reproduced in terms of configurations with two neutrons in the $2s_{1/2}$ and $1d_{3/2}$ orbits with a closed $^{28}_{14}Si_{14}$ core. From eq. (3.18) one finds with the MSDI matrix elements, evaluated in appendix B.4, the values for the binding and excitation energies as given in table 3.1.

Assume that the ground state and first excited state in ^{29}Si can be described as a ^{28}Si core with one extra neutron. The value for $e_{2s_{1/2}}$ follows from the observed difference in binding energy between the ^{28}Si and ^{29}Si ground states and thus is given by $e_{2s_{1/2}} = E^b(^{29}Si) - E^b(^{28}Si) = (-245.02 + 236.54)$ MeV $= -8.48$ MeV. The value for the spacing $e_{1d_{3/2}} - e_{2s_{1/2}}$ can then be estimated from the energy difference between the $J^\pi = \frac{1}{2}^+$ ground state of ^{29}Si (neutron in the $2s_{1/2}$ orbit) and the $J^\pi = \frac{3}{2}^+$ first excited state at 1.27 MeV (neutron in the $1d_{3/2}$ orbit). Inserting $e_{1d_{3/2}} - e_{2s_{1/2}} =$ 1.27 MeV and taking again as a trial value $A_1 = B = 25$ MeV/A = 0.8 MeV and $C = 0$, one obtains the level structure given in fig. 3.4a.

It is clear from fig. 3.4a that the agreement between theory and experiment for binding and excitation energies is very poor. Especially the second $J^\pi = 0^+$ level has a much too low excitation energy. The calculation in the $2s_{1/2}1d_{3/2}$ configuration space is not yet complete, however. It is not justified to assume that each nuclear state is described by only one pure configuration. As will be discussed in sect. 3.5, the residual interaction mixes the configurations and for a given state the nucleus has

Table 3.1
Energies in ^{30}Si calculated in a $2s_{1/2}1d_{3/2}$ model space as a function of the MSDI parameters A_1, B and C and the single-particle energies $e_{2s_{1/2}}$ and $e_{1d_{3/2}}$

Configuration	J^π	T	Binding energy with respect to the ^{28}Si core	Excitation energy
$(2s_{1/2})^2$	0^+	1	$-\ A_1 + B + C + 2e_{2s_{1/2}}$	0
$2s_{1/2}1d_{3/2}$	1^+	1	$B + C + e_{2s_{1/2}} + e_{1d_{3/2}}$	$A_1 + (e_{1d_{3/2}} - e_{2s_{1/2}})$
$2s_{1/2}1d_{3/2}$	2^+	1	$-0.8A_1 + B + C + e_{2s_{1/2}} + e_{1d_{3/2}}$	$0.2A_1 + (e_{1d_{3/2}} - e_{2s_{1/2}})$
$(1d_{3/2})^2$	0^+	1	$-2.0A_1 + B + C + 2e_{1d_{3/2}}$	$-1.0A_1 + 2(e_{1d_{3/2}} - e_{2s_{1/2}})$
$(1d_{3/2})^2$	2^+	1	$-0.4A_1 + B + C + 2e_{1d_{3/2}}$	$+0.6A_1 + 2(e_{1d_{3/2}} - e_{2s_{1/2}})$

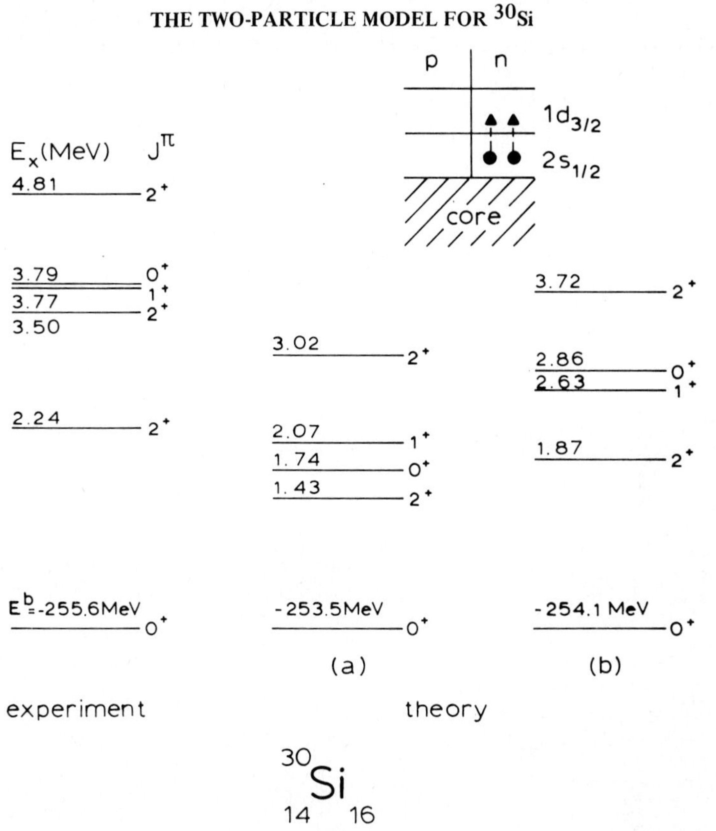

Fig. 3.4. A comparison between theory and experiment for the ground-state binding energy and the excitation energies of the low-lying states in ^{30}Si. The spectra have been calculated for two neutrons in the $2s_{1/2}$ and $1d_{3/2}$ orbits with the MSDI as effective interaction. (a) Calculated spectrum for pure configurations. (b) Calculated spectrum with configuration mixing taken into account.

only a certain probability to be in a particular configuration. This feature is called *configuration mixing.* Inclusion of configuration mixing results in a change of calculated energies. Anticipating the discussion of sect. 3.5, we show in fig. 3.4b the improvement obtained with a mixed-configuration calculation in the same model space.

The nucleus $^{42}_{21}Sc_{21}$ illustrates the situation of a proton and a neutron outside the doubly closed-shell core $^{40}_{20}Ca_{20}$, such that both $T = 0$ and $T = 1$ states can be formed. The simplest description of ^{42}Sc is obtained from a model with a $^{40}_{20}Ca_{20}$ core and both active nucleons occupying the $1f_{7/2}$ shell. From the MSDI matrix elements given in appendix B.4 one obtains the expressions for the excitation energies given in table 3.2. Since the active proton and neutron can couple to $T = 1$ and $T = 0$, one needs in addition to the parameters A_1, B and C for $T = 1$ matrix elements also the parameter A_0 for $T = 0$ matrix elements. Using again the very crude estimate $A_1 = A_0 = B =$

Table 3.2
Calculated excitation energies in ^{42}Sc for $(1f_{7/2})^2$ proton-neutron configurations as a function of the MSDI parameters A_1, A_0 and B

J^π	T	Excitation energy
0^+	1	0
1^+	0	$4.00A_1 - 2.10A_0 - 4B$
2^+	1	$3.05A_1$
3^+	0	$4.00A_1 - 0.99A_0 - 4B$
4^+	1	$3.53A_1$
5^+	0	$4.00A_1 - 0.94A_0 - 4B$
6^+	1	$3.77A_1$
7^+	0	$4.00A_1 - 1.63A_0 - 4B$

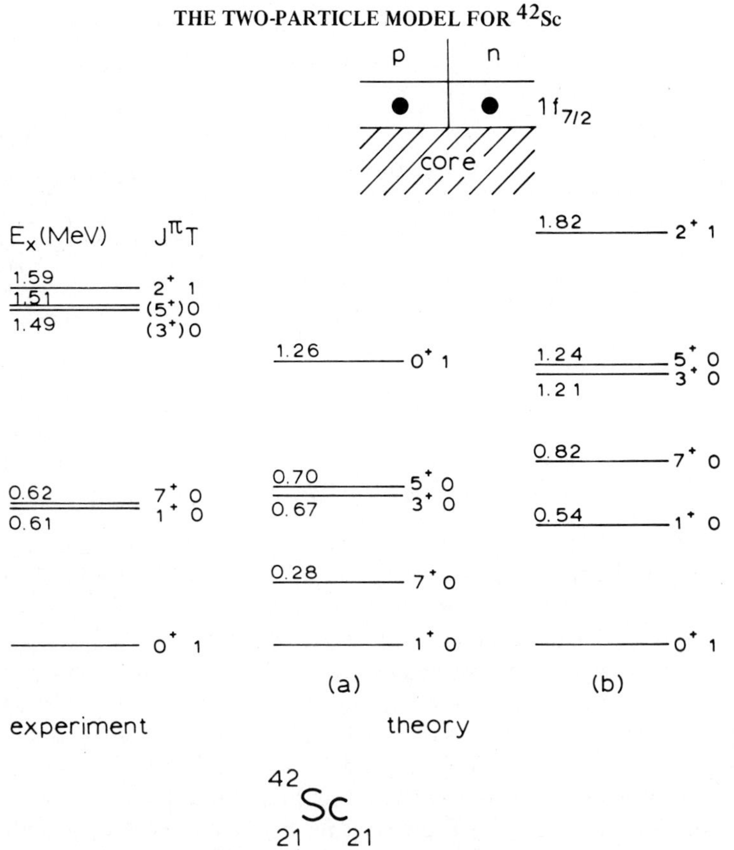

Fig. 3.5. The low-lying states in ^{42}Sc calculated with the MSDI as the two-body interaction for one proton and one neutron in the $1f_{7/2}$ orbit. (a) With the MSDI parameter values $A_0 = A_1 = B = 0.6$ MeV. (b) With $A_0 = A_1 = 0.6$ MeV and $B = 0.15$ MeV.

25 MeV/A = 0.6 MeV and C = 0, one obtains the spectrum given in fig. 3.5a for the lowest six levels of ^{42}Sc. It is seen that this simple $(1f_{7/2})^2$ model space does not produce the correct spin sequence for these low-lying states. Better agreement can be obtained when the $T = 0$ states are shifted upwards. This can be accomplished by taking B = 0.15 MeV instead of the first-guess value B = 0.6 MeV. The result with the improved B-value is given in fig. 3.5b.

3.4. Protons and neutrons filling different orbits

So far it has been assumed that a core consists of equal numbers, say n_a, of inactive protons and neutrons which make up doubly closed subshells with spin $J_a = 0$ and isospin $T_a = 0$. For the treatment of active particles outside such a core the isospin formalism is very convenient. For heavier nuclei the neutron excess may be so large that the additional neutrons, say n_b in number, fill one or more higher-lying subshells completely (see fig. 3.6). These excess neutrons are coupled to spin $J_b = 0$ and to isospin $T_b = (T_b)_z = \frac{1}{2}n_b$. Thus the total spin $\boldsymbol{J}_{core} = \boldsymbol{J}_a + \boldsymbol{J}_b$ and isospin $\boldsymbol{T}_{core} = \boldsymbol{T}_a + \boldsymbol{T}_b$ of such a core with excess neutrons is given by $J_{core} = 0$ and $T_{core} = \frac{1}{2}n_b \neq 0$. Active particles outside this core may be treated more efficiently in a proton-neutron formalism.

The situations that one may encounter with a two-particle system coupled to a core with $J_{core} = 0$ and $T_{core} \neq 0$ are illustrated schematically in fig. 3.7. We first discuss the cases (a), (b) and (c) and we assume that the neutron-excess core is inert. In cases (a) and (b) of fig. 3.7 the projection of the isospin for the two extra nucleons is given by $T''_z = -1$ or $+1$, respectively. The only possible isospin of the two-nucleon system then is $T'' = 1$. In case (c), however, the p-n pair possesses $T''_z = 0$ and the two isospins $t = \frac{1}{2}$ can couple as well to $T'' = 0$ as to $T'' = 1$. It should be realized that both values of T'' may contribute to the description of one particular state, since only the total isospin T of the nucleus is a good quantum number and both values $T'' = 0$ and $T'' = 1$ can couple with T_{core} to a total T when $T = T_{core} \neq 0$ according to the relation

$$\boldsymbol{T} = \boldsymbol{T}_{core} + \boldsymbol{T}'' . \tag{3.39}$$

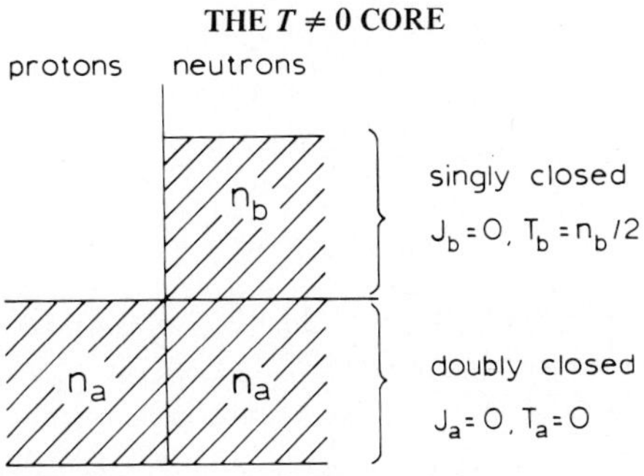

Fig. 3.6. Schematic illustration of a core with an unequal number of protons and neutrons.

TWO PARTICLES OUTSIDE A $T \neq 0$ CORE

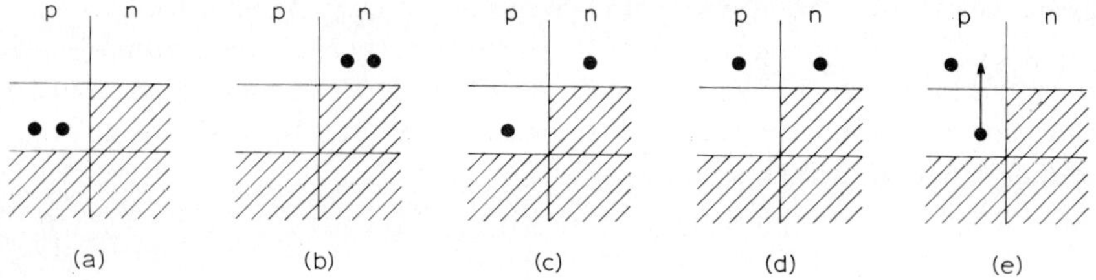

Fig. 3.7. The possibilities for two particles outside a core with $T_z > 0$. Hatching indicates closed orbits. For the cases (a), (b) and (c) the total isospin is well defined. The cases (d) and (e) lead to states of mixed isospin.

The proton-neutron configuration shown in fig. 3.7c is described as the product of a single-proton function and a single-neutron function with their spins coupled to J,

$$\Phi_{JM}(\boldsymbol{r}_\mathrm{p}, \boldsymbol{r}_\mathrm{n}) = \sum_{m_\mathrm{p}, m_\mathrm{n}} \langle j_\mathrm{p} m_\mathrm{p} j_\mathrm{n} m_\mathrm{n} | JM \rangle \, \phi_{j_\mathrm{p} m_\mathrm{p}}(\boldsymbol{r}_\mathrm{p}) \, \phi_{j_\mathrm{n} m_\mathrm{n}}(\boldsymbol{r}_\mathrm{n}) \,. \tag{3.40}$$

In the isospin formalism eq. (3.40) contains the product of a proton and a neutron isospinor that can be written as

$$|t = \tfrac{1}{2}, t_z = -\tfrac{1}{2}\rangle |t = \tfrac{1}{2}, t_z = +\tfrac{1}{2}\rangle = \sum_{T''=0}^{1} \langle \tfrac{1}{2} - \tfrac{1}{2} \tfrac{1}{2} \tfrac{1}{2} | T'' 0 \rangle | T'', 0 \rangle$$

$$= \sqrt{\tfrac{1}{2}} \{ |T'' = 1, T''_z = 0\rangle - |T'' = 0, T''_z = 0\rangle \}, \tag{3.41}$$

where the numerical values $+\sqrt{\frac{1}{2}}$ and $-\sqrt{\frac{1}{2}}$ of the isospin Clebsch-Gordan coefficients for $T'' = 1$ and $T'' = 0$, respectively, have been substituted. The proton-neutron wave function is thus seen to be a mixture of $T'' = 1$ and $T'' = 0$ states. The matrix elements of the residual interaction that are required, now assume the form

$$\langle \Phi_{JM}(\boldsymbol{r}_\mathrm{p}, \boldsymbol{r}_\mathrm{n}) | V | \Phi_{JM}(\boldsymbol{r}_\mathrm{p}, \boldsymbol{r}_\mathrm{n}) \rangle$$

$$= \tfrac{1}{2} \{ \langle J, T'' = 1 | V | J, T'' = 1 \rangle - \langle J, T'' = 1 | V | J, T'' = 0 \rangle$$

$$- \langle J, T'' = 0 | V | J, T'' = 1 \rangle + \langle J, T'' = 0 | V | J, T'' = 0 \rangle \}$$

$$= \tfrac{1}{2} \{ \langle J, T'' = 1 | V | J, T'' = 1 \rangle + \langle J, T'' = 0 | V | J, T'' = 0 \rangle \}, \tag{3.42}$$

where the charge independence of the nuclear interaction, i.e. isospin conservation, causes the matrix elements between states $T'' = 1$ and $T'' = 0$ to vanish. Instead of the relation (3.36) one now has for the expectation value of the residual interaction

$$E_J^{(1)}(\mathrm{p}, \mathrm{n}) = \tfrac{1}{2} \{ \langle \rho\lambda | V | \rho\lambda \rangle_{J, T''=1} + \langle \rho\lambda | V | \rho\lambda \rangle_{J, T''=0} \} \,. \tag{3.43}$$

Thus the interaction between the proton and neutron in a situation as pictured in fig. 3.7c can be written as the sum of $T'' = 1$ and $T'' = 0$ matrix elements.

It must be remarked here that for the configuration in figs. 3.7a, b and c the extra protons are restricted to orbits with counterparts that are completely filled by neutrons. Thus it is impossible to obtain a configuration where one of the extra protons is transformed into a neutron that occupies the same orbit. In other words, these configurations of a core plus proton(s) are all characterized by the property that the isospin-raising operator T_+ yields zero. The total isospin then is well defined and the projection assumes the maximum value, $T_z = T$. The situation becomes much more complex when the extra protons occupy orbits which are not filled completely by neutrons. For such cases other proton-neutron configurations must be admixed to obtain states of well-defined total isospin. A short discussion of this complication will be given now.

In fig. 3.7d a configuration of two nucleons outside a neutron-excess core is drawn for which the total isospin T is not well defined. The configuration of a core plus two particles can be represented by a product of isospin functions as

$$|\mathrm{core}\rangle|\mathrm{n}\rangle|\mathrm{p}\rangle = |T_\mathrm{c}, T_\mathrm{c}\rangle_\mathrm{c}|\tfrac{1}{2}, \tfrac{1}{2}\rangle_1|\tfrac{1}{2}, -\tfrac{1}{2}\rangle_1 , \tag{3.44}$$

where each of the isospin functions is given by $|T, T_z\rangle_k$ with k denoting the number of particles concerned. One thus obtains, coupling the isospins with Clebsch-Gordan coefficients, the equalities

$$\begin{aligned}
|T_\mathrm{c}, T_\mathrm{c}\rangle_\mathrm{c}|\tfrac{1}{2}, \tfrac{1}{2}\rangle_1|\tfrac{1}{2}, -\tfrac{1}{2}\rangle_1 &= \langle T_\mathrm{c}T_\mathrm{c}\tfrac{1}{2}\tfrac{1}{2}|T_\mathrm{c}+\tfrac{1}{2}, T_\mathrm{c}+\tfrac{1}{2}\rangle|T_\mathrm{c}+\tfrac{1}{2}, T_\mathrm{c}+\tfrac{1}{2}\rangle_{\mathrm{c}+1}|\tfrac{1}{2}, -\tfrac{1}{2}\rangle_1 \\
&= |T_\mathrm{c}+\tfrac{1}{2}, T_\mathrm{c}+\tfrac{1}{2}\rangle_{\mathrm{c}+1}|\tfrac{1}{2}, -\tfrac{1}{2}\rangle_1 \\
&= \langle T_\mathrm{c}+\tfrac{1}{2}, T_\mathrm{c}+\tfrac{1}{2}, \tfrac{1}{2}, -\tfrac{1}{2}|T_\mathrm{c}+1, T_\mathrm{c}\rangle|T_\mathrm{c}+1, T_\mathrm{c}\rangle_{\mathrm{c}+2} \\
&\quad + \langle T_\mathrm{c}+\tfrac{1}{2}, T_\mathrm{c}+\tfrac{1}{2}, \tfrac{1}{2}, -\tfrac{1}{2}|T_\mathrm{c}, T_\mathrm{c}\rangle|T_\mathrm{c}, T_\mathrm{c}\rangle_{\mathrm{c}+2} \\
&= \frac{1}{\sqrt{2T_\mathrm{c}+2}}|T_\mathrm{c}+1, T_\mathrm{c}\rangle_{\mathrm{c}+2} + \sqrt{\frac{2T_\mathrm{c}+1}{2T_\mathrm{c}+2}}|T_\mathrm{c}, T_\mathrm{c}\rangle_{\mathrm{c}+2} .
\end{aligned} \tag{3.45}$$

Here eq. (A.1.a5) has been used to introduce the two possible values of the total isospin $T_\mathrm{c}+1$ and T_c. The explicit values of the Clebsch-Gordan coefficients are given in eq. (A.1.a14).

The two components in eq. (3.45) each possess well-defined isospin and can be interpreted as follows. Let us consider the state $|T_\mathrm{c}+1, T_\mathrm{c}\rangle_{\mathrm{c}+2}$ first. The configuration of fig. 3.7c can be written as

$$|T_\mathrm{c}+1, T_\mathrm{c}+1\rangle_{\mathrm{c}+2} = |T_\mathrm{c}, T_\mathrm{c}\rangle_\mathrm{c}|1, 1\rangle_2 , \tag{3.46}$$

since the Clebsch-Gordan coefficient entering the right-hand side is equal to unity. Acting upon this state with the normalized isospin-lowering operator (cf. eq. (2.69)), one obtains

$$|T_c+1, T_c\rangle_{c+2} = \frac{T_-}{\sqrt{2T_c+2}}|T_c+1,\ T_c+1\rangle_{c+2} = \frac{T_-}{\sqrt{2T_c+2}}[|T_c, T_c\rangle_c|1,1\rangle_2]$$

$$= |T_c, T_c\rangle_c \frac{T_-}{\sqrt{2T_c+2}}|1,1\rangle_2 + |1,1\rangle_2 \frac{T_-}{\sqrt{2T_c+2}}|T_c, T_c\rangle_c$$

$$= \frac{1}{\sqrt{T_c+1}}|T_c, T_c\rangle_c|1,0\rangle_2 + \sqrt{\frac{T_c}{T_c+1}}|T_c, T_c-1\rangle_c|1,1\rangle_2 \ . \qquad (3.47)$$

The first term of eq. (3.47) represents a $T = 1$, $T_z = 0$ coupled nucleon pair outside the closed core. The second term describes a $T = 1$, $T_z = 1$ coupled neutron pair plus a configuration that is no longer closed in protons and in neutrons. One thus has for the first component of the state (3.45), writing eq. (3.47) in a pictorial notation,

$$|T_c+1, T_c\rangle_{c+2} = \frac{T_-}{\sqrt{2T_c+2}}$$ 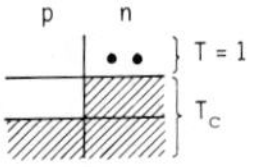

$$= \frac{1}{\sqrt{T_c+1}}$$ 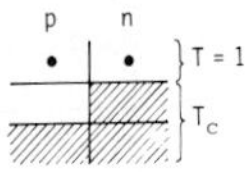

$$+ \sqrt{\frac{T_c}{T_c+1}}$$ 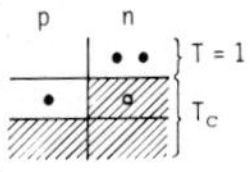

. (3.48)

It is seen that holes in the neutron-excess core must be taken into account. Since the isospin-lowering operator does not affect the angular momenta, the configuration $|T_c, T_c-1\rangle_c$ is still coupled to $J_c = 0$.

The other component in eq. (3.45), i.e. $|T_c, T_c\rangle_{c+2}$, is orthogonal to $|T_c+1, T_c\rangle_{c+2}$ and is given by

$$|T_c, T_c\rangle_{c+2} = \frac{T_c}{\sqrt{(2T_c+1)(T_c+1)}}|T_c, T_c\rangle_c|1,0\rangle_2 + \sqrt{\frac{T_c+1}{2T_c+1}}|T_c, T_c\rangle_c|0,0\rangle_2$$

$$- \sqrt{\frac{T_c}{(2T_c+1)(T_c+1)}}|T_c, T_c-1\rangle_c|1,1\rangle_2 \ . \qquad (3.49)$$

This expression can be verified by writing the left-hand side of eq. (3.45) as

$$|T_c, T_c\rangle_c|\tfrac{1}{2},\tfrac{1}{2}\rangle_1|\tfrac{1}{2},-\tfrac{1}{2}\rangle_1 = \sqrt{\tfrac{1}{2}}|T_c, T_c\rangle_c|1,0\rangle_2 + \sqrt{\tfrac{1}{2}}|T_c, T_c\rangle_c|0,0\rangle_2 \ , \qquad (3.50)$$

and inserting eqs. (3.47) and (3.49) into the right-hand side of eq. (3.45). In the pictorial notation used before we can represent the second component of the state (3.45) as

$$|T_c, T_c\rangle_{c+2} = \frac{T_c}{\sqrt{(2T_c+1)(T_c+1)}}$$

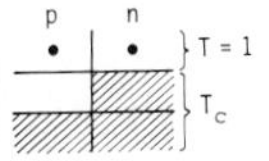

$$+ \sqrt{\frac{T_c+1}{2T_c+1}}$$

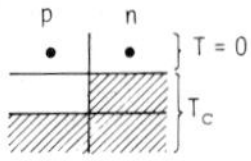

$$- \sqrt{\frac{T_c}{(2T_c+1)(T_c+1)}}$$

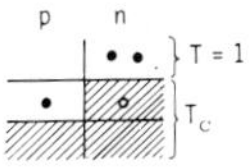

. (3.51)

It is clear now that the treatment of the configuration of fig. 3.7d requires more complicated proton-neutron wave functions in order to obtain states of well-defined isospin. The same holds for the configuration of fig. 3.7e. This is the case in general as soon as configurations are considered that consist of a neutron-excess core and one or more extra protons that occupy orbits, the counterparts of which are not completely filled by neutrons. In such a case one must break up the closed neutron core, which may destroy the simplicity of the proton-neutron formalism. It also occurs that configurations that are simple in the proton-neutron formalism are complicated to describe in the isospin formalism. Here we shall not discuss these cases any further and we restrict ourselves to configurations with a neutron-excess for which the isospin formalism is convenient.

An example is given for the nucleus ${}^{38}_{17}Cl_{21}$. Assume that the low-lying states can be described as a ${}^{36}_{16}S_{20}$ core plus a proton in the $1d_{3/2}$ shell and a neutron in the $1f_{7/2}$ shell. The binding energy of a state of ${}^{38}Cl$ with respect to the ${}^{36}S$ core is thus according to eq. (3.43) given by

$$E_J^b({}^{38}\mathrm{Cl}) = E_J^{(1)}(\mathrm{p},\mathrm{n}) + e_{1d_{3/2}} + e_{1f_{7/2}} = \tfrac{1}{2}\{\langle 1d_{3/2}1f_{7/2}|V|1d_{3/2}1f_{7/2}\rangle_{J,T=0}$$

$$+ \langle 1d_{3/2}1f_{7/2}|V|1d_{3/2}1f_{7/2}\rangle_{J,T=1}\} + e_{1d_{3/2}} + e_{1f_{7/2}}\,, \qquad (3.52)$$

where we have used the symbol T instead of T'' to denote the isospin of the two extra particles. The single-particle energies $e_{1d_{3/2}}$ and $e_{1f_{7/2}}$ are derived from the binding energies of ${}^{37}_{17}Cl_{20}$ and ${}^{37}_{16}S_{21}$ with respect to the ${}^{36}_{16}S_{20}$ core. The excitation

Table 3.3
Excitation energies in ${}^{38}Cl$ for $1d_{3/2}1f_{7/2}$ configurations as a function of the MSDI parameters A_0 and A_1

J^π	Excitation energy
2^-	0
3^-	$1.15A_0 - 0.19A_1$
4^-	$1.34A_0$
5^-	$0.99A_0 - 0.61A_1$

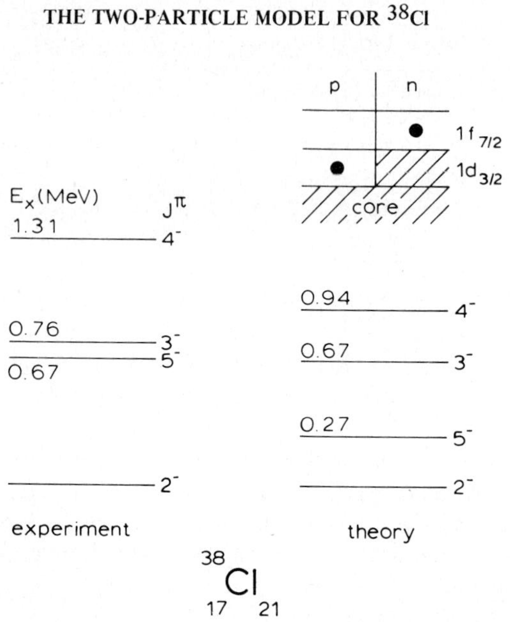

Fig. 3.8. The spectrum of ^{38}Cl calculated with the MSDI for a proton in the $1d_{3/2}$ orbit and a neutron in the $1f_{7/2}$ orbit outside the ^{36}S core.

energies in the given configuration space, however, are independent of the single-particle energies. When we employ again as effective interaction the MSDI to evaluate the matrix elements, the excitation energies are determined only by the strengths A_0 and A_1. Inserting the values of the two-body matrix elements from appendix B.4 into eq. (3.52), one obtains the expressions for the excitation energies given in table 3.3. Taking the usual first-guess value for the strength parameters $A_1 = A_0 = 25$ MeV/A = 0.7 MeV one finds the level scheme given in fig. 3.8. It is seen that the correct spin sequence of the lower states in ^{38}Cl can be reproduced. The agreement of the excitation energies is still poor, but can be improved by taking somewhat larger values for the strength parameters A_1 and A_0.

3.5. States of mixed configuration

Up till now we have restricted our discussion to unperturbed states $\Phi_\Gamma^{(0)}$. Each of these states represents a pure shell-model configuration. For example, considering two active orbits ρ and λ, one has pure states $\Phi_\Gamma^{(0)}(\rho_\alpha^n\lambda_\beta^m)$ each with a given particle distribution specified by ρ^n and λ^m and a given set of intermediate quantum numbers α and β with $\boldsymbol{J}_\alpha + \boldsymbol{J}_\beta = \boldsymbol{J}_\Gamma$ and $\boldsymbol{T}_\alpha + \boldsymbol{T}_\beta = \boldsymbol{T}_\Gamma$.

It follows from eq. (3.16) that the energy of the pure state $\Phi_\Gamma^{(0)}$ is given by the sum of two terms $E = E^{(0)} + E^{(1)}$. The contribution $E^{(0)}$ results from the Hamiltonian $H^{(0)}$, that describes the independent-particle motion. The contribution $E^{(1)}$ derives from the residual interaction $H^{(1)}$. Suppose there are g states $(\Phi_\Gamma^{(0)})_k$ with $k = 1, ..., g$ of which the energies $E_k = E_k^{(0)} + E_k^{(1)}$ are not very much different. In this case we cannot neglect that, due to the residual interaction, the nucleons may scatter from one state $(\Phi_\Gamma^{(0)})_k$ into the other. Thus the actual state must be given by a mixture of states $(\Phi_\Gamma^{(0)})_k$. The task is to find the appropriate linear combinations of $(\Phi_\Gamma^{(0)})_k$ that describe the many-particle system.

Let us write these combinations as

$$\Psi_p = \sum_{k=1}^{g} a_{kp}\, \Phi_k^{(0)} \qquad (p = 1, ..., g)\,, \tag{3.53}$$

where for brevity the label Γ denoting the fixed value of J_Γ and T_Γ has been suppressed. The normalization condition for Ψ_p is given by the relation

$$\sum_{k=1}^{g} a_{kp}^2 = 1 \qquad \text{with } p = 1, ..., g\,. \tag{3.54}$$

The square of the amplitude a_{kp} may be interpreted as the probability that the nucleus is in the state described by $\Phi_k^{(0)}$.

One now has to solve the eigenvalue equation

$$H|\Psi_p\rangle = E_p|\Psi_p\rangle\,. \tag{3.55}$$

Substituting the complete Hamiltonian (3.3) and the wave function (3.53) into the Schrödinger equation (3.55), one obtains

$$(H^{(0)} + H^{(1)})|\sum_{k=1}^{g} a_{kp}\,\Phi_k^{(0)}\rangle = E_p|\sum_{k=1}^{g} a_{kp}\,\Phi_k^{(0)}\rangle\,. \tag{3.56}$$

Multiplication on the left-hand side with $\langle\Phi_l^{(0)}|$ leads to

$$\sum_{k=1}^{g} \langle\Phi_l^{(0)}|H^{(0)} + H^{(1)}|\Phi_k^{(0)}\rangle\, a_{kp} = E_p a_{lp}\,, \tag{3.57}$$

where the orthonormality of the functions $\Phi_k^{(0)}$ has been used. Since the functions $\Phi_k^{(0)}$ are eigenstates of $H^{(0)}$ with

$$H^{(0)}\Phi_k^{(0)} = E_k^{(0)}\Phi_k^{(0)}\,, \tag{3.58}$$

one obtains for the matrix elements of H

$$H_{lk} \equiv \langle \Phi_l^{(0)} | H | \Phi_k^{(0)} \rangle = \langle \Phi_l^{(0)} | H^{(0)} + H^{(1)} | \Phi_k^{(0)} \rangle = \langle \Phi_l^{(0)} | H^{(0)} | \Phi_k^{(0)} \rangle + \langle \Phi_l^{(0)} | H^{(1)} | \Phi_k^{(0)} \rangle$$

$$= E_k^{(0)} \delta_{lk} + H_{lk}^{(1)} . \qquad (3.59)$$

The term $E_k^{(0)}$ represents the contribution from the single-particle energies and $H_{lk}^{(1)}$ that from the residual interaction.

Employing the abbreviated notation of eq. (3.59) one can rewrite eq. (3.57) as

$$\sum_{k=1}^{g} H_{lk} a_{kp} = E_p a_{lp} . \qquad (3.60)$$

Writing the amplitudes a_{kp} as column vectors for each value of p, one can give eq. (3.60) in explicit matrix form (multiplying, as usual, rows with columns) as

$$\begin{pmatrix} H_{11} & H_{12} & \cdots & H_{1g} \\ H_{21} & H_{22} & & \cdot \\ \cdot & & & \cdot \\ \cdot & & & \cdot \\ \cdot & & & \cdot \\ H_{g1} & \cdot & \cdots & H_{gg} \end{pmatrix} \begin{pmatrix} a_{1p} \\ a_{2p} \\ \cdot \\ \cdot \\ \cdot \\ a_{gp} \end{pmatrix} = E_p \begin{pmatrix} a_{1p} \\ a_{2p} \\ \cdot \\ \cdot \\ \cdot \\ a_{gp} \end{pmatrix} . \qquad (3.61)$$

Due to the hermiticity of H one obtains for the (real) matrix elements the relation

$$H_{lk} = H_{kl} , \qquad (3.62)$$

which implies that the matrix H_{lk} is symmetric. The condition that eq. (3.61) does possess solutions a_{kp}, requires a vanishing determinant

$$\begin{vmatrix} H_{11} - E_p & H_{12} & \cdots & H_{1g} \\ H_{21} & H_{22} - E_p & & \cdot \\ \cdot & & & \cdot \\ \cdot & & & \cdot \\ \cdot & & & \cdot \\ H_{g1} & \cdots & \cdot & H_{gg} - E_p \end{vmatrix} = 0 . \qquad (3.63)$$

This leads to an equation of degree g in E_p and thus to g roots E_p $(p = 1, 2, ..., g)$. Substitution of the different roots into eq. (3.61) then leads each time to an equation for the corresponding eigenvector a_{kp}.

The eigenvectors belonging to different eigenvalues are necessarily orthogonal and each can be normalized such that

$$\sum_{k=1}^{g} a_{kp} a_{kp'} = \delta_{pp'} \quad \text{for } E_p \neq E_{p'} \,. \tag{3.64}$$

For $E_p = E_{p'}$ with $p \neq p'$ the corresponding eigenvectors a_{kp} and $a_{kp'}$ can be made orthonormal with the aid of some *ad hoc* orthogonalization procedure. Multiplying eq. (3.60) with $a_{lp'}$ and summing over l, one obtains with the aid of eq. (3.64)

$$\sum_{l,k=1}^{g} a_{lp'} H_{lk} a_{kp} = E_p \delta_{pp'} \,. \tag{3.65}$$

Note that eqs. (3.55) and (3.65) are equivalent. For the latter, however, a particular representation of basis states $\Phi_k^{(0)}$ has been chosen. Writing eq. (3.65) in matrix notation one obtains

$$\begin{pmatrix} a_{11} & a_{21} & \cdots & a_{g1} \\ a_{12} & & & \cdot \\ \cdot & & & \cdot \\ \cdot & & & \cdot \\ \cdot & & & \cdot \\ a_{1g} & \cdots & \cdots & a_{gg} \end{pmatrix} \begin{pmatrix} H_{11} & H_{12} & \cdots & H_{1g} \\ H_{21} & & & \cdot \\ \cdot & & & \cdot \\ \cdot & & & \cdot \\ \cdot & & & \cdot \\ H_{g1} & \cdots & \cdots & H_{gg} \end{pmatrix} \begin{pmatrix} a_{11} & a_{12} & \cdots & a_{1g} \\ a_{21} & & & \cdot \\ \cdot & & & \cdot \\ \cdot & & & \cdot \\ \cdot & & & \cdot \\ a_{g1} & \cdots & \cdots & a_{gg} \end{pmatrix} = \begin{pmatrix} E_1 & 0 & \cdot & \cdot & \cdot & 0 \\ 0 & E_2 & \cdot & & & \cdot \\ \cdot & \cdot & \cdot & \cdot & & \cdot \\ \cdot & & \cdot & \cdot & \cdot & \cdot \\ \cdot & & & \cdot & \cdot & 0 \\ 0 & \cdot & \cdot & \cdot & 0 & E_g \end{pmatrix} . \tag{3.66}$$

Thus the matrices a_{kp} diagonalize the matrix H_{lk}. Eq. (3.64) implies that the coefficients a_{kp} constitute an orthogonal matrix, say A. The orthogonality of this matrix can be expressed by the relation $A^{-1} = A^{\mathrm{T}}$, i.e. the inverse matrix A^{-1} is given by the transposed matrix A^{T} (rows and columns interchanged). Eq. (3.66) can now be given in the compact form

$$A^{-1} H A = E \,, \tag{3.67}$$

where the right-hand side is a diagonal matrix.

It should be noted that the complication of the diagonalization procedure always occurs when the pure states $\Phi_k^{(0)}$ are so close in energy that the off-diagonal matrix elements H_{lk} and the energy difference of the pure states, given by $|E_k - E_l|$, are of the same order of magnitude. In such a case the relatively large off-diagonal matrix elements of the residual interaction cause a large-scale mixing of the unperturbed wave functions $\Phi_k^{(0)}$. The feature to form linear combinations of configurations to describe a particular state is referred to as *configuration mixing*.

Throughout this book configurations will be considered different when the numbers of particles in a given orbit and/or the intermediate coupling quantum numbers are not the same. Thus $\Phi_\Gamma^{(0)}(\rho_\alpha^n\lambda_\beta^m)$ and $\Phi_\Gamma^{(0)}(\rho_{\alpha'}^{n'}\lambda_{\beta'}^{m'})$ are different if $n, m \neq n', m'$ and/or $\alpha \neq \alpha'$ and/or $\beta \neq \beta'$.

One can summarize the procedure which leads to the determination of energies and wave functions as follows. The energy matrix is constructed from the matrix elements H_{lk}, defined in eq. (3.59). The unperturbed Hamiltonian $H^{(0)}$, leading to the single-particle energies, only contributes to the diagonal matrix elements. Diagonalization of the matrix H_{lk} leads to the required eigenvalues (energies) and eigenvectors (mixed-configuration wave functions) of the Hamiltonian.

It is difficult to say *a priori* how many configurations $\Phi_k^{(0)}$ should be taken into account. Often there are many states $\Phi_k^{(0)}$ with energies E_k lying rather close together. In such cases the speed and memory of the computer, needed to perform the diagonalization, may be the limiting factor. Some *ad hoc* truncation procedure must then be employed (see e.g. sect. 18.2).

For an evaluation of $H^{(1)}$ use is made of the assumption that the perturbation in the shell model can be written as a sum over two-particle interactions

$$H^{(1)} = \sum_{i<j} V(i, j) . \tag{3.68}$$

3.6. Application of configuration mixing

Suppose there are two states in a nucleus, both having the same spin J and isospin T, to be described by the orthonormal wave functions $\Phi_1^{(0)}$ and $\Phi_2^{(0)}$ (see fig. 3.9). Without configuration mixing the energies of the two states $\Phi_1^{(0)}$ and $\Phi_2^{(0)}$ are given by $H_{11} = \langle\Phi_1^{(0)}|H|\Phi_1^{(0)}\rangle$ and $H_{22} = \langle\Phi_2^{(0)}|H|\Phi_2^{(0)}\rangle$, respectively, as follows from eq. (3.16). Introduce two wave functions Ψ_p given by (see eqs. (3.53) and (3.54))

$$\Psi_p = a_{1p}\Phi_1^{(0)} + a_{2p}\Phi_2^{(0)} \qquad \text{with } a_{1p}^2 + a_{2p}^2 = 1 \qquad (p = 1, 2) . \tag{3.69}$$

Eq. (3.61) shows that with configuration mixing the energies are obtained from the

CONFIGURATION MIXING FOR TWO STATES

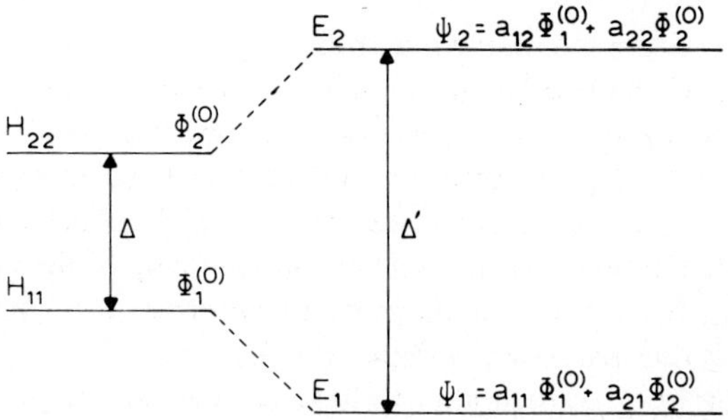

Fig. 3.9. The change in energy separation that results from the mixing of two states.

eigenvalue equation

$$\begin{pmatrix} H_{11} & H_{12} \\ H_{21} & H_{22} \end{pmatrix} \begin{pmatrix} a_{1p} \\ a_{2p} \end{pmatrix} = E_p \begin{pmatrix} a_{1p} \\ a_{2p} \end{pmatrix} \tag{3.70}$$

with the matrix elements $H_{lk} = H_{kl}$ defined in eq. (3.59). The eigenvalues $E_p = E_p^{(0)} + E_p^{(1)}$ follow from

$$\begin{vmatrix} H_{11} - E_p & H_{12} \\ H_{12} & H_{22} - E_p \end{vmatrix} = 0 \quad \text{or} \quad (H_{11} - E_p)(H_{22} - E_p) - H_{12}^2 = 0 \tag{3.71}$$

with the solutions given by

$$E_p = \tfrac{1}{2}\{H_{11} + H_{22} \pm \sqrt{(H_{11} - H_{22})^2 + (2H_{12})^2}\}. \tag{3.72}$$

For the two possible roots E_1 (lower sign) and E_2 (upper sign) of eq. (3.72) one obtains two different wave functions Ψ_1 and Ψ_2, respectively. The corresponding amplitudes a_{lp} can be calculated from eqs. (3.69) and (3.70) and one obtains for $p = 1$

$$\Psi_1 = a_{11}\Phi_1^{(0)} + a_{21}\Phi_2^{(0)} = \pm \frac{H_{12}\Phi_1^{(0)} + (E_1 - H_{11})\Phi_2^{(0)}}{\sqrt{(E_1 - H_{11})^2 + H_{12}^2}} \tag{3.73}$$

and for $p = 2$

$$\Psi_2 = a_{12}\Phi_1^{(0)} + a_{22}\Phi_2^{(0)} = \pm \frac{(E_2 - H_{22})\Phi_1^{(0)} + H_{12}\Phi_2^{(0)}}{\sqrt{(E_2 - H_{22})^2 + H_{12}^2}}. \tag{3.74}$$

Since eq. (3.72) yields $E_1 - H_{11} = -(E_2 - H_{22})$, one sees from eqs. (3.73) and (3.74) that the wave functions Ψ_1 and Ψ_2 are indeed orthogonal with $a_{12} = \pm a_{21}$ and $a_{11} = \mp a_{22}$. It also follows from these equations that for a vanishing residual interaction, i.e. $H_{12} = H_{12}^{(1)} \to 0$, each perturbed state goes over into one specific unperturbed state, i.e. $\Psi_k \to \Phi_k^{(0)}$ $(k = 1, 2)$. For a verification of this limit one must take into account that the differences $E_1 - H_{11}$ and $E_2 - H_{22}$ are proportional to H_{12}^2 for vanishing H_{12}, as follows from eq. (3.72).

In eqs. (3.73) and (3.74) the two wave functions Ψ_1 and Ψ_2 are determined only up to a sign, i.e. one may still provide either one of them or both with an overall minus sign. It is known from quantum mechanics that the phase of a wave function has no physical meaning, i.e. wave functions that differ only in phase do represent the same state.

The energy separation between the states, originally described by $\Phi_1^{(0)}$ and $\Phi_2^{(0)}$, changes when configuration mixing between these two states is taken into account. Let

$$\Delta = |H_{11} - H_{22}| \tag{3.75}$$

be their energy separation without configuration mixing (see fig. 3.9). From eq. (3.72) then follows that with configuration mixing the energy separation is given by

$$\Delta' = \sqrt{\Delta^2 + (2H_{12})^2} \; . \tag{3.76}$$

The level separation increases as a result of configuration mixing since $\Delta' \geqslant \Delta$. For the off-diagonal matrix element H_{12} one finds from eq. (3.76) the relations

$$2|H_{12}| = \Delta' \quad \text{for} \quad \Delta = 0 \, , \tag{3.77}$$

$$2|H_{12}| < \Delta' \quad \text{for} \quad \Delta \neq 0 \, . \tag{3.78}$$

Relation (3.78) can set an upper limit on the value for $|H_{12}|$ when Δ' is known experimentally.

A typical example that illustrates the effect of configuration mixing, when many states are taken into account, is given in fig. 3.10. In this case the matrix is constructed for all 273 states in ^{63}Cu with $J^\pi = \frac{5}{2}^-$ and $T = \frac{5}{2}$ that can be formed with seven active particles in a $2p_{3/2}1f_{5/2}2p_{1/2}$ configuration space (the nucleus ^{56}Ni with a closed $1f_{7/2}$ orbit is taken as an inert core). The number of states per MeV energy interval is plotted with and without configuration mixing. It is seen that configura-

CONFIGURATION MIXING FOR MANY STATES

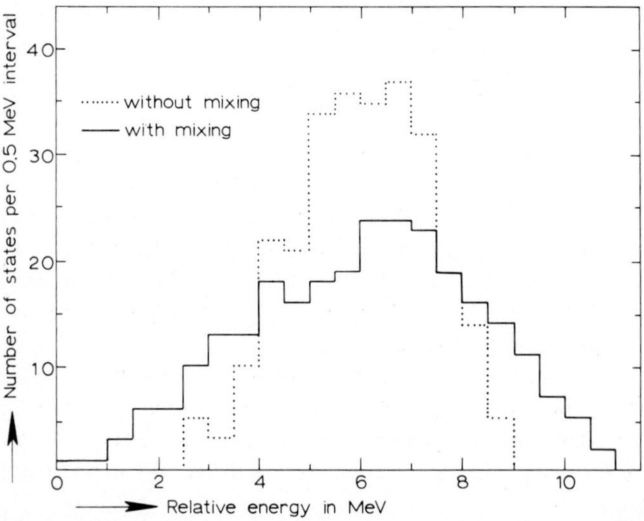

Fig. 3.10. Histogram of the distribution of the 273 states with $J^\pi = \frac{5}{2}^-$, $T = \frac{5}{2}$ in ^{63}Cu. The number of states per 0.5 MeV energy interval has been calculated with and without configuration mixing. This number is plotted as a function of the relative energy of the states with respect to the lowest eigenvalue. A model with seven particles in the $2p_{3/2}$, $1f_{5/2}$ and $2p_{1/2}$ orbits and the MSDI as effective interaction have been used.

tion mixing leads to a larger separation between the lowest- and the highest-lying state.

3.7. Examples

The excitation energies in ^{30}Si have been calculated in sect. 3.3 with the assumption that the states can be described by pure configurations. This time the effect of configuration mixing will be investigated. Let us restrict ourselves first to the $J^\pi = 0^+$, $T = 1$ levels with the configurations $|\Phi_1^{(0)}\rangle = |(2s_{1/2})^2\rangle_{01}$ and $|\Phi_2^{(0)}\rangle = |(1d_{3/2})^2\rangle_{01}$. Assuming that only these two states mix, one can use eq. (3.72) to obtain the energies of the perturbed states. For this purpose the values of the matrix elements $H_{kl} = \langle\Phi_k|H^{(0)} + H^{(1)}|\Phi_l\rangle$ must be available. In order to evaluate the matrix elements of the residual interaction $H^{(1)}$ we employ as before the MSDI. Since $H^{(0)}$ only contributes to the diagonal matrix elements, one obtains

$$H_{11} = \langle(2s_{1/2})^2|V(1,2)|(2s_{1/2})^2\rangle_{01} + 2e_{2s_{1/2}} = -A_1 + B + C + 2e_{2s_{1/2}} \,,$$

$$H_{22} = \langle(1d_{3/2})^2|V(1,2)|(1d_{3/2})^2\rangle_{01} + 2e_{1d_{3/2}} = -2A_1 + B + C + 2e_{1d_{3/2}} \,,$$

$$H_{12} = \langle(2s_{1/2})^2|V(1,2)|(1d_{3/2})^2\rangle_{01} = -1.41A_1 \,. \tag{3.79}$$

With the values $A_1 = B = 0.8$ MeV, $C = 0$, $e_{2s_{1/2}} = -8.48$ MeV and $e_{1d_{3/2}} = -7.21$ MeV as used before (see sect. 3.3), the values $H_{11} = -16.96$ MeV, $H_{22} = -15.22$ MeV and $H_{12} = -1.13$ MeV are obtained. Inserting these values in eq. (3.72) one obtains the eigenvalues $E_1(0^+) = -17.52$ MeV and $E_2(0^+) = -14.66$ MeV (see fig. 3.4b). The corresponding eigenvectors that follow from eqs. (3.73) and (3.74) are given by

$$|\Psi_1\rangle = \pm\{0.90\,|(2s_{1/2})^2\rangle_{01} + 0.44\,|(1d_{3/2})^2\rangle_{01}\} \,, \tag{3.80}$$

$$|\Psi_2\rangle = \pm\{0.44\,|(2s_{1/2})^2\rangle_{01} - 0.90\,|(1d_{3/2})^2\rangle_{01}\} \,, \tag{3.81}$$

respectively. The overall phases of Ψ_1 as well as Ψ_2 can still be chosen arbitrarily. Similarly for the $J^\pi = 2^+$, $T = 1$ levels one finds with configuration mixing of the states $|\Phi_1\rangle = |2s_{1/2}1d_{3/2}\rangle_{21}$ and $|\Phi_2\rangle = |(1d_{3/2})^2\rangle_{21}$ the results $H_{11} = -15.53$ MeV, $H_{22} = -13.94$ MeV and $H_{12} = +0.45$ MeV. The energies of the mixed states are then found to be $E_1(2^+) = -15.65$ MeV and $E_2(2^+) = -13.82$ MeV. The $J^\pi = 0^+$ and 2^+ states represent the only configuration mixing that can occur for two neutrons in the $2s_{1/2}1d_{3/2}$ shell. For the energy of the pure state $|2s_{1/2}1d_{3/2}\rangle_{11}$ one finds $E = -14.89$ MeV and one gets the level scheme given in fig. 3.4b.

It is seen that with mixed configurations a better agreement with experiment is obtained. The agreement can be improved further by taking the strength of the interaction larger than the crude estimate $A_1 = 0.8$ MeV used here. This larger value will lead to a stronger binding and a larger separation between the calculated levels. It can be shown that in that case the calculated second $J^\pi = 2^+$ state should be

SINGLE-PARTICLE STATES IN ^{57}Ni

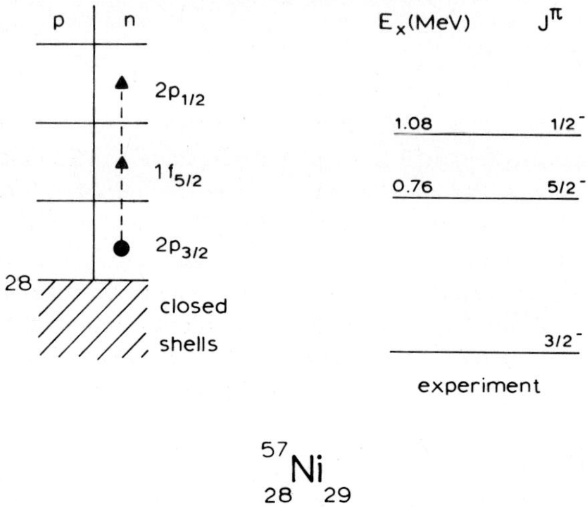

Fig. 3.11. The lower states in ^{57}Ni that are assumed to be described by single-particle states and a closed-shell core of 28 protons and 28 neutrons.

identified with the experimentally observed state at $E_x = 4.81$ MeV. The observed $J^\pi = 2^+$ level at $E_x = 3.50$ MeV then is not reproduced in this simple model space. However, it follows from more extended shell-model calculations [Wildenthal, McGrory, Halbert and Graber (1971)] that this state can be explained by admixing configurations in which $1d_{5/2}$ holes in the ^{28}Si core are explicitly taken into account.

A final example for which matrices of up to order five must be diagonalized is provided by a shell-model description of $^{58}_{28}Ni_{30}$. We will discuss this nucleus in terms of a model space where $^{56}_{28}Ni_{28}$ is taken as an inert core of closed $(1f_{7/2})^8$ proton and neutron orbits. The remaining two neutrons are assumed to occupy only the next higher orbits $2p_{3/2}$, $1f_{5/2}$ and $2p_{1/2}$. The fact that these orbits should be important is suggested by the spin and parities of the lowest three states of the core-plus-one-particle nucleus, $^{57}_{28}Ni_{29}$. The spins and parities in ^{57}Ni are given by $J^\pi = \frac{3}{2}^-, \frac{5}{2}^-$ and $\frac{1}{2}^-$ for $E_x = 0$, 0.76 and 1.08 MeV, respectively (see fig. 3.11). The single-particle energy spacings between the orbits $2p_{3/2}$, $1f_{5/2}$ and $2p_{1/2}$ can thus be taken from the experimental ^{57}Ni spectrum.

The MSDI two-body matrix elements for particles in the orbits $2p_{3/2}$, $1f_{5/2}$ and $2p_{1/2}$ needed for a description of ^{58}Ni can be found in appendix B.4. Only the matrix elements for $T = 1$ coupled pairs enter into the calculation, since we deal with identical active particles (neutrons). The only adjustable parameter affecting the calculated excitation energies is then given by the strength A_1. For a crude estimate of the strength we use again the value $A_1 = 25$ MeV/$A \approx 0.4$ MeV. The ^{58}Ni spectrum obtained this way is given in fig. 3.12.

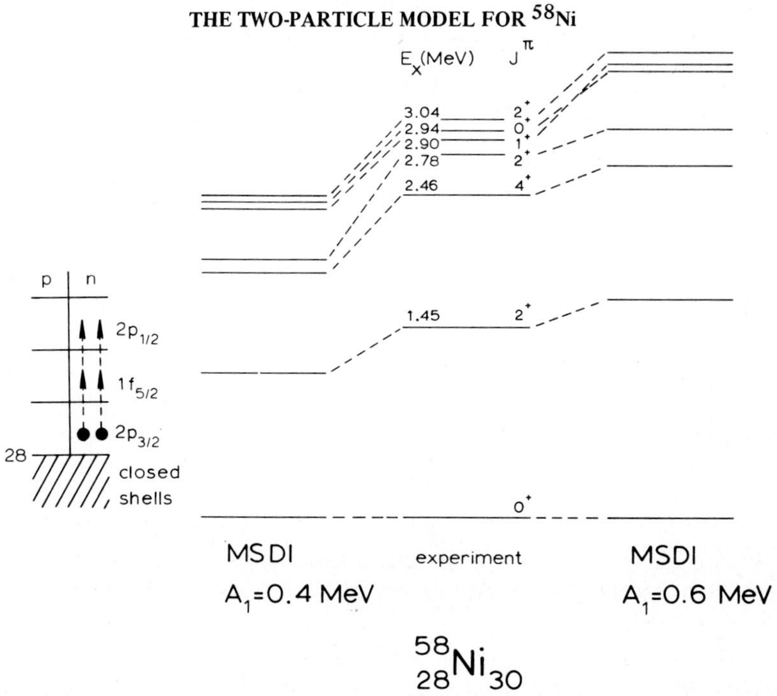

Fig. 3.12. The low-lying levels in ^{58}Ni calculated with two active neutrons in the orbits $2p_{3/2}$, $1f_{5/2}$ and $2p_{1/2}$. The spectra have been calculated for two values of the only parameter A_1 that occurs in the MSDI two-body matrix elements.

It is seen that the sequence of the lower levels is well reproduced, but that the level spacing is somewhat too small. The effect of variation of the strength parameter A_1 is illustrated by displaying in fig. 3.12 the spectrum with $A_1 = 0.6$ MeV together with that obtained from the smaller value used as a first guess. It is clear that for the intermediate value $A_1 \approx 0.5$ MeV theory and experiment will agree quite well for the excitation energies of low-lying states in ^{58}Ni. One should not be surprised about some disagreement, however, since the model space (two active neutrons only) and the interaction (MSDI) used in this example are both extremely simple.

CHAPTER 4

INTERACTING PARTICLES IN ONE ORBIT

We have seen in chapter 3 that in order to perform a shell-model calculation, one must be able to evaluate the matrix elements of the residual interaction between many-particle states Φ_Γ. In this chapter methods will be discussed that can be used to reduce the many-particle matrix elements $\langle\Phi_\Gamma|V|\Phi_\Gamma\rangle$ to sums over two-body matrix elements. In order to keep the formulas transparent, a pictorial notation is introduced in sect. 4.1 for the many-particle states that are angular-momentum coupled and antisymmetrized. In sect. 4.2 the coefficients of fractional parentage are introduced. These coefficients are very useful when a particle must be decoupled from an antisymmetric group of n particles in one orbit. Sect. 4.3 is concerned with the calculation of the interaction energy of more than two particles in one orbit. Double-parentage coefficients are introduced and applied in sect. 4.4. In sect. 4.5 the various quantum numbers, such as total spin and isospin, seniority and reduced isospin, which are necessary to specify a system of n particles in one orbit are discussed. The theoretical treatment considered in this chapter is illustrated in sect. 4.6 with a calculation of excitation energies in the nucleus ^{51}V.

4.1. Notation

Suppose one has two particles in one orbit, which is specified by n, l and j. Spins and isospins are coupled to $\boldsymbol{j}+\boldsymbol{j}=\boldsymbol{J}$ and $\boldsymbol{t}+\boldsymbol{t}=\boldsymbol{T}$ with $T=0$ or 1 since one has $t=\frac{1}{2}$. A two-particle wave function for particles numbered 1 and 2 can be written as a product of a spin- and an isospin-dependent part

$$\Phi_{JMTT_z}(1,2)=\Phi_{JM}(j(1)j(2))\Theta_{TT_z}(t(1)t(2))\,. \tag{4.1}$$

Usually a wave function is given by displaying all the quantum numbers necessary for its complete specification. Such a procedure becomes very cumbersome for wave functions of many particles distributed over several shells. Introducing a diagrammatic notation for the spin part of eq. (4.1) one can write in a transparent way [Macfarlane and French (1960)]

$$\Phi_{JM}(j(1)j(2))=\sum_{mm'}\langle jmjm'|JM\rangle\phi_{jm}(1)\phi_{jm'}(2)\equiv$$ 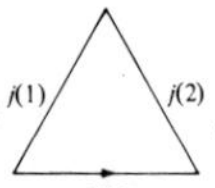

, (4.2)

where $\phi_{jm}(1)$ and $\phi_{jm'}(2)$ denote the single-particle states for particles 1 and 2 with their angular momenta j coupled to a total J. The diagram defined in eq. (4.2) contains all information that is relevant in most calculations. The coupling order is specified by the arrow, which is often important in connection with phases, as follows from eq. (2.81).

Analogously one can write the isospin dependent part as

$$\Theta_{TT_z}(t(1)t(2)) = \sum_{t_z t'_z} \langle t t_z t t'_z | T T_z \rangle \theta_{t t_z}(1) \theta_{t t'_z}(2) \equiv$$ 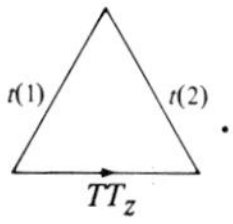

. (4.3)

The notation can even be condensed further when one denotes spin and isospin quantum numbers by one Greek symbol, e.g. $\rho \equiv (j, t)$ and $\Gamma \equiv (J, T)$. Thus eq. (4.1) can be rewritten as

$$\Phi_\Gamma(1, 2) =$$ 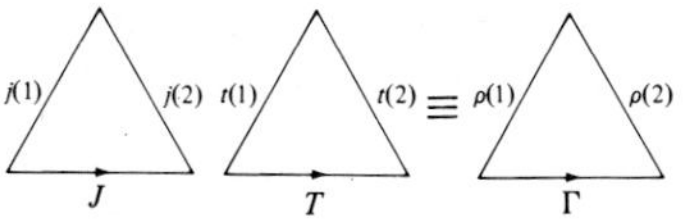

, (4.4)

where for brevity the projection quantum numbers M and T_z have been suppressed. This should cause no confusion, as in general the notation is used in expressions that are independent of the projection quantum numbers. In any case it is tacitly assumed that in an equation the final projection quantum numbers are the same on the left- and the right-hand side.

Antisymmetry of a wave function is indicated by a circular arc and one obtains for two particles in two different orbits ρ and λ

$$\Phi_\Gamma^{\rm as}(1, 2) \equiv$$ 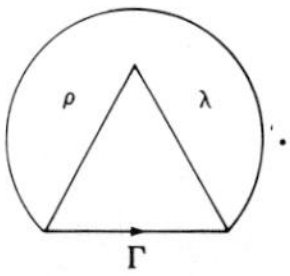

. (4.5)

For particles in the same orbit the notation can be further simplified as

$$\Phi_\Gamma^{\rm as}(1, 2) \equiv$$ 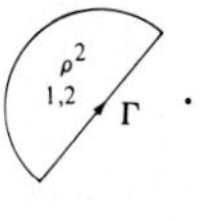

. (4.6)

Note that for this antisymmetric wave function the set of particle labels given by 1, 2 is displayed although one can no longer distinguish the two particles. The only reason is that by giving the sequence of the labels as 1, 2 the overall sign of the wave function is fixed. It is understood that one first constructs a many-particle product function with the given particle ordering and then antisymmetrizes. An odd permutation of the particle labels then introduces an overall minus sign. The diagrammatic notation can be extended easily to wave functions of more than two particles in one orbit ρ by writing

$\Phi^{as}_{\Gamma}(1, 2, ..., n) =$ 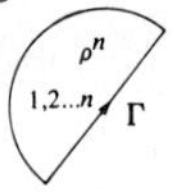 . (4.7)

It is assumed in eqs. (4.6) and (4.7) that only such values Γ are used that indeed an antisymmetric wave function results. Often the set of final spin and isospin, J_Γ and T_Γ, is not sufficient to specify the state. In such cases Γ will be understood to contain the extra quantum numbers as well.

4.2. Coefficients of fractional parentage

Let an n-particle function with all particles in one orbit ρ be given as

$\Phi_\Gamma(1, 2, ..., n) =$ 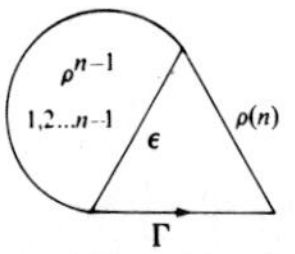 . (4.8)

The notation shows that this function is antisymmetrized in the first $n - 1$ particles, but not necessarily with respect to the last particle. The group ρ^{n-1} is coupled to $J_\epsilon, T_\epsilon, x_\epsilon$ with x_ϵ denoting all further quantum numbers needed to specify the state $|\rho^{n-1}\rangle_\epsilon$ uniquely. When the operator P_{ij} interchanges all coordinates of particles i and j, then one obtains for $i, j \leqslant n - 1$ due to the antisymmetry

P_{ij} 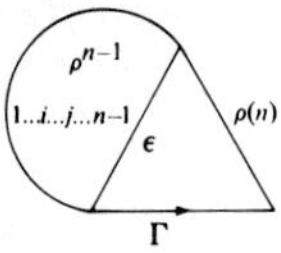 = 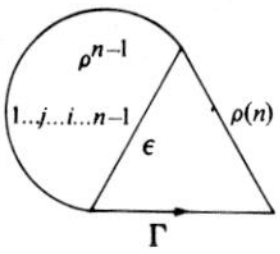 = − 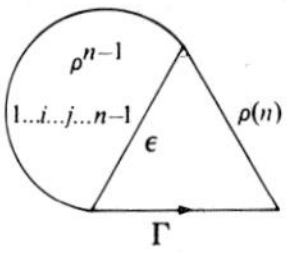 . (4.9)

The result of the permutation P_{ij} for i or j equal to n, however, cannot in general be represented by a simple expression in terms of the original function as in eq. (4.9). Since complete antisymmetrization of the n-particle wave function is a stronger restriction than the antisymmetrization given in eq. (4.9), it follows that the wave function

$\Phi^{as}_{\Gamma}(1, 2, ..., n) =$ 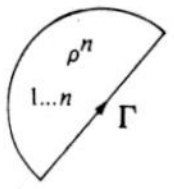 (4.10)

is contained in the space of the functions given in eq. (4.8). Therefore the wave function (4.10) can be expressed as a linear combination of the functions (4.8) for different values of ϵ, which yields

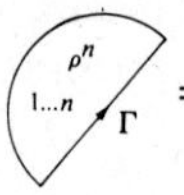 $= \sum_\epsilon \langle \rho^n \Gamma | \} \rho^{n-1} \epsilon \rangle$ 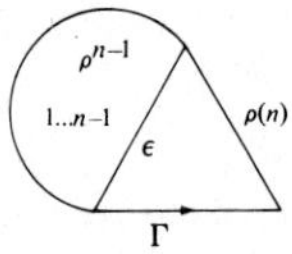 . (4.11)

The (real) expansion coefficients $\langle \rho^n \Gamma | \} \rho^{n-1} \epsilon \rangle$ introduced in eq. (4.11) are called *coefficients of fractional parentage* or c.f.p. The name derives from the fact that each state $|\rho^{n-1}\rangle_\epsilon$ can be considered as a "fractional parent" of the completely antisymmetric state $|\rho^n\rangle_\Gamma$.

The square of the c.f.p. $\langle \rho^n \Gamma | \} \rho^{n-1} \epsilon \rangle$ *gives the probability that when a single particle is removed from the antisymmetric state* ρ^n *(coupled to* Γ*) the remaining* $n-1$ *particles are in an antisymmetric state* ρ^{n-1} *(coupled to* ϵ*).*

The orthogonality of two wave functions $|\rho^n\rangle_\Gamma$ of different values of Γ is guaranteed by the Clebsch-Gordan coefficients that describe the coupling of the angular momenta Γ' and ρ of the wave functions $|\rho^{n-1}\rangle_{\Gamma'}$ and $|\rho\rangle$. Hence this orthogonality imposes no conditions on the corresponding c.f.p. If, however, we consider two orthogonal states $|\rho^n\rangle_\Gamma$ with the same values of Γ, an orthogonality condition for the c.f.p. results. Let the labels that distinguish the two orthogonal states $|\rho^n\rangle_{\Gamma x}$ be denoted by x, then the normalization and orthogonality lead to the condition

$$\sum_{\Gamma' x'} \langle \rho^n \Gamma x | \} \rho^{n-1} \Gamma' x' \rangle \langle \rho^n \Gamma x'' | \} \rho^{n-1} \Gamma' x' \rangle = \delta_{xx''} \,. \tag{4.12}$$

In the c.f.p. notation the symbol $|\}$ has been inserted to stress the fact that the c.f.p. express a projection from the larger space spanned by the functions (4.8) onto the smaller space spanned by the wave functions (4.10). Such a transformation has no inverse. The c.f.p. expansion given in eq. (4.11) is very useful when a particle must be singled out from a group of more than two particles described by an antisymmetric wave function. They are used therefore in all calculations of properties of states described by configurations with more than two active particles.

The phases in eq. (4.11) are defined such that the c.f.p. refer to the decoupling of the last particle from the state $\Phi_\Gamma^{\rm as}(1, 2, ..., k, ..., n)$. If one wishes to decouple the particle numbered k, then the simple reordering

$$\Phi_\Gamma^{\rm as}(1, 2, ..., k, ..., n) = (-1)^{n-k} \Phi_\Gamma^{\rm as}(1, 2, ..., n, k) \tag{4.13}$$

in the completely antisymmetric wave function leads to the expansion

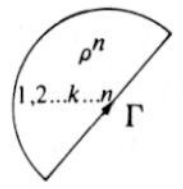

$$= (-1)^{n-k} \sum_{\epsilon} \langle \rho^n \Gamma | \} \rho^{n-1} \epsilon \rangle$$

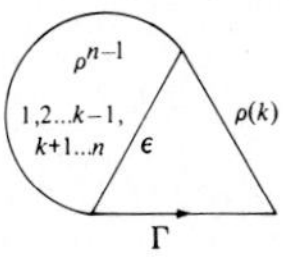

. (4.14)

A list of c.f.p. for some configurations j^n with $j = \frac{1}{2}, \frac{3}{2}$ and $\frac{5}{2}$ is given in appendix B.3.

It is instructive to discuss in detail the derivation of c.f.p. for the relatively simple case of three identical particles (i.e. maximum isospin) in one orbit with $j \leqslant \frac{7}{2}$. It is only for $j \leqslant \frac{7}{2}$ that three particles couple in an unique way to a given total spin J. The coupling of three single-particle wave functions to a non-antisymmetrized function of total spin J can be rendered in a diagram as

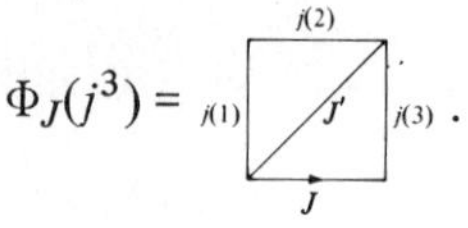

$$\Phi_J(j^3) = \quad\text{[diagram]}\quad . \tag{4.15}$$

A normalized antisymmetric wave function can be constructed by taking the combination

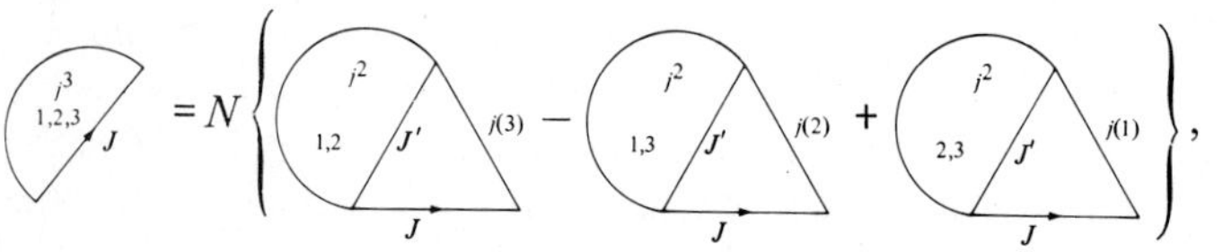

$$\text{[diagram]} = N\left\{\text{[diagram]} - \text{[diagram]} + \text{[diagram]}\right\}, \tag{4.16}$$

where N is a normalization factor. One easily verifies that an interchange of two particle labels leads to the opposite sign of this wave function. Since each term is taken to be antisymmetric in the first two particles, the intermediate spin J' must be restricted to even values only (see eq. (2.81)). As we wish to separate off the particle labeled 3, a recoupling of the last two terms of eq. (4.16) is required. This can be achieved by the aid of normalized Racah coefficients or U-coefficients, defined by the relation

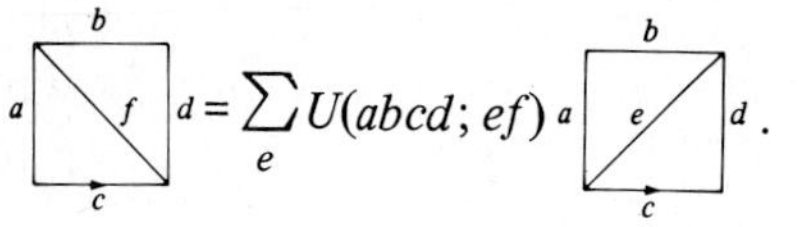

$$\text{[diagram]} = \sum_e U(abcd; ef) \, \text{[diagram]} . \tag{4.17}$$

These U-coefficients are summations over products of Clebsch-Gordan coefficients involved in the two coupling schemes (see appendix A.1).

Application of eqs. (2.80) and (4.17) to the second term of eq. (4.16) leads to

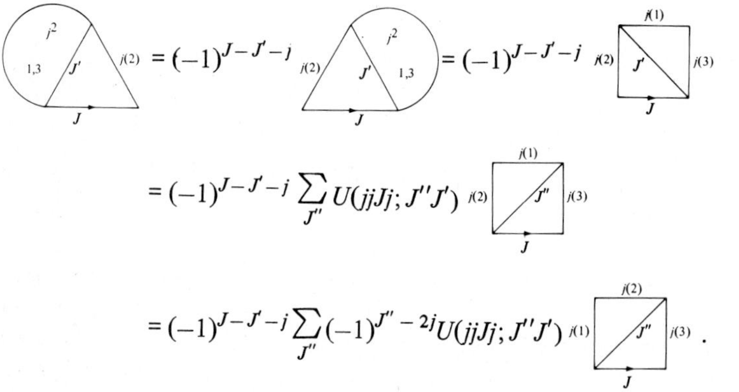

$$\text{[diagram]} = (-1)^{J-J'-j}\ \text{[diagram]} = (-1)^{J-J'-j}\ \text{[diagram]}$$

$$= (-1)^{J-J'-j}\sum_{J''} U(jjJj; J''J')\ \text{[diagram]}$$

$$= (-1)^{J-J'-j}\sum_{J''}(-1)^{J''-2j}U(jjJj; J''J')\ \text{[diagram]} . \tag{4.18}$$

A similar expression can be obtained for the third term in eq. (4.16). Thus one can write, utilizing the fact that $2j$ is odd and J' is even,

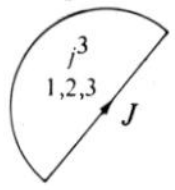

$$= N \sum_{J'} [\delta_{J'J''} + (-1)^{J-J'-j}\{(-1)^{J''} + 1\}\, U(jjJj; J''J')]$$

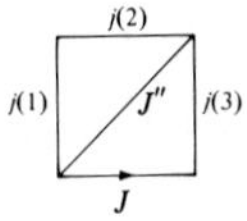

$$= N \sum_{J''=\text{even}} [\delta_{J'J''} + 2(-1)^{J-j} U(jjJj; J''J')]$$

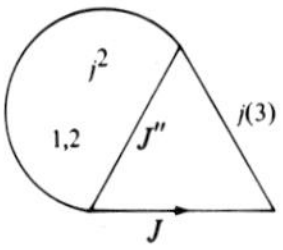

$$. \qquad (4.19)$$

It is obvious from the second term on the right-hand side of eq. (4.19) that odd values of J'' do not contribute. Therefore only states antisymmetric in particles 1 and 2 are present, which is indicated by the circular arc in the third member of eq. (4.19).

We now have succeeded in writing the fully antisymmetric wave function in terms of functions that are antisymmetric only in particles 1 and 2, and with particle 3 singled out. The functions on the right-hand side of eq. (4.19) with different values of J'' form an orthogonal and complete set for three equivalent particles in the j-orbit. Due to this orthogonality one can calculate the norm N from

$$N^2 \sum_{J''=\text{even}} [\delta_{J'J''} + 2(-1)^{J-j} U(jjJj; J''J')]^2 = 1 \, . \qquad (4.20)$$

The sum over J'' in this expression can be performed when one makes use of some properties of 6-j symbols with which the U-coefficient are closely related (see appendix A.1). Let us therefore write eq. (4.20) as

$$N^{-2} = \sum_{J''=\text{even}} (\delta_{J'J''})^2 + \sum_{J''=\text{even}} 4\delta_{J'J''}(-1)^{J-j} U(jjJj; J''J')$$

$$+ \sum_{\text{all } J''} 2\{1 + (-1)^{J''}\}[U(jjJj; J''J')]^2 \, . \qquad (4.21)$$

With the properties

$$\sum_{J''} [U(jjJj; J''J')]^2 = 1 \, , \qquad (4.22)$$

$$\sum_{J''} (-1)^{J''} [U(jjJj; J''J')]^2 = (-1)^{J-j} U(jjJj; J'J') \qquad (4.23)$$

one obtains

$$N^{-2} = 3 + 6(-1)^{J-j} U(jjJj; J'J') \, . \qquad (4.24)$$

The c.f.p. defined by the relation

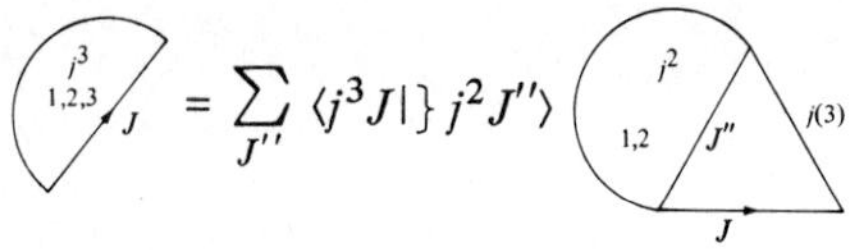

$$\qquad\qquad (4.25)$$

are thus given by

$$\langle j^3 J| \} j^2 J'' \rangle = \frac{\delta_{J'J''} + 2(-1)^{J-j} U(jjJj; J''J')}{\sqrt{3 + 6(-1)^{J-j} U(jjJj; J'J')}} \; . \qquad\qquad (4.26)$$

The values of the total spin J for the j^3 configuration not allowed by the Pauli principle lead to a vanishing expression (4.26), due to properties of the U-coefficients.

Although the c.f.p. in eq. (4.26) show an explicit dependence on the value of J', one can verify that any even value of J', compatible with the triangular conditions for coupled angular momenta, will lead to the same wave functions $|j^3\rangle_J$. The value of J' can affect the overall sign of the resulting wave function $|j^3\rangle_J$ only. The situation changes if the condition $j \leqslant \frac{7}{2}$ is no longer met. Then for different values of J' one may obtain different states $|j^3\rangle_J$. A method to construct c.f.p. for n particles in an arbitrary shell j is described in [DeShalit and Talmi (1963)].

4.3. The interaction energy for n particles

In this section it is shown that the interaction between n particles in one shell ρ can be expressed in terms of two-particle matrix elements, when it is assumed that only two-body forces contribute. The expectation value for the two-body part of the Hamiltonian of n particles coupled to a total $\Gamma \equiv (J, T)$ is given by

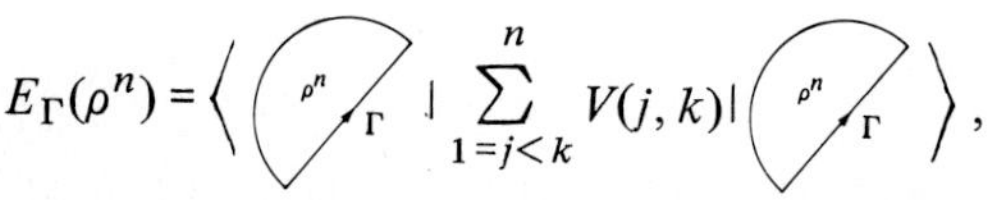

$$E_\Gamma(\rho^n) = \left\langle \; \middle| \sum_{1=j<k}^{n} V(j, k) | \; \right\rangle, \qquad\qquad (4.27)$$

where $V(j, k)$ denotes the interaction between particles j and k. The reduction of this n-particle matrix element will be performed in several steps. First it is shown that it can be expressed in terms of $(n-1)$-particle matrix elements.

Each term of $\Sigma^n_{1=j<k} V(j, k)$ in eq. (4.27) contributes the same amount, since the particles in shell ρ are indistinguishable. There are $\binom{n}{2} = \frac{1}{2}n(n-1)$ pairs among ρ^n and thus one can write

$$\left\langle \; \middle| \sum_{1=j<k}^{n} V(j, k) | \; \right\rangle = \frac{1}{2}n(n-1) \left\langle \; \middle| V(1, 2)| \; \right\rangle, \quad (4.28)$$

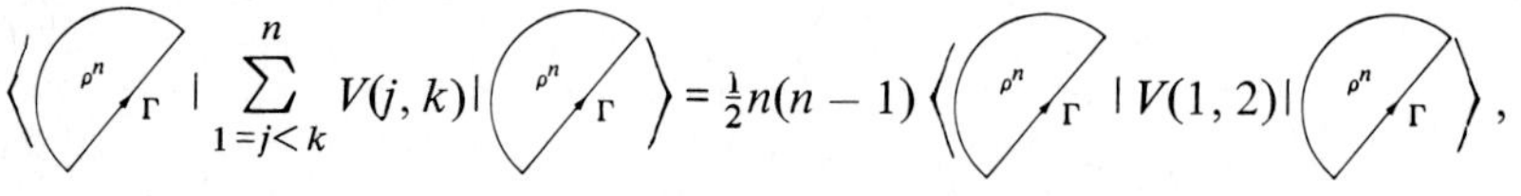

where the pair $(1, 2)$ has been chosen arbitrarily. For a two-body operator that acts on the first $n - 1$ particles only, one can write similarly

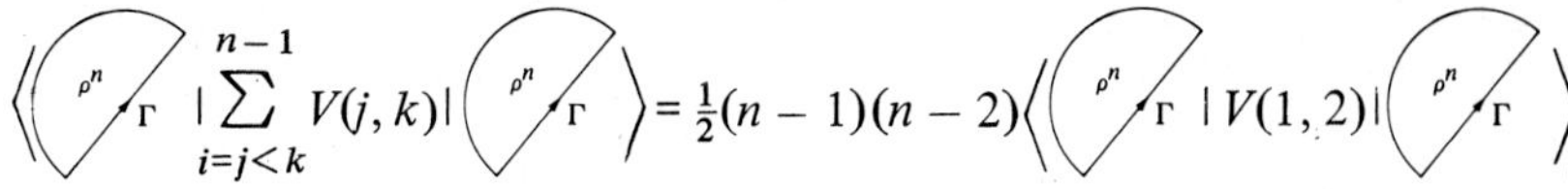

$$\left\langle \left.\vcenter{\hbox{ρ^n}}\middle/\Gamma \middle| \sum_{i=j<k}^{n-1} V(j,k) \middle| \vcenter{\hbox{ρ^n}}\middle/\Gamma \right\rangle = \tfrac{1}{2}(n-1)(n-2)\left\langle \vcenter{\hbox{ρ^n}}\middle/\Gamma \middle| V(1,2) \middle| \vcenter{\hbox{ρ^n}}\middle/\Gamma \right\rangle. \tag{4.29}$$

From eqs. (4.27), (4.28) and (4.29) follows immediately

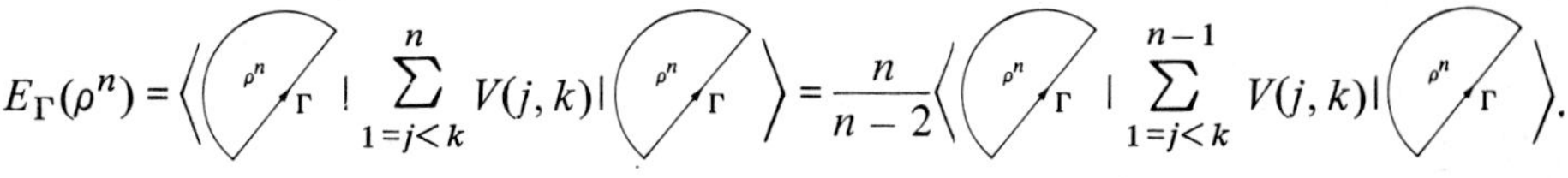

$$E_\Gamma(\rho^n) = \left\langle \vcenter{\hbox{ρ^n}}\middle/\Gamma \middle| \sum_{1=j<k}^{n} V(j,k) \middle| \vcenter{\hbox{ρ^n}}\middle/\Gamma \right\rangle = \frac{n}{n-2}\left\langle \vcenter{\hbox{ρ^n}}\middle/\Gamma \middle| \sum_{1=j<k}^{n-1} V(j,k) \middle| \vcenter{\hbox{ρ^n}}\middle/\Gamma \right\rangle. \tag{4.30}$$

Expanding the right-hand side of eq. (4.30) according to eq. (4.11), one obtains

$$E_\Gamma(\rho^n) = \frac{n}{n-2} \sum_\epsilon \sum_{\epsilon'} \langle \rho^n \Gamma| \}\rho^{n-1}\epsilon\rangle \langle \rho^n \Gamma| \}\rho^{n-1}\epsilon'\rangle$$

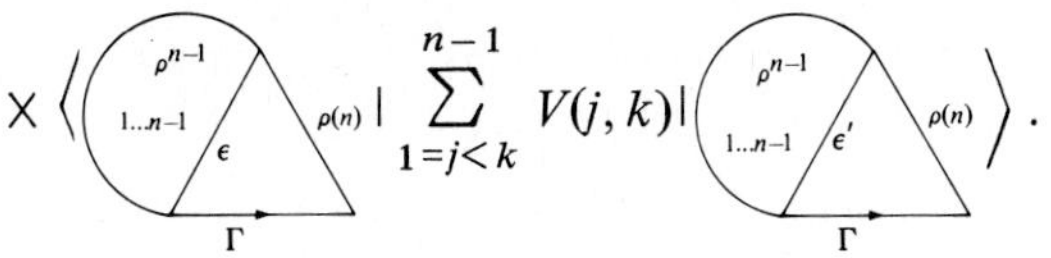

$$\times \left\langle \vcenter{\hbox{ρ^{n-1}}}\,{}_{1...n-1}\!\!\!\Big/\epsilon \;\rho(n)\; \middle| \sum_{1=j<k}^{n-1} V(j,k) \middle| \vcenter{\hbox{ρ^{n-1}}}\,{}_{1...n-1}\!\!\!\Big/\epsilon' \;\rho(n)\; \right\rangle. \tag{4.31}$$

It is seen that the operator in eq. (4.31) acts only on the $n - 1$ particles that are contained in the antisymmetrized part of the wave function.

We show now that the last particle labelled n, on which the operator does not act, can be removed completely from the matrix element. The wave functions in eq. (4.31) can be written explicitly as

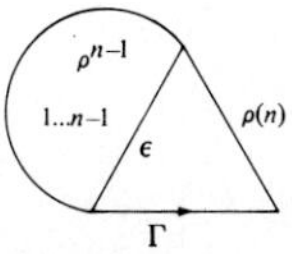

$$\vcenter{\hbox{ρ^{n-1}}}\,{}_{1...n-1}\!\!\!\Big/\epsilon \;\rho(n)\; = \sum_{\epsilon_z \rho_z} \langle \epsilon\epsilon_z \rho\rho_z | \Gamma\Gamma_z\rangle \, \Phi^{as}_{\epsilon\epsilon_z}(1,...,n-1)\phi_{\rho\rho_z}(n), \tag{4.32}$$

where $\langle \epsilon\epsilon_z \rho\rho_z | \Gamma\Gamma_z\rangle$, containing Greek symbols, denotes the product of a coordinate space and an isospace Clebsch-Gordan coefficient and Φ^{as} denotes an antisymmetric wave function. Inserting eq. (4.32) into the matrix element of eq. (4.31), one obtains

$$M \equiv \left\langle \vcenter{\hbox{ρ^{n-1}}}\,{}_{1...n-1}\!\!\!\Big/\epsilon \;\rho(n)\; \middle| \sum_{1=j<k}^{n-1} V(j,k) \middle| \vcenter{\hbox{ρ^{n-1}}}\,{}_{1...n-1}\!\!\!\Big/\epsilon' \;\rho(n)\; \right\rangle.$$

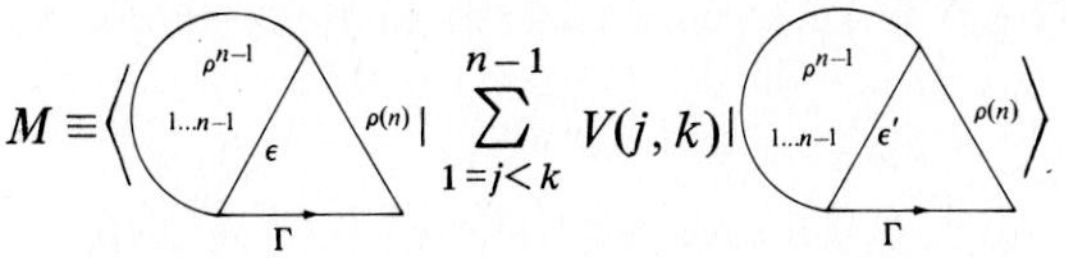

$$= \sum_{\epsilon_z \rho_z} \sum_{\epsilon'_z \rho'_z} \langle \epsilon\epsilon_z \rho\rho_z | \Gamma\Gamma_z\rangle \langle \epsilon'\epsilon'_z \rho\rho'_z | \Gamma\Gamma_z\rangle$$

$$\times \langle \Phi^{as}_{\epsilon\epsilon_z}(1,...,n-1)\phi_{\rho\rho_z}(n) | \sum_{1=j<k}^{n-1} V(j,k) | \Phi^{as}_{\epsilon'\epsilon'_z}(1,...,n-1)\phi_{\rho\rho'_z}(n) \rangle. \tag{4.33}$$

From the fact that the operator in eq. (4.33) does not act on the wave function $\phi_{\rho\rho_z}(n)$ of the last particle and from the orthonormality of the single-particle wave functions

$$\langle \phi_{\rho\rho_z}(n) | \phi_{\rho\rho'_z}(n) \rangle = \delta_{\rho_z\rho'_z} \, , \tag{4.34}$$

it follows that eq. (4.33) reduces to

$$M = \sum_{\epsilon_z\epsilon'_z\rho_z} \langle \epsilon\epsilon_z\rho\rho_z | \Gamma\Gamma_z \rangle \langle \epsilon'\epsilon'_z\rho\rho_z | \Gamma\Gamma_z \rangle \langle \Phi^{\mathrm{as}}_{\epsilon\epsilon_z}(1, ..., n-1) | \sum_{1=j<k}^{n-1} V(j,k) | \Phi^{\mathrm{as}}_{\epsilon'\epsilon'_z}(1, ..., n-1) \rangle \tag{4.35}$$

The two-body energy operators $V(j, k)$ are scalar in coordinate space as well as in isospace. Therefore the matrix element M vanishes for $J_\epsilon \neq J_{\epsilon'}$ or $T_\epsilon \neq T_{\epsilon'}$ and is independent of the projection quantum numbers $\epsilon_z \equiv (J_{\epsilon_z}, T_{\epsilon_z})$, i.e. the orientation in coordinate space and isospace. (The matrix element M does not necessarily vanish when other quantum numbers are different such as e.g. the seniority that may be contained in ϵ and ϵ'. Such quantum numbers are irrelevant for the present discussion.) Thus for $J_\epsilon = J_{\epsilon'}$ and $T_\epsilon = T_{\epsilon'}$ eq. (4.35) can be written as

$$M = \sum_{\epsilon_z\rho_z} \langle \epsilon\epsilon_z\rho\rho_z | \Gamma\Gamma_z \rangle^2 \langle \Phi^{\mathrm{as}}_{\epsilon\epsilon_z}(1, ..., n-1) | \sum_{1=j<k}^{n-1} V(j,k) | \Phi^{\mathrm{as}}_{\epsilon\epsilon_z}(1, ..., n-1) \rangle \, . \tag{4.36}$$

Since the matrix element in eq. (4.36) is independent of ϵ_z one obtains, using the normalization condition for the Clebsch-Gordan coefficients

$$\sum_{\epsilon_z\rho_z} \langle \epsilon\epsilon_z\rho\rho_z | \Gamma\Gamma_z \rangle^2 = 1 \, , \tag{4.37}$$

from eqs. (4.33) and (4.36) the result

$\Big\langle$ 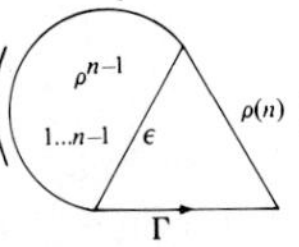 $\Big| \sum_{1=j<k}^{n-1} V(j,k) \Big|$ 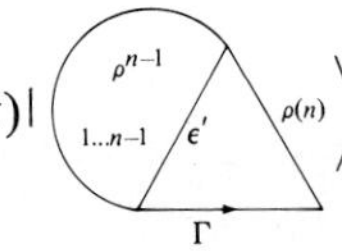 $\Big\rangle = \Big\langle$ 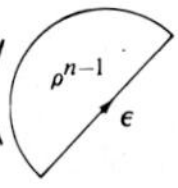 $\Big| \sum_{1=j<k}^{n-1} V(j,k) \Big|$ 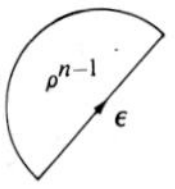 $\Big\rangle \delta_{\epsilon\epsilon'}$. (4.38)

Inserting eq. (4.38) into eq. (4.31) one obtains from eq. (4.30) the final expression

$E_\Gamma(\rho^n) = \Big\langle$ 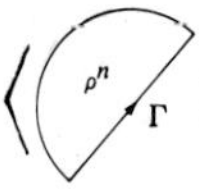 $\Big| \sum_{1=j<k}^{n} V(j,k) \Big|$ 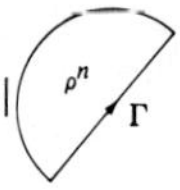 $\Big\rangle$

$= \dfrac{n}{n-2} \sum_{\epsilon} \langle \rho^n \Gamma | \} \rho^{n-1} \epsilon \rangle^2 \Big\langle$ 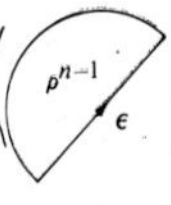 $\Big| \sum_{1=j<k}^{n-1} V(j,k) \Big|$ 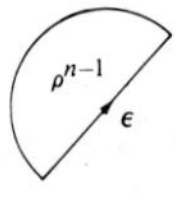 $\Big\rangle$ (4.39) or

$$E_\Gamma(\rho^n) = \frac{n}{n-2} \sum_\epsilon \langle \rho^n \Gamma | \} \rho^{n-1} \epsilon \rangle^2 E_\epsilon(\rho^{n-1}). \tag{4.40}$$

Thus the interaction energy in the group ρ^n is given by the probability (c.f.p.)^2 that $n-1$ particles are in the state $|\rho^{n-1}\rangle_\epsilon$ times the interaction energy in the state $|\rho^{n-1}\rangle_\epsilon$. The factor $n/(n-2)$ takes care of the fact that in the state ρ^n there are $\frac{1}{2}n(n-1)$ interacting pairs, while in the state ρ^{n-1} there are only $\frac{1}{2}(n-1)(n-2)$ pairs. Expression (4.40) is extremely useful, since it relates the interaction between n particles, occupying the same orbit, to the interaction between $n-1$ particles. Successive application thus yields an expression of the n-particle interaction in terms of two-particle interactions.

4.4. Double-parentage coefficients

Instead of expressing the interaction energy of an n-particle system in terms of that between $n-1$ particles with $n \to n-1$ c.f.p., it is sometimes useful for larger values of n to express the n-particle interaction directly in two-particle energies. The advantage of this method is that for an n-particle system only the $n \to n-1$ and $n-1 \to n-2$ c.f.p. are needed (i.e. not the complete sequence of $n-2 \to n-3 \to \ldots \to 3 \to 2$ c.f.p.). It has already been shown before that one can make the expansion

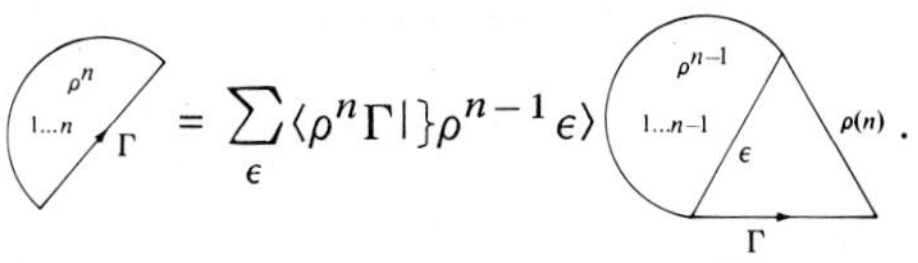

$$\left(\genfrac{}{}{0pt}{}{\rho^n}{1\ldots n}\right)_\Gamma = \sum_\epsilon \langle \rho^n \Gamma | \} \rho^{n-1} \epsilon \rangle \left(\genfrac{}{}{0pt}{}{\rho^{n-1}}{1\ldots n-1}\right)_\epsilon \, \rho(n) \, . \tag{4.41}$$

Applying the expression with c.f.p. once more to the antisymmetric state $|\rho^{n-1}\rangle_\epsilon$, one can split off a second particle to obtain

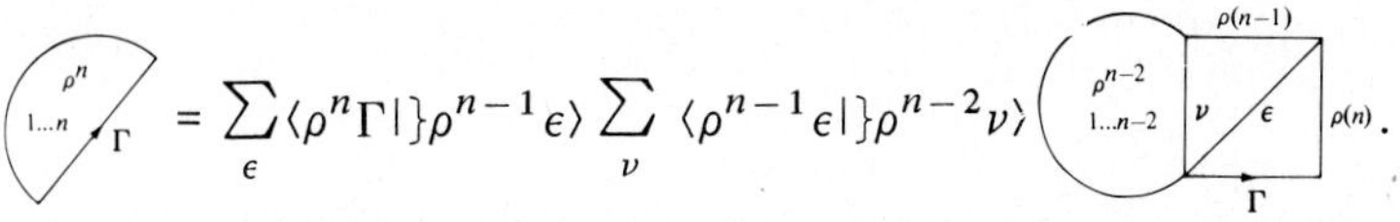

$$\left(\genfrac{}{}{0pt}{}{\rho^n}{1\ldots n}\right)_\Gamma = \sum_\epsilon \langle \rho^n \Gamma | \} \rho^{n-1} \epsilon \rangle \sum_\nu \langle \rho^{n-1} \epsilon | \} \rho^{n-2} \nu \rangle \left(\genfrac{}{}{0pt}{}{\rho^{n-2}}{1\ldots n-2}\right) \nu \, \epsilon \, \rho(n-1) \, \rho(n) \, . \tag{4.42}$$

By means of a simple recoupling of angular momenta one can rewrite eq. (4.42) such that the two particles labelled $n-1$ and n are separated off in states of specified angular momentum and isospin. This recoupling is achieved with normalized Racah coefficients U that are defined by the relation (see also appendix A.1)

$$\left[\genfrac{}{}{0pt}{}{b}{a \; e \; d}_c\right] = \sum_f U(abcd; ef) \left[\genfrac{}{}{0pt}{}{b}{a \; f \; d}_c\right] . \tag{4.43}$$

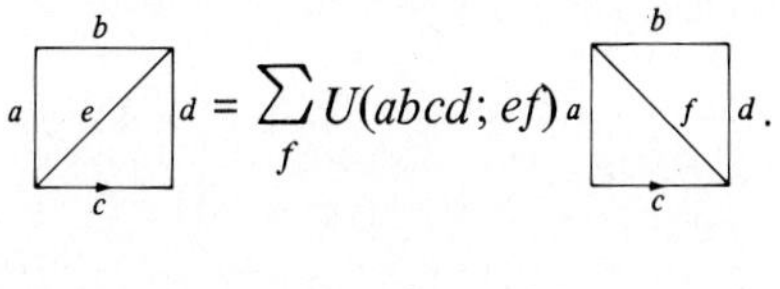

Application of eq. (4.43) to eq. (4.42) yields

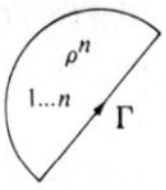

$$
\left\langle \begin{matrix} \rho^n \\ 1...n \end{matrix} \middle/ \Gamma \right. = \sum_\epsilon \langle \rho^n \Gamma | \} \rho^{n-1}\epsilon\rangle \sum_\nu \langle \rho^{n-1}\epsilon|\}\rho^{n-2}\nu\rangle \sum_\delta U(\nu\rho\Gamma\rho;\epsilon\delta) \left(\begin{matrix} \rho^{n-2} \\ 1...n-2 \end{matrix} \nu \middle\backslash \begin{matrix} \rho(n-1) \\ \delta \\ \rho(n) \end{matrix} \right)_\Gamma
$$

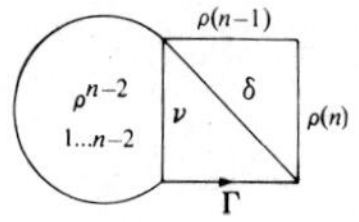

$$(4.44)$$

The U-coefficient with Greek symbols denotes a product of a coordinate space and isospace normalized Racah coefficient.

The left-hand side wave function in eq. (4.44) is antisymmetric in all n particles, including the particles labelled $n-1$ and n. The same must therefore hold also for the right-hand side. Thus nonzero contributions are obtained only for values of δ that correspond to an antisymmetric wave function for particles $n-1$ and n.

Defining *double-parentage coefficients* (d.p.c.) as

$$
\langle\rho^n\Gamma|\}\rho^{n-2}\nu(\rho^2\delta)\rangle\rangle \equiv \sum_\epsilon \langle\rho^n\Gamma|\}\rho^{n-1}\epsilon\rangle\langle\rho^{n-1}\epsilon|\}\rho^{n-2}\nu\rangle U(\nu\rho\Gamma\rho;\epsilon\delta) , \qquad (4.45)
$$

one can rewrite eq. (4.44) as

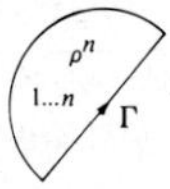

$$
\left\langle \begin{matrix} \rho^n \\ 1...n \end{matrix} \middle/ \Gamma \right. = \sum_{\nu\delta} \langle\rho^n\Gamma|\}\rho^{n-2}\nu(\rho^2\delta)\rangle\rangle \left(\begin{matrix}\rho^{n-2}\\1...n-2\end{matrix}\nu \middle\backslash \begin{matrix}\rho^2\\ \delta \\ n-1,n\end{matrix} \right)_\Gamma .
$$

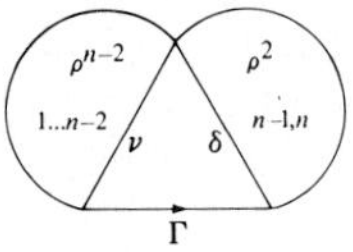

$$(4.46)$$

Applying eq. (4.28), but now taking the term $V(n-1,n)$ as representative, one obtains with eq. (4.46)

$$
\left\langle \left. \begin{matrix}\rho^n\\ \end{matrix}\middle/\Gamma \right| \sum_{1=j<k}^n V(j,k) \middle| \begin{matrix}\rho^n\\ \end{matrix}\middle/\Gamma \right\rangle = \tfrac12 n(n-1) \left\langle \left.\begin{matrix}\rho^n\\1...n\end{matrix}\middle/\Gamma\right| V(n-1,n) \middle| \begin{matrix}\rho^n\\1...n\end{matrix}\middle/\Gamma \right\rangle
$$

$$
= \tfrac12 n(n-1) \sum_{\nu\delta} \langle\rho^n\Gamma|\}\rho^{n-2}\nu(\rho^2\delta)\rangle\rangle^2 \left\langle \left.\begin{matrix}\rho^2\\n-1,n\end{matrix}\middle/\delta\right| V(n-1,n) \middle| \begin{matrix}\rho^2\\n-1,n\end{matrix}\middle/\delta \right\rangle . \qquad (4.47)
$$

The removal of the group $\rho_\nu^{n-2}(1,...,n-2)$ on which $V(n-1,n)$ does not act, is achieved along the same lines as shown in eqs. (4.32)–(4.38). Denoting the interaction energy of a group of n equivalent particles by $E(\rho^n)$ one can write

$$
E_\Gamma(\rho^n) = \tfrac12 n(n-1) \sum_{\nu\delta} \langle\rho^n\Gamma|\}\rho^{n-2}\nu(\rho^2\delta)\rangle\rangle^2 E_\delta(\rho^2) . \qquad (4.48)
$$

The d.p.c. defined in eqs. (4.45) and (4.46) are also useful for the analysis of two-nucleon transfer reactions as will be shown in chapter 8.

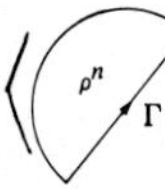

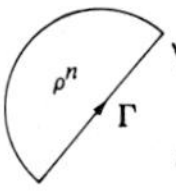

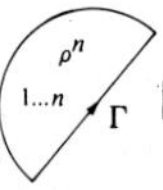

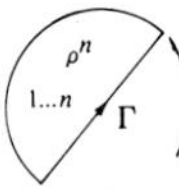

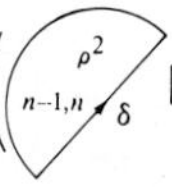

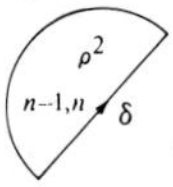

4.5. Allowed J, T combinations for n particles

It has been shown in sect. 2.4 that the wave function for two particles occupying the same orbit is antisymmetric only when their total spin J and isospin T obey the condition $J + T =$ odd. The restrictions that are imposed on the total J and T for more than two nucleons in the same orbit and described by an antisymmetrized wave function cannot be summarized by a simple rule. The allowed configurations for particles in the orbits $j = \frac{1}{2}, \frac{3}{2}$ and $\frac{5}{2}$ are given in appendix B.2.

Consider as an example three particles in the $1f_{7/2}$ shell. The value of the total J follows from the vector coupling $\boldsymbol{J} = \boldsymbol{j} + \boldsymbol{j} + \boldsymbol{j}$ with $j = \frac{7}{2}$. We shall show below that, e.g. for $T = \frac{3}{2}$, the values $J = \frac{21}{2}, \frac{19}{2}, \frac{17}{2}, \frac{13}{2}$ and $\frac{1}{2}$ are excluded. One can derive also that for $T = \frac{1}{2}$ only $J = \frac{21}{2}$ is excluded, while the values $J = \frac{5}{2}, \frac{9}{2}, \frac{11}{2}$ and $\frac{13}{2}$ occur twice and $\frac{7}{2}$ even three times. This means that there are three independent states with $J = \frac{7}{2}, T = \frac{1}{2}$. Therefore additional labels are required for a unique specification of such states.

Although in general the methods of group theory are required to determine the allowed values of J and T for a configuration ρ^n, one can do without these advanced methods in some special cases. In the case of maximum total isospin $T = n/2$, e.g. for a configuration of n identical particles, the allowed total J values can be derived by a straightforward enumeration of all states in the m-scheme.

As an example we consider the configuration $|(1f_{7/2})^3\rangle_{J,T=3/2}$. In the m-scheme the individual quantum numbers $nljm$ for each particle are specified and thus the total wave function for the identical particles is given by a Slater determinant. The projection quantum number of the total spin is given by

$$M = \sum_{k=1}^{3} m(k) , \tag{4.49}$$

where because of the Pauli exclusion principle no two values of $m(k)$ may be the same. Thus the maximum value of M for the case of $(1f_{7/2})^3$ amounts to $\frac{7}{2} + \frac{5}{2} + \frac{3}{2} = \frac{15}{2}$. The M-values that correspond to all possible combinations of values of $m(k)$ are enumerated in table 4.1 (only the positive M-values are listed; the negative values result after sign reversal of all projection quantum numbers). It is seen that there is one state $J = \frac{15}{2}$ ($M = +J, +J - 1, ..., -J$) but no state $J = \frac{13}{2}$, since the only available projection $M = \frac{13}{2}$ is already needed for $J = \frac{15}{2}$. Almost all other states with $J < \frac{15}{2}$ occur exactly once. The exception is the state with $J = \frac{1}{2}$, which is not possible since all projections $M = \frac{1}{2}$ are used already for other J values.

It should be remarked that this simple method of enumeration of the states in the m-scheme no longer applies when the configuration is not coupled to maximum isospin. In such a case the coordinate space and isospace parts of the wave function are characterized by mixed symmetry, i.e. they are each separately neither completely symmetric nor antisymmetric. Then one has to rely on methods of group theory,

Table 4.1
Enumeration of the projection quantum numbers $M = m(1) + m(2) + m(3)$ that correspond to the states $|(1f_{7/2})^3\rangle_{JM}$ with $M > 0$

M	$\lvert m(1)\, m(2)\, m(3)\rangle$					
$\frac{15}{2}$	$\lvert\frac{7}{2}\,\frac{5}{2}\,\frac{3}{2}\rangle$					
$\frac{13}{2}$	$\lvert\frac{7}{2}\,\frac{5}{2}\,\frac{1}{2}\rangle$					
$\frac{11}{2}$	$\lvert\frac{7}{2}\,\frac{5}{2}-\frac{1}{2}\rangle$	$\lvert\frac{7}{2}\,\frac{3}{2}\,\frac{1}{2}\rangle$				
$\frac{9}{2}$	$\lvert\frac{7}{2}\,\frac{5}{2}-\frac{3}{2}\rangle$	$\lvert\frac{7}{2}\,\frac{3}{2}-\frac{1}{2}\rangle$	$\lvert\frac{5}{2}\,\frac{3}{2}\,\frac{1}{2}\rangle$			
$\frac{7}{2}$	$\lvert\frac{7}{2}\,\frac{5}{2}-\frac{5}{2}\rangle$	$\lvert\frac{7}{2}\,\frac{3}{2}-\frac{3}{2}\rangle$	$\lvert\frac{7}{2}\,\frac{1}{2}-\frac{1}{2}\rangle$	$\lvert\frac{5}{2}\,\frac{3}{2}-\frac{1}{2}\rangle$		
$\frac{5}{2}$	$\lvert\frac{7}{2}\,\frac{5}{2}-\frac{7}{2}\rangle$	$\lvert\frac{7}{2}\,\frac{3}{2}-\frac{5}{2}\rangle$	$\lvert\frac{7}{2}\,\frac{1}{2}-\frac{3}{2}\rangle$	$\lvert\frac{5}{2}\,\frac{3}{2}-\frac{3}{2}\rangle$	$\lvert\frac{5}{2}\,\frac{1}{2}-\frac{1}{2}\rangle$	
$\frac{3}{2}$	$\lvert\frac{7}{2}\,\frac{3}{2}-\frac{7}{2}\rangle$	$\lvert\frac{7}{2}\,\frac{1}{2}-\frac{5}{2}\rangle$	$\lvert\frac{7}{2}-\frac{1}{2}-\frac{3}{2}\rangle$	$\lvert\frac{5}{2}\,\frac{3}{2}-\frac{5}{2}\rangle$	$\lvert\frac{5}{2}\,\frac{1}{2}-\frac{3}{2}\rangle$	$\lvert\frac{3}{2}\,\frac{1}{2}-\frac{1}{2}\rangle$
$\frac{1}{2}$	$\lvert\frac{7}{2}\,\frac{1}{2}-\frac{7}{2}\rangle$	$\lvert\frac{7}{2}-\frac{1}{2}-\frac{5}{2}\rangle$	$\lvert\frac{5}{2}\,\frac{3}{2}-\frac{7}{2}\rangle$	$\lvert\frac{5}{2}\,\frac{1}{2}-\frac{5}{2}\rangle$	$\lvert\frac{5}{2}-\frac{1}{2}-\frac{3}{2}\rangle$	$\lvert\frac{3}{2}\,\frac{1}{2}-\frac{3}{2}\rangle$

where one uses Young diagrams to specify the required intermediate symmetries [Flowers (1952); cf. appendix B.2].

Besides the rotational symmetries leading to angular-momentum and isospin quantum numbers, there exists for many-particle systems another symmetry, leading to the quantum numbers of *seniority* and *reduced isospin.* We shall discuss these without relying on group theory.

A state $|\rho^n\rangle_\Gamma$ may contain a number of particles that are coupled pairwise to $J_\delta = 0$. Since only antisymmetric combinations are permitted, these pairs should couple to an isospin $T_\delta = 1$. *The seniority v can be defined as the number of unpaired particles in the state* $|\rho^n\rangle_\Gamma$. For example, the state $|\rho^2\rangle_\Gamma$ possesses seniority $v = 0$ for $J_\Gamma = 0$ and $v = 2$ for $J_\Gamma \neq 0$. A state with v particles in shell ρ is characterized by seniority v if it is impossible to remove any pair ρ^2 coupled to $J_\delta = 0$, $T_\delta = 1$. This can be formulated in terms of d.p.c. by the condition

$$\langle \rho^v \Gamma | \} \rho^{v-2} \Delta(\rho^2 \delta) \rangle = 0 \,, \tag{4.50}$$

for every Δ and $J_\delta = 0$, $T_\delta = 1$.

The state $|\rho^n\rangle_\Gamma$ possesses seniority v when it can be constructed from a state $|\rho^v\rangle_\Delta$ of seniority v by successive addition of $\frac{1}{2}(n - v)$ pairs coupled to $J_\delta = 0$, $T_\delta = 1$, and subsequent antisymmetrization. Thus the state $|\rho^n\rangle_\Gamma$ must have the same spin as the state $|\rho^v\rangle_\Delta$, i.e. $J_\Gamma = J_\Delta$, but the isospins are *not* necessarily equal. From the states $|\rho^v\rangle_\Delta$ one can, by mere addition of pairs coupled to $J_\delta = 0$, $T_\delta = 1$ and subsequent antisymmetrization, obtain *all* states $|\rho^n\rangle_\Gamma$ of seniority v with $J_\Gamma = J_\Delta$. For a further specification of this construction, and thus a further characterization of the state $|\rho^n\rangle_\Gamma$, one should also give the isospin of the state $|\rho^v\rangle_\Delta$. This isospin is referred to as the reduced isospin t. In other words *the reduced isospin is defined as the total isospin of all unpaired nucleons.* The state of a single nucleon is characterized by $v = 1, t = \frac{1}{2}$. The two-particle configuration $|\rho^2\rangle_\Gamma$ with $J_\Gamma = 0$ possesses $v = 0$ and $t = 0$. The state $|\rho^2\rangle_\Gamma$ with $J_\Gamma \neq 0$ has $v = 2$ and $t = T_\Gamma = 0$ or 1. States with $v = 3$ have reduced isospin $t = \frac{1}{2}$ or $\frac{3}{2}$.

It should be noted that one can reach the state $|\rho^n\rangle_\Gamma$ along different isospin-coupling schemes when adding $\frac{1}{2}(n - v)$ pairs with $J_\delta = 0, T_\delta = 1$ to the state $|\rho^v\rangle_\Delta$. The only condition on the total isospin T_0 of the $\frac{1}{2}(n - v)$ pairs coupled to $J_0 = 0$ is given by the triangular restriction

$$|T_\Gamma - t| \leqslant T_0 \leqslant T_\Gamma + t\,. \tag{4.51}$$

The different, allowed values of T_0 do not necessarily lead to the same antisymmetric state $|\rho^n\rangle_\Gamma$. This situation can occur for particles in orbits with $j \geqslant \frac{5}{2}$. In such cases one needs another quantum number. As long as no systematic procedure has been found to obtain a complete set of quantum numbers, all one can do is to add some *ad hoc* number, say $x = 1, 2, 3, ...$, that labels the states to be distinguished.

For identical nucleons the reduced isospin is fixed by the seniority through the relation $t = \frac{1}{2}v$, since then one should couple to maximum isospin. Two wave functions $\Phi_\Gamma(\rho^n)$ and $\Phi_\Delta(\rho^n)$ with different seniorities or reduced isospins are orthogonal. For a proof of this statement the reader is referred to [DeShalit and Talmi (1963) ch. 34].

Since it is found that nuclear forces lead to strongly bound $J_\delta = 0$ coupled pairs, one uses sometimes the seniority quantum number to set up a truncated configuration space. In this procedure only the states with low seniority, i.e. with very few $J_\delta \neq 0$ coupled pairs, are taken into account for the description of low-lying nuclear levels. It is then assumed that the break-up of $J_\delta = 0$ coupled pairs will lead to states lying at much higher excitation energies, such that they can be ignored in the calculation.

4.6. Examples

The theory developed so far for nuclei that can be described by n particles in the same orbit will be illustrated by a calculation of energy levels in ^{51}V. The simplest description of $^{51}_{23}V_{28}$ is given by the configuration with three protons in the $1f_{7/2}$ orbit and a closed $1f_{7/2}$ neutron shell (see fig. 4.1). The isospin of the three-proton system is given by $T = \frac{3}{2}$, i.e. the maximum value, since the system consists of identical particles only. The allowed J-values are, according to sect. 4.5, given by $J = \frac{3}{2}, \frac{5}{2}, \frac{7}{2}, \frac{9}{2}, \frac{11}{2}$ and $\frac{15}{2}$, and the parity of the wave functions must be negative for three particles in $l = 3$ states.

With eq. (4.40) one can express the interaction between the three particles in terms of two-body energies as

$$E_{J,T=3/2}(1f_{7/2}^3) = 3 \sum_{J_\epsilon T_\epsilon} \langle f_{7/2}^3 J \tfrac{3}{2} | \} f_{7/2}^2 J_\epsilon T_\epsilon \rangle^2 E_{J_\epsilon T_\epsilon}(1f_{7/2}^2)\,. \tag{4.52}$$

THE $(1f_{7/2})^3$ PROTON CONFIGURATION FOR ^{51}V

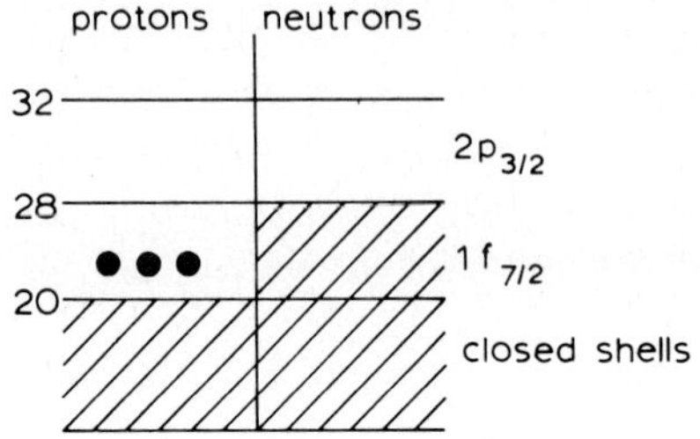

Fig. 4.1. The simplest representation of $^{51}_{23}V_{28}$ with three active protons in the $1f_{7/2}$ orbit. Hatching indicates fully occupied orbits.

The c.f.p. that enter into eq. (4.52) can be calculated with eq. (4.26) and are listed in table 4.2. Nonvanishing contributions to the sum in eq. (4.52) are obtained for $T_\epsilon = 1$ only, since one cannot couple two identical particles to isospin $T_\epsilon = 0$.

Let us take the values for the two-particle energies $E_{J_\epsilon T_\epsilon}(1f^2_{7/2})$ from two different sources: (i) empirical values and (ii) from matrix elements calculated with the MSDI. The empirical matrix elements can be obtained directly from the experimental information on $^{50}_{22}Ti_{28}$. In this approach it is assumed that the structure of the lowest $J^\pi = 0^+, 2^+, 4^+$ and 6^+ states in ^{50}Ti shown in fig. 4.2 derives from the coupling of two protons in the $(1f_{7/2})^2$ configuration with the neutron shell being closed for $N = 28$. In that case the spectra of ^{50}Ti with $(1f_{7/2})^2$ and ^{51}V with $(1f_{7/2})^3$ proton configurations are related according to eq. (4.52).

The excitation energies of ^{50}Ti are given by $E_x(J^\pi_\epsilon, T_\epsilon = 1) = 0$, 1.55, 2.68 and

Table 4.2
Coefficients of fractional parentage $\langle f^3_{7/2}J | \} f^2_{7/2}J' \rangle$ for three particles coupled to maximum isospin

J \	$J' = 0$	$J' = 2$	$J' = 4$	$J' = 6$
$\frac{3}{2}$	0	0.463	−0.886	0
$\frac{5}{2}$	0	0.782	0.246	−0.573
$\frac{7}{2}$	0.500	−0.373	−0.500	−0.601
$\frac{9}{2}$	0	0.321	−0.806	0.497
$\frac{11}{2}$	0	0.527	−0.444	−0.725
$\frac{15}{2}$	0	0	0.477	−0.879

THE $(1f_{7/2})^n$ MODEL FOR ^{50}Ti AND ^{51}V

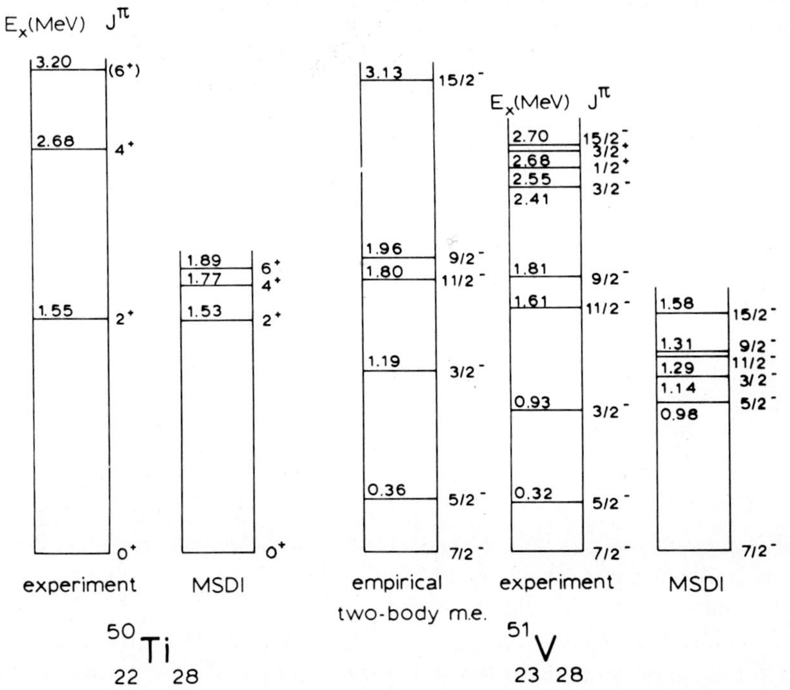

Fig. 4.2. The spectra of ^{50}Ti and ^{51}V calculated for configurations $(1f_{7/2})^n$. Both the MSDI and the empirical two-body matrix elements from ^{50}Ti have been used. The experimental data are from [Nuclear Data Sheets (1970); Horoshko, Cline and Lesser (1970)].

3.20 MeV for $J^\pi_\epsilon = 0^+, 2^+, 4^+$ and 6^+, respectively. Since these excitation energies are defined with respect to the ^{50}Ti ground state, application of eq. (4.52) leads to the result

$$E_{J,T=3/2}(1f^3_{7/2}) = 3 \sum_{J_\epsilon T_\epsilon} \langle f^3_{7/2} J \tfrac{3}{2} | \} f^2_{7/2} J_\epsilon T_\epsilon \rangle^2 \{E_{0,1}(1f^2_{7/2}) + E_x(J_\epsilon T_\epsilon)\} . \qquad (4.53)$$

In this equation the two-body matrix element $E_{0,1}(1f^2_{7/2})$ represents the interaction energy of two protons, coupled to $J = 0$, outside a closed ^{48}Ca core. Because of eq. (4.12) its contribution to $E_{J,T=3/2}(1f^3_{7/2})$ is independent of J and hence it is irrelevant for the calculation of the excitation energies of the three-particle system of ^{51}V. Similarly the single-particle energy of the three-particle system of ^{51}V is shifted by a constant amount compared to the two-particle system of ^{50}Ti. One thus obtains from eq. (4.52) and table 4.2 the spectrum of ^{51}V given in fig. 4.2. It is seen that the calculated spectrum of ^{51}V agrees quite well with the experimentally observed one.

Table 4.3
Calculated excitation energies for configurations $|(f_{7/2})^n\rangle_{J,\,T=T_{max}}$ as a function of the MSDI parameter A_1

$n = 2$		$n = 3$	
J^π	E_x	J^π	E_x
0^+	0	$\frac{7}{2}^-$	0
2^+	$3.05\,A_1$	$\frac{5}{2}^-$	$1.95\,A_1$
4^+	$3.53\,A_1$	$\frac{3}{2}^-$	$2.28\,A_1$
6^+	$3.77\,A_1$	$\frac{11}{2}^-$	$2.57\,A_1$
		$\frac{9}{2}^-$	$2.62\,A_1$
		$\frac{15}{2}^-$	$3.15\,A_1$

The approach with the matrix elements of the MSDI given in appendix B.4 yields the excitation energies listed in table 4.3. The strength A_1 is the only parameter and by choosing as before the value $A_1 = 25$ MeV/A = 25 MeV/51 = 0.5 MeV, one obtains the MSDI spectra shown in fig. 4.2. It is seen that the MSDI reproduces correctly the spin sequence of the lower states in ^{50}Ti and ^{51}V. The excitation energies in ^{51}V are poorly reproduced, however. Especially the $J^\pi = \frac{5}{2}^-$ state calculated from the MSDI matrix elements is found at too high an excitation energy. This excitation is mainly determined by the separation between $|(1f_{7/2})^2\rangle_{J_\epsilon T_\epsilon}$ states with $J_\epsilon^\pi = 2^+$ and 4^+, as can be derived from the coefficients given in table 4.2. The empirical matrix elements obtained from ^{50}Ti yield a separation of 1.13 MeV, while the MSDI gives a value of 0.25 MeV only.

The appearance of positive-parity states in the experimental spectrum of ^{51}V shows that the model space spanned by the states $|(1f_{7/2})^3\rangle_\Gamma$ is too simple. These positive-parity states can be explained e.g. by taking into account an odd number of holes in the closed 2s1d shell. One then has an even number of nucleons in the 1f2p shell, which leads to positive-parity states. Such a calculation is too complex to be discussed at this stage, however. Nevertheless the simple description given above is a useful illustration of the methods discussed in this chapter. The assumption of pure wave functions $|(1f_{7/2})^3\rangle_\Gamma$ will be used again later for a calculation of other properties of the low-lying states of ^{51}V.

CHAPTER 5

PARTICLES IN TWO ACTIVE ORBITS

When more than two particles outside a closed-shell system are allowed to occupy several orbits, the calculation of the interaction between these particles becomes rather complex. Such calculations can in general be done well only with the help of a computer. When more than two orbits are taken into account, the most convenient way to reduce the many-particle, multishell matrix elements in terms of two-body matrix elements is presented by the second-quantization formalism. The principles of this formalism are given in chapters 13 and 14. Such an approach and a computer program developed along these lines, are described in [French, Halbert, McGrory and Wong (1969)]. When only two active orbits are involved, however, there is no need to make use of the second-quantization formalism. In this chapter a technique is discussed, which can be used as well. It is a logical extension of the theory described so far.

Some basic angular-momentum recoupling rules and the formulas required to express a totally antisymmetric two-orbit wave function in terms of antisymmetric single-orbit wave functions are treated in sect. 5.1. In sect. 5.2 it is shown that the matrix elements of the interaction for particles in two orbits can be classified in four categories. The matrix elements that are diagonal in particle partition are discussed in detail in sect. 5.3. In sect. 5.4 some sum rules, which can be used to check numerical calculations, are derived. In sect. 5.5 the formulas are applied to the calculation of the excitation energy of the first excited state in ^{31}Si. The matrix elements that are off-diagonal in particle distribution are treated in sects. 5.6 and 5.7.

5.1. Coupling rules and antisymmetry

The rules pertinent to the vector coupling and the antisymmetrization of wave functions that are often needed in shell-model calculations are summarized in this section. Some of them have been used before but are given again for completeness.

The diagrammatic notation, introduced in chapter 4, can be summarized as follows

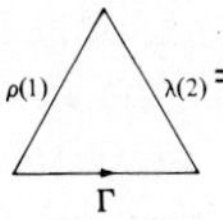

$$= \sum_{m_\rho m_\lambda} \langle j_\rho m_\rho j_\lambda m_\lambda | J_\Gamma M_\Gamma\rangle \, \phi_{j_\rho m_\rho}(1)\, \phi_{j_\lambda m_\lambda}(2)$$

$$\times \sum_{t_{\rho z} t_{\lambda z}} \langle t_\rho t_{\rho z} t_\lambda t_{\lambda z} | T_\Gamma T_{\Gamma z}\rangle \theta_{t_\rho t_{\rho z}}(1)\, \theta_{t_\lambda t_{\lambda z}}(2)\,, \qquad (5.1)$$

where $\langle aa_z bb_z | cc_z \rangle$ is a Clebsch-Gordan coefficient, ϕ denotes the single-particle wave function in coordinate space and θ represents the single-particle isospinor. The Greek symbols in the diagrams each refer to a set of quantum numbers necessary to completely specify the wave functions. For example, ρ in the diagram of eq. (5.1) denotes the spin j_ρ as well as the isospin t_ρ of a particle in the ρ orbit. The symbol Γ stands for the set of quantum numbers $J_\Gamma, T_\Gamma, v_\Gamma, t_\Gamma$ and x_Γ, where J_Γ denotes the spin, T_Γ the isospin, v_Γ the seniority, t_Γ the reduced isospin and x_Γ all other labels that may be required to completely characterize the wave function.

Antisymmetrization of a wave function is denoted by a circular arc. Thus one has for n particles in the ρ orbit

P_{jk} 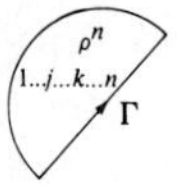

$=$ 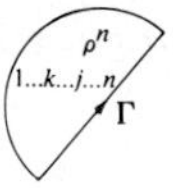

$= -$ 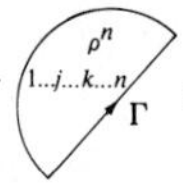

, (5.2)

where P_{jk} is the operator that interchanges all coordinates of the two particles labelled j and k.

The coefficients of fractional parentage (c.f.p.) are defined by the relation

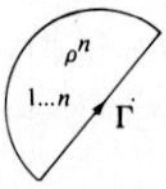

$= \sum_{\epsilon} \langle \rho^n \Gamma | \} \rho^{n-1} \epsilon \rangle$ 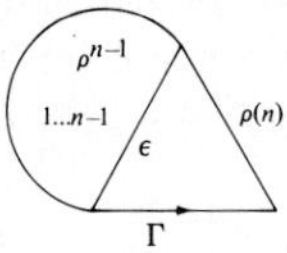

, (5.3)

where the right-hand side wave function is antisymmetric in the particles numbered $1, ..., n-1$ only. A list of some c.f.p. for orbits with $j = \frac{1}{2}, \frac{3}{2}$ and $\frac{5}{2}$ is given in appendix B.3.

An antisymmetric two-orbit wave function can be decomposed into wave functions that are antisymmetric only in the two orbits separately. One can show [Macfarlane and French (1960)] that the following relation holds

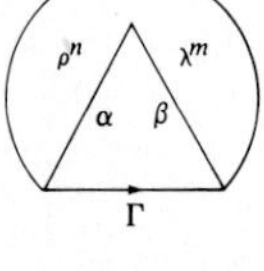

$= \dfrac{1}{\sqrt{(n+m)!}} \sum_s \Pi_s P_s$ 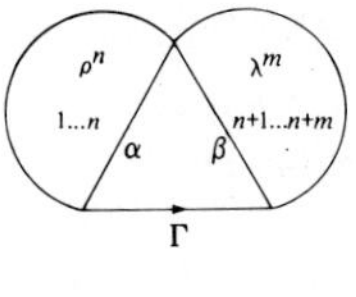

$= \sqrt{\dfrac{n!m!}{(n+m)!}} \sum_r \hat{\Pi}_r \hat{P}_r$ 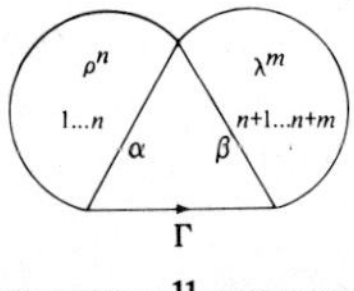

for $\rho \neq \lambda$, (5.4)

where $\Sigma_s \Pi_s P_s$ denotes a sum over all even and odd permutations P_s, each multiplied by the corresponding phase factor $\Pi_s = +1$ and $\Pi_s = -1$, respectively. Since the wave functions on the right-hand side of eq. (5.4) are antisymmetric in ρ^n and λ^m separately, it is superfluous to perform the $n!$ and $m!$ permutations among the particles of each group and thus the number of actual terms in the summation can be reduced appreciably. The necessary permutations that are to be performed on the right-hand side of eq. (5.4) can be defined uniquely as the so-called *order-preserving permutations* $\hat{P}_r$. An alternative approach is presented in appendix A.6.

To start with, assign in eq. (5.4) the numbers $1, 2, ..., n$ to the particles in ρ^n and the numbers $n+1, n+2, ..., n+m$ to those in λ^m. The circumflex over the permutation operator $\hat{P}_r$ indicates that only those permutations are performed that preserve the ascending order of the particle numbers within ρ^n as well as within λ^m. This means firstly that permutations among particles within one orbit are indeed excluded. Secondly that an interchange of particles in different orbits in general should be followed by a reshuffling of the particles of each orbit in order that the net result be an order-preserving permutation. The permutations to be summed over always include the identity. Each permutation is multiplied by a phase factor $\hat{\Pi}_r$ defined by

$$\hat{\Pi}_r = +1 \quad \text{for } \hat{P}_r \text{ an even permutation ,} \tag{5.5a}$$

$$\hat{\Pi}_r = -1 \quad \text{for } \hat{P}_r \text{ an odd permutation .} \tag{5.5b}$$

With a summation over all permutations in eq. (5.4) rather than over the order-preserving permutations only, the normalization factor is $[(n+m)!]^{-1/2}$ instead of $[n!m!/(n+m)!]^{1/2}$. This change of normalization factor makes up for the suppression of the $n!m!$ permutations (except for the identity) among particles in functions that are already antisymmetric.

Eq. (5.4) illustrates the reduction of a totally antisymmetric multishell wave function in terms of coupled antisymmetric single-shell wave functions. It is very useful for the reduction of multishell matrix elements of one- and two-body operators. For a somewhat different approach to the antisymmetrization procedure the reader is referred to appendix A.6.

As an example consider the antisymmetric four-particle wave function

$\Phi_\Gamma =$ 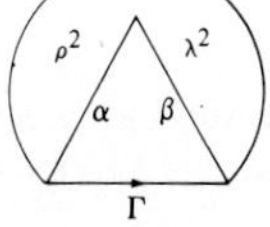 . (5.6)

The order-preserving permutations required for the application of eq. (5.4) are either the identity $P_r = 1$ or contain at least one of the transpositions that interchange particles between the groups ρ^2 (particle numbers 1 and 2) and λ^2 (particle numbers 3 and 4), i.e. P_{13}, P_{14}, P_{23} and P_{24}. Application of these permutations in eq. (5.4) does not always lead to ascending orders of the particle numbers within ρ^2 and λ^2, but still subsequent reorderings within an orbit are required. Thus eq. (5.4) becomes explicitly

$\Phi_\Gamma = \sqrt{\tfrac{1}{6}}\,[1 + P_{23}P_{13} - P_{24}P_{13}P_{14} - P_{23} + P_{23}P_{24} + P_{13}P_{24}]$ 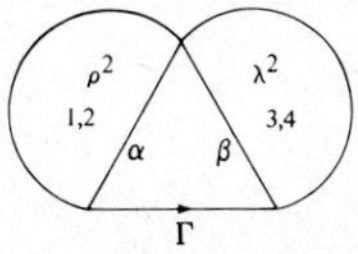 . (5.7)

Eq. (5.7) contains six order-preserving permutations P_r, written as products of transpositions P_{kl}. The sign $\hat{\Pi}_r$ that accompanies each order-preserving permutation is immediately determined by the number of transpositions. All $4! = 24$ permutations of the four particles would be obtained if also the four permutations within ρ^2 and λ^2 separately were taken into account, i.e. $P_r = 1, P_{12}, P_{34}$ and $P_{12}P_{34}$. Suppression of the latter three reduces the summation to the $24/4 = 6$ terms of eq. (5.7).

Introducing for brevity the notation

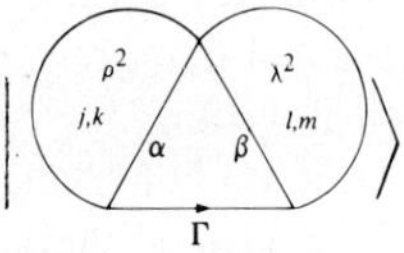

$$\equiv |jk, lm\rangle \,, \tag{5.8}$$

one obtains from eq. (5.7)

$$\Phi_\Gamma = \sqrt{\tfrac{1}{6}}\,[|12,34\rangle + |23,14\rangle - |24,13\rangle - |13,24\rangle + |14,23\rangle + |34,12\rangle] \,. \tag{5.9}$$

It is easily verified that the wave function (5.9) is antisymmetric in all particles, i.e. $P_{jk}\Phi_\Gamma = -\Phi_\Gamma$ for all pairs $j \neq k$, if one remembers that each term is already antisymmetrized in the groups ρ^2 and λ^2 separately.

The coupling order, denoted by an arrow, defines a phase of the wave function, as is clear from the relation

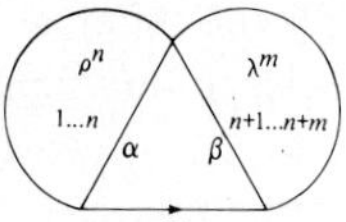

$$= (-1)^{\Gamma-\alpha-\beta}$$

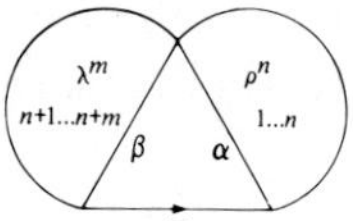

$$. \tag{5.10}$$

The phase factor in eq. (5.10) must be understood as

$$(-1)^{\Gamma-\alpha-\beta} = (-1)^{(J_\Gamma + T_\Gamma) - (J_\alpha + T_\alpha) - (J_\beta + T_\beta)} \,. \tag{5.11}$$

Eq. (5.10) follows from the definition (5.1) and the symmetry property of Clebsch-Gordan coefficients given by

$$\langle jmj'm'|JM\rangle = (-1)^{J-j-j'} \langle j'm'jm|JM\rangle \,. \tag{5.12}$$

Once a particular coupling order of orbits in an actual shell-model calculation is chosen, it is recommended to maintain this order in all calculations with these wave functions. A change of this order introduces extra phase factors, as follows from the relation

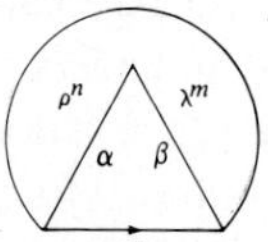

$$= (-1)^{\Gamma-\alpha-\beta-nm}$$

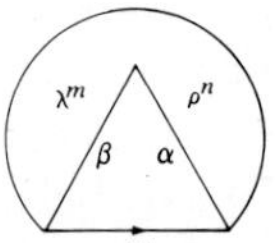

$$, \tag{5.13}$$

which holds for totally antisymmetric wave functions. One part of the phase factor, $(-1)^{\Gamma-\alpha-\beta}$, in eq. (5.13) has a purely geometric origin, just as in eq. (5.10). The other part, $(-1)^{nm}$, stems from the antisymmetry of the complete wave function when the particles are reordered from $1, \ldots, n, n+1, \ldots, n+m$ into $n+1, \ldots, n+m, 1, \ldots, n$ which requires nm transpositions. Eq. (5.13) can be verified when one applies eq.

(5.4) to the two sides and uses eq. (5.10). For the simple case with $n = m = 1$ one thus obtains directly

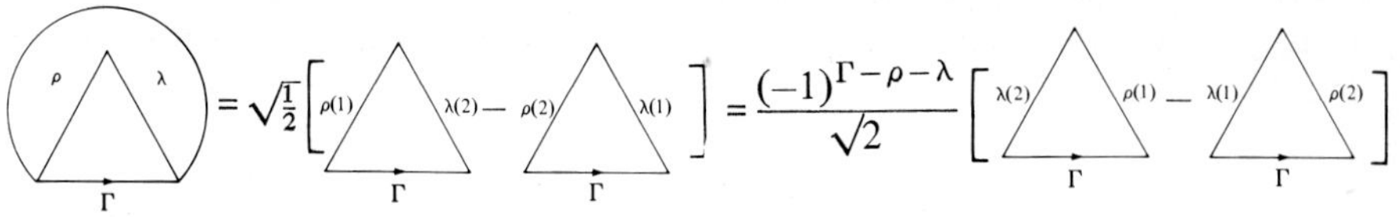

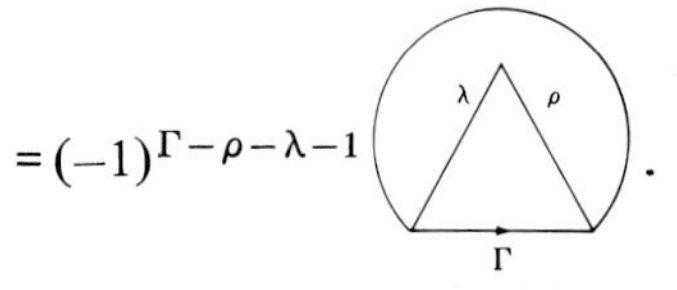

$$\left(\bigtriangleup_\rho{}^\lambda\right)_\Gamma = \sqrt{\tfrac{1}{2}}\left[\,{}_{\rho(1)}\!\bigtriangleup\!{}_{\lambda(2)}\,-\,{}_{\rho(2)}\!\bigtriangleup\!{}_{\lambda(1)}\,\right]_\Gamma = \frac{(-1)^{\Gamma-\rho-\lambda}}{\sqrt{2}}\left[\,{}_{\lambda(2)}\!\bigtriangleup\!{}_{\rho(1)}\,-\,{}_{\lambda(1)}\!\bigtriangleup\!{}_{\rho(2)}\,\right]_\Gamma$$

$$= (-1)^{\Gamma-\rho-\lambda-1}\left(\bigtriangleup_\lambda{}^\rho\right)_\Gamma . \tag{5.14}$$

with the convention $(-1)^\Gamma \equiv (-1)^{J_\Gamma + T_\Gamma}$ etc. Eq. (5.14) is useful when phase relations are to be established between two-body matrix elements that are given for different coupling orders of the orbits ρ and λ.

When expressing antisymmetric matrix elements in terms of non-antisymmetrized two-body functions, one should be careful about possible factors of $\sqrt{2}$. From eq. (5.4) one derives by taking $n = m = 1$ for a diagonal two-body matrix element

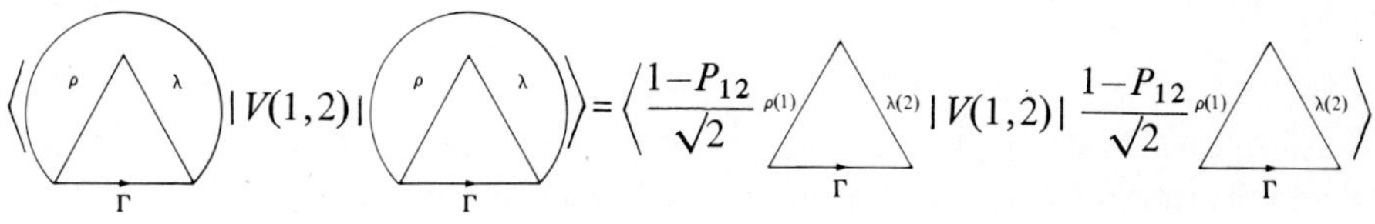

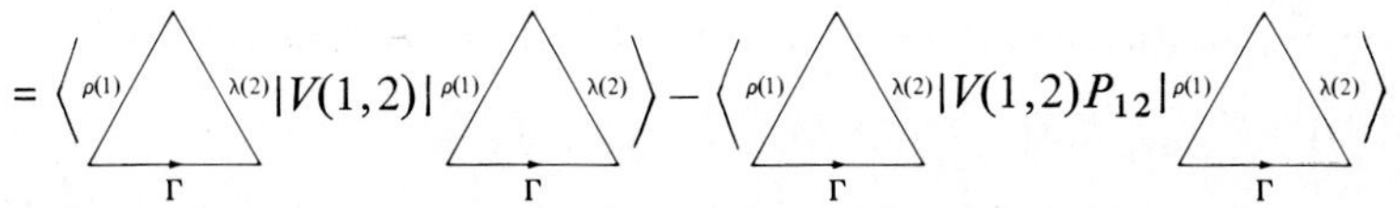

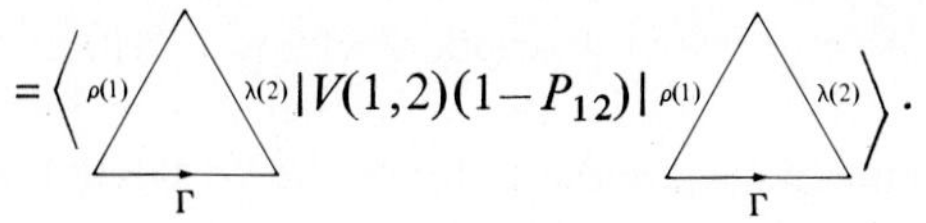

$$\left\langle\left(\bigtriangleup_\rho{}^\lambda\right)_\Gamma\,|V(1,2)|\,\left(\bigtriangleup_\rho{}^\lambda\right)_\Gamma\right\rangle = \left\langle\frac{1-P_{12}}{\sqrt{2}}\,{}_{\rho(1)}\!\bigtriangleup\!{}_{\lambda(2)}\,|V(1,2)|\,\frac{1-P_{12}}{\sqrt{2}}\,{}_{\rho(1)}\!\bigtriangleup\!{}_{\lambda(2)}\right\rangle$$

$$= \left\langle{}_{\rho(1)}\!\bigtriangleup\!{}_{\lambda(2)}\,|V(1,2)|\,{}_{\rho(1)}\!\bigtriangleup\!{}_{\lambda(2)}\right\rangle - \left\langle{}_{\rho(1)}\!\bigtriangleup\!{}_{\lambda(2)}\,|V(1,2)P_{12}|\,{}_{\rho(1)}\!\bigtriangleup\!{}_{\lambda(2)}\right\rangle$$

$$= \left\langle{}_{\rho(1)}\!\bigtriangleup\!{}_{\lambda(2)}\,|V(1,2)(1-P_{12})|\,{}_{\rho(1)}\!\bigtriangleup\!{}_{\lambda(2)}\right\rangle . \tag{5.15}$$

For an off-diagonal matrix element one obtains

$$\left\langle\left(\bigtriangleup{}^{\rho^2}\right)_\Gamma\,|V(1,2)|\,\left(\bigtriangleup_\rho{}^\lambda\right)_\Gamma\right\rangle = \left\langle\left(\bigtriangleup{}^{\rho^2}_{1,2}\right)_\Gamma\,|V(1,2)\frac{1-P_{12}}{\sqrt{2}}|\,{}_{\rho(1)}\!\bigtriangleup\!{}_{\lambda(2)}\right\rangle$$

$$= \sqrt{2}\left\langle\left(\bigtriangleup{}^{\rho^2}_{1,2}\right)_\Gamma\,|V(1,2)|\,{}_{\rho(1)}\!\bigtriangleup\!{}_{\lambda(2)}\right\rangle , \tag{5.16}$$

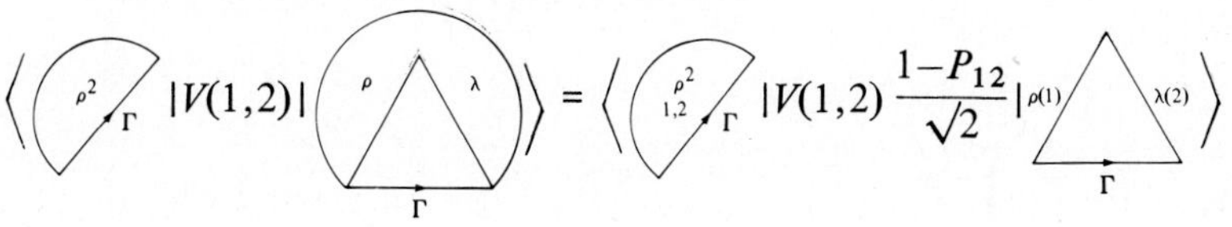

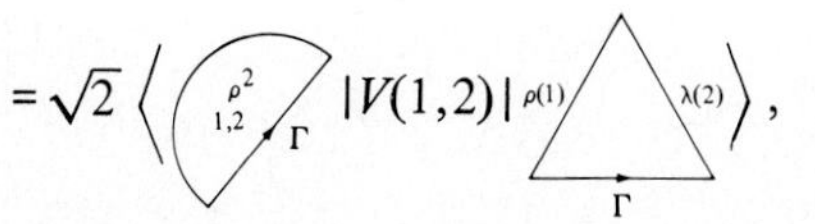

where for the last equality use has been made of the fact that the operator P_{12}, when acting to the left, yields a factor -1, due to the antisymmetry of the configuration ρ^2 and the symmetry of the interaction $V(1,2)$.

In general one can express the antisymmetric two-body matrix elements in terms of those for non-antisymmetrized states as

$$\left\langle\left(\begin{array}{c}\rho\\\lambda\end{array}\right)|V(1,2)|\left(\begin{array}{c}\sigma\\\mu\end{array}\right)\right\rangle = \frac{\left\langle\left(\begin{array}{c}\rho(1)\quad\lambda(2)\end{array}\right)|V(1,2)(1-P_{12})|\left(\begin{array}{c}\sigma(1)\quad\mu(2)\end{array}\right)\right\rangle}{\sqrt{(1+\delta_{\rho\lambda})(1+\delta_{\sigma\mu})}}.$$

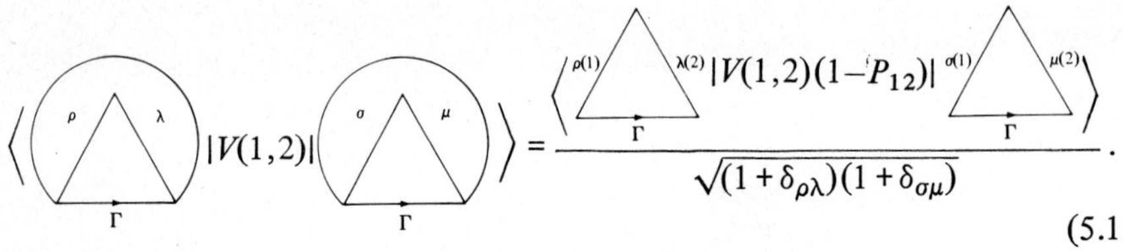

$$(5.17)$$

For the recoupling of three angular momenta one can make use of the normalized Racah coefficients or U-coefficients defined by the relations

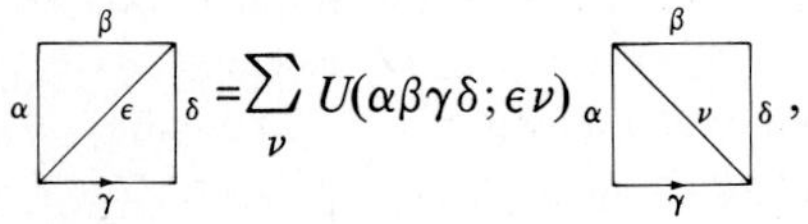

$$\begin{array}{c}\beta\\\alpha\quad\epsilon\quad\delta\\\gamma\end{array} = \sum_{\nu} U(\alpha\beta\gamma\delta;\epsilon\nu)\begin{array}{c}\beta\\\alpha\quad\nu\quad\delta\\\gamma\end{array},\qquad(5.18)$$

$$\begin{array}{c}\beta\\\alpha\quad\nu\quad\delta\\\gamma\end{array} = \sum_{\epsilon} U(\alpha\beta\gamma\delta;\epsilon\nu)\begin{array}{c}\beta\\\alpha\quad\epsilon\quad\delta\\\gamma\end{array}.\qquad(5.19)$$

The left-hand side of eq. (5.18) specifies the coupling of α and β to ϵ and then with δ to the final γ. On the right-hand side the β and δ are first coupled to ν and then α is coupled with ν to the final γ. The Greek symbols denote J, T pairs and the U-coefficients must be understood as products of spin and isospin coefficients

$$U(\alpha\beta\gamma\delta;\epsilon\nu) \equiv U(J_\alpha J_\beta J_\gamma J_\delta; J_\epsilon J_\nu) \times U(T_\alpha T_\beta T_\gamma T_\delta; T_\epsilon T_\nu).\qquad(5.20)$$

The relation between U-coefficients and 6-j symbols is given in appendix A.1. The triangular conditions to be satisfied by the various quantum numbers in order to obtain nonzero U-coefficients follow directly from the diagrams of eqs. (5.18) and (5.19).

The recoupling of four angular momenta is given in terms of the 9-j symbols as

$$\begin{array}{c}\alpha_2\quad\alpha_3\\\alpha_1\quad\quad\quad\alpha_4\\\Gamma_{12}\ \Gamma_{34}\\\Gamma\end{array} = \sum_{\Gamma_{13}\Gamma_{24}} \sqrt{(2\Gamma_{12}+1)(2\Gamma_{34}+1)(2\Gamma_{13}+1)(2\Gamma_{24}+1)}$$

$$\times \left\{\begin{array}{ccc}\alpha_1 & \alpha_2 & \Gamma_{12}\\\alpha_3 & \alpha_4 & \Gamma_{34}\\\Gamma_{13} & \Gamma_{24} & \Gamma\end{array}\right\}\begin{array}{c}\alpha_3\quad\alpha_2\\\alpha_1\quad\quad\quad\alpha_4\\\Gamma_{13}\ \Gamma_{24}\\\Gamma\end{array}.\qquad(5.21)$$

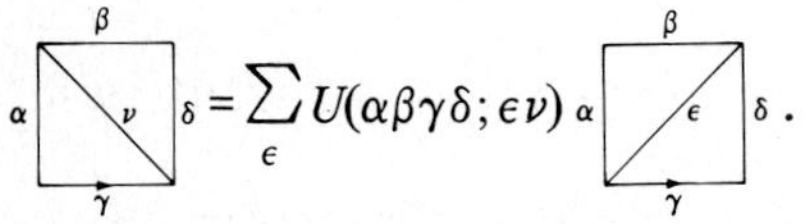

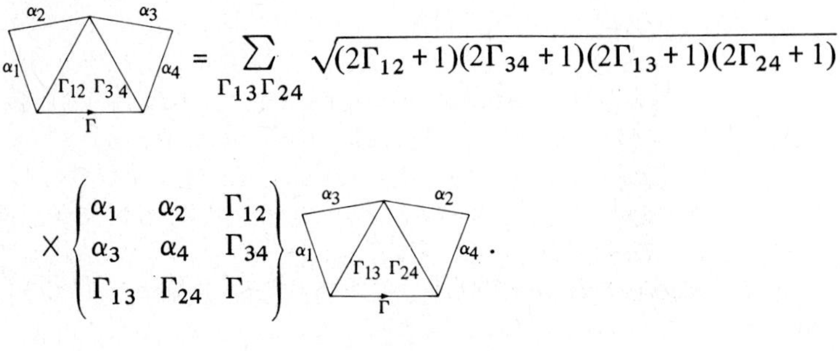

This relation can be applied, for example, to establish a relation between two-body wave functions obtained in L-S coupling and in j-j coupling. Substituting $\alpha_1 = l_1, \alpha_2 = l_2, \alpha_3 = s_1$ and $\alpha_4 = s_2$ one has for L-S coupling $\boldsymbol{l}_1 + \boldsymbol{l}_2 = \boldsymbol{L}_{12}, \boldsymbol{s}_1 + \boldsymbol{s}_2 = \boldsymbol{S}_{12}$ and then $\boldsymbol{L}_{12} + \boldsymbol{S}_{12} = \boldsymbol{J}_{12}$ for the left-hand side wave function. The right-hand side then gives the coupling of $\boldsymbol{l}_1 + \boldsymbol{s}_1 = \boldsymbol{j}_1, \boldsymbol{l}_2 + \boldsymbol{s}_2 = \boldsymbol{j}_2$ and $\boldsymbol{j}_1 + \boldsymbol{j}_2 = \boldsymbol{J}_{12}$.

5.2. Several particles in two active orbits

Now we have the tools ready to express the interaction matrix elements in terms of two-body matrix elements when many particles in more than one orbit are involved. The procedure will be outlined only for particles in two active orbits, but can in principle also be used in more complex cases involving more orbits.

The interaction V, assumed to be a pure two-body interaction, can change the orbits of at most two particles. The matrix elements to be evaluated thus have the form

$\langle V \rangle = \Big\langle$ 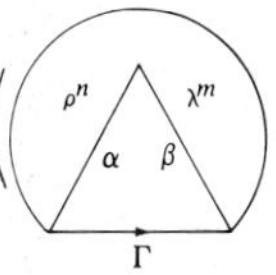 $\Big| \sum_{1=j<k}^{n+m} V(j,k) \Big|$ 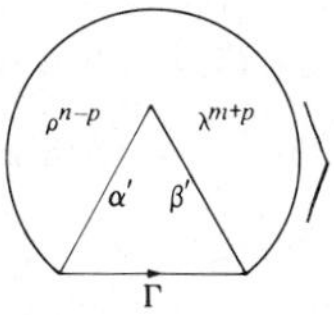 $\Big\rangle$ (5.22)

with $|p| \leqslant 2$.

One can classify the matrix elements $\langle V \rangle$ into four different classes, given by

$$
\begin{aligned}
&\text{category I}: && p = 0\,, \quad \alpha = \alpha'\,, \quad \text{and } \beta = \beta'\,,\\
&\text{category II}: && p = 0\,, \quad \alpha \neq \alpha'\,, \quad \text{and/or } \beta \neq \beta'\,,\\
&\text{category III}: && |p| = 1\,,\\
&\text{category IV}: && |p| = 2\,.
\end{aligned}
\qquad (5.23)
$$

Category I represents all diagonal matrix elements of the interaction matrix $\langle V \rangle$. All other categories represent off-diagonal matrix elements giving rise to configuration mixing.

5.3. Matrix elements of categories I and II

In order to decompose the many-particle matrix elements given in eq. (5.22) in terms of two-particle matrix elements, one must undo the antisymmetrization of the particles in the ρ orbit with respect to those in the λ orbit. The first step to this goal can be made by writing the complete antisymmetric $(n + m)$-particle wave functions in terms of those antisymmetric in the ρ and λ orbits separately. Applying eq. (5.4) to the bra wave function of eq. (5.22) one obtains for $p = 0$

$$\langle V \rangle = \sqrt{\frac{n!\,m!}{(n+m)!}} \sum_r \Big\langle \hat{\Pi}_r \hat{P}_r \Big(\!\!\!\begin{smallmatrix}\rho^n & \lambda^m\\ 1...n & n+1...n+m\\ \alpha & \beta\end{smallmatrix}\!\!\!\Big)_\Gamma \Big| \sum_{1=j<k}^{n+m} V(j,k) \Big| \Big(\!\!\!\begin{smallmatrix}\rho^n & \lambda^m\\ \alpha' & \beta'\end{smallmatrix}\!\!\!\Big)_\Gamma \Big\rangle \quad (5.24)$$

with the permutation operator $\hat{P}_r$ acting on the bra function only.

All terms of the sum Σ_r are of the same magnitude and of the same sign, as can be seen as follows. Denoting the matrix elements of eq. (5.24) by $\langle \hat{\Pi}_r \hat{P}_r \Phi_\Gamma | V | \Phi'_\Gamma \rangle$, one can write

$$\langle \hat{\Pi}_r \hat{P}_r \Phi_\Gamma | V | \Phi'_\Gamma \rangle = \langle \hat{P}_r \Phi_\Gamma | V | \hat{\Pi}_r \Phi'_\Gamma \rangle$$

$$= \langle \hat{P}_r \Phi_\Gamma | V | \hat{P}_r \Phi'_\Gamma \rangle$$

$$= \langle \hat{P}_r \Phi_\Gamma | \hat{P}_r V \hat{P}_r^{-1} | \hat{P}_r \Phi'_\Gamma \rangle \, . \quad (5.25)$$

In this derivation use has been made of the fact that the permutation $\hat{P}_r$ possesses the signature $\hat{\Pi}_r$ when acting on the completely antisymmetric state Φ'_Γ and also that the interaction V is fully symmetric in the particle coordinates, i.e. $V = \hat{P}_r V \hat{P}_r^{-1}$. In eq. (5.25) one must integrate over all coordinates, and thus one has

$$\langle \hat{\Pi}_r \hat{P}_r \Phi_\Gamma | V | \Phi'_\Gamma \rangle = \langle \hat{P}_r \Phi_\Gamma | \hat{P}_r V \hat{P}_r^{-1} | \hat{P}_r \Phi'_\Gamma \rangle = \langle \Phi_\Gamma | V | \Phi'_\Gamma \rangle \, , \quad (5.26)$$

since the permutations cause only a renumbering of all integration variables.

There are $(n+m)!/n!m!$ terms in the sum over r in eq. (5.24) and thus one obtains, taking the particle numbering for $P_r = 1$,

$$\langle V \rangle = \sqrt{\frac{(n+m)!}{n!\,m!}} \Big\langle \Big(\!\!\!\begin{smallmatrix}\rho^n & \lambda^m\\ 1...n & n+1...n+m\\ \alpha & \beta\end{smallmatrix}\!\!\!\Big)_\Gamma \Big| \sum_{1=j<k}^{n+m} V(j,k) \Big| \Big(\!\!\!\begin{smallmatrix}\rho^n & \lambda^m\\ \alpha' & \beta'\end{smallmatrix}\!\!\!\Big)_\Gamma \Big\rangle \, . \quad (5.27)$$

Application of eq. (5.4) to the ket in eq. (5.27) yields

$$\langle V \rangle = \Big\langle \Big(\!\!\!\begin{smallmatrix}\rho^n & \lambda^m\\ 1...n & n+1...n+m\\ \alpha & \beta\end{smallmatrix}\!\!\!\Big)_\Gamma \Big| \sum_{1=j<k}^{n+m} V(j,k) \Big| \sum_r \hat{\Pi}_r \hat{P}_r \Big(\!\!\!\begin{smallmatrix}\rho^n & \lambda^m\\ 1...n & n+1...n+m\\ \alpha' & \beta'\end{smallmatrix}\!\!\!\Big)_\Gamma \Big\rangle \quad (5.28)$$

where the product of the factorials given in eqs. (5.4) and (5.27) leads to unity.

The interaction $V = \Sigma_{j<k} V(j,k)$ can always be rewritten as

$$V = V_\rho + V_\lambda + V_{\rho\lambda} \quad (5.29)$$

with

$$V_\rho \equiv \sum_{1=j<k}^{n} V(j,k) \, , \quad V_\lambda \equiv \sum_{n+1=j<k}^{n+m} V(j,k) \, , \quad V_{\rho\lambda} \equiv \sum_{j=1}^{n} \sum_{k=n+1}^{n+m} V(j,k) \quad (5.30)$$

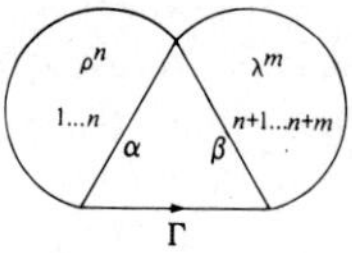

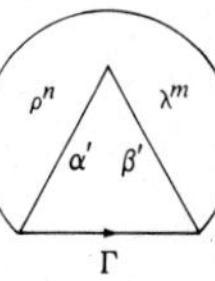

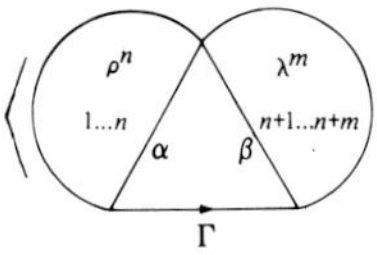

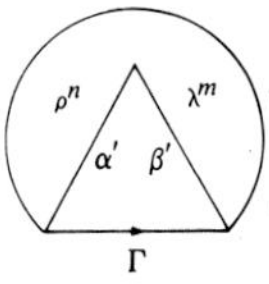

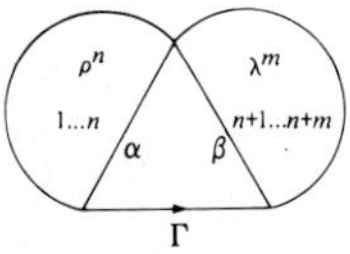

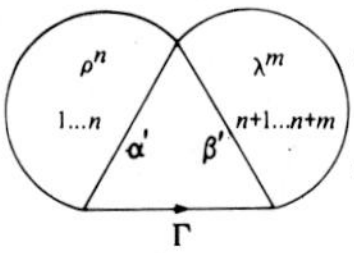

For the particle labelling assigned to the bra function in eq. (5.28) V_ρ acts only on particles in the ρ orbit and V_λ on those in the λ orbit, whereas $V_{\rho\lambda}$ describes the interaction between particles in two different orbits.

Consider the contribution from V_ρ first. One has to calculate the matrix element (see eq. (5.28))

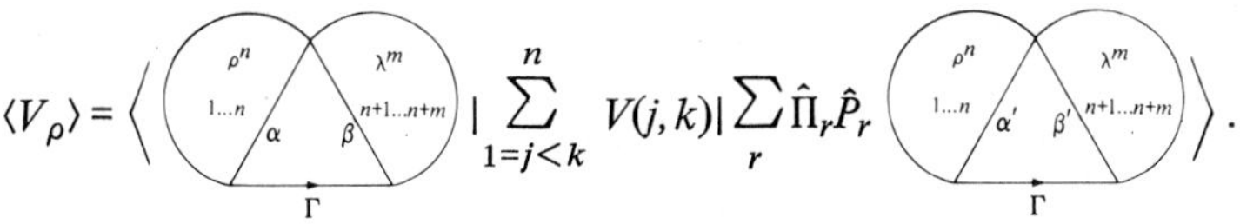

$$\langle V_\rho \rangle = \left\langle \begin{array}{c} \rho^n \quad \lambda^m \\ \overset{1...n}{\underset{\alpha}{\diagup}} \overset{n+1...n+m}{\underset{\beta}{\diagup}} \\ \Gamma \end{array} \;\middle|\; \sum_{1=j<k}^{n} V(j,k) \middle| \sum_r \hat{\Pi}_r \hat{P}_r \; \begin{array}{c} \rho^n \quad \lambda^m \\ \overset{1...n}{\underset{\alpha'}{\diagup}} \overset{n+1...n+m}{\underset{\beta'}{\diagup}} \\ \Gamma \end{array} \right\rangle . \tag{5.31}$$

The order-preserving permutations $\hat{P}_r$ interchange only particles between the ρ and λ orbits. Consider the permutations $\hat{P}_r \neq 1$. Then at least one particle labelled l with $l \in \{n+1, ..., n+m\}$ of the λ orbit is transferred to the ρ orbit. Since the operator $\Sigma_{1=j<k}^{n} V(j,k)$ in eq. (5.31) does not act on particles l with $l > n$, all resulting matrix elements must contain a factor $\langle \lambda(l)|\rho(l)\rangle$, which vanishes because of the orthogonality of the single-particle states $|\lambda(l)\rangle$ and $|\rho(l)\rangle$. Therefore only the term with $P_r = 1$ contributes and eq. (5.31) can be written as

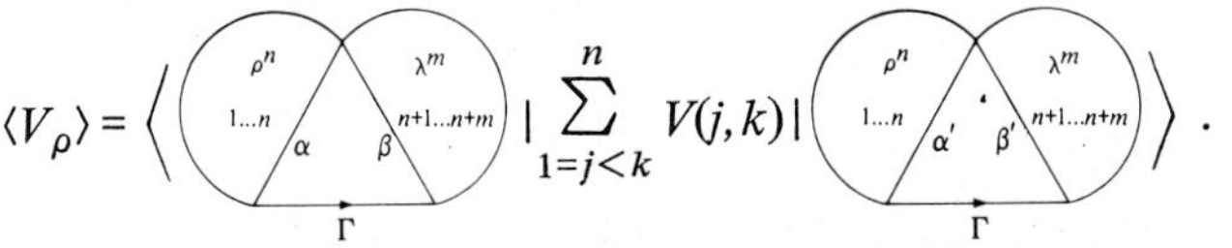

$$\langle V_\rho \rangle = \left\langle \begin{array}{c} \rho^n \quad \lambda^m \\ \overset{1...n}{\underset{\alpha}{\diagup}} \overset{n+1...n+m}{\underset{\beta}{\diagup}} \\ \Gamma \end{array} \;\middle|\; \sum_{1=j<k}^{n} V(j,k) \middle| \; \begin{array}{c} \rho^n \quad \lambda^m \\ \overset{1...n}{\underset{\alpha'}{\diagup}} \overset{n+1...n+m}{\underset{\beta'}{\diagup}} \\ \Gamma \end{array} \right\rangle . \tag{5.32}$$

Since the operator does not act on particles in the λ orbit, it follows from a procedure similar to that used to obtain eq. (4.38) that one has

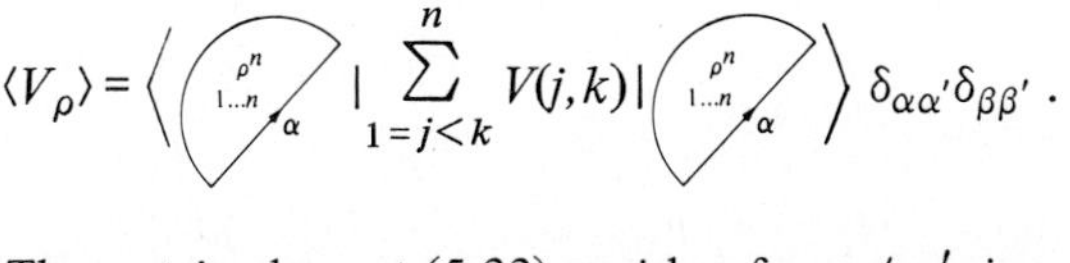

$$\langle V_\rho \rangle = \left\langle \begin{array}{c} \rho^n \\ \overset{1...n}{\underset{\alpha}{\diagup}} \end{array} \;\middle|\; \sum_{1=j<k}^{n} V(j,k) \middle|\; \begin{array}{c} \rho^n \\ \overset{1...n}{\underset{\alpha}{\diagup}} \end{array} \right\rangle \delta_{\alpha\alpha'} \delta_{\beta\beta'} . \tag{5.33}$$

The matrix element (5.33) vanishes for $\alpha \neq \alpha'$ since the interaction V_ρ is scalar. Therefore this term contributes only to the diagonal matrix elements defined by eq. (5.23) as category I. The final expression (5.33) can be treated as outlined in chapter 4, since only particles in one orbit are involved.

The term V_λ defined in eq. (5.30) can be reduced in analogy with the term V_ρ, thus yielding

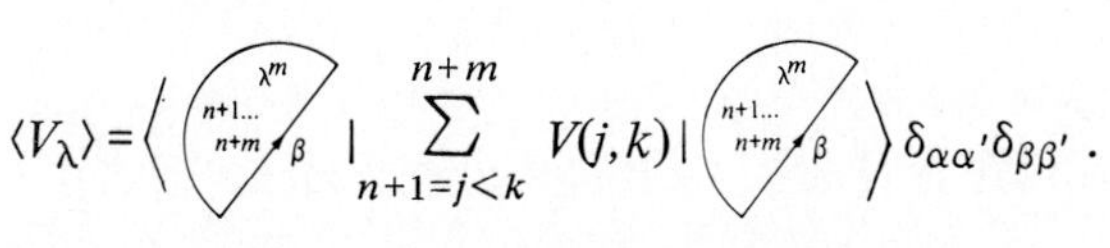

$$\langle V_\lambda \rangle = \left\langle \begin{array}{c} \lambda^m \\ \overset{n+1...}{\underset{n+m}{\diagup}} \underset{\beta}{} \end{array} \;\middle|\; \sum_{n+1=j<k}^{n+m} V(j,k) \middle|\; \begin{array}{c} \lambda^m \\ \overset{n+1...}{\underset{n+m}{\diagup}} \underset{\beta}{} \end{array} \right\rangle \delta_{\alpha\alpha'} \delta_{\beta\beta'} . \tag{5.34}$$

The last term of eq. (5.29) deals with the interaction between particles in different orbits. Now one has to evaluate the matrix element

$\langle V_{\rho\lambda}\rangle = \Big\langle$ 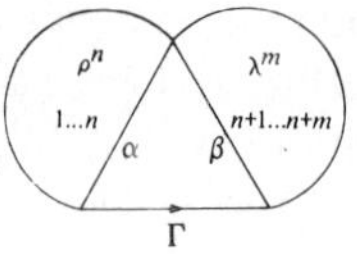

$\Big| \sum_{j=1}^{n} \sum_{k=n+1}^{n+m} V(j,k) \Big| \sum_r \hat{\Pi}_r \hat{P}_r$ 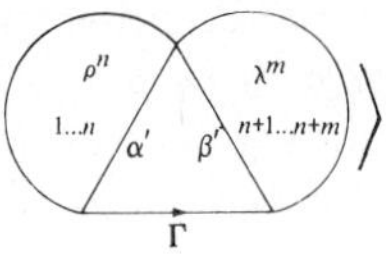

$\Big\rangle$. (5.35)

From the orthogonality of the single-particle wave functions it follows that for each term $V(j,k)$ there are only two order-preserving permutations that will give a non-vanishing contribution, i.e. $P_r = 1$ and $\hat{P}_r = \hat{P}_{jk}$. For given j and k therefore the sum $\Sigma_r \hat{\Pi}_r \hat{P}_r$ reduces to $1 + \hat{\Pi}_{jk}\hat{P}_{jk}$ and eq. (5.35) can be written as

$\langle V_{\rho\lambda}\rangle = \Big\langle$ 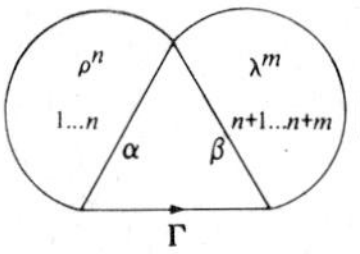

$\Big| \sum_{j=1}^{n} \sum_{k=n+1}^{n+m} V(j,k)(1 + \hat{\Pi}_{jk}\hat{P}_{jk}) \Big|$ 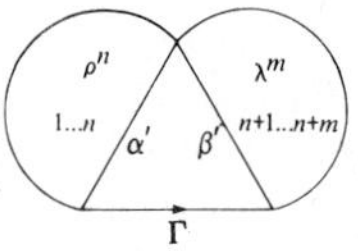

$\Big\rangle$. (5.36)

The summation in eq. (5.36) runs over $n \times m$ terms. As the particles $\rho^n(1, ..., n)$ as well as the particles $\lambda^m(n+1, ..., n+m)$ are antisymmetrized on *both* sides of the matrix element, each term $\langle | V(j,k)(1 + \hat{\Pi}_{jk}\hat{P}_{jk}) | \rangle$ will lead to a contribution of the same magnitude and sign. Choosing the term with $j = n$ and $k = n + m$, one obtains

$\langle V_{\rho\lambda}\rangle = nm \Big\langle$ 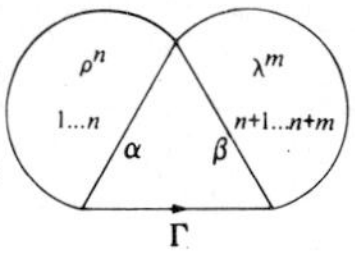

$\big| V(n, n+m)(1 - P_{n,n+m}) \big|$ 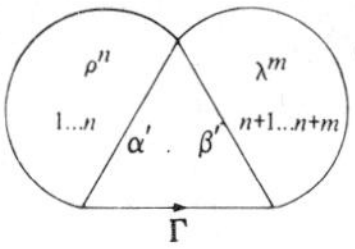

$\Big\rangle$, (5.37)

since for one transposition one has $\hat{\Pi}_{n,n+m} = -1$.

In order to reduce the many-particle matrix element of eq. (5.37) in terms of two-particle matrix elements, one must decouple the particles on which the operator $V(n, n+m)$ acts. Applying the c.f.p. expansion given in eq. (5.3) for the decoupling of the particle labelled n from the group ρ^n and the particle labelled $n + m$ from the group λ^m, one obtains

$$\langle V_{\rho\lambda}\rangle = nm \sum_{\epsilon\eta\epsilon'\eta'} \langle \rho^n \alpha | \} \rho^{n-1}\epsilon\rangle \langle \rho^n \alpha' | \} \rho^{n-1}\epsilon'\rangle \langle \lambda^m \beta | \} \lambda^{m-1}\eta\rangle \langle \lambda^m \beta' | \} \lambda^{m-1}\eta'\rangle$$

$\times \Big\langle$ 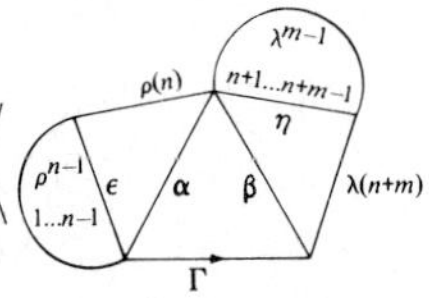

$\big| V(n, n+m)(1 - P_{n,n+m}) \big|$ 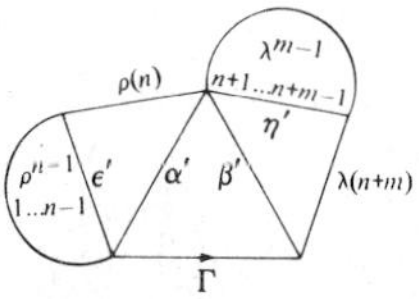

$\Big\rangle$. (5.38)

For a further reduction it is necessary to change the coupling order such that the particles labelled n and $n + m$ can be taken together, coupled to some well-defined value of spin and isospin. Then one can integrate over the coordinates of particles $1, 2, ..., n-1$ and $n+1, n+2, ..., n+m-1$. This procedure is performed most conveniently in a two-step reduction with the aid of eqs. (5.18) and (5.19). After the first step one obtains

$$\langle V_{\rho\lambda}\rangle = nm \sum_{\epsilon\eta\epsilon'\eta'} \langle\rho^n\alpha|\}\rho^{n-1}\epsilon\rangle\langle\rho^n\alpha'|\}\rho^{n-1}\epsilon'\rangle\langle\lambda^m\beta|\}\lambda^{m-1}\eta\rangle\langle\lambda^m\beta'|\}\lambda^{m-1}\eta'\rangle$$

$$\times \sum_{\pi\pi'} U(\epsilon\rho\Gamma\beta;\alpha\pi)\, U(\epsilon'\rho\Gamma\beta';\alpha'\pi')$$

$\times\Big\langle$ 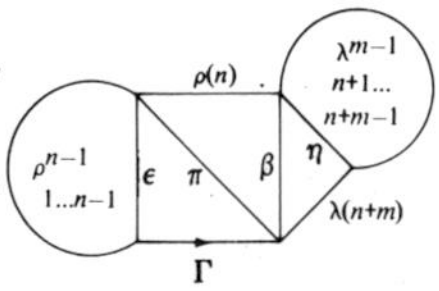

$| V(n, n+m)(1 - P_{n,n+m})|$ 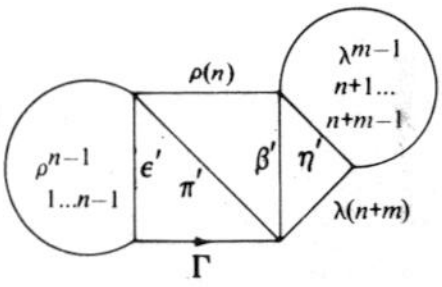

$\Big\rangle$. (5.39)

It should be remarked that only the angular momenta involved in the recoupling are relevant; whether these momenta refer to antisymmetrized groups or not, does not affect the angular-momentum coupling. In eq. (5.39) the coordinates of particles 1, 2, ..., $n-1$ can be integrated over, which leads to a Kronecker delta $\delta_{\epsilon\epsilon'}$. One obtains after (i) the interchange of the bra vectors $\langle\lambda^{m-1}|_\eta$ and $\langle\lambda(n+m)|$ and of the ket vectors $|\lambda^{m-1}\rangle_{\eta'}$ and $|\lambda(n+m)\rangle$, (ii) the application of eq. (5.19) and (iii) the integration over the coordinates of particles $n+1, n+2, \ldots, n+m-1$ (which leads to $\delta_{\eta\eta'}$) the expression

$$\langle V_{\rho\lambda}\rangle = nm \sum_{\epsilon\eta} \langle\rho^n\alpha|\}\rho^{n-1}\epsilon\rangle\langle\rho^n\alpha'|\}\rho^{n-1}\epsilon\rangle\langle\lambda^m\beta|\}\lambda^{m-1}\eta\rangle\langle\lambda^m\beta'|\}\lambda^{m-1}\eta\rangle$$

$$\times \sum_{\pi\theta} (2\pi+1)(2\theta+1)\sqrt{(2\alpha+1)(2\beta+1)(2\alpha'+1)(2\beta'+1)} \begin{Bmatrix} \epsilon & \rho & \alpha \\ \beta & \Gamma & \pi \end{Bmatrix} \begin{Bmatrix} \epsilon & \rho & \alpha' \\ \beta' & \Gamma & \pi \end{Bmatrix}$$

$\times \begin{Bmatrix} \eta & \beta' & \lambda \\ \rho & \theta & \pi \end{Bmatrix} \begin{Bmatrix} \eta & \beta & \lambda \\ \rho & \theta & \pi \end{Bmatrix} \Big\langle$ 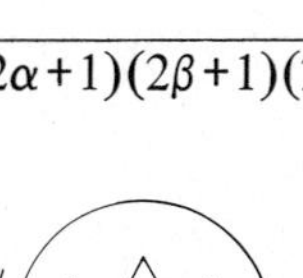

$|V|$ 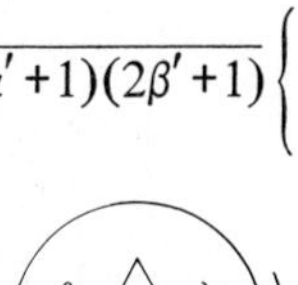

$\Big\rangle$ for $\rho \neq \lambda$, (5.40)

where the U-coefficients have been replaced by 6-j symbols. The two-particle matrix element between antisymmetric states enters into the right-hand side of this equation after application of eq. (5.17).

Summarizing the results for matrix elements of categories I and II one obtains

$\langle V\rangle = \Big\langle$ 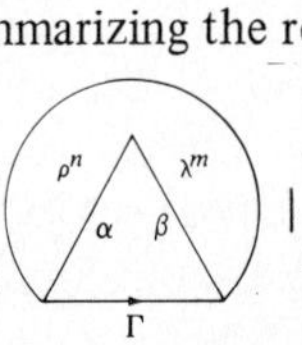

$\Big| \sum_{1=j<k}^{n+m} V(j,k) \Big|$ 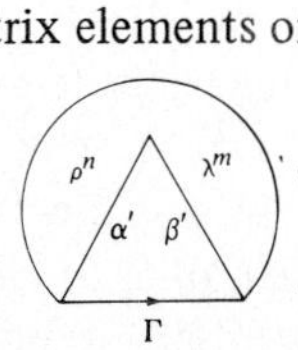

$\Big\rangle = \langle V_\rho\rangle + \langle V_\lambda\rangle + \langle V_{\rho\lambda}\rangle$, (5.41)

where $\langle V_\rho\rangle$ and $\langle V_\lambda\rangle$ contain the Kronecker delta symbols $\delta_{\alpha\alpha'}\,\delta_{\beta\beta'}$, i.e. they contribute only to the diagonal elements ($\alpha = \alpha'$ and $\beta = \beta'$) of the interaction matrix. The expressions for $\langle V_\rho \rangle$, $\langle V_\lambda \rangle$ and $\langle V_{\rho\lambda} \rangle$ are given in eqs. (5.33), (5.34) and (5.40), respectively.

5.4. Sum rules for diagonal matrix elements

It has been shown that the two-shell matrix elements $\langle V \rangle$ of an n-particle system, defined as categories I and II in eq. (5.23) can be expressed in terms of diagonal two-body matrix elements. Denoting the latter by x_k one may write

$$\langle V \rangle = \sum_l c_l x_l \,, \tag{5.42}$$

where l enumerates the contributing two-body matrix elements and the coefficients c_l follow from the Racah algebra discussed in the previous section. There is a simple check on the sum of the coefficients c_l, in case one makes the restriction to diagonal matrix elements only, i.e. category I.

Suppose that the two-body matrix elements x_l describing the interaction between a pair of nucleons depend neither on the single-particle orbits involved nor on the spin and isospin of the two-particle wave functions. In this case all two-body matrix elements will have the same value, say V_0. Since the number of interacting pairs in an n-particle system is equal to $\binom{n}{2} = \frac{1}{2}n(n-1)$, one finds that the expectation value $\langle V \rangle$ for the n-particle system must be equal to $\frac{1}{2}n(n-1)V_0$. Thus, using eq. (5.42), one has the relation

$$\langle V \rangle = \sum_l c_l \, V_0 = \tfrac{1}{2}n(n-1)V_0 \tag{5.43}$$

from which the sum rule

$$\sum_l c_l = \tfrac{1}{2}n(n-1) \tag{5.44}$$

follows directly. This sum rule holds for any many-particle multishell configuration as long as one deals with the diagonal matrix elements of the interaction matrix.

When $c_l^{(0)}$ and $c_m^{(1)}$ denote the coefficients of the two-body matrix elements for two-particle states that are coupled to $T' = 0$ and $T' = 1$, respectively, one can also determine the partial sums $\Sigma_l \, c_l^{(0)}$ and $\Sigma_m \, c_m^{(1)}$ separately, as is shown below.

Define the two-body isospin operator

$$V_{\mathrm{T}}(j,k) = \tfrac{1}{2}(\boldsymbol{t}(j) + \boldsymbol{t}(k))^2 \,. \tag{5.45}$$

The eigenvalues of $V_{\mathrm{T}}(j,k)$, operating on the two-particle system coupled to $\boldsymbol{T}' = \boldsymbol{t}(j) + \boldsymbol{t}(k)$, are given by $\frac{1}{2}T'(T'+1)$ and thus are equal to 0 and 1 for pairs coupled to $T' = 0$ and $T' = 1$, respectively. Hence the evaluation of the operator $\Sigma_{1=j<k}^{n} V_{\mathrm{T}}(j,k)$ for n-particle states yields the number of $T' = 1$ coupled pairs that contribute. This number is also given by $\Sigma_m c_m^{(1)}$. According to eq. (5.45) one can write

$$\sum_{1=j<k}^{n} V_{\mathrm{T}}(j,k) = \tfrac{1}{2} \sum_{1=j<k}^{n} (\boldsymbol{t}(j) + \boldsymbol{t}(k))^2 = \tfrac{1}{2} \sum_{1=j<k}^{n} (\boldsymbol{t}^2(j) + \boldsymbol{t}^2(k)) + \sum_{1=j<k}^{n} (\boldsymbol{t}(j) \cdot \boldsymbol{t}(k)) \,. \tag{5.46}$$

The last term of eq. (5.46) can be related to the total isospin T of the n-particle system by

$$\boldsymbol{T}^2 = \left(\sum_{j=1}^{n} \boldsymbol{t}(j)\right)^2 = \sum_{j=1}^{n} \boldsymbol{t}^2(j) + 2 \sum_{1=j<k}^{n} (\boldsymbol{t}(j)\cdot\boldsymbol{t}(k)) \,, \tag{5.47}$$

from which it follows that

$$\sum_{1=j<k}^{n} V_{\mathrm{T}}(j,k) = \tfrac{1}{2} \sum_{1=j<k}^{n} (\boldsymbol{t}^2(j) + \boldsymbol{t}^2(k)) + \tfrac{1}{2}\boldsymbol{T}^2 - \tfrac{1}{2}\sum_{j=1}^{n} \boldsymbol{t}^2(j) \,. \tag{5.48}$$

Substituting the eigenvalues $T(T+1)$ for $\boldsymbol{T}^2$ and $t(k)(t(k)+1) = \frac{3}{4}$ for $\boldsymbol{t}^2(k)$ and using the fact that the sum $\Sigma_{1=j<k}^{n}(\boldsymbol{t}^2(j) + \boldsymbol{t}^2(k))$ consists of $\frac{1}{2}n(n-1)$ terms that each contribute $\frac{3}{2}$, one obtains from eq. (5.48) for the sum of the coefficients of the $T' = 1$ coupled two-body matrix elements

$$\sum_m c_m^{(1)} = \tfrac{3}{8}\, n(n-2) + \tfrac{1}{2}\, T(T+1) \,. \tag{5.49}$$

From relation (5.44) it then follows directly that the sum of the coefficients of the $T' = 0$ coupled two-body matrix elements is given by

$$\sum_l c_l^{(0)} = \sum_l c_l - \sum_m c_m^{(1)} = \tfrac{1}{8} n(n+2) - \tfrac{1}{2}\, T(T+1) \,. \tag{5.50}$$

The sum rules (5.49) and (5.50) are useful not only as a check on the coefficients of two-body matrix elements, but also for a study of the effect of an isospin dependent term in the two-body interaction, as will be discussed in chapter 6.

5.5. Applications

To illustrate the treatment of many-nucleon matrix elements discussed above, the excitation energy of the first excited state in ${}^{31}_{14}\mathrm{Si}_{17}$ will be calculated. Let us assume that the $J^\pi = \frac{3}{2}^+$ ground state and $J^\pi = \frac{1}{2}^+$ first excited state can be described in a model space with a ${}^{28}_{14}\mathrm{Si}_{14}$ core and three neutrons in the $2s_{1/2}$ and $1d_{3/2}$ orbits (see fig. 5.1). Moreover assume that these configurations are given by

ψ (ground state) = 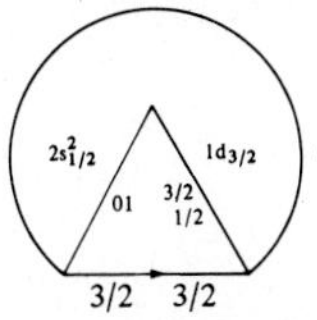

, ψ (first excited state) = 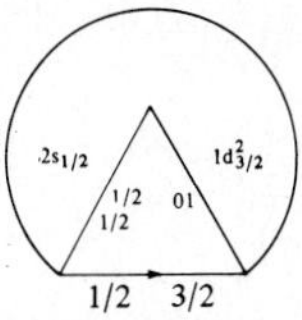

, (5.51)

where in the graphical notation spins and isospins are displayed explicitly.

The ground-state binding energy is given by (cf. eq. (3.34))

$$E^{\mathrm{b}}_{\mathrm{g.s.}} = E_{\mathrm{C}} + E^{\mathrm{b}}(\mathrm{core}) + 2e_{2s_{1/2}} + e_{1d_{3/2}} + E^{(1)}_{3/2\;3/2}((2s_{1/2})^2_{01}\, 1d_{3/2}\; {}_{1/2}) \,. \tag{5.52}$$

The interaction energy between the three active neutrons outside the core is given

THE TWO-ORBIT MODEL FOR ^{31}Si

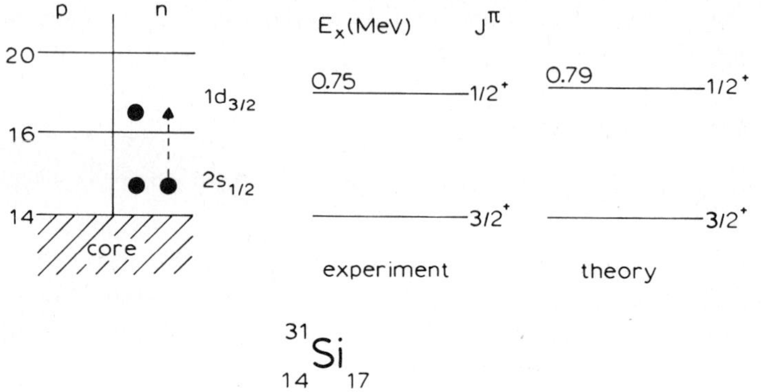

Fig. 5.1. The excitation energy of the first excited state in ^{31}Si described in terms of three active neutrons in the $2s_{1/2}$ and $1d_{3/2}$ orbits.

by the diagonal matrix element (see eq. (3.35)) as

$$\langle V\rangle_{\text{g.s.}} = E^{(1)}_{3/2\;3/2}(s^2_{01}d) = \langle s^2_{01}d|\sum_{1=j<k}^{3} V(j,k)|s^2_{01}d\rangle_{3/2\;3/2}\,, \tag{5.53}$$

where the notation $s = 2s_{1/2}$ and $d = 1d_{3/2}$ is used. After application of the reduction (5.41) one obtains finally

$$\langle V\rangle_{\text{g.s}} = \langle s^2|V|s^2\rangle_{01} + \tfrac{1}{4}\langle sd|V|sd\rangle_{11} + \tfrac{7}{4}\langle sd|V|sd\rangle_{21}\,. \tag{5.54}$$

Note that the coefficients of the two-body matrix elements satisfy the sum rules (5.44), (5.49) and (5.50).

The evaluation of the two-body matrix elements in eq. (5.54) with the MSDI, given in appendix B.4, yields for the total binding energy of ^{31}Si with the aid of eq. (5.52) the expression

$$E^{\text{b}}_{\text{g.s.}} = E_{\text{C}} + E^{\text{b}}(\text{core}) + 2\,e_{2s_{1/2}} + e_{1d_{3/2}} - 2.4\,A_1 + 3B + 3C\,. \tag{5.55}$$

A similar approach for the three-particle diagonal matrix element for ^{31}Si in its first excited state leads to

$$\langle V\rangle_{\text{e.s.}} = \langle d^2|V|d^2\rangle_{01} + \tfrac{3}{4}\langle sd|V|sd\rangle_{11} + \tfrac{5}{4}\langle sd|V|sd\rangle_{21} \tag{5.56}$$

with the binding energy of ^{31}Si in this state given by

$$E^{\text{b}}_{\text{e.s.}} = E_{\text{C}} + E^{\text{b}}(\text{core}) + e_{2s_{1/2}} + 2\,e_{1d_{3/2}} - 3A_1 + 3B + 3C\,. \tag{5.57}$$

The excitation energy of the first excited state follows from eqs. (5.55) and (5.57) when as usual the contributions E_{C} and $E^{\text{b}}(\text{core})$ are assumed to be independent of the excitation energy. One obtains

$$E_{\text{x}} = -0.6\,A_1 + e_{1d_{3/2}} - e_{2s_{1/2}}\,. \tag{5.58}$$

The difference of the single-particle energies can be obtained from ^{29}Si (see sect. 3.3) as $e_{1d_{3/2}} - e_{2s_{1/2}} = 1.27$ MeV. With the MSDI strength parameter $A_1 = 0.8$ MeV, which has also been used for the calculation of ^{30}Si (see sect. 3.3), one obtains from eq. (5.58) the calculated excitation energy of $(-0.48 + 1.27)$ MeV = 0.79 MeV. This agrees nicely with the experimental value for the excitation energy which is found to be 0.75 MeV.

5.6. Matrix elements of category III

Now the matrix elements of category III, defined in eqs. (5.22) and (5.23) will be discussed. They are given by

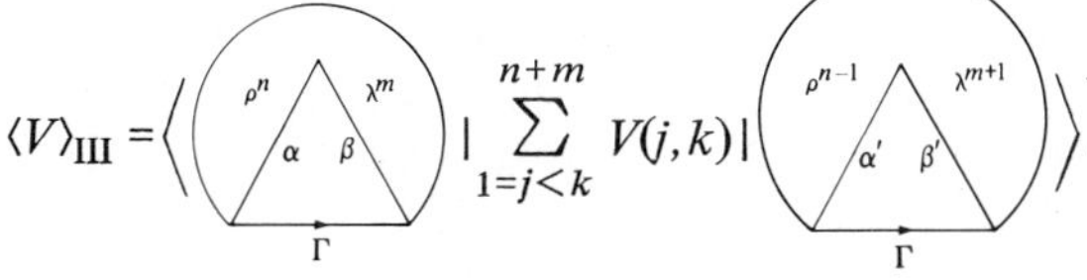

$$\langle V\rangle_{\text{III}} = \left\langle \left(\begin{smallmatrix} \rho^n & & \chi^m \\ & \alpha \ \ \beta & \\ & r & \end{smallmatrix} \right) \middle| \sum_{1=j<k}^{n+m} V(j,k) \middle| \left(\begin{smallmatrix} \rho^{n-1} & & \chi^{m+1} \\ & \alpha' \ \ \beta' & \\ & r & \end{smallmatrix} \right) \right\rangle . \tag{5.59}$$

We have to treat only the matrix elements of eq. (5.22) with $p = +1$, since the interaction is hermitian. The (real) matrix elements with $p = -1$ can be written as

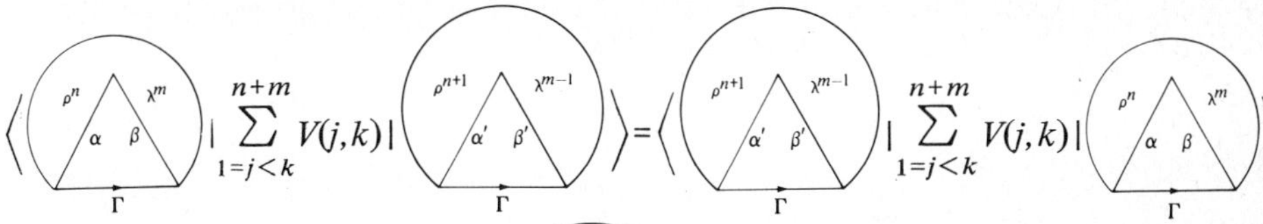

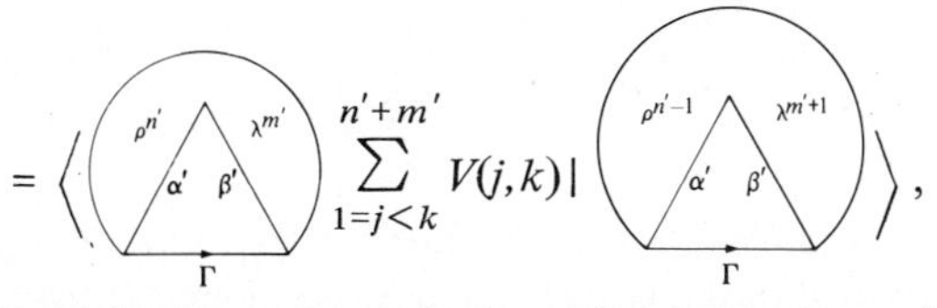

$$\left\langle \left(\begin{smallmatrix} \rho^n & & \chi^m \\ & \alpha \ \ \beta & \\ & r & \end{smallmatrix} \right) \middle| \sum_{1=j<k}^{n+m} V(j,k) \middle| \left(\begin{smallmatrix} \rho^{n+1} & & \chi^{m-1} \\ & \alpha' \ \ \beta' & \\ & r & \end{smallmatrix} \right) \right\rangle = \left\langle \left(\begin{smallmatrix} \rho^{n+1} & & \chi^{m-1} \\ & \alpha' \ \ \beta' & \\ & r & \end{smallmatrix} \right) \middle| \sum_{1=j<k}^{n+m} V(j,k) \middle| \left(\begin{smallmatrix} \rho^n & & \chi^m \\ & \alpha \ \ \beta & \\ & r & \end{smallmatrix} \right) \right\rangle$$

$$= \left\langle \left(\begin{smallmatrix} \rho^{n'} & & \chi^{m'} \\ & \alpha' \ \ \beta' & \\ & r & \end{smallmatrix} \right) \middle| \sum_{1=j<k}^{n'+m'} V(j,k) \middle| \left(\begin{smallmatrix} \rho^{n-1} & & \chi^{m+1} \\ & \alpha' \ \ \beta' & \\ & r & \end{smallmatrix} \right) \right\rangle , \tag{5.60}$$

where the latter corresponds to those given in eq. (5.59). Applying expansion (5.4) to the bra function in eq. (5.59) and taking into account the fact that all terms have the same magnitude and sign (see eq. (5.26)) one obtains

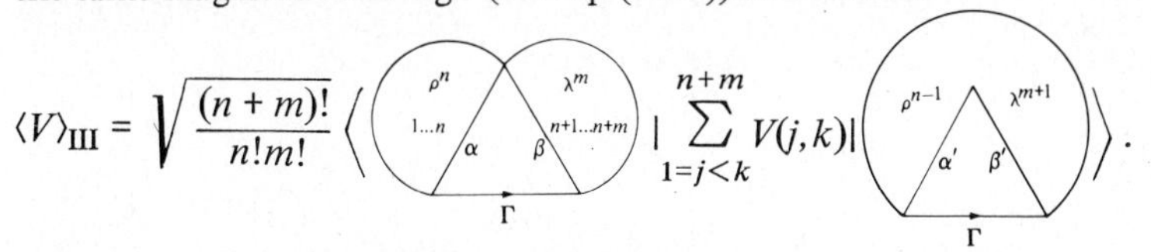

$$\langle V\rangle_{\text{III}} = \sqrt{\frac{(n+m)!}{n!m!}} \left\langle \left(\begin{smallmatrix} \rho^n & & \chi^m \\ 1...n & & n+1..n+m \\ & \alpha \ \ \beta & \\ & r & \end{smallmatrix} \right) \middle| \sum_{1=j<k}^{n+m} V(j,k) \middle| \left(\begin{smallmatrix} \rho^{n-1} & & \chi^{m+1} \\ & \alpha' \ \ \beta' & \\ & r & \end{smallmatrix} \right) \right\rangle . \tag{5.61}$$

Application of eq. (5.4) to the ket function in eq. (5.61) leads to

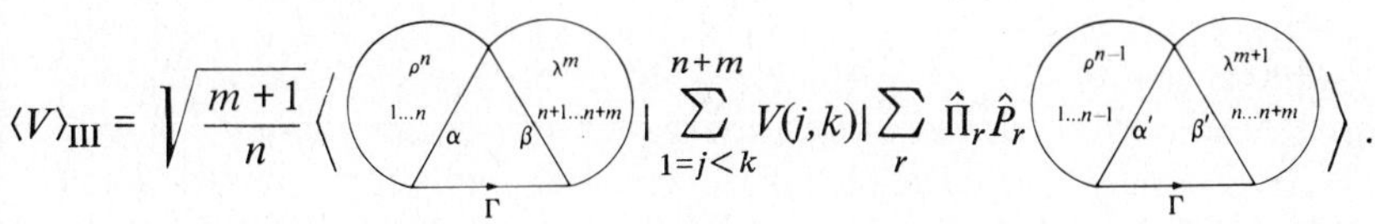

$$\langle V\rangle_{\text{III}} = \sqrt{\frac{m+1}{n}} \left\langle \left(\begin{smallmatrix} \rho^n & & \chi^m \\ 1...n & & n+1..n+m \\ & \alpha \ \ \beta & \\ & r & \end{smallmatrix} \right) \middle| \sum_{1=j<k}^{n+m} V(j,k) \sum_r \hat{\Pi}_r \hat{P}_r \middle| \left(\begin{smallmatrix} \rho^{n-1} & & \chi^{m+1} \\ 1...n-1 & & n...n+m \\ & \alpha' \ \ \beta' & \\ & r & \end{smallmatrix} \right) \right\rangle . \tag{5.62}$$

The order-preserving permutations $\hat{P}_r$ in eq. (5.62) must act on the particle labelled n (except for the identity $P_r = 1$) in order to obtain a nonvanishing contribution. This follows from the fact that any other order-preserving permutation will necessarily leave the particles numbered n in bra and ket functions in different orbits and in addition will cause two more particle numbers to correspond to different orbits. Such states cannot be connected by the two-body operator $V(j,k)$, since then each matrix element $\langle V(j,k)\rangle$ contains a factor $\langle\rho(l)\,|\,\lambda(l)\rangle = 0\ (l = 1, 2, \ldots \text{ or } n+m)$. Any one of the n permutations $P_r = 1, \hat{P}_{jn}\ (j = 1, \ldots, n-1)$ leads to a matrix element of the same magnitude and sign, as can be shown in analogy with the derivation of eq. (5.26). Evaluating the contribution for $P_r = 1$ and multiplying the result by n, one obtains for the matrix element of eq. (5.62)

$$\langle V\rangle_{\text{III}} = n\sqrt{\frac{m+1}{n}}\Bigg\langle$$
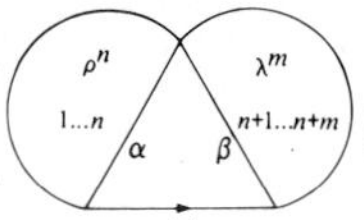

$$\Big|\sum_{1=j<k}^{n+m} V(j,k)\Big|$$
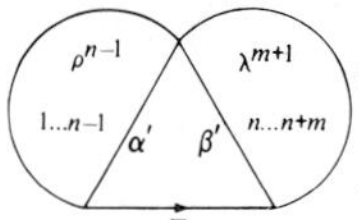

$$\Bigg\rangle. \tag{5.63}$$

In this equation only the terms $V(j,k)$ with $j = n$ or $k = n$ lead to a nonvanishing contribution, as the orbit of the particle labelled n differs for the bra vector and the ket vector. Therefore the operator $V(j,k)$ must act on this particle in order to prevent a factor $\langle\rho(n)\,|\,\lambda(n)\rangle = 0$. Because of the equivalence of the particles in the ρ orbit and also of the particles in the λ orbit, eq. (5.63) can be reduced further to

$$\langle V\rangle_{\text{III}} = \sqrt{n(m+1)}\Bigg\langle$$
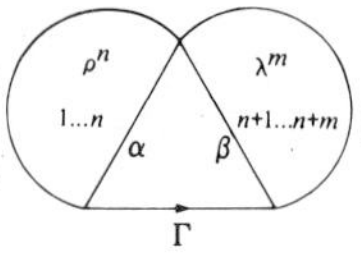

$$\big|(n-1)\,V(n-1,n) + m\,V(n,n+1)\big|$$
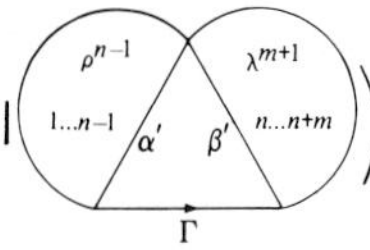

$$\Bigg\rangle. \tag{5.64}$$

For the calculation of expression (5.64) we treat the contributions $\langle V(n-1,n)\rangle_{\text{III}}$ and $\langle V(n,n+1)\rangle_{\text{III}}$ separately. Starting with the latter, one must decouple particles n and $n+1$ from the rest. After application of the c.f.p. expansion of eq. (5.3) and a recoupling as given by eq. (5.18), one has

$$\langle V(n,n+1)\rangle_{\text{III}} = \sum_{\epsilon} \langle\rho^n\alpha|\}\rho^{n-1}\epsilon\rangle \sum_{\omega} U(\epsilon\rho\Gamma\beta;\alpha\omega)$$

$$\times\,(-1)^{m-1}\Bigg\langle$$
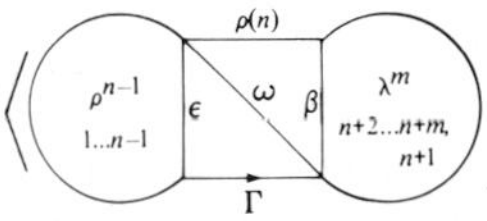

$$\big|V(n,n+1)\big|$$
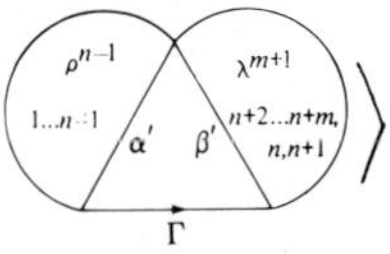

$$\Bigg\rangle, \tag{5.65}$$

where the phase factor $(-1)^{m-1}$ comes from shifting particle $n+1$ across the others in the bra vector $\langle\lambda^m|_\beta$. The reordering of the particles in the ket vector $|\lambda^{m+1}\rangle_{\beta'}$ involves an even permutation. These permutations are required for the application of c.f.p. in eq. (5.66). Integration over particles $1, 2, \ldots, n-1$ yields the Kronecker delta $\delta_{\epsilon\alpha'}$. Since the interaction is scalar, the resulting matrix element contains also the Kronecker delta $\delta_{\omega\beta'}$.

Now particles n and $n+1$ must be decoupled, which can be performed by writing (see sect. 4.4 for the double-parentage coefficients)

$$\langle V(n,n+1)\rangle_{\rm III} = \langle \rho^n\alpha|\}\rho^{n-1}\alpha'\rangle\, U(\alpha'\rho\Gamma\beta;\alpha\beta')(-1)^{m-1}\sum_{\eta\eta'\theta}\langle\lambda^m\beta|\}\lambda^{m-1}\eta\rangle$$

$$\times\langle\lambda^{m+1}\beta'|\}\lambda^{m-1}\eta'(\lambda^2\theta)\rangle\Big\langle$$ 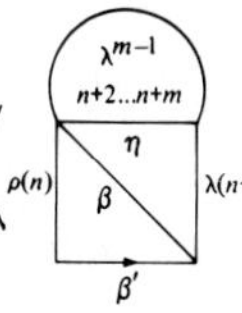

$|V(n,n+1)|$ 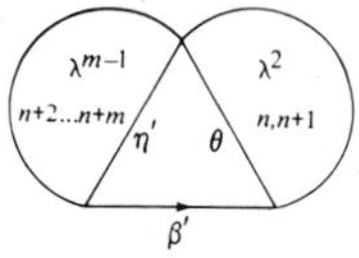

$\Big\rangle$. (5.66)

Recoupling the bra function as

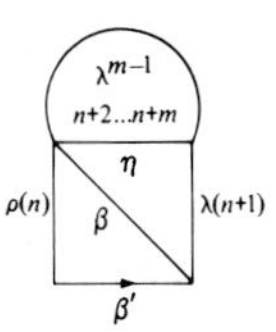

$= (-1)^{\beta-\lambda-\eta}$ 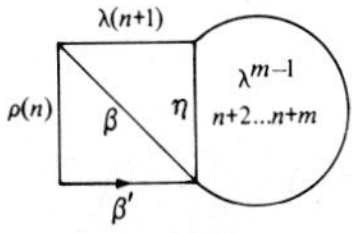

$$= (-1)^{\beta-\lambda-\eta}\sum_{\zeta} U(\rho\lambda\beta'\eta;\beta\zeta)$$ 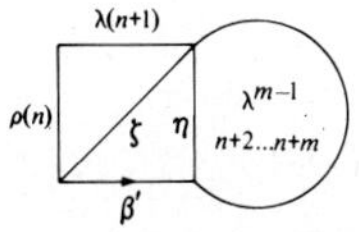

(5.67)

and interchanging the groups in the ket function with

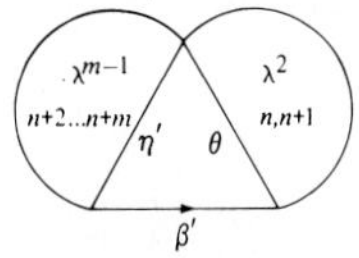

$= (-1)^{\beta'-\eta'-\theta}$ 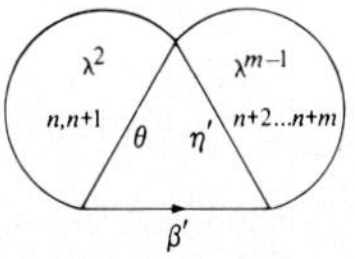

, (5.68)

one obtains for the matrix element on the right-hand side of eq. (5.66)

$\Big\langle$ 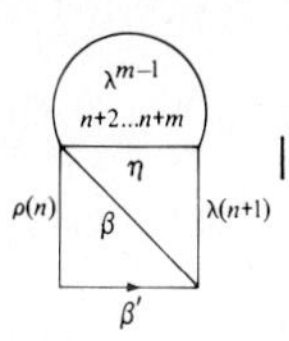

$|V(n,n+1)|$ 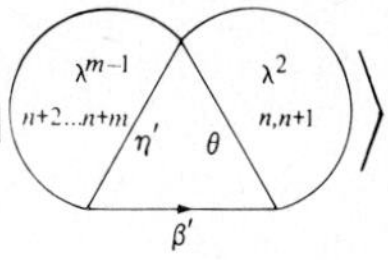

$\Big\rangle = (-1)^{\beta+\beta'-\lambda-\eta-\eta'-\theta}$

$$\times\sum_{\zeta} U(\rho\lambda\beta'\eta;\beta\zeta)\Big\langle$$ 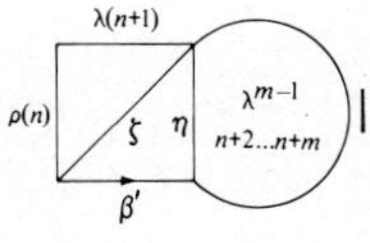

$|V(n,n+1)|$ 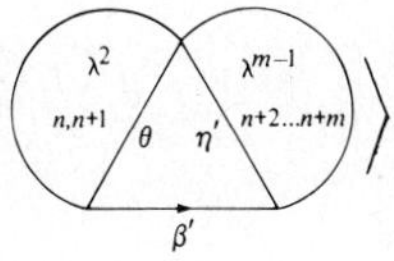

$\Big\rangle$. (5.69)

Integration over particles $n+2, ..., n+m$ yields the Kronecker delta $\delta_{\eta\eta'}$ and the resulting matrix element contains the Kronecker delta $\delta_{\zeta\theta}$. Thus eqs. (5.66) and (5.69) can be combined to give

$$\langle V(n,n+1)\rangle_{\mathrm{III}} = \langle \rho^n \alpha | \} \rho^{n-1} \alpha' \rangle \, U(\alpha' \rho \Gamma \beta; \alpha\beta')$$

$$\times \sum_{\eta\theta} \langle \lambda^m \beta | \} \lambda^{m-1} \eta \rangle \langle \lambda^{m+1} \beta' | \} \lambda^{m-1} \eta (\lambda^2 \theta) \rangle \, U(\rho\lambda\beta'\eta; \beta\theta)$$

$$\times (-1)^{m-1+\beta+\beta'-\lambda-\theta} \Big\langle$$ 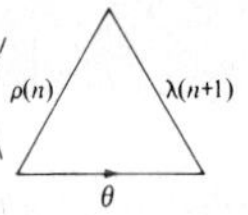

$$|V(n,n+1)|$$ 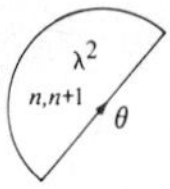

$$\Big\rangle . \qquad (5.70)$$

Proceeding similarly to calculate the other contribution to eq. (5.64), one finds in analogy to eqs. (5.65)–(5.69) the relation

$$\langle V(n-1,n)\rangle_{\mathrm{III}} = \sum_{\eta\eta'} \langle \lambda^{m+1} \beta' | \} \lambda^m \eta \rangle \, (-1)^{m+\eta+\lambda-\beta} \, U(\alpha' \lambda \Gamma \eta; \eta'\beta')$$

$$\times \Big\langle$$ 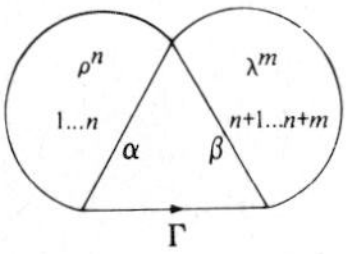

$$|V(n-1,n)|$$ 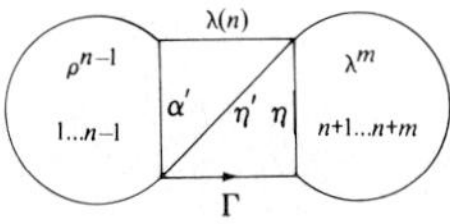

$$\Big\rangle . \qquad (5.71)$$

Integration over the coordinates of particles labelled $n+1, \ldots, n+m$ then yields the Kronecker delta $\delta_{\beta\eta}$ and the resulting matrix element contains the Kronecker delta $\delta_{\alpha\eta'}$. A decoupling of the particles labelled $n-1$ and n, on which the operator acts, yields

$$\langle V(n-1,n)\rangle_{\mathrm{III}} = \langle \lambda^{m+1} \beta' | \} \lambda^m \beta \rangle \, (-1)^{m+\beta+\lambda-\beta'} \, U(\alpha' \lambda \Gamma \beta; \alpha\beta')$$

$$\times \sum_{\epsilon\epsilon'\nu\nu'} \langle \rho^n \alpha | \} \rho^{n-2} \epsilon (\rho^2 \nu) \rangle \langle \rho^{n-1} \alpha' | \} \rho^{n-2} \epsilon' \rangle \, U(\epsilon' \rho \alpha \lambda; \alpha' \nu')$$

$$\times \Big\langle$$ 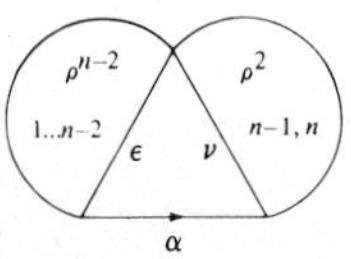

$$|V(n-1,n)|$$ 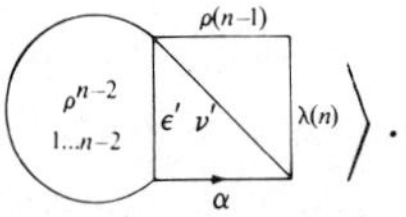

$$\Big\rangle . \qquad (5.72)$$

From the integration over the coordinates of the particles labelled $1, \ldots, n-2$, one obtains the Kronecker delta $\delta_{\epsilon\epsilon'}$ and the resulting matrix element contains the Kronecker delta $\delta_{\nu\nu'}$. Thus eq. (5.72) reduces to

$$\langle V(n-1,n)\rangle_{\mathrm{III}} = \langle \lambda^{m+1} \beta' | \} \lambda^m \beta \rangle \, (-1)^{m+\beta+\lambda-\beta'} \, U(\alpha' \lambda \Gamma \beta; \alpha\beta')$$

$$\times \sum_{\epsilon\nu} \langle \rho^n \alpha | \} \rho^{n-2} \epsilon (\rho^2 \nu) \rangle \, \langle \rho^{n-1} \alpha' | \} \rho^{n-2} \epsilon \rangle \, U(\epsilon \rho \alpha \lambda; \alpha' \nu)$$

$$\times \Big\langle$$ 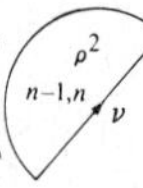

$$|V(n-1,n)|$$ 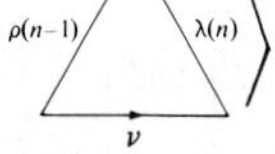

$$\Big\rangle . \qquad (5.73)$$

Substituting eqs. (5.70) and (5.73) into eq. (5.64), one obtains the final expression

$\langle V\rangle_{\text{III}} = \Big\langle$ 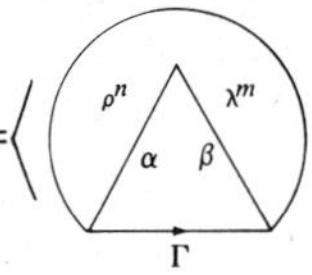

$\Big| \sum_{1=j<k}^{n+m} V(j,k) \Big|$ 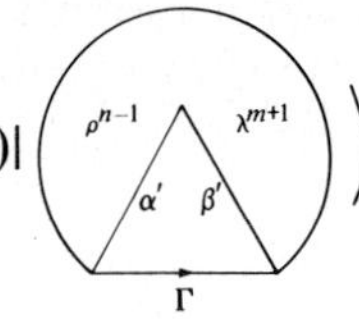

$\Big\rangle$

$$= (-1)^{m+\beta+\lambda-\beta'} \sqrt{\tfrac{1}{2}n(m+1)} \left[\left\{(n-1)\langle\lambda^{m+1}\beta'|\}\lambda^m\beta\rangle\, U(\alpha'\lambda\Gamma\beta;\alpha\beta')\right.\right.$$

$$\times \sum_{\epsilon\nu} \langle\rho^n\alpha|\}\rho^{n-2}\epsilon(\rho^2\nu)\rangle\,\langle\rho^{n-1}\alpha'|\}\rho^{n-2}\epsilon\rangle\, U(\epsilon\rho\alpha\lambda;\alpha'\nu)$$

$\times \Big\langle$ 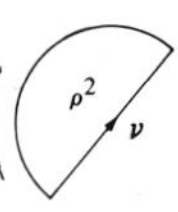

$|V(1,2)|$ 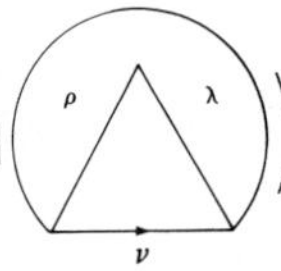

$\Big\rangle\Big\}$

$$-\Big\{ m\langle\rho^n\alpha|\}\rho^{n-1}\alpha'\rangle\, U(\alpha'\rho\Gamma\beta;\alpha\beta') \sum_{\eta\theta} (-1)^\theta \langle\lambda^m\beta|\}\lambda^{m-1}\eta\rangle\langle\lambda^{m+1}\beta'|\}\lambda^{m-1}\eta(\lambda^2\theta)\rangle$$

$\times\, U(\rho\lambda\beta'\eta;\beta\theta) \Big\langle$ 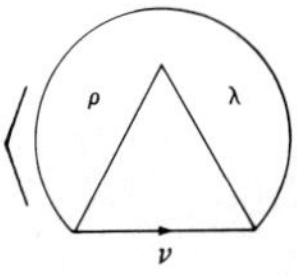

$|V(1,2)|$ 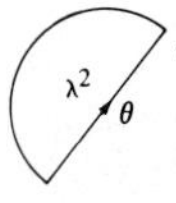

$\Big\rangle\Big\}\Big]$, (5.74)

where eq. (5.17) has been applied to obtain antisymmetric two-body matrix elements.

5.7. Matrix elements of category IV

The matrix elements of category IV were defined in eqs. (5.22) and (5.23). Due to the hermiticity of the interaction matrix it is sufficient to treat the case with $p = +2$ only. In analogy to eqs. (5.28) and (5.62) one obtains

$\langle V\rangle_{\text{IV}} = \Big\langle$ 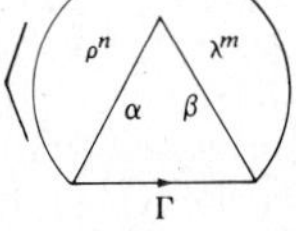

$\Big| \sum_{1=j<k}^{n+m} V(j,k) \Big|$ 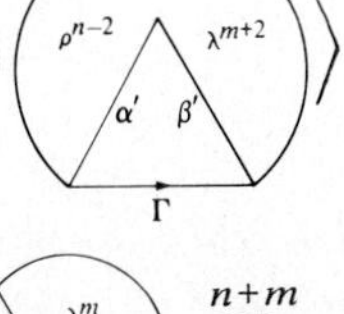

$\Big\rangle$

$= \sqrt{\dfrac{(m+1)(m+2)}{n(n-1)}} \Big\langle$ 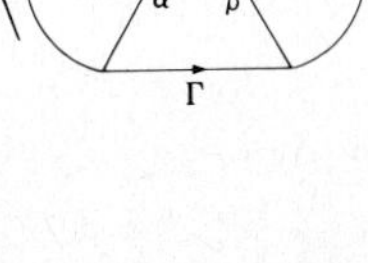

$\Big| \sum_{1=j<k}^{n+m} V(j,k) \Big| \sum_r \hat{\Pi}_r \hat{P}_r$ 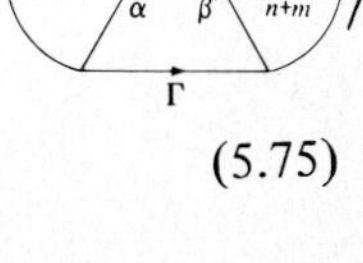

$\Big\rangle$.

(5.75)

The reduction of eq. (5.75) can be performed with methods similar to those discussed before. The only order-preserving permutations $\hat{P}_r$ that yield a nonvanishing contribution in eq. (5.75) are $P_r = 1, \hat{P}_r = \hat{P}_{jk}$ ($j = 1, 2, ..., n-2$ and $k = n-1, n$) and all products of two of these that do not involve either $n-1$ or n. This follows from the fact that any other order-preserving permutation will necessarily leave the particles numbered $n-1$ or n in different orbits and in addition will cause two more particle numbers to correspond to different orbits in bra and ket functions. In such cases the two-body interaction $V(j,k)$ leads to a zero contribution to the matrix element. The number of contributing permutations is equal to the number of ways one can select $n-2$ particle labels from $1, 2, ..., n$, which is given by $\binom{n}{n-2} = \frac{1}{2}n(n-1)$. Again as for the other categories, each contribution is of the same magnitude and sign. For $P_r = 1$ the only interaction term giving a nonvanishing contribution is $V(n-1, n)$, which connects the two particles in different orbits in bra and ket functions. Multiplying by $\frac{1}{2}n(n-1)$ one obtains

$$\langle V\rangle_{\mathrm{IV}} = \tfrac{1}{2}n(n-1)\sqrt{\frac{(m+1)(m+2)}{n(n-1)}}\ \Big\langle$$ 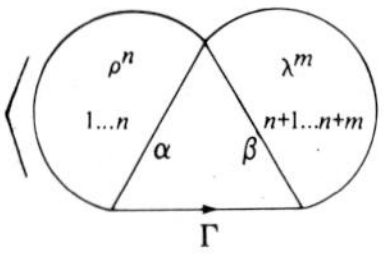 $$|V(n-1,n)|$$ 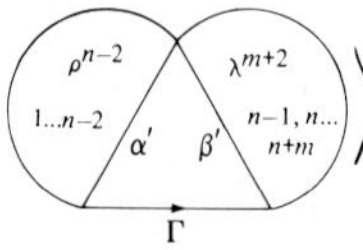 $$\Big\rangle\,. \qquad (5.76)$$

After decoupling two particles labelled $n-1$ and n with double-parentage coefficients one reduces the matrix element as follows:

$$\Big\langle$$ 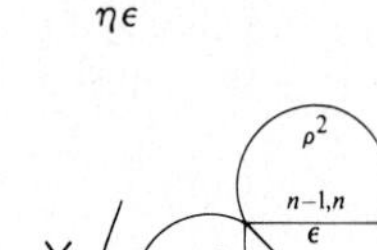 $$|V(n-1,n)|$$ 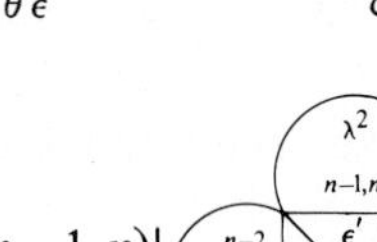 $$\Big\rangle$$

$$= \sum_{\eta\epsilon} \langle \rho^n \alpha |\} \rho^{n-2}\eta(\rho^2\epsilon)\rangle \sum_{\theta\epsilon'} (-1)^{\beta'-\epsilon'-\theta} \sum_{\omega} U(\eta\epsilon\Gamma\beta;\alpha\omega)\,\langle\lambda^{m+2}\beta'|\}\lambda^m\theta(\lambda^2\epsilon')\rangle$$

$$\times\Big\langle$$ 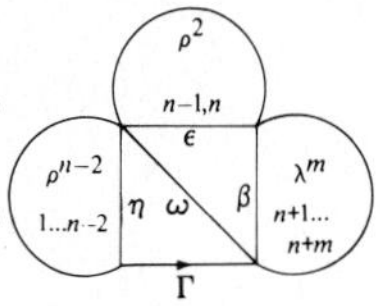 $$|V(n-1,n)|$$ 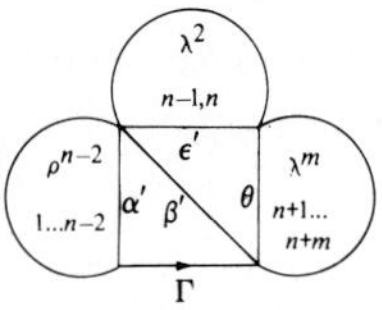 $$\Big\rangle\,. \qquad (5.77)$$

Integration over the coordinates of the sets ρ^{n-2} and λ^m yields the Kronecker deltas $\delta_{\eta\alpha'}\,\delta_{\beta\theta}$ and, since $V(n-1,n)$ is a scalar operator, one also has the Kronecker deltas $\delta_{\omega\beta'}\,\delta_{\epsilon\epsilon'}$. Thus one obtains finally for the matrix elements of category IV

$\langle V\rangle_{\mathrm{IV}} = \Big\langle$ 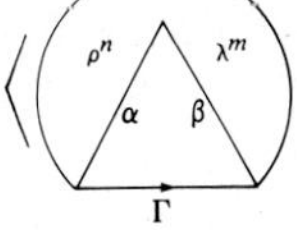

$\Big| \sum_{1=j<k}^{n+m} V(j,k) \Big|$ 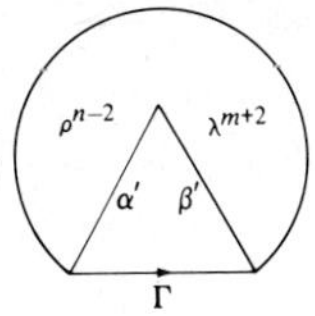

$\Big\rangle$

$$= \tfrac{1}{2}\sqrt{n(n-1)(m+1)(m+2)} \sum_{\epsilon} \langle \rho^n \alpha |\} \rho^{n-2}\alpha'(\rho^2\epsilon)\rangle \langle \lambda^{m+2}\beta' |\} \lambda^m \beta(\lambda^2\epsilon)\rangle$$

$\times\, U(\alpha'\epsilon\Gamma\beta;\alpha\beta')(-1)^{\beta'-\epsilon-\beta} \Big\langle$ 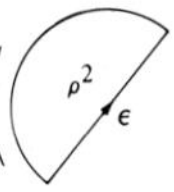

$|V(1,2)|$ 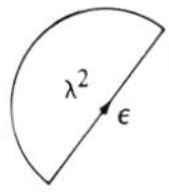

$\Big\rangle$. (5.78)

Thus all many-body matrix elements for several particles in two orbits have been expressed in terms of two-body matrix elements. The evaluation of the two-body matrix elements will be discussed in the next chapter.

CHAPTER 6

EFFECTIVE INTERACTIONS

In the preceding chapters it has been shown that in order to calculate an energy spectrum of a nucleus, one must solve the many-body Schrödinger equation $H\Psi = E\Psi$. For this purpose the energy matrix $\langle \Phi_k^{(0)} | H | \Phi_l^{(0)} \rangle$ must be constructed and then diagonalized. The eigenvalues obtained yield the required level energies. The matrix elements of a given interaction between many-particle states can be expressed in terms of two-body matrix elements. In this chapter the evaluation of the two-body matrix elements is discussed.

In sect. 6.1 three different approaches leading to the so-called empirical, realistic and schematic effective interactions are summarized. The explicit values for the matrix elements of the surface delta interaction (SDI), which is one of the mathematically simplest schematic interactions, are derived in sect. 6.2. In sect. 6.3 a modified version of the SDI (called the MSDI) leading to e.g. a much better reproduction of binding energies is discussed. As an illustration the MSDI is applied in sect. 6.4 to the calculation of low-lying states in ^{58}Ni and ^{210}Po. The empirical, realistic and schematic interactions and some spectra obtained from them are compared in sect. 6.5. The effect of the chosen configuration space on the calculated spectra is illustrated with some examples in sect. 6.6.

6.1. Evaluation of two-body matrix elements

Let $\psi_\Gamma(\rho_a\rho_b)$ represent an antisymmetric wave function of the two-body system with one particle in orbit ρ_a and one particle in orbit ρ_b, coupled to spin J_Γ and isospin T_Γ. The allowed values of Γ have been discussed in sect. 2.4. The expectation value of the effective residual two-body interaction is given according to eqs. (3.15) and (3.26) by

$$E_\Gamma^{(1)}(\rho_a\rho_b) = \langle \rho_a\rho_b | H_{12}^{(1)} | \rho_a\rho_b \rangle_\Gamma = \langle \rho_a\rho_b | V(1,2) | \rho_a\rho_b \rangle_\Gamma \,. \tag{6.1}$$

The value of the matrix element depends on the residual interaction $V(1,2)$, the single-particle wave functions $|\rho_a\rangle$ and $|\rho_b\rangle$ and on the total spin and isospin Γ of the two-particle system.

Three methods that can be used to evaluate the two-body matrix elements of eq. (6.1) will be discussed.

(a) Matrix elements from experimental spectra (empirical approach).

Let us assume that the states of a nucleus can be described by an inert core and two particles. In this case the level scheme is determined completely, according to eq. (3.34), by the two-body matrix elements of the residual effective interaction together with the single-particle energies of the active orbits involved. (The effect of the Coulomb interaction between active protons can be estimated separately, as will be discussed in sect. 18.3.) On the other hand, from the experimental spectrum one can obtain the values of the two-body matrix elements, once the single-particle energies are known. The single-particle energies are usually taken from the spectrum of the nucleus with the same core and only one nucleon (see, e.g., sect. 3.3).

The approach discussed above can be extended to nuclei described by a core with many active nucleons. Then one must express the many-particle matrix elements of the interaction in terms of the two-particle matrix elements, where the latter can be determined from a comparison with experimental data in several nuclei. Of course, this method only makes sense if one can assume that the two-body matrix elements of the effective interaction do not change in the mass region considered. It is clear that for this procedure to be meaningful, the number of two-body matrix elements has to be less than the number of experimental level energies. The optimum values of the two-body matrix elements can be obtained from a least-squares fit to the experimental data. The details of such an iterative fitting procedure are discussed in chapter 7.

An advantage of the empirical approach is that it is not necessary to explicitly specify the interaction in order to correlate experimental energy spectra. Moreover, the matrix elements obtained in this way may have optimum values with respect to a reproduction of experimental energies, i.e. this procedure should yield the most suitable effective two-body matrix elements in a given truncated shell-model space.

The disadvantage of this method is that in many cases the number of parameters is very large. For example, such an approach applied to the complete 2s1d shell leads to 63 two-body matrix elements (i.e. 28 diagonal and 35 off-diagonal matrix elements) describing the interaction of particles in the $1d_{5/2}$, $2s_{1/2}$ and $1d_{3/2}$ orbits.

Another objection is the fact that the selection of experimental states that are thought to be described well in the assumed model space, may become rather arbitrary. This is the more serious since the two-body matrix elements sometimes depend strongly on the set of experimental data taken into account. In order to minimize the effect of states that are erroneously included in the fit, one should use many more experimental data than there are two-body matrix elements to be determined. This way the probability that each two-body matrix element depends on several experimental data is larger. A practical ratio of the number of experimental data to the number of parameters is found to be three or larger.

A serious shortcoming of this empirical method stems from the fact that the calculated energies are insensitive to the sign of some off-diagonal matrix elements. This complication will be discussed in more detail in chapter 7. Due to the sign ambiguities, however, the wave functions thus obtained are often not useful for a calculation of phase-dependent properties such as cross sections of two-nucleon transfer reactions (chapter 8) and electromagnetic transition rates (chapters 9 and 10).

The conclusion, therefore, is that empirical matrix elements are useful for the correlation of binding energies and excitation energies when the number of two-body matrix elements is much smaller than the amount of experimental data. In practice this means that generally the number of orbits taken into account should not be larger than two.

(b) Matrix elements from realistic interactions.

In this approach the two-body matrix elements are not obtained from a fit to spectroscopic data, but they are calculated from the free nucleon-nucleon interaction. Starting from a parametrized form of the nucleon-nucleon interaction one can fit the parameters as well as possible to reproduce (i) the phase shifts observed in free nucleon-nucleon scattering experiments and (ii) some properties of the deuteron, such as its binding energy. The parametrization can be such that only the lower partial waves, say S-, P- and D-waves, are taken into account or that the phase shifts of all partial waves are described. The nucleon-nucleon scattering phases are considered for proton energies in the laboratory system with $E_p \lesssim 350$ MeV. For higher energies a description in terms of a potential loses its meaning due to meson production.

Potentials derived from the description of free nucleon-nucleon scattering are customarily referred to as *realistic interactions.* One of the interactions of this type, which is frequently used in shell-model calculations, is the one obtained by Hamada-Johnston, see e.g. [Kuo and Brown (1966)]. In another approach one derives two-body matrix elements in a particular single-particle basis directly from the scattering phase shifts. In this case intervention of the explicit form of the realistic interaction is avoided [Elliott, Jackson, Mavromatis, Sanderson and Singh (1968)].

Unfortunately, direct application of a realistic interaction in a shell-model calculation does not lead to an acceptable agreement with the spectroscopic data. This is due to the fact that a shell-model calculation is necessarily restricted to a finite, truncated model space. For a reasonably complete description in terms of a realistic interaction, one should take into account the scattering of nucleons into many more single-particle states. In particular, also the presence of the core (assumed to be inert in the model calculation) has a strong modifying influence on the interaction between the nucleons outside the core. This means that for a model calculation one needs a so-called *effective interaction.* For a given configuration space this effective interaction can in principle be constructed from the free nucleon-nucleon interaction when all processes that take place outside the chosen configuration space are accounted for in terms of perturbation theory. Such a derivation of an effective interaction is complicated and difficult, in particular because of problems of convergence of the perturbation expansions involved. In chapter 16 the relation between realistic and effective interactions will be discussed in more detail.

(c) Matrix elements from schematic interactions.

Certain rather simple two-body interactions can be used to successfully correlate many observed nuclear properties when a truncated shell-model basis is used. Some of these interactions are discussed below.

6.2. Exchange potentials

In its simplest form the nucleon-nucleon interaction is represented by a central, attractive potential that is characterized by a range R_0 and a strength V_0. Such potentials completely ignore the strong repulsion that sets in at very small internucleon distances.

Scattering experiments indicate that the nucleon-nucleon interaction possesses a certain amount of exchange character. This means that the interaction depends also on (i) the spins, (ii) the isospins of the nucleons and (iii) the parity of the states involved. Thus, in addition to the purely radial potential, there are three more potentials. Each of these four contributions is briefly discussed.

The Wigner term $W(r)$ depends on the internucleon distance r only. Besides the harmonic-oscillator and Saxon-Woods potentials (see eqs. (2.15) and (2.37)) some other potentials used for calculations are given by (see fig. 6.1)

$$W(r) = -V_0 \quad \text{for } r \leqslant R_0$$

$$W(r) = 0 \quad \text{for } r > R_0 \qquad \text{square-well potential,} \tag{6.2a}$$

$$W(r) = -V_0 e^{-r/R_0} \qquad \text{exponential potential,} \tag{6.2b}$$

$$W(r) = -V_0 e^{-r^2/R_0^2} \qquad \text{Gaussian potential,} \tag{6.2c}$$

$$W(r) = -V_0 e^{-r/R_0}/(r/R_0) \qquad \text{Yukawa potential.} \tag{6.2d}$$

The square-well, exponential and Gaussian potentials are used because of their mathematical simplicity. The Yukawa potential was predicted [Yukawa (1935)] when nuclear forces were first explained in terms of an exchange of mesons.

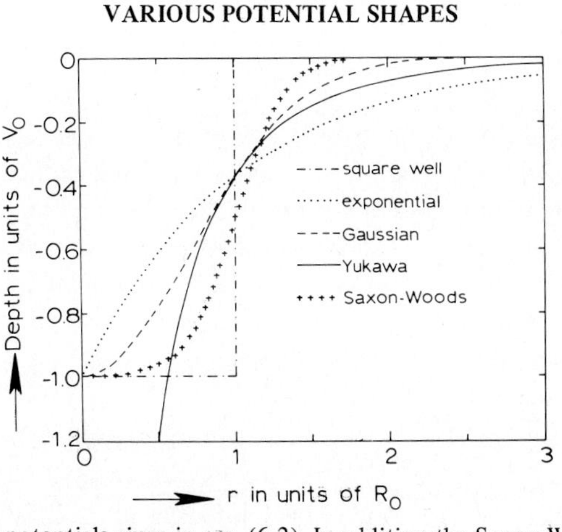

Fig. 6.1. Plots of the potentials given in eqs. (6.2). In addition the Saxon-Woods potential with a diffuseness parameter a = 0.7 is also shown.

The Bartlett term. This term is given by $B(r)\,P^{\sigma}$, where the spin exchange operator is defined by

$$P^{\sigma} = \tfrac{1}{2}(1 + \boldsymbol{\sigma}(1) \cdot \boldsymbol{\sigma}(2)) . \tag{6.3}$$

With the total spin $\boldsymbol{S}$ of the two-particle system defined by $\boldsymbol{S} = \boldsymbol{s}(1) + \boldsymbol{s}(2)$ one has

$$\boldsymbol{S}^2 = \boldsymbol{s}^2(1) + \boldsymbol{s}^2(2) + 2\boldsymbol{s}(1) \cdot \boldsymbol{s}(2) . \tag{6.4}$$

The eigenvalues of the operator $\boldsymbol{s}(1) \cdot \boldsymbol{s}(2) = \tfrac{1}{2}[\boldsymbol{S}^2 - \boldsymbol{s}^2(1) - \boldsymbol{s}^2(2)]$ are consequently given by $\tfrac{1}{2}[S(S+1) - \tfrac{3}{4} - \tfrac{3}{4}]$. With $\boldsymbol{s} = \tfrac{1}{2}\boldsymbol{\sigma}$ one finds for the expectation value

$$\langle \boldsymbol{\sigma}(1) \cdot \boldsymbol{\sigma}(2) \rangle_S = 2S(S+1) - 3 . \tag{6.5}$$

The spin exchange operator (6.3) acting on a two-particle wave function ψ thus leads to

$$P^{\sigma}\psi_{S=1} = \psi_{S=1} , \qquad P^{\sigma}\psi_{S=0} = -\psi_{S=0} , \tag{6.6}$$

for the triplet ($S = 1$) and singlet ($S = 0$) states, respectively. From eq. (6.6) one sees that, due to the action of P^{σ}, in the triplet state (symmetric in the spin coordinates of the two particles) no sign change of ψ occurs, whereas in the singlet state (antisymmetric in the spin coordinates) the spin of the wave function is changed. The operator P^{σ} can thus be interpreted as an operator that exchanges the spin coordinates of the two particles.

The Heisenberg term is given by $-H(r)P^{\tau}$ with the charge exchange operator defined by

$$P^{\tau} = \tfrac{1}{2}(1 + \boldsymbol{\tau}(1) \cdot \boldsymbol{\tau}(2)) . \tag{6.7}$$

From a derivation as given above for P^{σ} it follows

$$P^{\tau}\psi_{T=1} = \psi_{T=1} , \qquad P^{\tau}\psi_{T=0} = -\psi_{T=0} , \tag{6.8}$$

and thus P^{τ} exchanges the isospin coordinates of the two particles.

The Majorana term is given by $M(r)P^{r}$, where the space exchange operator P^{r} exchanges the position coordinates of the two particles. For a two-particle system this is equivalent to the inversion of the relative coordinate $\boldsymbol{r}(1) - \boldsymbol{r}(2) \Rightarrow -(\boldsymbol{r}(1) - \boldsymbol{r}(2))$, and thus the action of the operator P^{r} is seen to be equivalent to the parity operation for the two-particle system.

As nucleon wave functions must be antisymmetric under the exchange of all coordinates of any two particles, one has the relation

$$P^{\sigma}P^{\tau}P^{r} = -1 . \tag{6.9}$$

Summarizing one can now write the central potential as

$$V(r) = -V_0\{W(r) + B(r)P^{\sigma} - H(r)P^{\tau} - M(r)P^{\sigma}P^{\tau}\} , \tag{6.10}$$

Table 6.1
Some exchange mixtures

	W	B	H	M
Rosenfeld	−0.13	0.46	−0.26	0.93
Serber	0.5	0	0	0.5
Kurath	0	0.20	0	0.80
Soper	0.30	0.27	0	0.43

where the four functions of r allow different strengths and also different shapes. Taking, for simplicity, the same shape for the four radial dependences, one obtains

$$V(r) = -f(r)\{W + BP^{\sigma} - HP^{\tau} - MP^{\sigma}P^{\tau}\}, \tag{6.11}$$

where the coefficients W, B, H and M represent the relative contributions of the various potentials that can be normalized to $W + B + H + M = 1$. The signs in eq. (6.11) are chosen such that for the proton-neutron interaction in the deuteron one obtains

$$V_{\mathrm{d}}(r) = -f(r)\{W + B + H + M\} = -f(r). \tag{6.12}$$

Various exchange mixtures, i.e. sets of numerical values for the coefficients W, B, H and M, are in use (see e.g. table 6.1). These have been determined, together with the parameters in the radial dependence $f(r)$, from an adjustment to various sets of experimental results, mostly nucleon-nucleon scattering data and nuclear binding energies. The four coefficients W, B, H and M may also be interpreted as giving the different potentials for singlet or triplet states of even or odd parity. With the parity given by the product $-P^{\sigma}P^{\tau}$ one has the four equivalent linear combinations given in table 6.2.

A further inspection of the experimental data shows, however, discrepancies with the predictions of a central potential. The magnetic moment of the deuteron ground state is not equal to the algebraic sum of the magnetic moments of the proton and the neutron. Also the quadrupole moment does not vanish as it should for the spherically symmetric state that results for a central potential. These discrepancies can be explained by the presence of a non-central tensor force, i.e. a force that does not act along the line connecting the two interacting nucleons. Such refinements are not

Table 6.2
Exchange potentials

	Parity +1	Parity −1
singlet $S = 0$	$-f(r)\{W - B - H + M\}$	$-f(r)\{W - B + H - M\}$
triplet $S = 1$	$-f(r)\{W + B + H + M\}$	$-f(r)\{W + B - H - M\}$

considered here for the phenomenological interactions and neither are velocity-dependent forces taken into account.

6.3. Matrix elements of the surface delta interaction

An example of a mathematically simple interaction is the surface delta interaction (SDI) [Plastino, Arvieu and Moszkowski (1966)]. Due to the simplicity of the SDI and its success in accounting for many nuclear properties, this effective interaction will be discussed in detail.

For the SDI some very crude assumptions are made about the effective interaction (see also [Arvieu and Moszkowski (1966)]):

(a) The interaction takes place at the nuclear surface only.

A qualitative justification of this assumption might be [Faessler and Plastino (1967)]) that the local kinetic energy T of a nucleon moving in a shell-model potential $U(r)$ is larger in the nuclear interior than near the surface, since one has $T + U =$ constant. The scattering process in the nucleus is dominated by S-wave scattering of nucleons colliding head-on in the vicinity of the Fermi surface. This surface defines the energy below which all single-particle states are occupied. The relative kinetic energy of two nucleons in a head-on collision is smaller near the surface than in the nuclear interior. One has learned from nucleon-nucleon scattering experiments that the S-wave phase shifts increase when the relative velocity decreases. As a result the interaction between nucleons near the nuclear surface should be most important.

(b) The two-body force is a delta force.

The free nucleon-nucleon interaction is known to be a short-range interaction. Although the effective interaction for a spectroscopic calculation must not be expected to be very similar to the free nucleon-nucleon interaction, the short-range behaviour should still be one of its characteristics. One may now, in a schematic way, assume that the effective interaction can be represented as a delta force, which moreover has the advantage of mathematical simplicity.

(c) The probability of finding a particle at the nuclear surface is independent of the shell-model orbit in which the particle moves.

This assumption cannot be justified exactly. It is in reasonable agreement, however, with the radial wave functions $R_{nl}(r)$ calculated from a harmonic-oscillator or a Saxon-Woods potential (see fig. 6.2). The probability of finding a particle at a radius between r and $r + \Delta r$ is given by $4\pi r^2 \Delta r R_{nl}^2(r)$. It is seen that for $r < R_0$ these probabilities depend strongly on n and l but for $r \approx R_0$ they are of comparable magnitude.

It is clear that none of the assumptions mentioned above can be expected to hold rigorously. The best justification of this simple interaction is its success in correlating many experimental data.

The assumed delta force still has to be assigned a strength. This strength is regarded as a parameter that must be determined from experimental spectra. Usually it is assumed that the strength is constant in the mass region under consideration. It is known

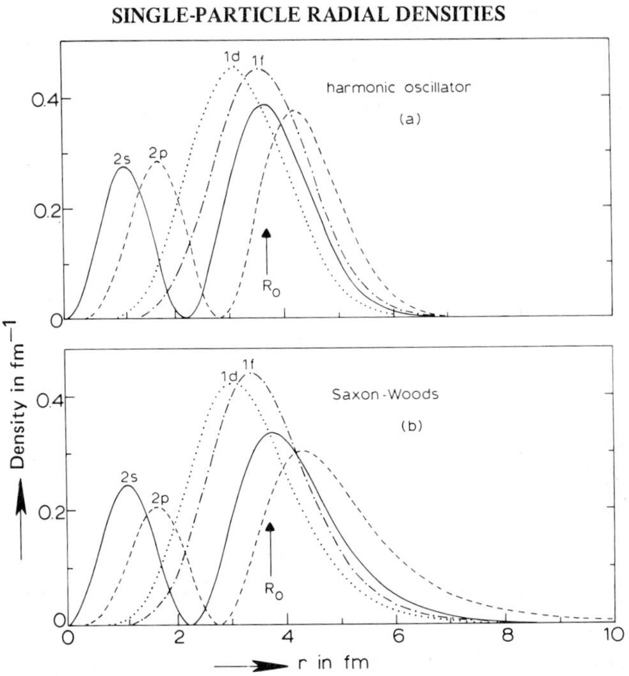

Fig. 6.2. The probability density $r^2R_{nl}^2(r)$ for a neutron in the 1d, 2s, 1f or 2p single-particle state calculated for the nucleus ^{29}Si. The plots illustrate that for both the harmonic-oscillator and the Saxon-Woods potential the probabilities near $r = R_0$ do not depend strongly on n and l.

from scattering experiments that the nucleon-nucleon interaction depends on the spin state of the two nucleons. Since each nucleon has intrinsic spin $s = \frac{1}{2}$, one obtains for the two-nucleon state with $\boldsymbol{S} = \boldsymbol{s}(1) + \boldsymbol{s}(2)$ the values $S = 0$ or 1. Therefore two strength parameters are introduced, which are given by $A'_{S=0}$ for the singlet state and $A'_{S=1}$ for the triplet state of the two interacting nucleons.

In *j-j* coupling it is not convenient to work with the total spin S. For a delta-force it can be related, however, to the total isospin T of the two-particle system. This can be shown as follows. The two-body wave function can be written in L-S coupling as

$$\psi_{JT}(1,2) = [\Phi_L(1,2) \times \Sigma_S(1,2)]^J \Theta_T(1,2), \tag{6.13}$$

where the total angular momentum $\boldsymbol{L}$ and total spin $\boldsymbol{S}$ are coupled to $\boldsymbol{J}$. The wave function $\psi_{JT}(1,2)$ must be totally antisymmetric. The orbital part $\Phi_L(1,2)$ depends only on the spatial coordinates of the particles 1 and 2. When for the evaluation of the two-body matrix elements one integrates over the spatial coordinates, the only contributions derive from the orbital part $\Phi_L(1,2)$ at $\boldsymbol{r}(1) = \boldsymbol{r}(2)$ because of the delta function. Therefore only symmetric functions $\Phi_L(1,2)$ can contribute, and so the spin-isospin part $\Sigma_S(1,2)\,\Theta_T(1,2)$ should be antisymmetric. It follows from sect.

2.4 that then one has either $S = 0, T = 1$ or $S = 1, T = 0$. Thus instead of the spin S one can use the isospin T to label the strength parameter and rather than $A'_{S=0}$ and $A'_{S=1}$ we shall use $A'_{T=1}$ and $A'_{T=0}$, respectively.

Taking into account the assumptions (*a*) and (*b*) one can write the following expression for the surface delta interaction between particles 1 and 2

$$V^{\text{SDI}}(1,2) = -4\pi A'_T \delta(\boldsymbol{r}(1) - \boldsymbol{r}(2))\, \delta(r(1) - R_0)\,, \tag{6.14}$$

where $\boldsymbol{r}(1)$ and $\boldsymbol{r}(2)$ are the position vectors of the interacting particles and R_0 is the nuclear radius. The factor 4π is introduced rather arbitrarily in order to avoid a similar factor $(4\pi)^{-1}$ in the final expression of a two-body matrix element, as will be shown below.

With the expression given for the SDI in eq. (6.14) one can evaluate the two-body matrix elements for particles in single-particle shell-model states. The two-body matrix elements are given by

$$\langle j_a j_b | V^{\text{SDI}}(1,2) | j_c j_d \rangle_{JT} = -4\pi A'_T \langle j_a j_b | \delta(\boldsymbol{r}(1) - \boldsymbol{r}(2))\, \delta(r(1) - R_0) | j_c j_d \rangle_{JT}\,. \tag{6.15}$$

For brevity of notation j_a stands for the complete set of single-particle quantum numbers n_a, l_a and j_a. The two-particle states are each coupled to total J and T. The matrix element does not depend on the orientation in coordinate space and isospace. Therefore, the projection quantum numbers M and T_z are suppressed.

The two-particle wave functions in the matrix element are products of functions of the position vectors $\boldsymbol{r}(1)$ and $\boldsymbol{r}(2)$, while the interaction depends on the relative distance $|\boldsymbol{r}(1) - \boldsymbol{r}(2)|$ only. For the evaluation of the matrix element it is useful to separate the spatial behaviour of the interaction into radial and angular parts. The transition to polar coordinates leads to

$$\delta(\boldsymbol{r}(1) - \boldsymbol{r}(2)) = \frac{\delta(r(1) - r(2))}{r(1)\,r(2)} \sum_{km} Y^*_{km}(\hat{\boldsymbol{r}}(1))\, Y_{km}(\hat{\boldsymbol{r}}(2))\,, \tag{6.16}$$

where the $Y_{km}(\hat{\boldsymbol{r}})$ are spherical harmonics of the angular coordinates $\hat{\boldsymbol{r}} = \boldsymbol{r}/r$. The surface delta interaction defined in eq. (6.14) can thus be written as

$$V^{\text{SDI}}(1,2) = -A'_T v(r(1), r(2))\, \delta(\Omega(1,2))\,. \tag{6.17}$$

In this expression the radial part is given by

$$v(r(1), r(2)) = \frac{\delta(r(1) - r(2))}{r(1)\,r(2)}\, \delta(r(1) - R_0) \tag{6.18}$$

and the angular part by

$$\delta(\Omega(1,2)) = 4\pi \sum_{km} Y^*_{km}(\hat{\boldsymbol{r}}(1))\, Y_{km}(\hat{\boldsymbol{r}}(2))\,. \tag{6.19}$$

Let us derive now an expression for the matrix elements of the SDI. The matrix elements can be factorized as

$$\langle j_a j_b | V^{SDI}(1,2) | j_c j_d \rangle_{JT} = -A'_T \langle M_{rad} \rangle \langle M_{ang} \rangle_{JT} . \tag{6.20}$$

Here the radial matrix element is evaluated with the radial functions $R_{nl}(r)$ as

$$\langle M_{rad} \rangle = \int R_{n_a l_a}(r(1)) R_{n_b l_b}(r(2))\, v(r(1), r(2))\, R_{n_c l_c}(r(1))\, R_{n_d l_d}(r(2))\, r^2(1)\, dr(1)\, r^2(2)\, dr(2) . \tag{6.21}$$

For the simple radial behaviour of the interaction given in eq. (6.18) this reduces to

$$\langle M_{rad} \rangle = R_{n_a l_a}(R_0) R_{n_b l_b}(R_0) R_{n_c l_c}(R_0) R_{n_d l_d}(R_0) R_0^2 . \tag{6.22}$$

With the assumption of the SDI that all radial wave functions $R_{nl}(r)$ for a given mass number have the same absolute value at $r = R_0$, it follows that the expression (6.22) is independent of the single-particle states involved, apart from a possible phase factor. It turns out that the radial function $R_{nl}(r)$ possessses no zeros for $r > R_0$. Thus the sign of $R_{nl}(R_0)$ is determined by the total number of radial nodes, $n - 1$, between $r = 0$ and $r = \infty$ if all $R_{nl}(r)$ are defined with positive values near the origin, which corresponds with the phase of the definition (2.21). Another phase convention, i.e. positive behaviour for $r \to \infty$, also occurs in the literature. It is remarked that once a choice has been made, one should use that convention throughout all calculations that depend on the phases of radial integrals. As a result one obtains (see also sect. 2.2)

$$R_{nl}(r{=}R_0) = (-1)^{n-1} |R_{nl}(r{=}R_0)| . \tag{6.23}$$

Since we have assumed the equalities

$$|R_{n_a l_a}(R_0)| = |R_{n_b l_b}(R_0)| = |R_{n_c l_c}(R_0)| = |R_{n_d l_d}(R_0)| , \tag{6.24}$$

eq. (6.22) can be written as

$$\langle M_{rad} \rangle = (-1)^{n_a + n_b + n_c + n_d} R^4_{n_a l_a}(R_0) R_0^2 = (-1)^{n_a + n_b + n_c + n_d} C(R_0) . \tag{6.25}$$

Note that the assumptions made for the SDI drastically simplify the evaluation of radial matrix elements. The only dependence of the SDI matrix elements on the single-particle states is an angular one, except for the phase factor given in eq. (6.25). The angular matrix element in eq. (6.20) can be written as

$$\langle M_{ang} \rangle_{JT} = \langle j_a j_b | \delta(\Omega(1,2)) | j_c j_d \rangle_{JT} = 4\pi \langle j_a j_b | \sum_k \boldsymbol{Y}_k(\hat{\boldsymbol{r}}(1)) \cdot \boldsymbol{Y}_k(\hat{\boldsymbol{r}}(2)) | j_c j_d \rangle_{JT} . \tag{6.26}$$

where it should be noted that only the angular parts of the wave functions are meant.

For a further evaluation of the two-particle matrix elements of the SDI it is helpful to postpone the complication of antisymmetry of the wave functions and therefore we consider matrix elements between non-antisymmetrized two-particle states. Instead of the matrix element in eq. (6.26) we evaluate first

$$\langle M_{\text{ang}}\rangle_J = 4\pi \langle j_{\text{a}}(1) j_{\text{b}}(2) | \sum_k \boldsymbol{Y}_k(\hat{\boldsymbol{r}}(1)) \cdot \boldsymbol{Y}_k(\hat{\boldsymbol{r}}(2)) | j_{\text{c}}(1) j_{\text{d}}(2)\rangle_J^{\text{n.a.s.}} , \tag{6.27}$$

where the single-particle angular momenta are coupled to $\boldsymbol{j}_{\text{a}} + \boldsymbol{j}_{\text{b}} = \boldsymbol{J}$ and $\boldsymbol{j}_{\text{c}} + \boldsymbol{j}_{\text{d}} = \boldsymbol{J}$. No antisymmetrization is performed on the resulting states and isospin coordinates are ignored.

One can write the matrix element in eq. (6.27) as a product of two factors. The first factor is, apart from a numerical factor, a Clebsch-Gordan coefficient and it describes in principle the dependence of the matrix element on the coordinate frame. The second factor, called the reduced matrix element, contains the information about the physical process being described. These reduced matrix elements are denoted by double-bar matrix elements. This separation into a factor that depends on the magnetic quantum numbers and a factor that is independent of these projection quantum numbers, is referred to as the Wigner-Eckart theorem (see appendix A.3). Application of this theorem to eq. (6.27) yields

$$\langle M_{\text{ang}}\rangle_J = \frac{4\pi}{\sqrt{2J+1}} \langle JM00 | JM\rangle \sum_k \langle j_{\text{a}}(1) j_{\text{b}}(2) \| \boldsymbol{Y}_k(\hat{\boldsymbol{r}}(1)) \cdot \boldsymbol{Y}_k(\hat{\boldsymbol{r}}(2)) \| j_{\text{c}}(1) j_{\text{d}}(2)\rangle_J^{\text{n.a.s.}} . \tag{6.28}$$

The operators $\boldsymbol{Y}_k$ in the reduced matrix element of eq. (6.28) each act on a specific particle. Therefore one can write the reduced matrix element as a product of reduced matrix elements for each particle separately. This factorization can be performed with eq. (A.3.d7). Since the Clebsch-Gordan coefficient in eq. (6.28) is equal to unity, one obtains

$$\langle M_{\text{ang}}\rangle_J = 4\pi (-1)^{j_{\text{b}}+j_{\text{c}}+J} \sum_k \begin{Bmatrix} j_{\text{a}} & j_{\text{b}} & J \\ j_{\text{d}} & j_{\text{c}} & k \end{Bmatrix} \langle j_{\text{a}}(1) \| \boldsymbol{Y}_k(\hat{\boldsymbol{r}}(1)) \| j_{\text{c}}(1)\rangle \langle j_{\text{b}}(2) \| \boldsymbol{Y}_k(\hat{\boldsymbol{r}}(2)) \| j_{\text{d}}(2)\rangle . \tag{6.29}$$

For the proper evaluation of the single-particle reduced matrix elements in eq. (6.29) it is necessary to specify first the coupling order of orbital angular momentum $\boldsymbol{l}$ and intrinsic spin $\boldsymbol{s}$ to the single-particle total spin $\boldsymbol{j}$. Let us fix this coupling order as $\boldsymbol{l} + \boldsymbol{s} = \boldsymbol{j}$ (rather than $\boldsymbol{s} + \boldsymbol{l} = \boldsymbol{j}$) for all calculations to follow. By the use of eq. (A.3.d9 we then get for the single-particle matrix element

$$\langle j_{\text{a}} \| \boldsymbol{Y}_k \| j_{\text{c}}\rangle = (-1)^{l_{\text{a}}+\frac{1}{2}+j_{\text{c}}+k} \sqrt{(2j_{\text{a}}+1)(2j_{\text{c}}+1)} \langle l_{\text{a}} \| \boldsymbol{Y}_k \| l_{\text{c}}\rangle \begin{Bmatrix} l_{\text{a}} & l_{\text{c}} & k \\ j_{\text{c}} & j_{\text{a}} & \frac{1}{2} \end{Bmatrix} . \tag{6.30}$$

The reduced matrix element occurring in eq. (6.30) can be evaluated (see eq. (A.3.e3)) with the relation

$$\langle l_{\text{a}} \| \boldsymbol{Y}_k \| l_{\text{c}}\rangle = (-1)^{l_{\text{a}}} \sqrt{\frac{(2l_{\text{a}}+1)(2k+1)(2l_{\text{c}}+1)}{4\pi}} \begin{pmatrix} l_{\text{a}} & k & l_{\text{c}} \\ 0 & 0 & 0 \end{pmatrix} \tag{6.31}$$

One thus obtains

$$\langle j_a \| Y_k \| j_c \rangle = \frac{(-1)^{j_c+\frac{1}{2}+k}}{\sqrt{4\pi}} \sqrt{(2k+1)(2j_a+1)(2j_c+1)(2l_a+1)(2l_c+1)} \begin{pmatrix} l_a & k & l_c \\ 0 & 0 & 0 \end{pmatrix} \begin{Bmatrix} l_a & l_c & k \\ j_c & j_a & \frac{1}{2} \end{Bmatrix}. \tag{6.32}$$

We are now in a position to evaluate the SDI matrix elements numerically. After one more reduction, however, the expression (6.32) obtains a somewhat more convenient form, since the product of 3-*j* and 6-*j* symbols can be rewritten according to eq. (A.1. b12) as

$$\sqrt{(2l_a+1)(2l_c+1)} \begin{pmatrix} l_a & k & l_c \\ 0 & 0 & 0 \end{pmatrix} \begin{Bmatrix} l_a & l_c & k \\ j_c & j_a & \frac{1}{2} \end{Bmatrix} = -\begin{pmatrix} j_a & k & j_c \\ -\frac{1}{2} & 0 & \frac{1}{2} \end{pmatrix} \tfrac{1}{2}\{1+(-1)^{l_a+k+l_c}\}. \tag{6.33}$$

The vanishing of eq. (6.33) for odd values of $l_a + k + l_c$ reflects the conservation of parity for the matrix element in eq. (6.31).

Substitution of eq. (6.32) and an analogous expression for $\langle j_b \| Y_k \| j_d \rangle$ into eq. (6.29) now yields the result for the non-antisymmetrized angular matrix element

$$\langle M_{ang} \rangle_J = \tfrac{1}{2}\sqrt{(2j_a+1)(2j_b+1)(2j_c+1)(2j_d+1)}(-1)^{j_b+j_d+J}$$

$$\times \sum_k (2k+1)[1+(-1)^{l_a+l_c+k}] \begin{Bmatrix} j_a & j_b & J \\ j_c & j_d & k \end{Bmatrix} \begin{pmatrix} j_a & k & j_c \\ -\frac{1}{2} & 0 & \frac{1}{2} \end{pmatrix} \begin{pmatrix} j_b & k & j_d \\ -\frac{1}{2} & 0 & \frac{1}{2} \end{pmatrix}. \tag{6.34}$$

Here the relation

$$\tfrac{1}{2}\{1+(-1)^{l_a+k+l_c}\} \times \tfrac{1}{2}\{1+(-1)^{l_b+k+l_d}\} = \tfrac{1}{2}\{1+(-1)^{l_a+l_c+k}\} \tag{6.35}$$

has been used, which follows from the fact that $l_a + l_b + l_c + l_d$ must be even for a nonvanishing matrix element, i.e. left- and right-hand side two-particle wave functions must have the same parity. Expression (6.33) can be simplified further with the relations

$$\sum_k (2k+1) \begin{Bmatrix} j_a & j_b & J \\ j_a & j_c & k \end{Bmatrix} \begin{pmatrix} j_a & k & j_c \\ -\frac{1}{2} & 0 & \frac{1}{2} \end{pmatrix} \begin{pmatrix} j_b & k & j_d \\ -\frac{1}{2} & 0 & \frac{1}{2} \end{pmatrix} = (-1)^{j_b+j_d+J} \begin{pmatrix} j_b & j_a & J \\ -\frac{1}{2} & -\frac{1}{2} & 1 \end{pmatrix} \begin{pmatrix} j_c & j_d & J \\ \frac{1}{2} & \frac{1}{2} & -1 \end{pmatrix}, \tag{6.36}$$

$$\sum_k (2k+1)(-1)^k \begin{Bmatrix} j_a & j_b & J \\ j_d & j_c & k \end{Bmatrix} \begin{pmatrix} j_a & k & j_c \\ -\frac{1}{2} & 0 & \frac{1}{2} \end{pmatrix} \begin{pmatrix} j_b & k & j_d \\ -\frac{1}{2} & 0 & \frac{1}{2} \end{pmatrix} = (-1)^{J-2j_d} \cdot \begin{pmatrix} j_b & j_a & J \\ \frac{1}{2} & -\frac{1}{2} & 0 \end{pmatrix} \begin{pmatrix} j_c & j_d & J \\ \frac{1}{2} & -\frac{1}{2} & 0 \end{pmatrix}. \tag{6.37}$$

Eqs. (6.36) and (6.37) are not proven here, but they can be derived directly from eqs. (A.1.a8) and (A.1.b11).

$$\left[\text{Hint: } (-1)^k \begin{pmatrix} j_b & k & j_d \\ -\frac{1}{2} & 0 & \frac{1}{2} \end{pmatrix} = (-1)^{j_b+j_d} \begin{pmatrix} j_b & k & j_d \\ \frac{1}{2} & 0 & -\frac{1}{2} \end{pmatrix}\right].$$

Thus one obtains finally

$$\langle M_{\text{ang}}\rangle_J = -\tfrac{1}{2}\sqrt{(2j_a+1)(2j_b+1)(2j_c+1)(2j_d+1)}$$

$$\times\left[(-1)^{j_b+j_d+l_a+l_c}\begin{pmatrix} j_a & j_b & J\\ \frac{1}{2} & -\frac{1}{2} & 0\end{pmatrix}\begin{pmatrix} j_c & j_d & J\\ \frac{1}{2} & -\frac{1}{2} & 0\end{pmatrix}-\begin{pmatrix} j_a & j_b & J\\ \frac{1}{2} & \frac{1}{2} & -1\end{pmatrix}\begin{pmatrix} j_c & j_d & J\\ \frac{1}{2} & \frac{1}{2} & -1\end{pmatrix}\right]\delta^{\text{even}}_{l_a+l_b+l_c+l_d}. \tag{6.38}$$

The delta symbol indicates that the matrix element vanishes for odd values of $l_a + l_b + l_c + l_d$.

The expression of SDI matrix elements for non-antisymmetrized two-particle states follows after insertion of eqs. (6.25) and (6.38) into eq. (6.20). Instead of the strength parameter A'_T we use A' here, since we still ignore T. One finds

$$\langle j_a j_b | V^{\text{SDI}}(1,2) | j_c j_d\rangle_J = \tfrac{1}{2}A'C(R_0)(-1)^{n_a+n_b+n_c+n_d}\sqrt{(2j_a+1)(2j_b+1)(2j_c+1)(2j_d}$$

$$\times\left[(-1)^{j_b+j_d+l_a+l_c}\begin{pmatrix} j_a & j_b & J\\ \frac{1}{2} & -\frac{1}{2} & 0\end{pmatrix}\begin{pmatrix} j_c & j_d & J\\ \frac{1}{2} & -\frac{1}{2} & 0\end{pmatrix}-\begin{pmatrix} j_a & j_b & J\\ \frac{1}{2} & \frac{1}{2} & -1\end{pmatrix}\begin{pmatrix} j_c & j_d & J\\ \frac{1}{2} & \frac{1}{2} & -1\end{pmatrix}\right]\delta^{\text{even}}_{l_a+l_b+l_c+l_d}. \tag{6.39}$$

For physical applications in the isospin formalism, the SDI matrix elements must be evaluated between states that are antisymmetric in all coordinates, i.e. coordinate space and isospace. The value $T = 1$ corresponds to symmetry in the isospin part and thus must be combined with an antisymmetric coordinate space part, while for $T = 0$ states the coordinate space part must be symmetric. This condition is fulfilled by combining the non-antisymmetrized wave functions as (cf. eq. (5.17))

$$\langle j_a j_b | V^{\text{SDI}}(1,2) | j_c j_d\rangle_{JT} = \frac{\langle j_a(1) j_b(2) | V^{\text{SDI}}(1,2)\{1+(-1)^T P_{12}\} | j_c(1) j_d(2)\rangle_J^{\text{n.a.s.}}}{\sqrt{(1+\delta_{ab})(1+\delta_{cd})}}. \tag{6.40}$$

The action of the permutation operator P_{12} on a non-antisymmetrized two-particle function is given by (see eq. (2.80))

$$P_{12}|j_c(1) j_d(2)\rangle_{JM}^{\text{n.a.s.}} = |j_c(2) j_d(1)\rangle_{JM}^{\text{n.a.s.}} = (-1)^{J-j_c-j_d}|j_d(1) j_c(2)\rangle_{JM}^{\text{n.a.s.}}. \tag{6.41}$$

Thus the matrix element (6.40) can be written as

$$\langle j_a j_b | V^{\text{SDI}}(1,2) | j_c j_d\rangle_{JT}$$

$$= \frac{\langle j_a(1) j_b(2) | V^{\text{SDI}}(1,2) | j_c(1) j_d(2)\rangle_J^{\text{n.a.s.}} + (-1)^{J-j_c-j_d+T}\langle j_a(1) j_b(2) | V^{\text{SDI}}(1,2) | j_d(1) j_c(2)\rangle_J^{\text{n}}}{\sqrt{(1+\delta_{ab})(1+\delta_{cd})}} \tag{6.42}$$

Both matrix elements between non-antisymmetrized states can be evaluated with expression (6.39), where for the second matrix element only the labels c and d must be interchanged. Application of symmetry properties of 3-j symbols (see appendix A.1) leads to

$$\langle j_a j_b | V^{SDI}(1,2) | j_c j_d \rangle_{JT} = \tfrac{1}{2} A'_T C(R_0) (-1)^{n_a+n_b+n_c+n_d} \sqrt{\frac{(2j_a+1)(2j_b+1)(2j_c+1)(2j_d+1)}{(1+\delta_{ab})(1+\delta_{cd})}}$$

$$\times \left\{ (-1)^{j_b+j_d+l_b+l_d} \begin{pmatrix} j_a & j_b & J \\ \frac{1}{2} & -\frac{1}{2} & 0 \end{pmatrix} \begin{pmatrix} j_c & j_d & J \\ \frac{1}{2} & -\frac{1}{2} & 0 \end{pmatrix} [1-(-1)^{J+T+l_c+l_d}] \right.$$

$$\left. - \begin{pmatrix} j_a & j_b & J \\ \frac{1}{2} & \frac{1}{2} & -1 \end{pmatrix} \begin{pmatrix} j_c & j_d & J \\ \frac{1}{2} & \frac{1}{2} & -1 \end{pmatrix} [1+(-1)^T] \right\} . \qquad (6.43)$$

Replacing the 3-j symbols in eq. (6.43) by Clebsch-Gordan coefficients one obtains finally

$$\langle j_a j_b | V^{SDI}(1,2) | j_c j_d \rangle_{JT} = (-1)^{n_a+n_b+n_c+n_d} \frac{A_T}{2(2J+1)} \sqrt{\frac{(2j_a+1)(2j_b+1)(2j_c+1)(2j_d+1)}{(1+\delta_{ab})(1+\delta_{cd})}}$$

$$\times \{ (-1)^{j_b+j_d+l_b+l_d} \langle j_b - \tfrac{1}{2} j_a \tfrac{1}{2} | J0 \rangle \langle j_d - \tfrac{1}{2} j_c \tfrac{1}{2} | J0 \rangle [1-(-1)^{l_a+l_b+J+T}]$$

$$- \langle j_b \tfrac{1}{2} j_a \tfrac{1}{2} | J1 \rangle \langle j_d \tfrac{1}{2} j_c \tfrac{1}{2} | J1 \rangle [1+(-1)^T] \} . \qquad (6.44)$$

Here A_T is defined as the product of the strength A'_T and the value of the radial integral $C(R_0)$, such that

$$A_T = A'_T C(R_0) . \qquad (6.45)$$

The coefficients A_T, possessing the dimension of an energy, are quoted as the strengths of the SDI. Expression (6.44) will be used for further discussions and applications. The relation between the matrix element (6.44) with $\boldsymbol{j}_a + \boldsymbol{j}_b = \boldsymbol{J}$ and $\boldsymbol{j}_c + \boldsymbol{j}_d = \boldsymbol{J}$ and that for the coupling order $\boldsymbol{j}_b + \boldsymbol{j}_a = \boldsymbol{J}$ and/or $\boldsymbol{j}_d + \boldsymbol{j}_c = \boldsymbol{J}$ follows from eq. (5.13).

It may be useful to summarize once more the assumptions that were made to establish the phase of the SDI matrix elements: (i) the coupling order $\boldsymbol{j} = \boldsymbol{l} + \boldsymbol{s}$ is used; (ii) the radial wave functions are taken to be positive near the origin.

6.4. The modified surface delta interaction

It turns out that the spectra obtained with the SDI show some systematic discrepancies with respect to the experimentally observed level energies. The deviations occur for the spacing of the $T = 0$ and $T = 1$ centroids of level energies. The centroids are defined by the relation

$$\bar{E}_T = \sum_J (2J+1) E_{JT} \Big/ \sum_J (2J+1) , \qquad (6.46)$$

where the weighting factor $2J+1$ accounts for the degeneracy of $M=-J, -J+1, \ldots, J-1, J$. It has also been observed that the SDI matrix elements reproduce the binding energies quite poorly. It turns out that the agreement with experiment can be improved substantially by the *ad hoc* addition of two J-independent terms given by $B'(\boldsymbol{\tau}(1)\cdot\boldsymbol{\tau}(2))+C'$. This expression can be looked at as a linear combination of Heisenberg and Wigner terms discussed in sect. 6.2. The resulting modified surface delta interaction (MSDI) is thus given by

$$V^{\mathrm{MSDI}}(1,2)=-4\pi A'_T\,\delta(\boldsymbol{r}(1)-\boldsymbol{r}(2))\,\delta(r(1)-R_0)+B'(\boldsymbol{\tau}(1)\cdot\boldsymbol{\tau}(2))+C'\,. \tag{6.47}$$

Note that both additional terms are constants in coordinate space and thus they contribute only to the diagonal two-body matrix elements.

In analogy with the derivation of eq. (6.5) one obtains the expectation value

$$\langle\boldsymbol{\tau}(1)\cdot\boldsymbol{\tau}(2)\rangle_T=2T(T+1)-3\,. \tag{6.48}$$

Thus the contribution of the additional terms is given by

$$\langle B(\boldsymbol{\tau}(1)\cdot\boldsymbol{\tau}(2))+C\rangle=\begin{cases}-3B+C & \text{for}\quad T=0\\ B+C & \text{for}\quad T=1\end{cases}, \tag{6.49}$$

where B and C denote the products of B' and C' with the radial integral $C(R_0)$. The modification of the SDI does not affect the wave functions, but only shifts the energies of calculated states. This stems from the fact that the extra terms leave off-diagonal matrix elements unaffected, while all diagonal matrix elements of matrices for a given mass number and isospin are changed by the same amount. The resulting shift for a state with n active particles and isospin T is given by [cf. eq. (6.49)]

$$D_T^{(n)}=(B+C)\sum_m c_m^{(1)}+(-3B+C)\sum_l c_l^{(0)}\,, \tag{6.50}$$

where $\Sigma_m c_m^{(1)}$ and $\Sigma_l c_l^{(0)}$ denote the sum of the expansion coefficients of the many-particle matrix elements in terms of the $T'=1$ and $T'=0$ coupled diagonal two-body matrix elements, respectively. Inserting the earlier derived sum rules, given in eqs. (5.49) and (5.50), one obtains

$$\begin{aligned}D_T^{(n)}&=(B+C)\left[\tfrac{3}{8}n(n-2)+\tfrac{1}{2}T(T+1)\right]+(-3B+C)\left[\tfrac{1}{8}n(n+2)-\tfrac{1}{2}T(T+1)\right]\\&=\tfrac{1}{2}n^2C-\tfrac{1}{2}n(3B+C)+2T(T+1)B\,.\end{aligned} \tag{6.51}$$

The shift $D_T^{(n)}$ is thus independent of the configuration and spin J of a many-particle state for a given number of active particles n. From eq. (6.51) it follows directly that when n is fixed, the position of $T=T_1$ states is shifted with respect to $T=T_2$ states by an amount

$$D_{T_1}^{(n)}-D_{T_2}^{(n)}=2[T_1(T_1+1)-T_2(T_2+1)]\,B\,. \tag{6.52}$$

THE EFFECT OF THE MONOPOLE TERM

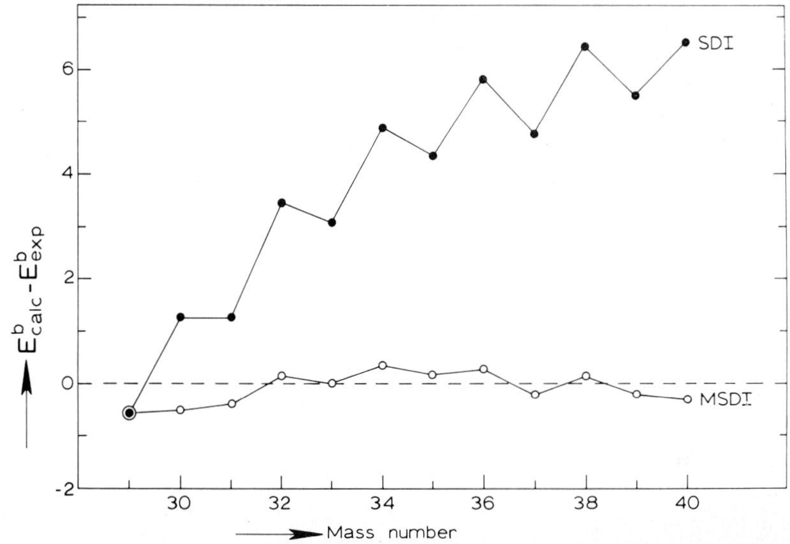

Fig. 6.3. The differences between the calculated and experimental binding energies E^b_{calc} and E^b_{exp} (with $E^b < 0$) are shown for A = 29–40 nuclei. The curve labelled MSDI is obtained for B = 0.7 MeV and C = 0.1 MeV and the curve SDI results when $B = C = 0$. In the latter case all other parameters, i.e., the strengths A_1 and A_0 as well as the single-particle energies, are kept equal to those of the MSDI approach. The calculations are performed in a $2s_{1/2}1d_{3/2}$ configuration space taking ^{28}Si as an inert core [Glaudemans, Brussaard and Wildenthal (1967)].

Expressions (6.51) and (6.52) can be used to study the effect of the additional B- and C-dependent terms on binding energies and on the separation between states of different isospin. An illustration is given in fig. 6.3 for a calculation of binding energies in A = 29–40 nuclei.

It is found empirically that the value of the coefficient C in eq. (6.51) is often very small. Sometimes it can even be quite appropriate to impose the restriction $C = 0$, when fitting the parameters to the experimental data. This is because usually also the single-particle energies e_ρ are considered as adjustable parameters. We shall show that under certain conditions the parameters C and e_ρ occur in such a way that they cannot be determined separately.

The sum of the expansion coefficients that express a diagonal many-particle matrix element in terms of two-body matrix elements is equal to $\frac{1}{2}n(n-1)$, where n denotes the number of active particles. The sum of the coefficients of the single-particle energies e_ρ is equal to n. Thus, when the parameter C is changed by an amount ΔC and all single-particle energies by an amount Δe_ρ, one finds that the values of all diagonal many-particle matrix elements are changed by an amount

$$\Delta E = \tfrac{1}{2}n(n-1)\,\Delta C + n\Delta e_\rho\ . \tag{6.53}$$

It then follows that the variations ΔC and Δe_ρ have no effect on the values of the diagonal many-particle matrix elements, when Δe_ρ and ΔC are related by

$$\Delta e_\rho = -\tfrac{1}{2}(n-1)\,\Delta C\,. \qquad (6.54)$$

When fitting the parameters to experimental energies for one mass number (i.e. a fixed number of active particles n), a unique determination of C and e_ρ is impossible, since variations in C and e_ρ satisfying condition (6.54) leave the calculated energies of the states unaffected.

Usually a fit is performed to experimental data in a restricted mass region. Let us assume that one deals with a number of active particles n with the restriction $n_{\rm min} \leqslant n \leqslant n_{\rm max}$. For $n_{\rm max} - n_{\rm min}$ small compared to n, relation (6.54) will still hold approximately for all nuclei considered, if one takes $n = \tfrac{1}{2}(n_{\rm min} + n_{\rm max})$. Thus also in these cases the parameters C and e_ρ cannot be determined separately without large uncertainties.

Some values of A_T, B and C obtained from fits to experimental data in various mass regions are given in table 6.3. From such calculations one can obtain an empirical estimate of the parameters A_T, B and C as a function of the mass number A. The results can be summarized by the approximate evaluations

$$A_0 \approx A_1 \approx B \approx (25/A)\ \text{MeV}\,, \qquad C \approx 0\,. \qquad (6.55)$$

It should be stressed that these values give only a very crude estimate as follows from a comparison with the values given in table 6.3. It is mainly the value of A_1 that satis-

Table 6.3
Strength parameters of the MSDI obtained from fits to experimental spectra in various mass regions

Mass region A	Core	Active orbits[a]	Strengths (MeV) A_1	A_0	B	C
8–16[b]	^{4}He	$1p_{3/2}\,1p_{1/2}$	2.6	1.2	1.4	−0.2
17–22[c]	^{16}O	$1d_{5/2}\,2s_{1/2}\,1d_{3/2}$	1.0	0.8	0.7	−0.3
24–28[d]	^{16}O	$1d_{5/2}\,2s_{1/2}\,1d_{3/2}$ *	1.0	0.7	0.8	0.03
27–29[e]	^{16}O	$1d_{5/2}\,2s_{1/2}\,1d_{3/2}$ *	1.0	1.0	0.9	0.2
30–34[f]	^{16}O	$1d_{5/2}\,2s_{1/2}\,1d_{3/2}$ *	0.9	0.7	0.5	0.3
35–40[g]	^{16}O	$1d_{5/2}\,2s_{1/2}\,1d_{3/2}$	1.0	0.4	0.6	−0.1
57–68[h]	^{56}Ni	$2p_{3/2}\,1f_{5/2}\,2p_{1/2}$	0.5	0.3	0.4	0.07

a) An asterisk indicates that the given space has been truncated.
b) Saayman, De Kock and Van der Merwe (1973).
c) Halbert, McGrory, Wildenthal and Pandya (1971).
d) Meurders, Glaudemans, Timmer and Van Hienen (1976).
e) Wildenthal and McGrory (1973).
f) Wildenthal, McGrory, Halbert and Graber (1971).
g) Wildenthal, Halbert, McGrory and Kuo (1971).
h) Koops and Glaudemans (1977).

fies the estimate (6.55) rather well. The estimates are useful, however, as starting values for an iterative least-squares fitting procedure such as discussed in chapter 7.

We now derive some properties of the MSDI from the general expression for an SDI matrix element given in eq. (6.44). Starting with the discussion of diagonal matrix elements (i.e. $\{n_a, l_a, j_a\} = \{n_c, l_c, j_c\}$ and $\{n_b, l_b, j_b\} = \{n_d, l_d, j_d\}$) one has (with $(-1)^{j_b+j_d+l_b+l_d} = (-1)^{2j_b+2l_b} = -1$)

$$\langle j_a j_b | V^{\mathrm{MSDI}}(1,2) | j_a j_b \rangle_{JT} = -A_T \frac{(2j_a+1)(2j_b+1)}{2(2J+1)(1+\delta_{ab})}$$

$$\times \{\langle j_b -\tfrac{1}{2} j_a \tfrac{1}{2} | J0 \rangle^2 [1-(-1)^{l_a+l_b+J+T}] + \langle j_b \tfrac{1}{2} j_a \tfrac{1}{2} | J1 \rangle^2 [1+(-1)^T]\} + [2T(T+1)-3]B + C. \tag{6.56}$$

From this equation an inequality follows, which is given by

$$\langle j_a j_b | V^{\mathrm{MSDI}}(1,2) | j_a j_b \rangle \leqslant 0 \qquad \text{for } A_T > 0, \qquad B = C = 0\,. \tag{6.57}$$

Since the strength A_T has always been found to be positive, the MSDI produces bound states when one has vanishing strengths B and C. A possible repulsive interaction can only derive from the B- and C-dependent parts in eq. (6.56).

For diagonal $T = 1$ matrix elements eq. (6.56) reduces further to

$$\langle j_a j_b | V^{\mathrm{MSDI}}(1,2) | j_a j_b \rangle_{J,T=1} = -A_1 \frac{(2j_a+1)(2j_b+1)}{2(2J+1)(1+\delta_{ab})} \langle j_b -\tfrac{1}{2} j_a \tfrac{1}{2} | J0 \rangle^2 [1+(-1)^{l_a+l_b+J}] + B + C. \tag{6.58}$$

It is seen that the first term in eq. (6.58) vanishes for odd values of $l_a + l_b + J$ and one obtains the relation

$$\langle j_a j_b | V^{\mathrm{MSDI}}(1,2) | j_a j_b \rangle_{J,T=1} = B + C \quad \text{for} \quad l_a + l_b + J = \text{odd}\,. \tag{6.59}$$

This means that matrix elements of the MSDI for two-particle states of even parity (i.e. even values of $l_a + l_b$) are identical for J = odd and $T = 1$. Similarly odd-parity two-particle states have identical matrix elements for J = even and $T = 1$.

Eq. (6.58) can be simplified further when the two interacting particles are in the same orbit. In this case one has $l_a = l_b$, $j_a = j_b = j$ and J = even. Hence one finds

$$\langle j^2 | V^{\mathrm{MSDI}}(1,2) | j^2 \rangle_{J,T=1} = -A_1 \frac{(2j+1)^2}{2(2J+1)} \langle j -\tfrac{1}{2} j \tfrac{1}{2} | J0 \rangle^2 + B + C\,. \tag{6.60}$$

Inserting the value of the Clebsch-Gordan coefficient for $J = 0$,

$$\langle j -\tfrac{1}{2} j \tfrac{1}{2} | 00 \rangle^2 = \frac{1}{2j+1}\,, \tag{6.61}$$

into eq. (6.60) one obtains

$$\langle j^2 | V^{\mathrm{MSDI}}(1,2) | j^2 \rangle_{J=0,T=1} = -\tfrac{1}{2}A_1(2j+1) + B + C\,. \tag{6.62}$$

This means that the absolute value of the binding of two particles in a j^2 configuration and coupled to $J = 0$ and $T = 1$ increases with j.

It follows from eqs. (6.44) and (6.56) that the values of off-diagonal matrix elements can be written in terms of diagonal matrix elements if for the latter one takes $B = C = 0$ (i.e. the original SDI). One finds the relation

$$|\langle j_a j_b | V^{\mathrm{SDI}}(1,2) | j_c j_d \rangle_{JT}| = R\sqrt{\langle j_a j_b | V^{\mathrm{SDI}}(1,2) | j_a j_b \rangle_{JT} \langle j_c j_d | V^{\mathrm{SDI}}(1,2) | j_c j_d \rangle_{JT}}\,, \tag{6.63}$$

with $R = 1$ unless one has $l_a + l_b + J$ = odd and $T = 0$. Relation (6.63) has the consequence that for a vanishing diagonal SDI matrix element the corresponding off-diagonal matrix elements vanish too.

6.5. Applications

Let us, as an application of eqs. (6.62) and (6.63), calculate the excitation energy of the first excited $J^\pi = 0^+$ state in ${}^{58}_{28}\mathrm{Ni}_{30}$. In this calculation a ${}^{56}_{28}\mathrm{Ni}_{28}$ core is assumed with two active neutrons in the orbits $2\mathrm{p}_{3/2}$ and $1\mathrm{f}_{5/2}$. Since we deal with identical active nucleons, only $T = 1$ two-body matrix elements are needed. The necessary two-body matrix elements follow from eqs. (6.62) and (6.63) and are given by

$$\langle 2\mathrm{p}^2_{3/2} | V^{\mathrm{MSDI}}(1,2) | 2\mathrm{p}^2_{3/2} \rangle_{01} = -2A_1 + B + C\,,$$

$$\langle 1\mathrm{f}^2_{5/2} | V^{\mathrm{MSDI}}(1,2) | 1\mathrm{f}^2_{5/2} \rangle_{01} = -3A_1 + B + C\,,$$

$$|\langle 2\mathrm{p}^2_{3/2} | V^{\mathrm{MSDI}}(1,2) | 1\mathrm{f}^2_{5/2} \rangle_{01}| = A_1\sqrt{6}\,. \tag{6.64}$$

It should be remarked that the explicit calculation yields a negative sign for the last matrix element, but this sign does not enter into our example.

In this case one can neglect the contribution from the strengths B and C in the diagonal matrix elements, since these terms do not affect the spacing of states with the same isospin T. We assume the strength parameter of the MSDI to have a value $A_1 = 0.5$ MeV, as suggested by the estimates (6.55). From the first excited state in ${}^{57}\mathrm{Ni}$ (see fig. 3.11) one obtains the difference in single-particle energies given by $e_{1\mathrm{f}_{5/2}} - e_{2\mathrm{p}_{3/2}} = 0.76$ MeV. After a diagonalization of the two-by-two matrix, a calculated excitation energy of $E_x^{\mathrm{th}}(0^+) = 2.67$ MeV results. This value is not far from the experimental value given by $E_x^{\mathrm{exp}}(0^+) = 2.94$ MeV. The possible admixture of the $2\mathrm{p}_{1/2}$ state into the configuration space is expected to be small since the relevant off-diagonal matrix elements are small as follows from eqs. (6.62) and (6.63). The effect of variations in the strength parameter A_1 on a calculated spectrum has been illustrated before in fig. 3.12 with the nucleus $^{58}_{28}Ni_{30}$. In that example the $2p_{1/2}$ orbit was also taken into account.

Up to here we have mentioned only some effects of the MSDI strength parameters on spectra calculated in a given configuration space. Due to its nature, however, an effective interaction must depend also on the configuration space employed. Hence the MSDI parameters are not independent of the model space. This can be illustrated clearly with a calculation on the nucleus $^{210}_{84}Po_{126}$. Consider this nucleus as

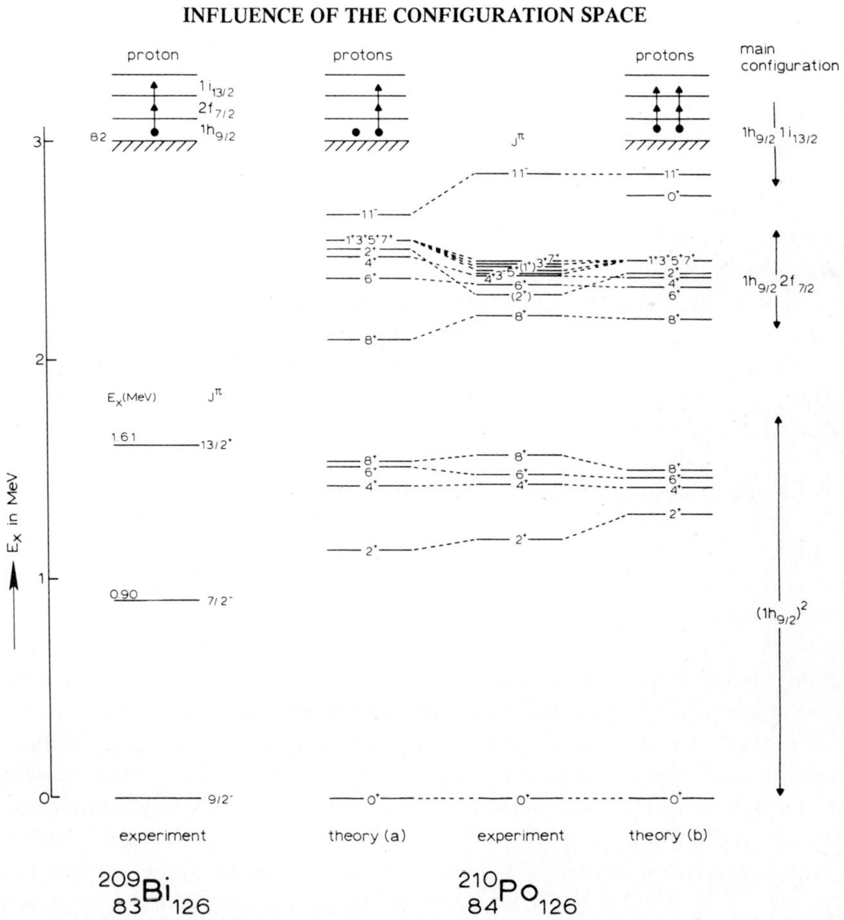

Fig. 6.4. The effect of the configuration space on the MSDI parameter A_1 is illustrated with ^{210}Po. In case (a) only the proton configurations $(1h_{9/2})^2$, $1h_{9/2}2f_{7/2}$ and $1h_{9/2}1i_{13/2}$ are taken into account leading to an optimum value $A_1 = 0.33$ MeV. In case (b) both active protons occupy the lowest three orbits and one finds the optimum value $A_1 = 0.17$ MeV. The experimental data are taken from [Jardine, Prussin and Hollander (1972)].

a closed-shell core of $^{208}_{82}\mathrm{Pb}_{126}$ plus two extra protons. The lowest orbits available for the extra protons are given by $1h_{9/2}$, $2f_{7/2}$ and $1i_{13/2}$. Their relative energies follow from the excitation energies of the lowest $J^\pi = \frac{9}{2}^+, \frac{7}{2}^-$ and $\frac{13}{2}^+$ states in $^{209}_{83}\mathrm{Bi}_{126}$ (see fig. 6.4). The two-body matrix elements needed for the calculation of ^{210}Po with two active protons depend on A_1 only, since the terms B and C do not affect the spacings between $T = 1$ two-particle states. Let us first choose a configuration space with one proton remaining in the $1h_{9/2}$ orbit and the other proton being allowed to occupy also the $2f_{7/2}$ or $1i_{13/2}$ orbits. In this model space the optimum agreement with experiment is obtained for the value $A_1 = 0.33$ MeV. The result of this calculation is shown in fig. 6.4(a). When both protons are allowed to occupy the next two orbits, one obtains a slightly better agreement with experiment (see also fig. 6.4(b)). In the latter case one finds, however, that the best value of the strength parameter is given by $A_1 = 0.17$ MeV.

This example demonstrates that the MSDI parameters may depend strongly on the configuration space taken into account and thus do not depend on the nuclear forces and radial overlaps only. The smaller strength parameter obtained in the extended configuration space for ^{210}Po reproduces better the experimentally observed narrow spacing between the levels at approximately 1.4 and 2.3 MeV.

It may be surprising that the large gap between the $J^\pi = 0^+$ ground state and lowest $J^\pi = 2^+$ state is preserved, despite the smaller strength A_1 in the extended space. This effect is due, however, to a strong configuration mixing of two $J^\pi = 0^+$ states. The ground state and the $J^\pi = 0^+$ state, calculated at about 2.8 MeV, have repelled each other (see also fig. 3.9).

6.6. Comparison of various two-body matrix elements

In sect. 6.1 three methods were mentioned that can be used to obtain two-body matrix elements, i.e. the empirical, realistic and schematic procedures. In this section some results of these approaches will be compared with each other.

In fig. 6.5 matrix elements of the MSDI are shown together with those obtained empirically from a fit to 35 experimental energies in $A = 8-16$ nuclei. For the empirical determination of the two-body matrix elements a closed $1s_{1/2}$ orbit (^{4}He) was assumed with active particles in the $1p_{3/2}$ and $1p_{1/2}$ orbits. The comparison shows that the empirical and MSDI values of two-body matrix elements are very similar. It should be realized that the MSDI matrix elements contain only four parameters (A_1, A_0, B and C), which were kept constant for all matrix elements and that the 15 empirical two-body matrix elements were all considered to be free parameters.

In fig. 6.6 the $T = 1$ matrix elements of the MSDI for particles in the $2p_{3/2}$, $1f_{5/2}$ and $2p_{1/2}$ orbits are compared with those obtained from the realistic Hamada-Johnston interaction. In this case the MSDI matrix elements contain only the two parameters A_1 and $(B + C)$. The similarity between the two sets of matrix elements is striking, especially if one realizes that they are obtained from quite different approaches to the effective two-nucleon interaction.

A COMPARISON OF TWO-BODY MATRIX ELEMENTS IN THE lp SHELL

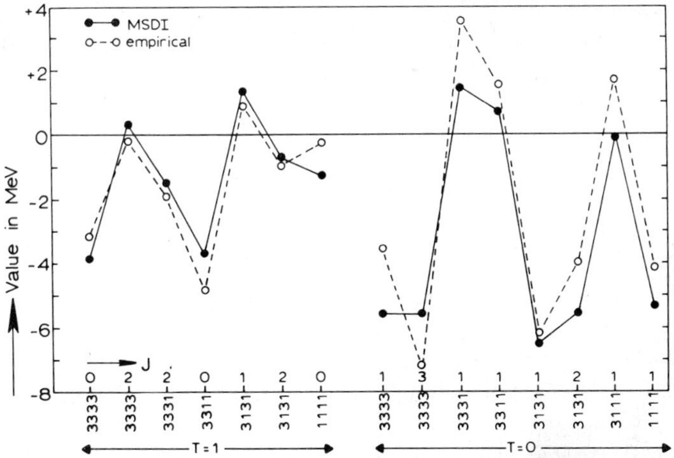

Fig. 6.5. Values of the two-body matrix elements in the 1p shell calculated from the MSDI (with $A_1 = 2.64$ MeV, $A_0 = 1.15$ MeV, $B = 1.40$ MeV and $C = -0.19$ MeV) are compared with those obtained empirically [Cohen and Kurath (1965)]. The *nlj* values are specified by 3 for $1p_{3/2}$ and 1 for $1p_{1/2}$. For example the notation 3331 denotes the matrix element $\langle 33|V|31\rangle$.

Diagonal two-body matrix elements of the effective interaction can be obtained also directly from experimentally determined level energies by selecting nuclei that are assumed to be described by a core of closed shells plus two extra nucleons. Some

A COMPARISON OF TWO-BODY MATRIX ELEMENTS IN THE 1f2p SHELL

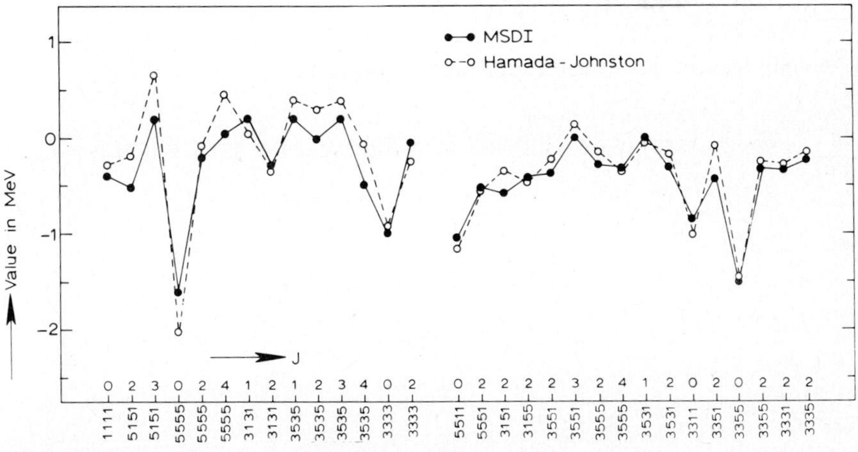

Fig. 6.6. Values of the $T = 1$ two-body matrix elements in the fp shell calculated from the MDSI (with $A_1 = 0.6$ MeV, $B = 0.2$ MeV and $C = 0$) are compared with matrix elements obtained from a realistic Hamada-Johnston potential [Lawson, Macfarlane and Kuo (1966)]. The *nlj* values are specified by 1 for $2p_{1/2}$, 3 for $2p_{3/2}$ and 5 for $1f_{5/2}$.

examples of such nuclei are ${}^{34}_{17}Cl_{17}({}^{32}_{16}S_{16} + p + n)$, ${}^{50}_{21}Sc_{29}({}^{48}_{20}Ca_{28} + p + n)$, ${}^{92}_{41}Nb_{51}({}^{90}_{40}Zr_{50} + p + n)$ and ${}^{210}_{84}Po_{126}({}^{208}_{82}Pb_{126} + 2p)$.

Ignoring configuration mixing, one can write the binding energy of a state described by a core and two particles in orbits ρ_a and ρ_b according to eqs. (3.34) and (3.36) as

$$E_\Gamma^b(\text{core} + \rho_a + \rho_b) = E_C + E^b(\text{core}) + e_{\rho_a} + e_{\rho_b} + \langle \rho_a \rho_b | V | \rho_a \rho_b \rangle_\Gamma \,. \tag{6.65}$$

The binding energies in this expression follow directly from the experimental data. Correcting if necessary for E_C as explained in sect. 18.3, one finds the value of the two-body matrix element from the experimental data, once the single-particle energies e_{ρ_a} and e_{ρ_b} are known. The values for e_ρ can be obtained from the experimental binding and excitation energies of the nucleus that can be described as the core-plus-one nucleon. This approach can be improved and extended [Schiffer (1971); Schiffer and True (1976)] when one takes into account configuration mixing between the two-particle states.

The behaviour of the diagonal two-body matrix elements as a function of the spin J of the two-particle states is very characteristic when their values are plotted in a particular way. Let us consider two particles in orbits j_a and j_b with $\boldsymbol{J} = \boldsymbol{j}_a + \boldsymbol{j}_b$. One can write then

$$\boldsymbol{J}^2 = (\boldsymbol{j}_a + \boldsymbol{j}_b)^2 = \boldsymbol{j}_a^2 + \boldsymbol{j}_b^2 + 2\boldsymbol{j}_a \cdot \boldsymbol{j}_b = j_a^2 + j_b^2 + 2 j_a j_b \cos\theta_{ab} \,, \tag{6.66}$$

where θ_{ab} is the angle between the vectors $\boldsymbol{j}_a$ and $\boldsymbol{j}_b$ (see fig. 6.7). Since the length of a vector $\boldsymbol{j}$ is given by $\sqrt{j(j+1)}$ one obtains from eq. (6.66) in a semiclassical picture

$$\cos\theta_{ab} = \frac{J(J+1) - j_a(j_a+1) - j_b(j_b+1)}{2\sqrt{j_a(j_a+1)\, j_b(j_b+1)}} \,. \tag{6.67}$$

We do not distinguish between $\boldsymbol{l}$ and $\boldsymbol{j}$ in this semiclassical treatment.

A SEMICLASSICAL DESCRIPTION OF ANGULAR-MOMENTUM COUPLING

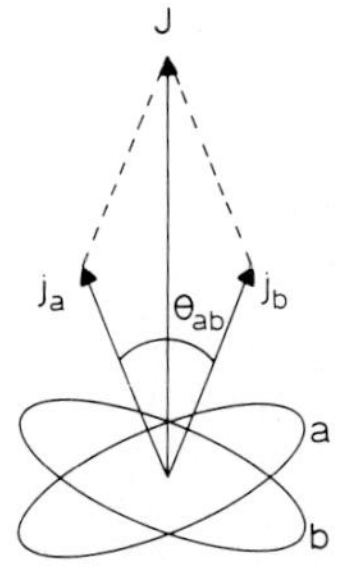

Fig. 6.7. The relation between the angle θ_{ab} and the corresponding single-particle orbits j_a and j_b with $\boldsymbol{j}_a + \boldsymbol{j}_b = \boldsymbol{J}$.

The J-dependence of the matrix elements $\langle j_a j_b | V | j_a j_b \rangle_{JT}$ can thus be plotted as a function of the angle θ_{ab} defined above. The radial overlaps of the particle orbits for light nuclei differ from those for heavy nuclei. The ensuing mass dependence can be removed [Schiffer (1971)] by dividing each matrix element by the absolute value of the average two-body energy. For two particles in the same orbit j this quantity $\bar{E}$ is defined by

$$\bar{E}(j^2) = \left| \frac{\sum_{JT} (2J+1) \langle j^2 | V | j^2 \rangle_{JT}}{\sum_{J} (2J+1)} \right| , \tag{6.68}$$

where J and T are summed over all possible values for the two-particle states $|j^2\rangle_{JT}$. The matrix elements extracted from the experimental data as indicated above and divided by the absolute value of the centroid energy, $\bar{E}(j^2)$, are plotted in fig. 6.8 as a function of θ_{ab} for two particles in the same orbit.

The two-body matrix elements for two active particles in different orbits outside a $T_z \neq 0$ core are obtained from nuclei assumed to be described by a proton in one specific orbit and a neutron in another. It is explained in sect. 3.4 that such proton-neutron configurations correspond to nucleon pairs having mixed isospin and one finds

$$E_J(\mathrm{p,n}) = \tfrac{1}{2} \{ \langle j_a j_b | V | j_a j_b \rangle_{J,T=1} + \langle j_a j_b | V | j_a j_b \rangle_{J,T=0} \} . \tag{6.69}$$

MATRIX ELEMENTS FROM IDENTICAL-ORBIT SPECTRA

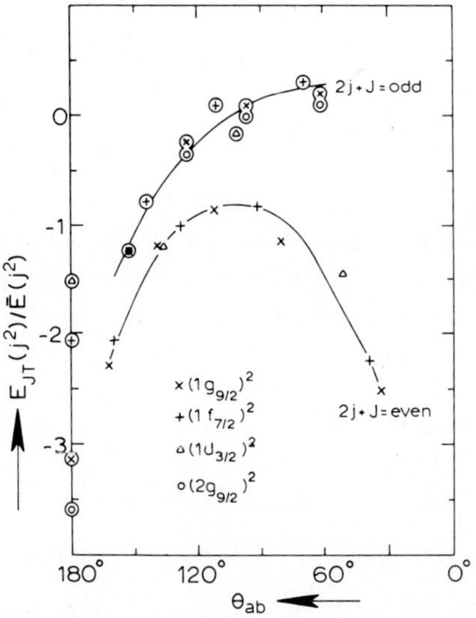

Fig. 6.8. Normalized values of empirically determined matrix elements for two particles in identical orbits [Schiffer (1971)].

AN INTERPRETATION OF THE ^{210}Bi SPECTRUM

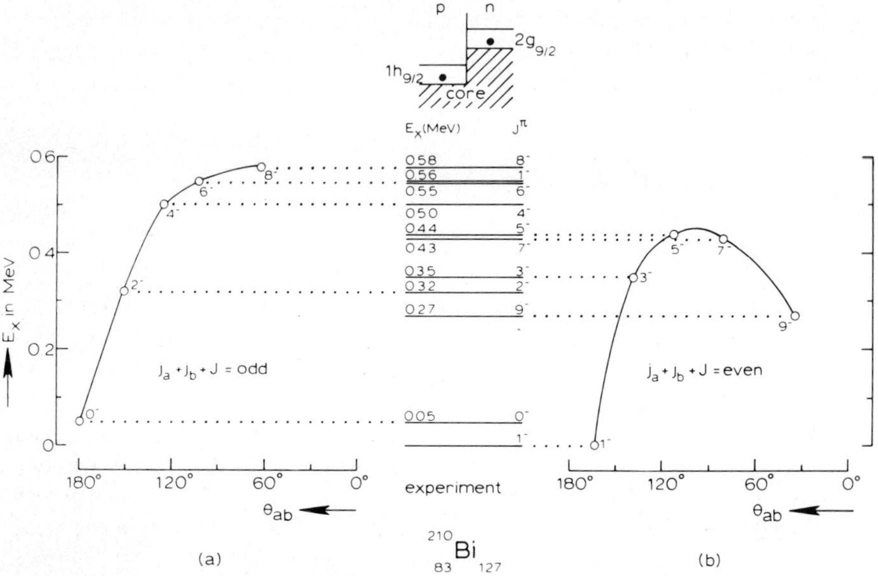

Fig. 6.9. The experimental spectrum of ^{210}Bi [Motz, Jurney, Shera and Sheline (1971)]. The J^{π} values can be reproduced in a configuration space with a proton in the $1h_{9/2}$ orbit and a neutron in the $2g_{9/2}$ orbit, except for the 1^- state at 0.56 MeV. For the latter state a larger number of active orbits must be taken into account.

The nucleus ^{210}Bi offers a nice example to illustrate the behaviour of the two-body matrix elements that are extracted from the observed spectrum. The low-lying states of this nucleus are plotted in fig. 6.9.

Describing the nucleus $^{210}_{83}\mathrm{Bi}_{127}$ as a closed core $^{208}_{82}\mathrm{Pb}_{126}$ with an extra $1h_{9/2}$ proton and an extra $1g_{9/2}$ neutron, one obtains states of spin and parity $J^{\pi} = 0^-, 1^-, 2^-, ..., 9^-$. The parity is negative since orbital angular momenta $l = 5$ and $l = 4$ are combined. It is seen that all states with these J^{π} values have been observed experimentally. Plotting the excitation energies of these states as a function of the corresponding angle θ_{ab} (determined according to eq. (6.67)), one can draw the two smooth curves shown in fig. 6.9. Case (a) shows the behaviour for odd values of $j_a + j_b + J$ and case (b) that for even values of $j_a + j_b + J$. In fig. 6.10 the results obtained [Schiffer (1971)] from many such nuclei are given. Here, for proton and neutron in different orbits, the absolute value of the average two-body energy is given by

$$\overline{E} = \left| \frac{\sum_J (2J+1) E_j}{\sum_J (2J+1)} \right| , \tag{6.70}$$

MATRIX ELEMENTS FROM NONIDENTICAL-ORBIT SPECTRA

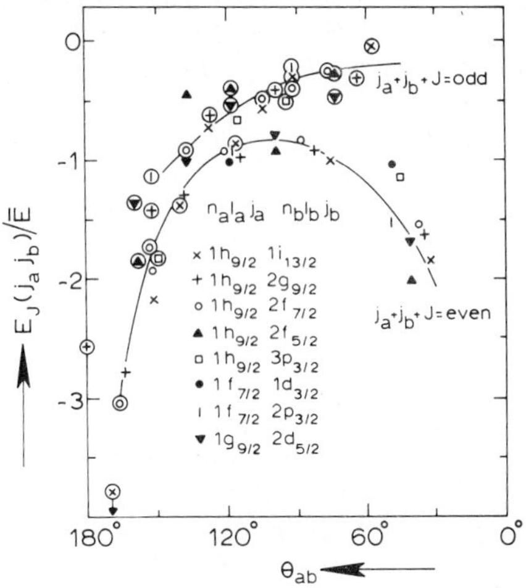

Fig. 6.10. Normalized values of empirically determined two-body matrix elements for a proton in the $n_a l_a j_a$ orbit and a neutron in the $n_b l_b j_b$ orbit with $n_a l_a j_a \neq n_b l_b j_b$ [Schiffer (1971)].

with E_J defined by eq. (6.69). It is seen that in all cases a similar pattern is obtained.

It turns out that a semiclassical discussion allows us to interpret to some extent the shapes of the curves presented in figs. 6.8 and 6.10. This is illustrated in fig. 6.11. For $\theta_{ab} = 180°$, shown in case (a), the orbits of the two interacting particles, moving in opposite directions, have a large overlap. Since the nuclear force is of short range the interaction will be strong (i.e. large and attractive). For $\theta_{ab} = 90°$, case (b), the particle orbits have a small overlap, which results in a weak interaction. This interpretation makes clear why the curves in figs. 6.8 and 6.10 have a positive slope for θ_{ab} varying from 180° to 90°. For smaller angles θ_{ab} the Pauli exclusion principle becomes important. For $\theta_{ab} = 0$ and $j_a = j_b$, case (c), one must distinguish the two possibilities of isospin coupling, i.e. $T = 0$ and $T = 1$. In the former case the particles oc-

SEMICLASSICAL OVERLAPS

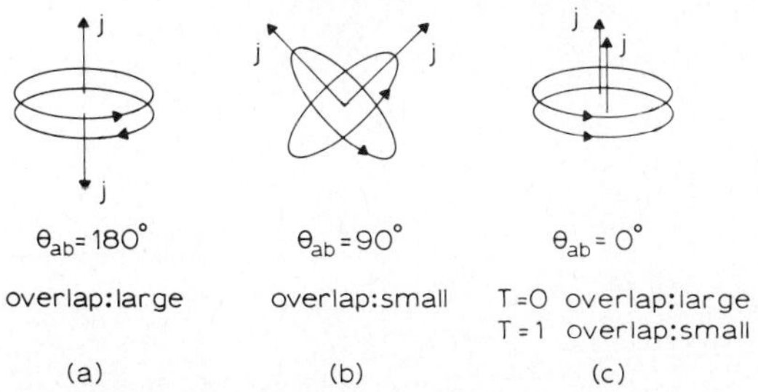

Fig. 6.11. A schematic semiclassical illustration of the various possibilities for the orbital overlaps of two interacting particles given as a function of the angle θ_{ab}.

cupy a spatially symmetric two-particle state which, due to the strong short-range attraction, leads to a large negative matrix element. In the $T = 1$ case the two particles form a spatially antisymmetric state and hence their relative distance increases for decreasing angle $\theta_{ab} \to 0$.

This very qualitative discussion is given here for particles in identical orbits, $j_a = j_b$, where $T = 0$ corresponds to $j_a + j_b + J =$ even and $T = 1$ corresponds to $j_a + j_b + J =$ odd. Investigation of the two-body matrix elements of a delta force shows that for the general case, i.e. j_a and j_b arbitrary, it is decisive whether $j_a + j_b + J$ is even or odd [Molinari, Johnson, Bethe and Alberico (1975)]. In figs. 6.10 and 6.13 the two-body matrix elements are plotted to show this behaviour.

It is interesting to investigate whether the MSDI matrix elements have the empirically obtained properties discussed above. The centroid two-body energy $\bar{E}$ defined in eqs. (6.68) and (6.70) can be given as an explicit expression for the SDI interaction. This is not derived here but the result follows after some manipulations with the Clebsch-Gordan coefficients in the SDI expression given in eq. (6.44) as

$$\bar{E}_{\mathrm{SDI}} = \tfrac{1}{4}(A_1 + 3A_0) . \tag{6.71}$$

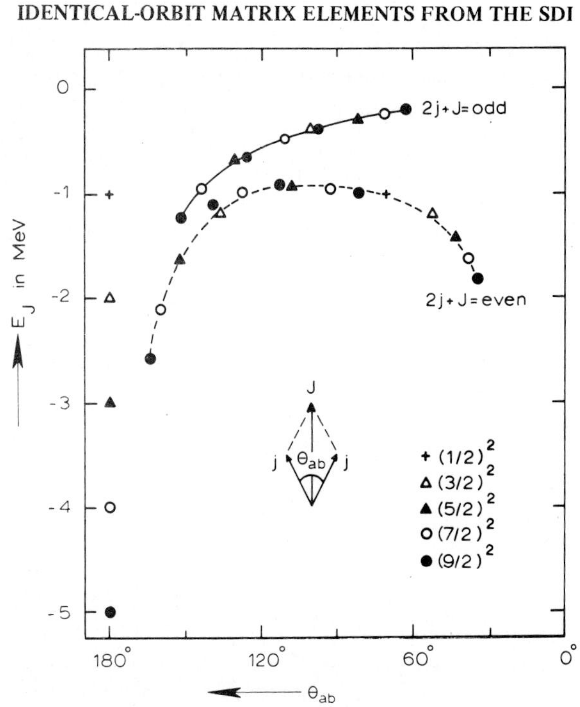

Fig. 6.12. Values of two-body matrix elements calculated from the SDI ($A_0 = A_1 = 1$ MeV) for two particles in the same orbit given as a function of the angle θ_{ab}. The values at $\theta_{ab} = 180°$ satisfy the relation $E_{J=0} = -(j + \frac{1}{2})$ MeV (cf. eq. (6.62)).

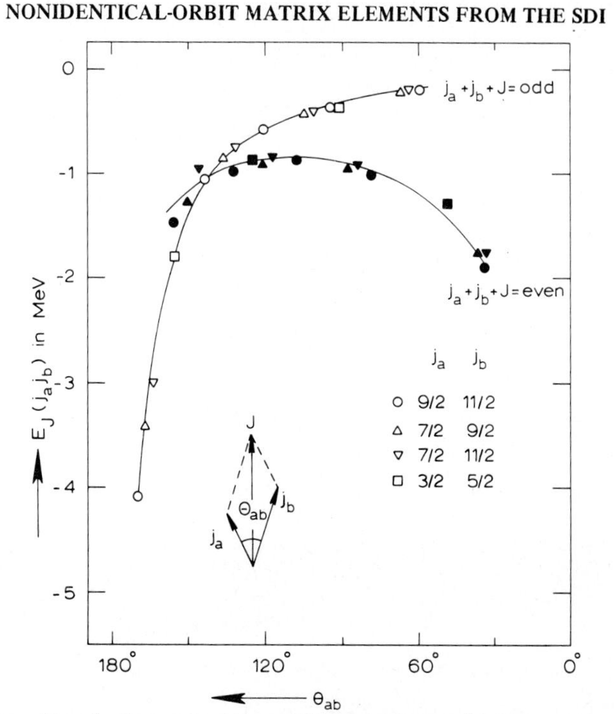

Fig. 6.13. Values of two-body matrix elements calculated from the SDI for a proton and a neutron in different orbits. The values plotted are given by $E_J(j_a j_b) = \frac{1}{2}(E_{JT=0} + E_{JT=1})$ for $A_0 = A_1 = 1$ MeV.

From eq. (6.71) it follows that for $B = C = 0$ (i.e. employing SDI instead of MSDI) the centroid energy $\bar{E}_{\text{SDI}}$ is independent of the orbits involved. Plots of the normalized SDI matrix elements versus the angle θ_{ab} are given in fig. 6.12 for two particles in the same orbit. In fig. 6.13 a plot of SDI matrix elements with $j_a \neq j_b$ is given. It is seen that these matrix elements show the same smooth behaviour with θ_{ab} as the empirical ones given in figs. 6.8 and 6.10, respectively.

The j-dependence of the values of the SDI matrix elements for $\theta_{ab} = 180°$ (i.e. $J = 0$ coupled pairs) follows directly from eq. (6.62). This is in qualitative agreement with the experimental values shown in fig. 6.8. Also the behaviour of SDI matrix elements for small angles θ_{ab} agrees with the pattern given in figs. 6.8 and 6.11.

6.7. Spectra from different interactions

Different sets of two-body matrix elements may produce level schemes and other properties of low-lying states that are very similar. In this section some examples are given of spectra calculated with two-body matrix elements obtained along the three approaches mentioned in sect. 6.1. In fig. 6.14 the spectra are given of ^{19}F calculated

A COMPARISON OF TWO INTERACTIONS FOR ^{19}F

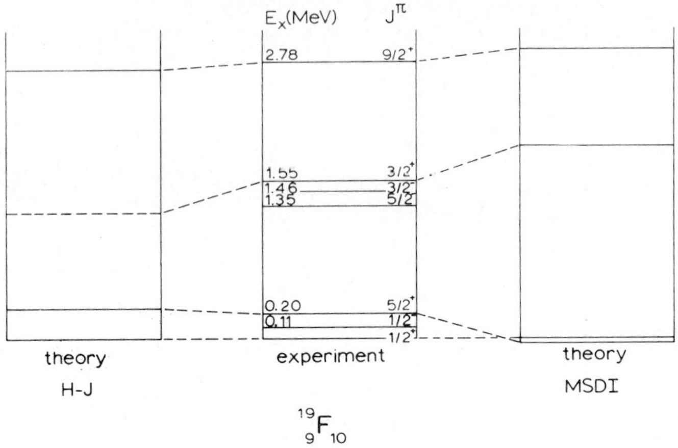

Fig. 6.14. A comparison of the spectra of ^{19}F obtained with two-body matrix elements from th realistic Hamada-Johnston interaction (*H-J*) and the MSDI. Dashed lines connect corresponding states. In both cases the full $1d_{5/2}\,2s_{1/2}\,1d_{3/2}$ configuration space is taken into account [Halber McGrory, Wildenthal and Pandya (1971)]. The experimental spectrum is taken from the compila tion [Ajzenberg-Selove (1972)].

A COMPARISON OF TWO INTERACTIONS FOR ^{27}Al

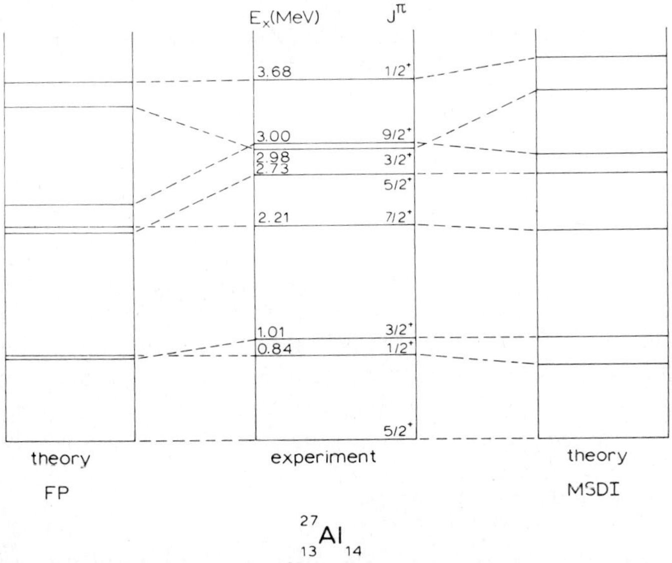

Fig. 6.15. A comparison of the spectra of ^{27}Al obtained with two-body matrix elements from the empirical free-parameter approach (FP) and from the MSDI. Dashed lines connect corresponding states. In both cases the $1d_{5/2}\,2s_{1/2}$ configuration space is taken into account [Van Hienen, Glaudemans and Van Lidt de Jeude (1974)].

in the model space of a ^{16}O core with the three extra nucleons in the orbits $1d_{5/2}$, $2s_{1/2}$ and $1d_{3/2}$. The comparison is made for the MSDI and an effective interaction derived from the realistic Hamada-Johnston potential. It is seen that very similar spectra are obtained with the two interactions. The negative-parity states cannot be reproduced, of course, since single-particle states of positive parity only are taken into account. These spectra are part of a description of low-lying positive-parity states in the mass region $A = 17-20$ with only one set of two-body matrix elements for each of the interactions employed.

In fig. 6.15 the level scheme of ^{27}Al is compared with the theoretical spectra obtained from empirical matrix elements and MSDI matrix elements, respectively. The same model space (a ^{16}O core and active orbits $1d_{5/2}$ and $2s_{1/2}$) has been used for both interactions. A total of 80 low-lying positive-parity states in the mass region $A = 23-28$ are fitted with one single set of 16 two-body matrix elements for FP c.q. 4 strength parameters for MSDI. One may thus conclude that calculated spectra are not always very sensitive to the interaction employed.

6.8. Effects of the configuration space

In this section some comparisons are made between spectra calculated for a given nucleus in different configuration spaces. Of the three approaches that were made to

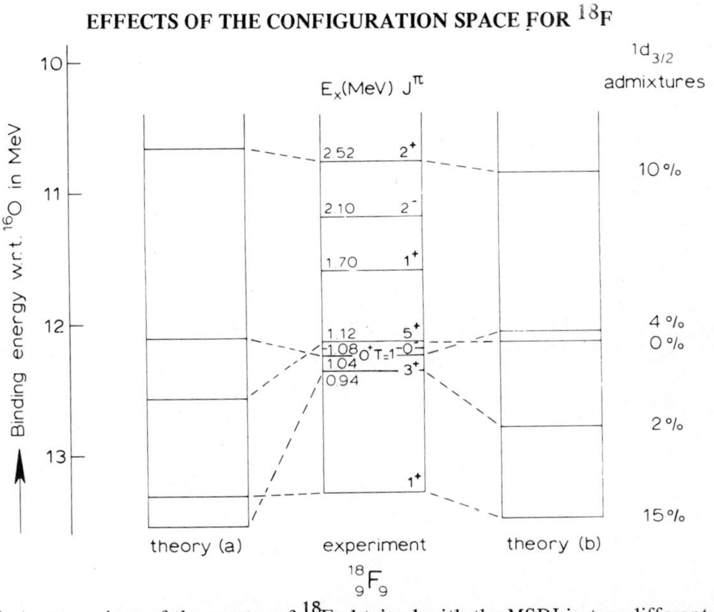

Fig. 6.16. A comparison of the spectra of ^{18}F obtained with the MSDI in two different configuration spaces. (a) Two particles in the active orbits $1d_{5/2}$ and $2s_{1/2}$. (b) Two particles in the active orbits $1d_{5/2}$, $2s_{1/2}$ and $1d_{3/2}$. In the latter space the $1d_{3/2}$ admixtures are given on the right-hand side. Dashed lines connect corresponding states. The experimental spectrum is taken from the compilation [Ajzenberg-Selove (1972)].

obtain effective two-body matrix elements (cf. sect. 6.1) the one with empirical matrix elements is not meaningful for such a comparison. This is because the number of two-body matrix elements (i.e. parameters) increases strongly with the number of active orbits and thus a fair comparison is made impossible. When on the other hand the MSDI is used, the number of parameters is independent of the model-space.

In fig. 6.16 the results for ^{18}F are shown that derive from an MSDI calculation on all nuclei in the mass region $A = 17-20$. The results for a model space with a $^{16}_{8}O_8$ core plus two active particles in the orbits $1d_{5/2}$ and $2s_{1/2}$ are compared with those for the same core and the orbits $1d_{5/2}$, $2s_{1/2}$ and $1d_{3/2}$. It is seen that the three-orbit approach works much better for the position of the lowest $J^\pi = 3^+$ state, although the admixtures of $1d_{3/2}$ components are small.

In the example discussed above both the two-orbit and the three-orbit approaches reproduce the correct number of experimentally known positive-parity states at low excitation energy. Sometimes, however, more low-lying states are known experimentally than can be obtained from a theoretical calculation. This is illustrated in fig. 6.17 with the results for ^{31}Si. In the two-orbit calculation a ^{28}Si core of a closed

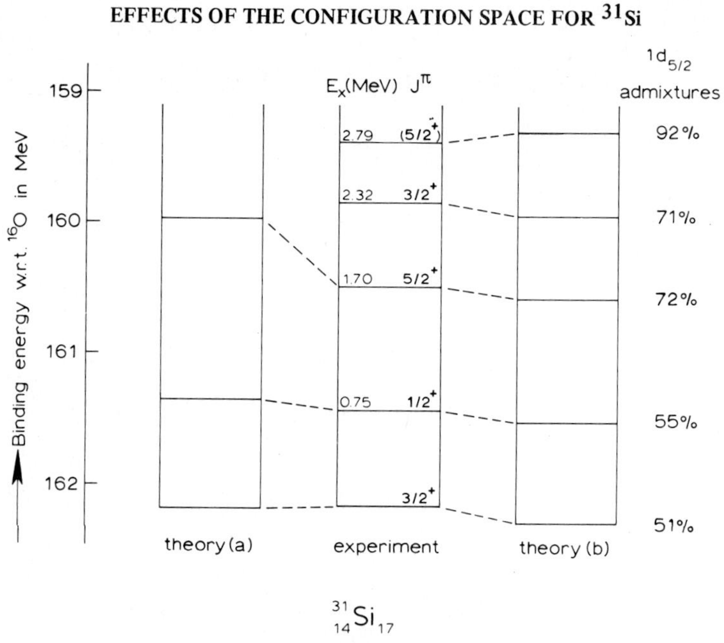

Fig. 6.17. A comparison of the spectra of ^{31}Si obtained with the MSDI in two different configuration spaces. (a) A ^{28}Si core and three particles in the active orbits $2s_{1/2}$ and $1d_{3/2}$. (b) Up to two holes in the $1d_{5/2}$ orbit and particles in the $2s_{1/2}$ and $1d_{3/2}$ orbits [Wildenthal, McGrory, Halbert and Graber (1971)]. Dashed lines connect corresponding states. The experimental spectrum is taken from the compilation [Endt and Van der Leun (1973)].

$1d_{5/2}$ shell is assumed with three neutrons in the $2s_{1/2}$ and $1d_{3/2}$ orbits. This yields the spectrum given in fig. 6.17a. When excitations of at most two particles from the $1d_{5/2}$ shell are also taken into account, one obtains the level scheme of fig. 6.17b. It is clear that, although the binding energy of the ground state and excitation energy of the first excited state are well reproduced in both model spaces, it is only the three-orbit model that can reproduce the second $J^\pi = \frac{3}{2}^+$ and $\frac{5}{2}^+$ states.

For a more detailed investigation of the model space that should be used for an adequate description of the states involved, one must include additional experimental information. This is provided e.g. by spectroscopic factors, electromagnetic transition rates, multipole moments and beta decay. Their evaluation is discussed in detail in chapters 8 through 12.

CHAPTER 7

DETERMINATION OF EMPIRICAL EFFECTIVE INTERACTIONS

In the previous chapters it has been shown that energy levels of nuclei can be calculated, once a set of active single-particle orbits has been selected and restrictions, if any, have been made on the distributions of the active nucleons over these orbits. In the treatment thus far it has been assumed that the values of single-particle energies and two-body matrix elements, necessary for the numerical construction of the Hamiltonian, are already known from some source. In fact reasonable values of single-particle energies and two-body matrix elements are often not available beforehand. This problem can be solved, however, in an approach in which the single-particle energies and two-body matrix elements are regarded as parameters. The values of these parameters can then be obtained from a fit of calculated energies (expressed in terms of these parameters) to experimental data on energy levels. It should be stressed that this approach is only useful, if a limited number of parameters suffices to correlate a large body of experimental data. The aim of this chapter is to discuss a technique of adjusting these parameters that leads to an optimum fit to the data.

The general procedure, each step of which will be outlined below, is illustrated schematically in fig. 7.1. First the eigenvalues of the Hamiltonian are expressed linearly in terms of the parameters. This can be done, as is discussed in sect. 7.1, once the Hamiltonian matrix H is diagonalized for an initial set of (guessed) parameters. The eigenvalues obtained from the initial set of parameters will in general not yield the optimum agreement with the experimental data. It is explained in sect. 7.2 that one can obtain an improved set of parameters in a second step from a least-squares fit to the data one wants to reproduce. With the new set of parameters, one con-

THE LEAST-SQUARES FITTING PROCEDURE

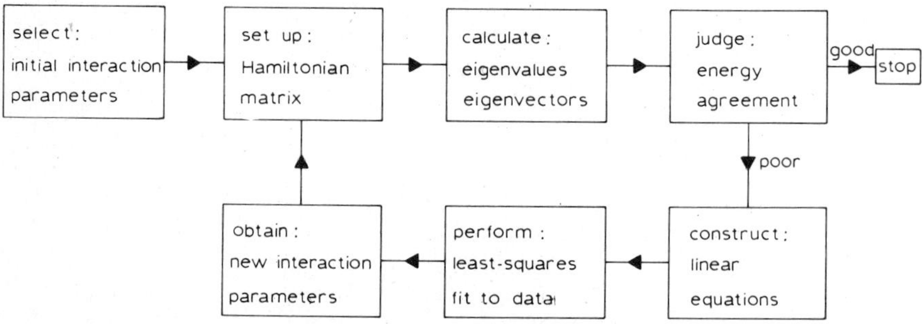

Fig. 7.1. Schematic illustration of the various steps necessary to obtain the effective-interaction parameters from a fit to experimental energies.

structs and diagonalizes the Hamiltonian again. The parameters can be further improved by repeating the procedure discussed above. This iteration process, as outlined in sect. 7.3, is repeated until sufficient convergence is obtained. Some remarks about the selection of experimental data are made in sect. 7.4. Phase ambiguities that may occur in the fitted parameters are discussed in sect. 7.5.

7.1. Construction of linear equations

The determination of the single-particle energies and two-body matrix elements from a comparison between calculated and experimentally determined energy levels is not a linear problem. The energy levels are obtained as the eigenvalues of the Hamiltonian matrices. Only in the trivial case of a 1 × 1 matrix does one obtain the eigenvalue immediately expressed as a linear combination of the parameters. For a 2 × 2 matrix the eigenvalues follow from the more complicated expression (cf. eq. (3.72))

$$E_{\mathrm{a,b}} = \tfrac{1}{2}\left[H_{11} + H_{22} \pm \sqrt{(H_{11} - H_{22})^2 + 4H_{12}^2}\right], \tag{7.1}$$

where H_{11} and H_{22} are the diagonal elements and H_{12} is the off-diagonal matrix element of the Hamiltonian. Algebraic procedures for the diagonalization of matrices are discussed in e.g. [Wilkinson (1965)]. Each of the elements H_{kl} $(k, l = 1, ..., n)$ of the n-dimensional (symmetric) matrix, however, depends *linearly* on the single- and two-particle matrix elements. We shall use this feature for an iteration procedure, which turns out to converge rapidly to a final solution.

It has been explained before that the energies of a nuclear system are determined by solving the eigenvalue problem for the Hamiltonian

$$H\Psi = E\Psi . \tag{7.2}$$

Each eigenvector Ψ_p $(p = 1, ..., n)$, belonging to the eigenvalue E_p, can be expanded in terms of the basis states Φ_k as

$$\Psi_p = a_{1p}\Phi_1 + a_{2p}\Phi_2 + ... + a_{np}\Phi_n . \tag{7.3}$$

The Schrödinger equation (7.2) can now be rewritten in matrix form as

$$\begin{pmatrix} H_{11} & \cdots & H_{1n} \\ \vdots & & \vdots \\ H_{n1} & \cdots & H_{nn} \end{pmatrix} \begin{pmatrix} a_{1p} \\ \vdots \\ a_{np} \end{pmatrix} = E_p \begin{pmatrix} a_{1p} \\ \vdots \\ a_{np} \end{pmatrix} \qquad \text{for } p = 1, 2, ..., n . \tag{7.4}$$

The matrix elements $H_{kl} = H_{lk}$ have been discussed in detail in chapters 4 and 5. It was seen in chapter 3 that the n eigenvalue equations (7.4) can be represented by one matrix equation as

$$A^{-1}HA = A^THA = \begin{pmatrix} a_{11} & \cdots & a_{n1} \\ \vdots & & \vdots \\ a_{1p} & & a_{np} \\ \vdots & & \vdots \\ a_{1n} & \cdots & a_{nn} \end{pmatrix} \begin{pmatrix} H_{11} & \cdots & H_{1n} \\ & & \\ \vdots & & \vdots \\ & & \\ H_{n1} & \cdots & H_{nn} \end{pmatrix} \begin{pmatrix} a_{11} & .. & a_{1p} & .. & a_{1n} \\ & & & & \\ \vdots & & & & \vdots \\ & & & & \\ a_{n1} & .. & a_{np} & .. & a_{nn} \end{pmatrix} = \begin{pmatrix} E_1 & & & & 0 \\ & \ddots & & & \\ & & E_p & & \\ & & & \ddots & \\ 0 & & & & E_n \end{pmatrix} . \tag{7.5}$$

Here the orthogonal matrix A is obtained by juxtaposition of the n column vectors a_{kp} $(k = 1, 2, ..., n)$. Since the matrix A is orthogonal, the inverse and transposed are equal, $A^{-1} = A^{\mathrm{T}}$. Eq. (7.5) reads with the summations in explicit form,

$$\langle A^{-1}HA\rangle_{p'p} = \sum_{j=1}^{n}\sum_{i=1}^{n} a_{jp'}H_{ji}a_{ip} = E_p\delta_{p'p} \qquad \text{for } p', p = 1, ..., n . \tag{7.6}$$

This equation is equivalent to the relation

$$\langle\Psi_{p'}|H|\Psi_p\rangle = E_p\delta_{p'p} \qquad \text{for } p', p = 1, ..., n . \tag{7.7}$$

Since each matrix element H_{ji} of the Hamiltonian is a linear combination of the single-particle energies and/or two-body matrix elements (both regarded as parameters x_r) we can write

$$H_{ji} = H_{ij} = \sum_{r=1}^{N_x} c_r^{(ij)}x_r , \tag{7.8}$$

where N_x gives the total number of parameters x_r and the geometrical coefficients $c_r^{(ij)}$ derive from the Racah algebra as discussed in chapters 4 and 5. Substitution of eq. (7.8) into eq. (7.6) yields

$$\sum_{j=1}^{n} a_{jp} \sum_{i=1}^{n} (\sum_{r=1}^{N_x} c_r^{(ij)}x_r)a_{ip} = E_p . \tag{7.9}$$

A rearrangement of the coefficients then leads to a set of simultaneous linear equations in the parameters x_r given by

$$\sum_{r=1}^{N_x} b_r^{(p)}x_r = E_p \qquad \text{for } p = 1, ..., n , \tag{7.10}$$

with

$$b_r^{(p)} = \sum_{j=1}^{n} a_{jp} \sum_{i=1}^{n} a_{ip}c_r^{(ij)} . \tag{7.11}$$

Let the Hamiltonian be evaluated for some initial "best-guess" set of parameters and subsequently be diagonalized. This diagonalization leads to a matrix a_{ij}. Then eq. (7.11) will provide us with an initial set of coefficients $b_r^{(p)}$ to be used in eq. (7.10). Substitution of the "best-guess" set of parameters into eq. (7.10) leads to the same eigenvalues E_p that were obtained already from the diagonalization of the Hamiltonian. One cannot expect that these eigenvalues E_p reproduce the experimental data exactly. Let us now replace the right-hand side of eq. (7.10) by the corresponding experimental energies $E_{\exp}^{(p)}$ and consider the x_r as unknown parameters.

This leads to a set of linear equations

$$\sum_{r=1}^{N_x} b_r^{(p)} x_r = E_{\text{exp}}^{(p)} \qquad \text{with } p = 1, ..., n\,, \tag{7.12}$$

where the coefficients $b_r^{(p)}$ are defined in eq. (7.11). It should be noted that $E_{\text{exp}}^{(p)}$ represents the binding energy of the state p with respect to the core with the Coulomb energy subtracted.

Up to here the discussion has been restricted to those eigenstates of one nucleus that are characterized by a given spin J and isospin T. It is assumed moreover that each eigenvalue can be identified with an experimental energy. In general, however, only some of the lower eigenvalues of a given matrix can be compared with experimentally determined energies. This implies that out of the n eqs. (7.12) only a limited number can be used for the determination of the parameters x_r.

It is not necessary to consider only one nucleus at a time for the fitting procedure. Usually one takes into account many levels of different spin J and isospin T in several neighbouring nuclei simultaneously. The total number of parameters N_x then remains the same of course, but the number of equations to be satisfied increases appreciably. Therefore, from now on we replace the index p (labelling states of one matrix) by the index q, which labels the complete set of equations that result from all matrices taken together

$$\sum_{r=1}^{N_x} b_r^{(q)} x_r = E_{\text{exp}}^{(q)} \qquad \text{with } q = 1, ..., N_q\,. \tag{7.13}$$

In order to obtain a meaningful solution of this set of N_q equations in N_x parameters with a least-squares fitting procedure, the condition $N_q > N_x$ must be satisfied.

So far we have restricted ourselves to the determination of interaction parameters with eq. (7.13), where the values $E_{\text{exp}}^{(q)}$ denote the Coulomb-corrected binding energies of the states labelled q. Since the Coulomb contribution is usually assumed to be equal for ground-state and excited-state binding energies of one nucleus, it has no effect on differences of binding energies. Thus knowledge of the Coulomb contribution is in general not necessary when only experimental excitation energies instead of binding energies are used in the fit. In this approach one determines the parameters from the set of equations

$$\sum_{r=1}^{N_x} (b_r^{(q)} - b_r^{(q_0)})\, x_r = E_{\text{exp}}^{(q)} - E_{\text{exp}}^{(q_0)}\,, \tag{7.14}$$

where the coefficients $b_r^{(q)}$ refer to excited states and the coefficients $b_r^{(q_0)}$ to the corresponding ground states. The right-hand side of eq. (7.14) denotes the experimental excitation energy of level q.

It may be remarked here that for a reproduction of excitation energies only, i.e. when binding energies themselves are not considered, a smaller number of parameters will suffice than for a reproduction of binding energies. For example, a change of all single-particle energies e_ρ by the same amount Δ, such that $e'_\rho = e_\rho + \Delta$, results in different binding energies but it leaves the excitation energies unaffected. Thus in order to avoid the problem of undetermined single-particle energies e_ρ one must either fit only their differences $e_\rho - e_\lambda$ or one must keep one of them fixed at an arbitrary value.

7.2. The least-squares fitting procedure

Suppose we have the set of linear equations (cf. eq. (7.13))

$$\begin{array}{ccccc} b_1^{(1)}x_1 & + b_2^{(1)}x_2 & + \ldots + & b_{N_x}^{(1)}x_{N_x} & = E_{\text{exp}}^{(1)} \\ \vdots & \vdots & & \vdots & \vdots \\ b_1^{(N_q)}x_1 & + b_2^{(N_q)}x_2 & + \ldots + & b_{N_x}^{(N_q)}x_{N_x} & = E_{\text{exp}}^{(N_q)} \end{array} \tag{7.15}$$

We wish to determine the parameters x_r such that the left-hand side approximates the experimental energies as closely as possible. In the least-squares method one minimizes the function

$$Q^2 = \sum_{q=1}^{N_q} \left(\sum_{i=1}^{N_x} b_i^{(q)}x_i - E_{\text{exp}}^{(q)}\right)^2 \tag{7.16}$$

by varying the parameters x_i. Here it is assumed that the experimental energies are uncorrelated. All weighting factors are assumed to be the same and are chosen equal to unity, see e.g. [Wapstra, Nijgh and Van Lieshout (1959)]. The minimum value of Q^2 is reached when the partial derivatives satisfy the relations

$$\frac{\partial Q^2}{\partial x_r} = 0 \qquad \text{for} \qquad r = 1, \ldots, N_x\,. \tag{7.17}$$

Insertion of eq. (7.16) into eq. (7.17) leads to

$$\frac{\partial Q^2}{\partial x_r} = \sum_{q=1}^{N_q} \left(\sum_{i=1}^{N_x} b_i^{(q)}x_i - E_{\text{exp}}^{(q)}\right) b_r^{(q)} = 0 \qquad \text{for } r = 1, \ldots, N_x\,, \tag{7.18}$$

or

$$\sum_{i=1}^{N_x} \sum_{q=1}^{N_q} b_r^{(q)} b_i^{(q)} x_i = \sum_{q=1}^{N_q} b_r^{(q)} E_{\text{exp}}^{(q)} \qquad \text{with } r = 1, \ldots, N_x\,. \tag{7.19}$$

The set of N_x linear equations in the N_x parameters given above can be vizualized better if one employs a matrix notation. Introducing a matrix B with elements $B_{qi} = b_i^{(q)}$ ($i = 1, \ldots, N_x$ and $q = 1, \ldots, N_q$), a column vector X with components x_i

and a column vector $E_{\rm exp}$ with components $E^{(q)}_{\rm exp}$, one can rewrite eq. (7.19) as

$$\begin{pmatrix} b_1^{(1)} \dots b_1^{(N_q)} \\ \vdots \quad\quad \vdots \\ b_{N_x}^{(1)} \dots b_{N_x}^{(N_q)} \end{pmatrix} \begin{pmatrix} b_1^{(1)} & \dots & b_{N_x}^{(1)} \\ \vdots & & \vdots \\ b_1^{(N_q)} & \dots & b_{N_x}^{(N_q)} \end{pmatrix} \begin{pmatrix} x_1 \\ \vdots \\ x_{N_x} \end{pmatrix} = \begin{pmatrix} b_1^{(1)} \dots b_1^{(N_q)} \\ \vdots \quad\quad \vdots \\ b_{N_x}^{(1)} \dots b_{N_x}^{(N_q)} \end{pmatrix} \begin{pmatrix} E_{\rm exp}^{(1)} \\ \vdots \\ E_{\rm exp}^{(N_q)} \end{pmatrix} \tag{7.20}$$

or

$$B^{\rm T}BX = B^{\rm T}E_{\rm exp}. \tag{7.21}$$

Thus we have obtained N_x linear, non-homogeneous equations for the N_x parameters $x_1, x_2, \dots, x_{N_x}$ that can be solved with standard procedures leading to a new set of parameters $x_r^{(1)}$.

It is noted that the matrix B is not a square matrix and has no inverse, except in the case $N_x = N_q$. Thus if in an exceptional case the number of parameters N_x equals the number of data points N_q, then eq. (7.21) shows that the best fit is obtained for the exact solution of eq. (7.15), i.e. $X = B^{-1}E_{\rm exp}$, which is no surprise, of course.

7.3. The iteration procedure

With the supposedly improved set of parameters $x_r^{(1)}$ one recalculates the matrix elements of the Hamiltonian. After diagonalization a new set of eigenvectors a_{kq} is obtained. From these one constructs a new set of equations (7.13) with coefficients $b_r^{(q)}$. After a least-squares fitting this leads to a second set of parameters $x_r^{(2)}$. This procedure must be repeated until convergence is obtained, i.e. until $x_r^{(n)} \approx x_r^{(n-1)}$. It is found from experience that the number of iterations needed is of the order of the number of parameters, but only if the number of parameters N_x is at least three times smaller than the number of equations N_q. For $N_q >> N_x$ a faster convergence can be expected.

An example of an iteration procedure is the treatment of the $A = 29$–40 nuclei in a model space where a closed $1d_{5/2}$ core of $^{28}_{14}Si_{14}$ is assumed with active nucleons in the $2s_{1/2}$ and $1d_{3/2}$ orbit. The 15 two-body matrix elements and two single-particle energies are all considered as parameters. The fit has been made to 55 energy levels and thus the number of parameters is approximately three times smaller than the number of experimental data. One finds that the experimental energies are reproduced with an average deviation of 0.11 MeV. The point we want to show here is that even if one takes all initial parameter values equal to +1 MeV, a rapid convergence occurs. After approximately ten iterations no further improvement is obtained, as is illustrated in fig. 7.2. The RMS deviation is defined as

$$\Delta_{\rm RMS} = \sqrt{\sum_{i=1}^{N_q} (E^{(i)}_{\rm calc} - E^{(i)}_{\rm exp})^2/(N_q - N_x)}\,, \tag{7.22}$$

where $E^{(i)}_{\rm calc}$ and $E^{(i)}_{\rm exp}$ denote the calculated and experimentally determined energies

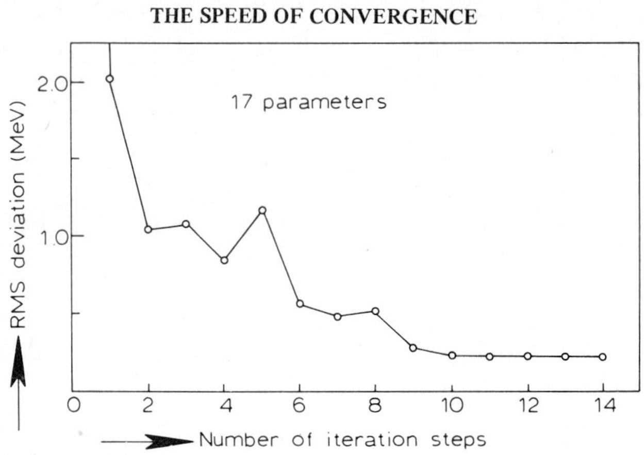

Fig. 7.2. The RMS deviation as a function of the number of iteration steps for a fit of 15 two-body matrix elements and two single-particle energies. The fit to 55 experimental level energies is performed for nuclei in the mass region $A = 29–40$ in a $2s_{1/2}1d_{3/2}$ configuration space. The initial-guess value of each parameter was taken to be 1.0 MeV.

of the *i*th level, respectively; N_q is the number of levels fitted and N_x is the number of parameters. The final parameter values are given in table 7.1. These values differ from those determined earlier [Glaudemans, Wiechers and Brussaard (1964)] due to a more recent and somewhat different set of experimental data.

Table 7.1
The values of the two-body matrix elements and single-particle energies resulting from a fit to 55 experimental energies in $A = 29–40$ nuclei in a $2s_{1/2}1d_{3/2}$ model space.

Matrix element [a]	Value (MeV)	Matrix element [a]	Value [b] (MeV)
$\langle s^2 \vert V \vert s^2 \rangle_{01}$	−1.29	$\langle d^2 \vert V \vert d^2 \rangle_{30}$	−2.50
$\langle s^2 \vert V \vert s^2 \rangle_{10}$	−2.31	$\langle s^2 \vert V \vert sd \rangle_{10}$	0.50
$\langle sd \vert V \vert sd \rangle_{10}$	−3.64	$\langle s^2 \vert V \vert d^2 \rangle_{01}$	−1.48
$\langle sd \vert V \vert sd \rangle_{11}$	1.47	$\langle s^2 \vert V \vert d^2 \rangle_{10}$	−0.14
$\langle sd \vert V \vert sd \rangle_{20}$	−1.41	$\langle sd \vert V \vert d^2 \rangle_{10}$	0.60
$\langle sd \vert V \vert sd \rangle_{21}$	−0.80	$\langle sd \vert V \vert d^2 \rangle_{21}$	−0.56
$\langle d^2 \vert V \vert d^2 \rangle_{01}$	−2.06	e_s	−8.52
$\langle d^2 \vert V \vert d^2 \rangle_{10}$	−1.48	e_d	−7.20
$\langle d^2 \vert V \vert d^2 \rangle_{21}$	0.18		

a) The symbols s and d denote $2s_{1/2}$ and $1d_{3/2}$, respectively. The subscripts give the J and T values of the two-particle states.

b) The signs of the off-diagonal matrix elements $\langle sd | V | d^2 \rangle_{JT}$ and $\langle s^2 | V | sd \rangle_{10}$ are consistent with the SDI for radial wave functions that are positive near the origin and with the coupling order $j = l + s$ (see sect. 7.5).

Sometimes rapid convergence does not occur. This may be due to the fact that some of the parameters are not well determined by the experimental data. These poorly determined parameters can usually be traced as those that vary wildly during the iteration process. In such cases it is recommended not to search on these parameters, but to keep their values fixed at a reasonable value. Such a value may be obtained e.g. from a realistic interaction or from a schematic effective interaction as has been discussed in chapter 6.

A somewhat different approach is possible when one restricts the variations in the parameters, instead of keeping some parameter values completely fixed. This may occur, for example, when a best-guess effective interaction reproduces the gross structure, but not the details of the spectra one wishes to describe. To this end a set of extra equations for $x_r^{(n)}$ given by

$$x_r^{(n)} = x_r^{(n-1)} \qquad \text{for } r = 1, ..., N_x , \tag{7.23}$$

is added to those given in eq. (7.15). Here the $x_r^{(0)}$ represent the matrix elements of the best-guess effective interaction. The additional set of equations (7.23) is then solved simultaneously with the set (7.15). This procedure can be used even when the number of two-body matrix elements and single-particle energies x_r is about equal to that of the experimental energies available for the fit. When after n iterations one observes that e.g. the parameter $x_r^{(n)}$ is still close to the value $x_r^{(0)}$, one may draw the conclusion that either the selected value for $x_r^{(0)}$ is a very good guess or that the parameter x_r is not well determined by the experimental data.

An illustration of this approach is shown in fig. 7.3 for nuclei in the mass region $A = 23–28$ and a $1d_{5/2}2s_{1/2}1d_{3/2}$ model space. Here the values $x_r^{(0)}$ were taken from

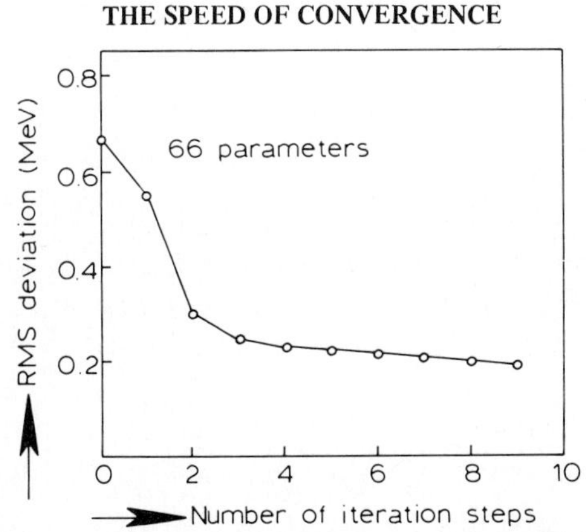

Fig. 7.3. The RMS deviation as a function of the number of iteration steps for an adjustment of 63 two-body matrix elements and three single-particle energies. The fit to 67 experimental level energies is performed for nuclei in the mass region $A = 24–28$ in a $1d_{5/2}2s_{1/2}1d_{3/2}$ configuration space. The equations (7.23) were added with $x_r^{(0)}$ given by MSDI matrix elements [Meurders, Glaudemans, Van Hienen and Timmer (1976)].

the MSDI, i.e. the effective interaction discussed in chapter 6. The strength parameters of the MSDI matrix elements were obtained from a fit to 67 experimental energies. In a second step all 63 two-body matrix elements and the three single-particle energies needed in the $1d_{5/2}2s_{1/2}1d_{3/2}$ configuration space are considered as free parameters $x_r^{(n)}$. The same 67 experimental energies, which were taken into account to obtain the set $x_r^{(0)}$ are used for the adjusted set of MSDI matrix elements (ASDI).

It follows from fig. 7.3 that the average absolute deviation between theoretical and experimental energies decreases very rapidly in the first few iteration steps. It is no surprise that this procedure leads to good energies, of course. It turns out, however, that the adjustment of an effective interaction with the sets of equations (7.15) and (7.23) may lead to a considerable improvement in the reproduction of many other properties, e.g., excitation energies of levels that were not taken along in the fit, spectroscopic factors, electromagnetic transition rates, etc. This approach also solves the problems arising from the phase ambiguities to be discussed in sect. 7.5.

It has been remarked before that some parameters x_r may not be well determined by the experimental data. Moreover, the parameters may be correlated. There is a method, which we call the diagonal correlation matrix (DCM) method, that allows one to derive which particular combinations of the parameters are most important for the spectra.

Let the square symmetric matrix $F \equiv B^{\mathrm{T}}B$ (see eq. (7.21)) possess the eigenvectors $v^{(k)}$ ($k = 1, 2, ..., N_x$) with eigenvalues f_k. Thus we can write eq. (7.19) as

$$\sum_{i=1}^{N_x} F_{ri}x_i = \sum_{q=1}^{N_q} B^{\mathrm{T}}_{rq}E^{(q)}_{\mathrm{exp}} \qquad \text{for } r = 1, ..., N_x\,, \tag{7.24}$$

with

$$F_{ri} = \sum_{q=1}^{N_q} B^{\mathrm{T}}_{rq}B_{qi}\,, \tag{7.25}$$

where the quantities x_i denote the adjustable parameters (two-body matrix elements and single-particle energies) and $E^{(k)}_{\mathrm{exp}}$ the experimental data that are to be reproduced. The eigenvectors $v^{(k)}$ diagonalizing the matrix F satisfy the relations

$$\sum_{ri} v_r^{(k)}F_{ri}v_i^{(l)} = f_k\delta_{kl}\,, \tag{7.26}$$

$$\sum_{l} v_i^{(l)}v_j^{(l)} = \delta_{ij}\,. \tag{7.27}$$

The left-hand side of eq. (7.24) can be rewritten with eq. (7.27) as

$$\sum_i F_{ri}x_i = \sum_i F_{ri}\sum_j \delta_{ij}x_j = \sum_i F_{ri}\sum_j\sum_l v_i^{(l)}v_j^{(l)}x_j\,. \tag{7.28}$$

Multiplying both sides of eq. (7.24) by $\Sigma_r\, v_r^{(k)}$ one thus obtains with eq. (7.26)

$$\sum_{rijl} v_r^{(k)} F_{ri} v_i^{(l)} v_j^{(l)} x_j = f_k \sum_j v_j^{(k)} x_j = \sum_r v_r^{(k)} \sum_q B_{rq}^{\mathrm{T}} E_{\mathrm{exp}}^{(q)} \tag{7.29}$$

or

$$f_k y_k = \sum_r v_r^{(k)} \sum_q B_{rq}^{\mathrm{T}} E_{\mathrm{exp}}^{(q)} \tag{7.30}$$

with

$$y_k = \sum_j v_j^{(k)} x_j \,. \tag{7.31}$$

Here y_k represents a particular combination of the adjustable parameters. The sets $\{x_r\}$ and $\{y_k\}$ are equivalent for the determination of the Hamiltonian. It can be shown that the parameter y_{k_1} that corresponds to the largest eigenvalue f_{k_1} is most accurately determined of all parameters by the original set of linear equations (7.24). Any other linear combination of the adjustable parameters is less well determined.

This is borne out by the correlation matrix of the probability distribution of the parameters. Similarly the one but largest eigenvalue f_{k_2} is associated with the next best determined parameter y_{k_2}, and so on.

The correlation matrix of the probability distribution of the parameters y_k is diagonal, i.e. the y_k values are not correlated. If one applies the same changes successively to all parameters y_k by adding a fixed amount, then the change of parameter y_{k_1} will cause the strongest deterioration of the calculated spectra. Thus one can define a procedure to select a number of adjustable parameters each representing a specific combination of the original one- and two-body matrix elements x_r that are most important for the description of particular spectra. An application of the DCM method to sd-shell nuclei is given by [Chung (1976)].

7.4. Selection of experimental data

One of the crucial points in obtaining the matrix elements of an effective interaction from experimentally determined level schemes is the selection of the data that should be taken into account. It is important that the set of experimental data is as large as possible. This way one reduces the probability (i) that some parameter values are not well determined, or (ii) that levels which cannot be described in the given model space (as one sometimes finds out after the fit has been performed) affect the parameter values too much. The latter possibility refers to the fact that all lower-lying states are not always reproduced correctly in a truncated model space. In other words, core excitation or the excitation of nucleons into higher-lying orbits outside the model space cannot be ignored if one wants to obtain a reasonable description of some states. Thus one should expect to treat successfully only those states whose important components lie in the configuration space which is taken into account. It is found empirically that in a not too small model space one generally can reproduce the lowest two states of each J^π, T combination reasonably well. Therefore one may start the fitting procedure assuming that indeed these low-lying states can be reproduced. When the iteration has converged one makes up the average absolute deviation defined by

$$\Delta_{\text{av}} = \frac{\sum_{i=1}^{N_q} |E^{(i)}_{\text{calc}} - E^{(i)}_{\text{expl}}|}{N_q} , \tag{7.32}$$

where N_q is the total number of levels $E^{(i)}$ used in the fit. As a rule of thumb it is recommended that states, for which the deviation between theory and experiment is more than about three times the average deviation Δ_{av} should be excluded from the fitting procedure.

The average deviation Δ_{av} of course depends strongly on the model space, the effective interaction and the ratio of the numbers of parameters and fitted levels. A typical value of the average deviation Δ_{av} for the lowest five to ten states obtained with the effective two-body matrix elements from the MSDI is roughly given by

$$\Delta_{\text{av}} \approx (10/A_{\text{av}})\ \text{MeV} , \tag{7.33}$$

where A_{av} is the average mass number of the nuclei considered.

It should be clear that not all experimentally available levels of well-defined J^π, T values can be used for a fit. The set of experimental levels of given J^π, T should not leave open the possibility that a state is missed, in order that no incorrect association between theoretical and experimental energies be made. States of well-defined J^π, T values lying above states whose J^π, T values are unknown, should not be used in a fit. They may be useful, however, to test the model predictions.

A final check on the assumed correspondence between calculated and experimentally determined states follows only from a detailed comparison of other measurable quantities such as spectroscopic factors (chapter 8), electromagnetic transition rates (chapters 9 and 10), multipole moments (chapter 11) and log *ft* values (chapter 12).

7.5. Phase ambiguities

In chapter 6 it has been mentioned that a serious shortcoming of the fitting procedure stems from the fact that the calculated energies are insensitive to the sign of some off-diagonal matrix elements. A particular case follows from eq. (7.1). It is clear that a change in the sign of the matrix element H_{12} does not affect the eigenvalues. The ambiguity in phase is a much more general problem, however, than in this simple case of a 2 X 2 matrix.

Suppose one changes the phase of a single-particle radial wave function. This changes also the phase of all off-diagonal two-body matrix elements in which this single-particle wave function occurs one or three times. For example, a change of the phase of the $2s_{1/2}$ single-particle wave function results in a sign change of the matrix elements $\langle(2s_{1/2})^2|V(1,2)|2s_{1/2}1d_{3/2}\rangle_{JT}$ and $\langle 2s_{1/2}1d_{3/2}|V(1,2)|(1d_{3/2})^2\rangle_{JT}$. The calculated energies, i.e. the eigenvalues of the energy matrix, cannot depend on these phase conventions. Thus one may obtain from a fit to the experimental energies several sets of two-body matrix elements that are each consistent with a particular sign convention. However, the result of the sign change of a single-particle state is that all amplitudes of the components corresponding to configurations with an odd number of particles in that particular orbit do also flip sign. Thus relative signs of amplitudes in a mixed-configuration wave function are affected by this ambiguity. This has important consequences, since for a calculation of e.g. E2 transition rates, one must know which phase convention is used for the construction of the wave function, i.e. whether a radial wave function has a positive or negative asymptotic behaviour. This ambiguity in the present procedure cannot be solved without assumptions about the explicit radial dependence of the effective residual interaction. In principle one could, simultaneously with the level energies, also fit phase-dependent data like, i.e. electromagnetic transition rates. However, this leads in most cases to far too complicated fitting procedures.

Another ambiguity in the sign of off-diagonal matrix elements concerns the fact that in an empirical approach it is not specified whether the coupling order $\boldsymbol{j} = \boldsymbol{l} + \boldsymbol{s}$ or $\boldsymbol{j} = \boldsymbol{s} + \boldsymbol{l}$ is used. A knowledge of the convention chosen for the coupling order, however, is very important for the calculation of electromagnetic transition rates. The convention affects the signs of interfering transition amplitudes (see chapter 10).

The conclusion therefore is that empirical matrix elements can be very useful for the correlation of binding energies and excitation energies when the number of two-body matrix elements is much smaller than the number of experimental data. When the phase problems discussed above occur, then the wave functions from this approach may be inappropriate for a calculation of phase-sensitive properties.

The sign ambiguities do not occur when parameters of a schematic interaction are fitted or when the extra equations (7.23) are included in the fit. Let us restrict ourselves to the MSDI discussed in chapter 6. Each two-body matrix element can be expressed linearly in terms of the parameters A_T, B and C. One can fit these strengths with the procedures discussed above. In this case signs of off-diagonal matrix elements are well established once the phases of the radial wave functions and the coupling order of $\boldsymbol{l}$ and $\boldsymbol{s}$ to $\boldsymbol{j}$ are specified as explained in sect. 6.3.

A fit of the parameters of a schematic interaction has the additional great advantage that the number of parameters is reduced considerably as compared to the empirical approach. For example, the MSDI contains at most four parameters regardless of the number of orbits taken into account.

It should be remarked that the fitting procedures discussed in this chapter may be useful also to determine the optimum values of the single-particle energies solely if one employs parameter-free two-body matrix elements derived from realistic interactions.

CHAPTER 8

ONE- AND TWO-NUCLEON TRANSFER REACTIONS

So far we have only discussed calculations that are directly related to the energies of nuclear states. It is mentioned in chapter 3, however, that from a diagonalization of the interaction matrix H one obtains not only eigenvalues (energies), but also eigenvectors (wave functions). With the wave functions expressed in terms of shell-model basis states, one can calculate the various measurable quantities, in particular dynamical properties of the nuclei.

In this chapter a method is outlined which can be used to calculate that part of the cross section for one- or two-nucleon transfer reactions that depends on the detailed structure of the nuclear states involved.

In sect. 8.1 a brief introduction to single-particle transfer reactions is given. The calculation of spectroscopic factors for stripping reactions with wave functions having one or two active orbits is discussed in sect. 8.2. Some examples illustrating these calculations are given in sect. 8.3. Single-particle pick-up reactions are treated in sect. 8.4. The sensitivity of calculated spectroscopic factors to the chosen configuration space is illustrated with some examples in sect. 8.5. Sum rules for spectroscopic factors are discussed in sect. 8.6. An introduction to two-particle transfer reactions is given in sect. 8.7. The corresponding spectroscopic amplitudes for one- and two-orbit wave functions are derived in sect. 8.8.

8.1. Single-particle transfer reactions

Single-particle transfer is realized experimentally in stripping or pick-up reactions. In the former, one nucleon is stripped from the incoming projectile when it passes the target nucleus and in the latter one nucleon is picked up by the projectile. These reactions can thus be written as

$$\mathrm{A + a \rightarrow B + b} \qquad \text{or} \qquad \mathrm{A(a,b)B}\,, \tag{8.1}$$

where A denotes the target nucleus, a the projectile, B the final nucleus and b the outgoing particle. For a single-particle transfer reaction the mass numbers of A and B, and of course also of a and b, differ by one unit.

Experimentally, many types of reactions may cause a single-particle transfer. Some frequently used combinations (a,b) are listed in table 8.1.

When the single-particle transfer takes place with a minimum of rearrangement of the nucleons in the nuclei involved, one speaks of a *direct reaction*. This process differs from a *compound-nucleus* reaction, where first an intermediate nucleus is formed, which then after rearrangement of several nucleons decays by emission of

Table 8.1
Examples of single-particle transfer reactions

Proton transfer		Neutron transfer	
stripping	pick-up	stripping	pick-up
(d,n)	(n,d)	(d,p)	(p,d)
(^{3}He,d)	(d,^{3}He)	(t,d)	(d,t)
(α,t)	(t,α)	(α,^{3}He)	(^{3}He,α)

a (composite) particle. When the energy of the incoming projectile is high enough (for a (d,p) reaction say $E_d > 10$ MeV), then the probability that a direct reaction takes place is usually much larger than that for a compound process.

Often one can distinguish experimentally between compound-nucleus reactions and direct reactions. For direct reactions the intensity of the outgoing particles is peaked in forward directions and the cross section is not very sensitive to the energy of the incoming projectiles. This does not hold for compound-nucleus reactions.

The cross section $\sigma_l(\theta)$ of a direct-reaction process for transfer of a particle with orbital angular momentum l can be written as a product of two parts. Apart from some numerical factors, the expression reads

$$\sigma_l(\theta) \propto S\sigma_l^{\mathrm{DW}}(\theta) . \tag{8.2}$$

A derivation of this relation will not be given here. The interested reader is referred to books dealing with this subject, for example [McCarthy (1968)]. The quantity $\sigma_l^{\mathrm{DW}}(\theta)$ depends only on the reaction part of the process, that is, for instance, on energies and scattering angles, but it is not affected by the structure of the initial and final nuclei. This structure is taken into account by the *spectroscopic factor S*.

The cross-section $\sigma_l^{\mathrm{DW}}(\theta)$ is usually calculated with a distorted wave Born approximation (DWBA) in the optical model. The spectroscopic factor S is determined experimentally as the quotient of the measured value of $\sigma_l(\theta)$ and the theoretical value of $\sigma_l^{\mathrm{DW}}(\theta)$ (see eq. (8.2)). This experimental spectroscopic factor can then be compared with a theoretical spectroscopic factor obtained from a description of initial and final state in a nuclear model.

It should be remarked that all single-particle transfer reactions that start from a given initial state and lead to the same final state are associated with the same spectroscopic factor S, independent of the projectiles used. The observed differences in cross sections for e.g. the reactions (d,n), (^{3}He,d) and (α,t) should be completely contained in the function $\sigma_l^{\mathrm{DW}}(\theta)$.

The angular momentum of the transferred nucleon determines the shape of the angular distribution of the outgoing particles. In the case of a stripping reaction this concerns the l-value of the nucleon captured by the target, and for a pick-up reaction the l-value of the nucleon removed from the target. From the measured angular distribution one can extract the l-value as is shown with some examples in fig. 8.1.

ANGULAR DISTRIBUTIONS OF THE REACTION $^{26}Mg(d,p)^{27}Mg$

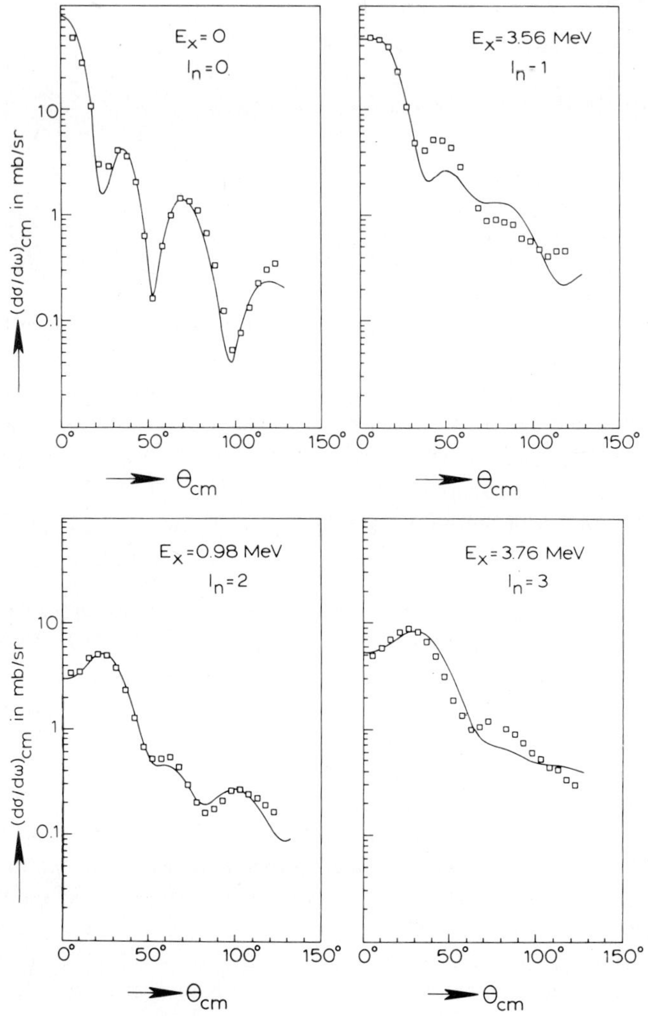

Fig. 8.1. Measurement of the differential cross section $\sigma(\theta_{\text{c.m.}})$ of a single-particle transfer reaction allows the determination of the orbital angular momentum of the captured nucleon. The angle $\theta_{\text{c.m.}}$ represents the direction of the outgoing particle in the centre-of-mass system. The experimental values for the reaction $^{26}Mg(d,p)^{27}Mg$ with $E_d = 12$ MeV are given by the open squares; the solid line gives the calculated values in the DWBA [Meurders and Van der Steld (1974)]. The position of the peak in the forward direction shifts to larger angles with increasing values of the orbital angular momentum l_n of the transferred neutron.

Let the spins of the initial and final nuclear states be given by J_i and J_f, respectively. From the conservation of angular momentum one then has the relation

$$J_i = J_f \pm j\,, \tag{8.3}$$

with $\boldsymbol{j} = \boldsymbol{l} + \boldsymbol{s}$ denoting the vector sum of the orbital angular momentum and intrinsic spin of the transferred nucleon.

Experimentally it is not always possible to determine the j-value of the transferred particle, since for a given l-value the angular distribution is usually very insensitive to the coupling of $\boldsymbol{l}$ and $\boldsymbol{s}$ (i.e. whether one has $j = l + \frac{1}{2}$ or $j = l - \frac{1}{2}$). Often, however, there is no such problem. In particular if J_f is known from other experiments and the initial state is characterized by $J_i = 0$, one has, due to eq. (8.3), $j = J_f$.

The parities of initial and final states given by Π_i and Π_f, respectively, should satisfy the relation $\Pi_i \Pi_l = \Pi_f$, where the parity of the wave function of the transferred particle is given by $\Pi_l = (-1)^l$. Thus one has the restriction on the orbital angular momentum of the transferred particle

$$\Pi_i \Pi_f = (-1)^l\,. \tag{8.4}$$

Consider as an example the neutron-transfer reaction ^{31}P(d,p)^{32}P. Since the ground state of ^{31}P possesses spin and parity $J^\pi = \frac{1}{2}^+$, the ground state of ^{32}P with $J^\pi = 1^+$ can be reached according to eq. (8.3) with both $j = \frac{1}{2}$ and $j = \frac{3}{2}$. As the orbital angular momentum of the transferred neutron must be even (see eq. (8.4)), both $l = 0$ ($s_{1/2}$) as well as $l = 2$ ($d_{3/2}$) transfer is possible. From a simple shell-model description it follows, however, that in $^{31}_{15}P_{16}$ the $2s_{1/2}$ neutron shell is already filled and thus only a neutron in the $1d_{3/2}$ orbit can be transferred. From the experimental data it follows indeed that the transition involves almost pure $l = 2$ transfer [Endt (1977)].

If initial and/or final states are described by mixed configurations one can sometimes extract information about these mixtures from stripping or pick-up reactions. This will be illustrated with the reaction ^{30}Si(d,p)^{31}Si.

The ground state of ^{30}Si possesses spin, parity and isospin given by $J^\pi = 0^+$, $T = 1$ and that of ^{31}Si has $J^\pi = \frac{3}{2}^+$, $T = \frac{3}{2}$. It follows from relations (8.3) and (8.4) that the stripped particle must have $j = \frac{3}{2}$ and an even l-value. Therefore it must be captured in a $d_{3/2}$ orbit. The wave function for the ^{30}Si ground state is given in eq. (3.80) as

$$\Psi(^{30}\mathrm{Si})_{01} = 0.90\;|(2s_{1/2})^2\rangle_{01} + 0.44\;|(1d_{3/2})^2\rangle_{01}\,. \tag{8.5}$$

Assuming that the active particles are restricted to the orbits $2s_{1/2}$ and $1d_{3/2}$, one can write the ^{31}Si ground-state wave function as

$$\Psi(^{31}\mathrm{Si})_{3/2^+\,3/2} = a_1\,|(2s_{1/2})^2_{01}\,1d_{3/2}\rangle_{3/2\,3/2} + a_2|2s_{1/2}(1d_{3/2})^2_{21}\rangle_{3/2\,3/2} + a_3|(1d_{3/2})^3\rangle_{3/2\,3/2}\,. \tag{8.6}$$

Here a_1, a_2 and a_3 are the amplitudes of the various components. From the wave functions (8.5) and (8.6) it follows that only the first and the third component of the ^{31}Si wave function can contribute to the cross section of the (d,p) reaction. In the following sections it will be shown how one can calculate the spectroscopic factor S from the contributions of the various components in the initial- and final-state wave functions.

8.2. Spectroscopic factors for stripping reactions

For a stripping reaction one can derive [Satchler (1964)] the relation for the cross section which is given by

$$\sigma_l^{\mathrm{str}}(\theta) = \frac{2J_\mathrm{f}+1}{2J_\mathrm{i}+1} N\sigma_l^{\mathrm{DW}}(\theta)\langle C\rangle^2 S \qquad \text{with } \langle C\rangle = \langle T_\mathrm{i} T_{\mathrm{i}z} \tfrac{1}{2} t_z | T_\mathrm{f} T_{\mathrm{f}z}\rangle\,. \tag{8.7}$$

The factor $(2J_\mathrm{f}+1)/(2J_\mathrm{i}+1)$ is a statistical weight and N is a normalization factor depending on the interaction between the transferred nucleon and the outgoing particle. Some frequently used values of N are given in table 8.2. In the isospin formalism the theoretical spectroscopic factor S does not distinguish between proton and neutron stripping. In a given experiment, however, only one of the two nucleons is transferred. The isospin Clebsch-Gordan coefficient $\langle C\rangle$ takes care of the fact that the stripped nucleon is either a proton or a neutron. The value $t_z = +\frac{1}{2}$ holds for neutron transfer and $t_z = -\frac{1}{2}$ for proton transfer. The values of $\langle C\rangle^2$ can be simply derived from the expressions given in table 8.3.

The spectroscopic factor S can be expressed in terms of an overlap integral I as

$$S(\rho) = n\,[I(\rho)]^2\,. \tag{8.8}$$

Here the symbol ρ specifies all quantum numbers of the transferred nucleon and n is the number of active particles in the final state (i.e. the number of particles outside closed shells). The factor n comes in since the stripped particle may be any of these particles in the antisymmetric final state. The overlap integral $I(\rho)$ in eq. (8.8)

Table 8.2
Semi-empirical values of the normalization factor N entering the experimental cross section for single-particle stripping reactions

Reaction	N [a)]
(d,p)	1.53
(^{3}He,d)	4.42
(t,d)	5.06
(α,^{3}He)	46
(α,t)	46

a) See e.g. [Bassel (1966); Lee, Schiffer, Zeidman, Satchler, Drisko and Bassel (1964)].

Table 8.3
Expressions for the square of the isospin Clebsch-Gordan coefficient for single-particle transfer reactions. (The symbols T_i and T_f denote the isospin of the initial and final state, respectively, with t_z (neutron) $= +\frac{1}{2}$)

	Stripping		Pick-up	
	proton	neutron	proton	neutron
$T_\mathrm{f} = T_\mathrm{i} - \frac{1}{2}$	$\dfrac{T_\mathrm{i} + T_{\mathrm{i}z}}{2T_\mathrm{i} + 1}$	$\dfrac{T_\mathrm{i} - T_{\mathrm{i}z}}{2T_\mathrm{i} + 1}$	$\dfrac{T_\mathrm{f} - T_{\mathrm{f}z} + 1}{2T_\mathrm{f} + 1}$	$\dfrac{T_\mathrm{f} + T_{\mathrm{f}z} + 1}{2T_\mathrm{f} + 1}$
$T_\mathrm{f} = T_\mathrm{i} + \frac{1}{2}$	$\dfrac{T_\mathrm{i} - T_{\mathrm{i}z} + 1}{2T_\mathrm{i} + 1}$	$\dfrac{T_\mathrm{i} + T_{\mathrm{i}z} + 1}{2T_\mathrm{i} + 1}$	$\dfrac{T_\mathrm{f} + T_{\mathrm{f}z}}{2T_\mathrm{f} + 1}$	$\dfrac{T_\mathrm{f} - T_{\mathrm{f}z}}{2T_\mathrm{f} + 1}$

is defined as

$$I(\rho) \equiv \langle [\Psi^{\mathrm{as}}_{\Gamma_\mathrm{i}}(1, ..., n-1) \times \rho(n)]^{\Gamma_\mathrm{f}} \,|\, \Psi^{\mathrm{as}}_{\Gamma_\mathrm{f}}(1, ..., n)\rangle , \tag{8.9}$$

where the symbol $\times$ denotes vector coupling. Thus the value of $I(\rho)$ depends on the overlap between the final state $\Psi^{\mathrm{as}}_{\Gamma_\mathrm{f}}(1, ..., n)$ (which is completely antisymmetric in the n active particles) and the state formed by coupling the initial state $\Psi^{\mathrm{as}}_{\Gamma_i}(1, ..., n-1)$ (which is antisymmetric in $n-1$ particles) with the transferred particle to a coupled-channel state Γ_f. Maximum overlap yields $|I(\rho)| = 1$.

One active orbit. Suppose that the initial- and final-state wave functions are described by active particles occupying only one orbit ρ, such that

$\Phi_\mathrm{i} =$ 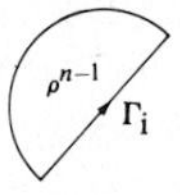

, $\Phi_\mathrm{f} =$ 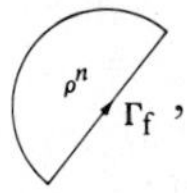

, (8.10)

where the diagrammatic notation has been explained in sect. 5.1. All other particles are assumed to belong to a core of closed shells. The overlap integral defined by eq. (8.9) can now be written as

$I(\rho) =$ 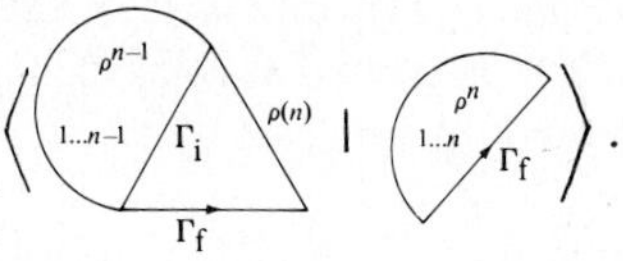

. (8.11)

In order to calculate the integral given in eq. (8.11), the ket wave function must be expanded in terms of the bra wave function. This can be performed with the c.f.p. expansion given in eq. (5.3) and one obtains

$I(\rho) = \sum_{\epsilon} \langle \rho^n \Gamma_\mathrm{f} | \} \rho^{n-1} \epsilon \rangle$ 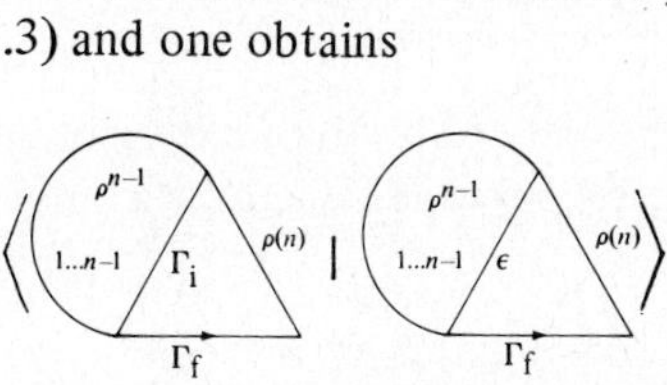

$= \langle \rho^n \Gamma_\mathrm{f} | \} \rho^{n-1} \Gamma_\mathrm{i} \rangle$, (8.12)

where from the orthonormality of bra and ket wave functions in the overlap integral one obtains a nonvanishing contribution only for $\epsilon = \Gamma_i$. Insertion of expression (8.12) into eq. (8.8) results in the final expression

$$S(\rho) = n\,[I(\rho)]^2 = n\langle \rho^n \Gamma_f | \} \rho^{n-1}\Gamma_i\rangle^2 \,. \tag{8.13}$$

Note that the factor n represents the number of particles in the active shell of the final nucleus, i.e. the heavier of the two nuclei involved.

Since the c.f.p. are normalized and therefore not larger than one, eq. (8.13) implies the inequality $S \leqslant n$. This upper limit for S no longer holds as soon as the wave functions used for the description of the initial and final state are less simple than assumed in eq. (8.10), i.e. when more active orbits are involved.

This can be illustrated as follows. Let us consider the reaction ^{33}S(d,p)^{34}S and only assume active particles in the $1d_{3/2}$ orbit for the ground-state configurations in both nuclei. Suppose that all lower-lying orbits are fully occupied, i.e. we consider ^{32}S as a closed core. One then has the transition $|1d_{3/2}\rangle_{3/2\,1/2} \rightarrow |(1d_{3/2})^2\rangle_{01}$, since the ground states of $^{33}_{16}S_{17}$ and $^{34}_{16}S_{18}$ have $J^\pi = \frac{3}{2}^+$, $T = \frac{1}{2}$ and $J^\pi = 0^+$, $T = 1$, respectively. According to eq. (8.13) one finds for the spectroscopic factor $S = 2$, since the corresponding c.f.p. is given by $\langle d^2 01 | \} d\, \frac{3}{2}\, \frac{1}{2}\rangle = 1$. Lifting the restriction that the $2s_{1/2}$ orbit be filled completely, one can also have a contribution to the spectroscopic factor from the transition $|(1d_{3/2})^5\rangle_{3/2\,1/2} \rightarrow |(1d_{3/2})^6\rangle_{01}$, i.e. the $2s_{1/2}$ orbit is assumed to be empty. If this were the only configuration that contributes, one would find for the spectroscopic factor $S = 6\,\langle d^6 01 | \} d^5 \frac{3}{2}\, \frac{1}{2}\rangle^2 = 6 \times \frac{5}{9} = 3.3$. It is seen that the latter value of S is considerably larger than that obtained for a closed $2s_{1/2}$ orbit. More complicated cases for two active orbits are discussed below.

The only strict limitation of the number n in eq. (8.13) is given by the relation $n \leqslant N_\rho$, where $N_\rho = (2\rho + 1)$ denotes the maximum number of nucleons in the shell ρ to which the transferred nucleon belongs (e.g. for $\rho = d_{3/2}$ one has $N_\rho = (2j_\rho + 1)(2t_\rho + 1) = 4 \times 2 = 8$).

Some examples of one-particle stripping reactions interpreted in a single-orbit description are shown in table 8.4. For the values of the c.f.p. see appendix B.3.

Two active orbits. The calculation of spectroscopic factors for states described by a configuration with two active orbits ρ and λ can be treated as follows.

Suppose that the initial- and final-state wave functions are given by

$\Phi_i =$ 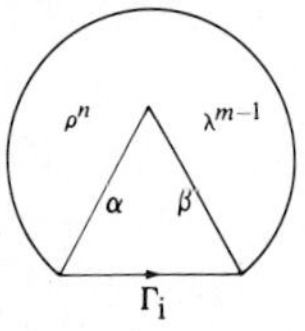

, $\Phi_f =$ 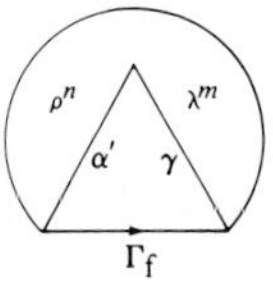

. (8.14)

The final state Φ_f can thus be reached by the addition of a nucleon to the orbit λ in the initial state Φ_i. Then the spectroscopic factor is obtained from expression (8.8), which yields

$$S(\lambda) = (n + m)\,[I(\lambda)]^2 \,. \tag{8.15}$$

Table 8.4
Some examples of stripping spectroscopic factors calculated with pure ρ^n configurations of lowest seniority and reduced isospin

Model space	Reaction	n	$(c.f.p.)^2$	Spectroscopic factor S	
				theory [a]	experiment [b]
$(d_{5/2})^n$	$^{20}Ne(d,p)^{21}Ne(1)$	5	0.13	0.65	0.71 ± 0.11
	$^{24}Mg(d,p)^{25}Mg(0)$	9	0.037	0.33	0.37 ± 0.08
$(d_{3/2})^n$	$^{33}S(d,p)^{34}S(0)$	2	1	2	1.9 ± 0.3
	$^{35}Cl(d,n)^{36}Ar(0)$	4	1	4	5.3 ± 0.5
	$^{36}Ar(d,p)^{37}Ar(0)$	5	0.10	0.50	0.49 ± 0.06
$(f_{7/2})^n$	$^{40}Ca(d,p)^{41}Ca(0)$	1	1	1	0.85 ± 0.09
	$^{42}Ca(d,p)^{43}Ca(0)$	3	0.25	0.75	0.58 ± 0.06

[a] The theoretical spectroscopic factors are given by $S = n \times (c.f.p.)^2$.
[b] From the review paper [Endt (1977)].

The overlap integral is defined according to eq. (8.9) by

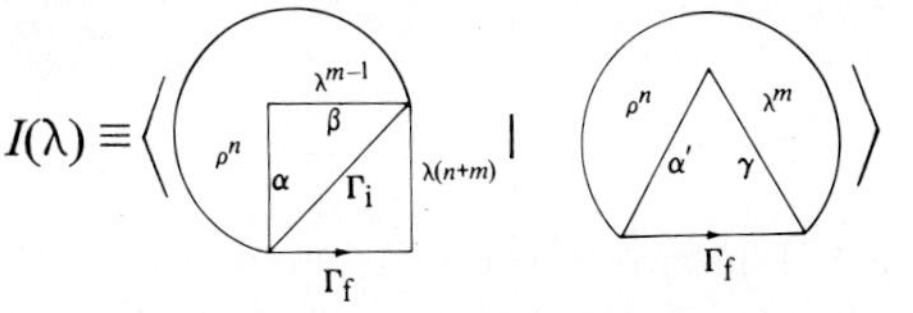

$$I(\lambda) \equiv \left\langle \left(\begin{array}{c} \rho^n \end{array} \right) \middle| \left(\begin{array}{c} \rho^n \end{array} \right) \right\rangle . \tag{8.16}$$

The factor $n + m$ in eq. (8.15) reflects the fact that in this case there are $n + m$ places available for the last nucleon, but only one possibility (having the transferred particle in the last position) is taken into account by the amplitude $I(\lambda)$.

The evaluation of the overlap integral $I(\lambda)$ given in eq. (8.16) requires several steps. It should be realized that the group ρ^n is not affected by the transfer of a λ-particle. The effect of the group ρ^n on $I(\lambda)$ will be investigated first. In order to single out the groups ρ^n on both sides, wave functions must be constructed that are antisymmetric in the ρ and λ parts separately. First eq. (5.4) is applied to the bra wave function in eq. (8.16). This yields

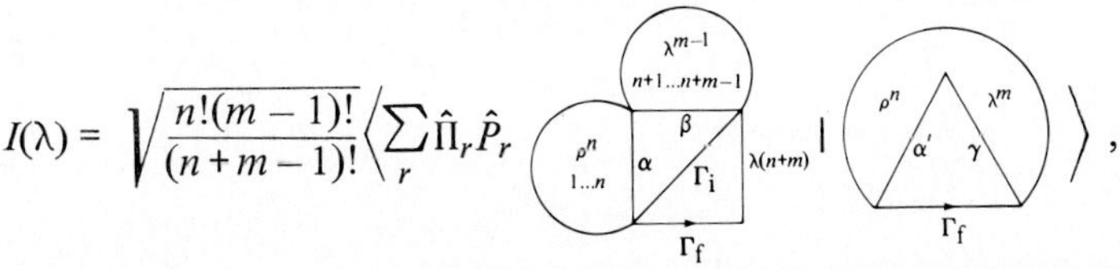

$$I(\lambda) = \sqrt{\frac{n!(m-1)!}{(n+m-1)!}} \left\langle \sum_r \hat{\Pi}_r \hat{P}_r \left(\begin{array}{c} \rho^n \end{array} \right) \middle| \left(\begin{array}{c} \rho^n \end{array} \right) \right\rangle , \tag{8.17}$$

where the permutation operators $\hat{P}_r$ are supposed to ignore particle $\lambda(n + m)$. All terms of the sum Σ_r are of the same magnitude and sign. This can be shown along the same lines as in the derivation of eq. (5.26). One can evaluate the term with $P_r = 1$ and multiply the result by the number of terms, $(n + m - 1)!/n!(m - 1)!$.

One thus obtains

$$I(\lambda) = \sqrt{\frac{(n+m-1)!}{n!(m-1)!}} \Big\langle$$ 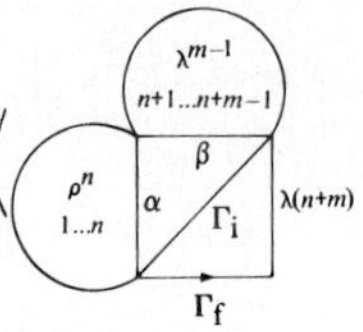 $$\Big|$$ 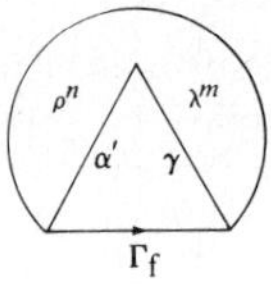 $$\Big\rangle . \qquad (8.18)$$

The expansion of the ket wave function in terms of functions that are antisymmetric in the groups ρ^n and λ^m separately yields with eq. (5.4)

$$I(\lambda) = \sqrt{\frac{(n+m-1)!}{n!(m-1)!}} \sqrt{\frac{n!m!}{(n+m)!}} \Big\langle$$ 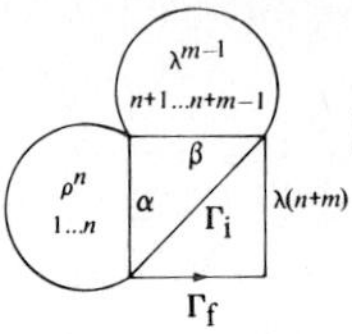 $$\Big| \sum_r \hat{\Pi}_r \hat{P}_r$$ 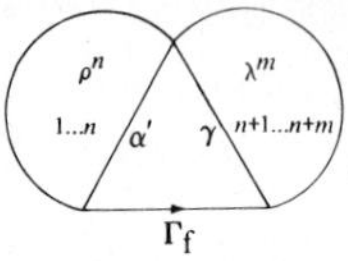 $$\Big\rangle . \qquad (8.19)$$

Only the term with $P_r = 1$ contributes, since for $\hat{P}_r \neq 1$ the groups ρ^n in bra and ket wave functions contain different particles and due to orthogonality the result vanishes. Hence one can write

$$I(\lambda) = \sqrt{\frac{m}{n+m}} \Big\langle$$ 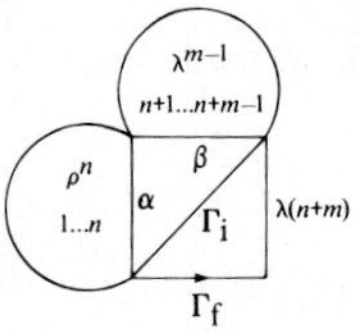 $$\Big|$$ 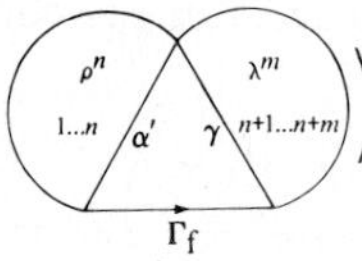 $$\Big\rangle . \qquad (8.20)$$

The spectroscopic factor S can be evaluated directly when there are no λ particles present in the initial state. In this case one has $m = 1$ and insertion of eq. (8.20) into eq. (8.15) yields

$$S(\lambda) = (n+1)[I(\lambda)]^2 = \Big\langle$$ 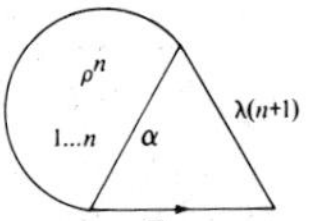 $$\Big|$$ 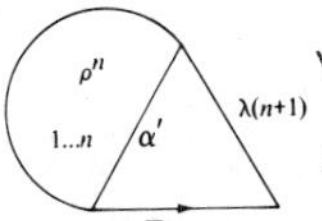 $$\Big\rangle^2 = \delta_{\alpha\alpha'} . \qquad (8.21)$$

For $m > 1$, however, the particle labelled $n + m$ must be decoupled in the ket wave function Φ_f of eq. (8.20). This can be achieved with the c.f.p. expansion of eq. (5.3) and a change of coupling order with eq. (5.19). One finds

$$\Phi_f =$$ 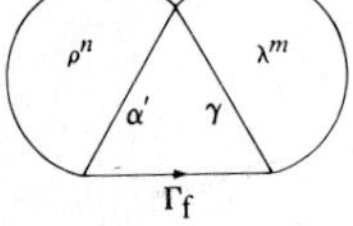 $$= \sum_\epsilon \langle \lambda^m \gamma | \} \lambda^{m-1} \epsilon \rangle$$ 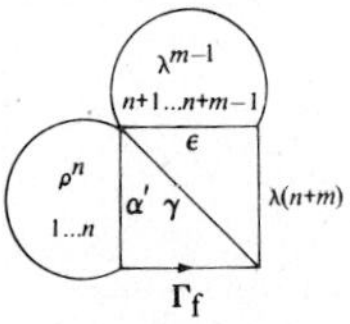

$$= \sum_\epsilon \langle \lambda^m \gamma | \} \lambda^{m-1} \epsilon \rangle \sum_\nu U(\alpha' \epsilon \Gamma_f \lambda; \nu \gamma)$$ 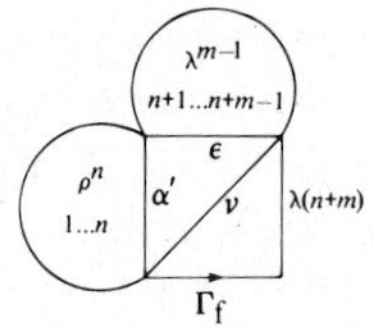 $$. \qquad (8.22)$$

From eqs. (8.20) and (8.22) one obtains

$$I(\lambda) = \sqrt{\frac{m}{n+m}} \sum_{\epsilon} \langle \lambda^m \gamma | \} \lambda^{m-1} \epsilon \rangle$$

$$\times \sum_{\nu} U(\alpha' \epsilon \Gamma_f \lambda; \nu\gamma) \Big\langle$$ 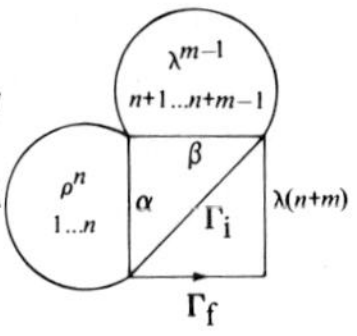

$\Big|$ 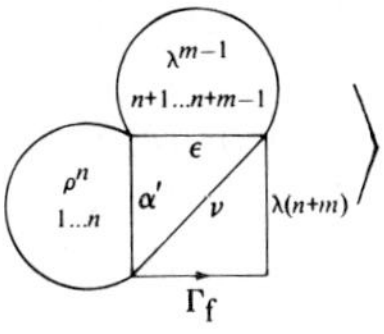

$\Big\rangle$. (8.23)

Due to orthogonality conditions this equation reduces to

$$I(\lambda) = \sqrt{\frac{m}{n+m}} \sum_{\epsilon} \langle \lambda^m \gamma | \} \lambda^{m-1} \epsilon \rangle \sum_{\nu} U(\alpha' \epsilon \Gamma_f \lambda; \nu\gamma) \delta_{\alpha\alpha'} \delta_{\beta\epsilon} \delta_{\Gamma_i \nu} \,. \tag{8.24}$$

Insertion of eq. (8.24) into eq. (8.15) finally yields an expression for the spectroscopic factor

$$S(\lambda) = m [\langle \lambda^m \gamma | \} \lambda^{m-1} \beta \rangle \, U(\alpha\beta\Gamma_f \lambda; \, \Gamma_i \gamma)]^2 \delta_{\alpha\alpha'} \qquad \text{for} \begin{cases} \Phi_i = |\rho_\alpha^n \lambda_\beta^{m-1}\rangle_{\Gamma_i} \\ \Phi_f = |\rho_{\alpha'}^n \lambda_\gamma^m \rangle_{\Gamma_f} \,. \end{cases} \tag{8.25}$$

Note that although the total number of particles outside closed shells appears in eq. (8.15), it is the number of nucleons in the group to which the transferred nucleon belongs, that emerges as a factor in the final expression (8.25).

Expression (8.25) reduces to the result for one active orbit when ρ^n represents a closed orbit. In this case one has $\alpha = \alpha' = 0$ (see eq. (8.14)) and also $\beta = \Gamma_i$ and $\gamma = \Gamma_f$. The normalized Racah coefficient in eq. (8.25) then has the value $U(0\Gamma_i\Gamma_f\lambda; \Gamma_i\Gamma_f) = 1$ and one obtains

$$S(\lambda) = m \langle \lambda^m \Gamma_f | \} \lambda^{m-1} \Gamma_i \rangle^2 \,, \tag{8.26}$$

which is exactly the single-orbit expression given in eq. (8.13).

The conclusion is that a closed orbit may be neglected. When the closed orbit is replaced by a set of closed orbits a similar result is obtained. Thus it can be stated that closed shells do not contribute in a calculation of S-factors. This holds also for all groups $\rho_k^{n_k}$ coupled to $\alpha_k = \alpha_k' = 0$, regardless of the number of particles n_k in such orbits ρ_k.

When a particle in the orbit ρ instead of the orbit λ is coupled to the initial state given in eq. (8.14), some recoupling rules can be applied to reduce this case to the one discussed above.

Suppose that initial and final states are given by

$\Phi_i =$ 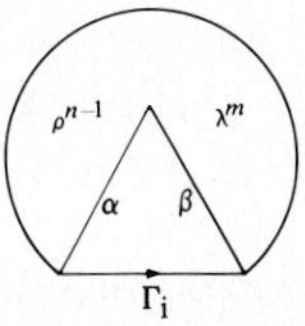

, $\Phi_f =$ 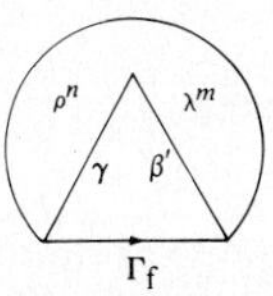

. (8.27)

According to eq. (8.15) the spectroscopic factor S then is given by

$$S(\rho) = (n+m)[I(\rho)]^2 \tag{8.28}$$

with

$I(\rho) =$ 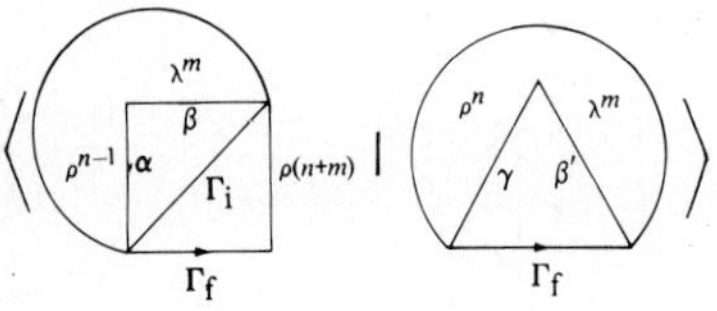

. (8.29)

In order to compare this expression with eq. (8.16) one must interchange the groups ρ and λ. Application of eq. (5.13) yields

$\Phi_i =$ 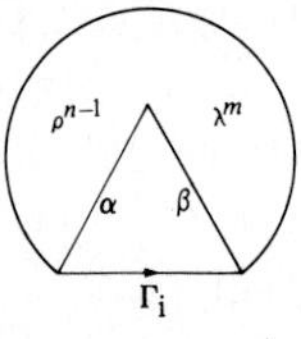

$= (-1)^{\Gamma_i - \alpha - \beta - (n-1)m}$ 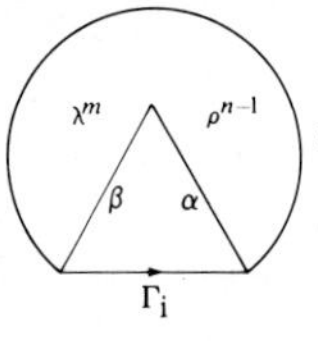

, (8.30)

$\Phi_f =$ 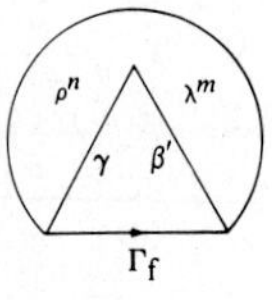

$= (-1)^{\Gamma_f - \gamma - \beta' - nm}$ 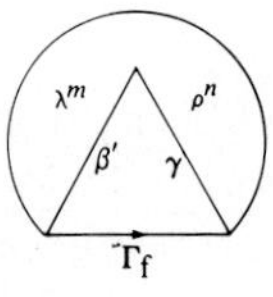

. (8.31)

Inserting these relations into expression (8.29) one obtains

$I(\rho) = (-1)^{\Gamma_i + \Gamma_f - \alpha - \beta - \gamma - \beta' + m}$ 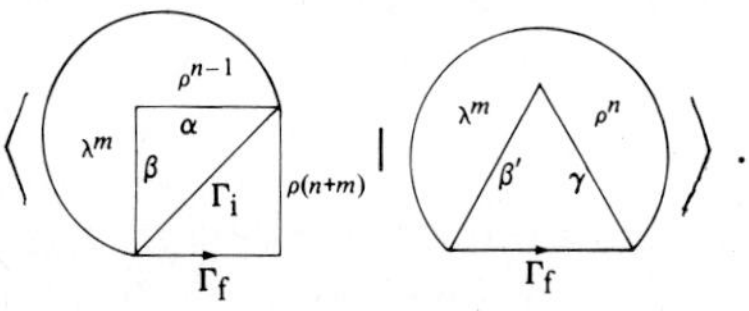

. (8.32)

Expression (8.32) is similar to eq. (8.16) apart from the phase factor. Thus the steps outlined in eqs. (8.17)–(8.24) yield

$$I(\rho) = (-1)^{\Gamma_i + \Gamma_f - \alpha - \gamma + m} \sqrt{\frac{n}{n+m}} \langle \rho^n \gamma | \} \rho^{n-1} \alpha \rangle \, U(\beta \alpha \Gamma_f \rho; \Gamma_i \gamma) \delta_{\beta\beta'} \tag{8.33}$$

for the wave functions specified in eq. (8.27). The phase factor $(-1)^{-\beta-\beta'} = (-1)^{-J_\beta - T_\beta - J_{\beta'} - T_{\beta'}} = +1$ drops out due to the Kronecker delta $\delta_{\beta\beta'}$. Thus the spectroscopic factor becomes

$$S(\rho) = n[\langle \rho^n \gamma | \} \rho^{n-1} \alpha \rangle \, U(\beta \alpha \Gamma_f \rho; \Gamma_i \gamma)]^2 \delta_{\beta\beta'} \qquad \text{for} \begin{cases} \Phi_i = |\rho_\alpha^{n-1} \lambda_\beta^m \rangle_{\Gamma_i} \\ \Phi_f = |\rho_\gamma^n \lambda_\beta^m \rangle_{\Gamma_f} . \end{cases} \tag{8.34}$$

The phase factor in eq. (8.33) is important only when initial and/or final states are described by mixed configurations. The factor $(-1)^{\Gamma_i+\Gamma_f}$ depends on the total spin J and isospin T of the initial and final states only, but an overall phase does not affect the spectroscopic factor, which is proportional to the square of $I(\rho)$.

Let the initial and final states be given by the mixed configurations $\Psi_i = \Sigma_k a_k \Phi_k^{(i)}$ and $\Psi_f = \Sigma_l b_l \Phi_l^{(f)}$, respectively. The wave functions $\Phi_k^{(i)}$ and $\Phi_l^{(f)}$ describe pure configurations of the type given in eqs. (8.14) or (8.27). When for the final state Ψ_f a model space is used with N_a active particles outside a core, one obtains the spectroscopic factor from the expression

$$S = N_a \left[\sum_{kl} a_k b_l I_{kl}\right]^2 , \tag{8.35}$$

where the overlap integrals I_{kl} are defined by eqs. (8.24) or (8.33) for transfer of a ρ- or λ-particle, respectively. The various contributions to the spectroscopic factor defined in eq. (8.35) can add constructively or destructively, depending on the signs of a_k, b_l and I_{kl}. Therefore the phase consistency is quite important. For instance, once a set of c.f.p. has been chosen for the construction of the wave functions, the same set of c.f.p. should be used for the calculation of spectroscopic factors.

8.3. Examples

Let us discuss first a single-particle transfer reaction that can be treated with one active orbit. In sect. 4.6 the nuclei $^{50}_{22}Ti_{28}$ and $^{51}_{23}V_{28}$ were described in a $(1f_{7/2})^3$ model space, which leads to a reasonable reproduction of the excitation energies of the lower states in both nuclei. Here we shall test these simple $|\rho^n\rangle_\Gamma$ wave functions in more detail with a calculation of spectroscopic factors.

The spectroscopic factor S for the reaction $^{50}Ti(^3He,d)^{51}V$ leading to the $J_f^\pi = \frac{7}{2}^-$ ground state of ^{51}V can involve only transfer of a $1f_{7/2}$ particle since the ^{50}Ti ground state has spin and parity $J_i^\pi = 0^+$ (see eqs. (8.3) and (8.4)). Thus a particle is transferred that belongs to the active orbit in the present model. Application of eq. (8.13) leads to

$$S(1f_{7/2}) = 3 \times \langle f^3 \tfrac{7}{2}\tfrac{3}{2} | \} f^2 01 \rangle^2 = 3 \times 0.25 = 0.75 , \tag{8.36}$$

where the value of the c.f.p. is taken from table 4.2. The theoretical value of S compares favourably with the experimental value $S_{exp} = 0.8$ [O'Brien, Dorenbusch, Belote and Rapaport (1967)]. Population of the $J^\pi = \frac{5}{2}^-$ first excited state and $J^\pi = \frac{3}{2}^-$ second excited state in ^{51}V can only be achieved by transfer of a $1f_{5/2}$ and a $2p_{3/2}$ particle, respectively, due to the selection rules (8.3) and (8.4). In our simple $(1f_{7/2})^n$ model we do not take into account configurations with active orbits $1f_{5/2}$ and $2p_{3/2}$, however, and thus one has $S = 0$ for transfer to the first and second excited state. Experimentally one does in fact find very small S-factors for these states, ($S \leqslant 0.02$), which does not contradict the results of the simple theory.

As an example for two active orbits we consider again the reaction $^{30}Si(d,p)^{31}Si$. From earlier calculations a simple, mixed-configuration wave function was constructed for the ^{30}Si ground state (see eq. (8.5)). This wave function and the simplest pure-configuration wave function for the ground state and first excited state in ^{31}Si are given by

$$\text{ground state } |^{30}\text{Si}(0)\rangle = 0.90|(2s_{1/2})^2\rangle_{01} + 0.44|(1d_{3/2})^2\rangle_{01} , \tag{8.37a}$$

$$\text{ground state } |^{31}\text{Si}(0)\rangle = |(2s_{1/2})^2_{01}\, 1d_{3/2\ 1/2}\rangle_{3/2\ 3/2} , \tag{8.37b}$$

$$\text{first excited state } |^{31}\text{Si}(1)\rangle = |2s_{1/2\ 1/2}(1d_{3/2})^2_{01}\rangle_{1/2\ 3/2} . \tag{8.37c}$$

The spectroscopic factor for the reaction to the ^{31}Si ground state is found after application of eq. (8.25), which yields

$$S(1d_{3/2}) = [0.90\,\langle d^1\tfrac{3}{2}\tfrac{1}{2}|\}\, d^0 00\rangle\, U(00\tfrac{3}{2}\tfrac{3}{2};0\tfrac{3}{2})\, U(10\tfrac{3}{2}\tfrac{1}{2};1\tfrac{1}{2})]^2 = 0.81 . \tag{8.38}$$

Similarly one finds from eq. (8.34) for the transition to the first excited state in ^{31}Si

$$S(2s_{1/2}) = [0.44\,\langle s^1\tfrac{1}{2}\tfrac{1}{2}|\}\, s^0 00\rangle\, U(00\tfrac{1}{2}\tfrac{1}{2};0\tfrac{1}{2})\, U(10\tfrac{3}{2}\tfrac{1}{2};1\tfrac{1}{2})]^2 = 0.19 . \tag{8.39}$$

The c.f.p. and U-coefficients are all equal to unity in the expressions given above. The measured values of the spectroscopic factors for the transitions to the ground state and first excited state are given by $S(l = 2) = 0.86$ and $S(l = 0) = 0.27$, respectively [Wildenthal and Glaudemans (1968)]. The uncertainty in the experimental values is usually estimated to be of the order of 30%. Thus the simple model accounts well for the measured S-factors. With the specific wave functions used here, one has the relation $S(1d_{3/2}) + S(2s_{1/2}) = 1$ due to the normalization of the ^{30}Si ground state wave function. It should be remarked that in this example one could have obtained the theoretical S-factors directly from eq. (8.21), thus bypassing the explicit introduction of c.f.p. and U-coefficients as in eqs. (8.25) and (8.34).

Finally we shall calculate the spectroscopic factors for the reaction ^{58}Ni(d,p)^{59}Ni that correspond to the lower two $J^\pi = \frac{3}{2}^-$ final states. To this end we employ the ^{58}Ni and ^{59}Ni wave functions that are listed in appendix B.7. In this example both the initial- and final-state wave functions contain more than one component. The ^{58}Ni ground-state wave function ($J^\pi = 0^+$) is given by

$$\Psi_{\text{g.s.}}(^{58}\text{Ni})_{\substack{J=0\\T=1}} = +0.555|(1f_{5/2})^2\rangle_{01} + 0.784|(2p_{3/2})^2\rangle_{01} + 0.280|(2p_{1/2})^2\rangle_{01} . \tag{8.40}$$

From eqs. (8.3) and (8.4) it follows that for a $J^\pi = \frac{3}{2}^-$ final state only a $p_{3/2}$ particle can be transferred. The wave functions of the lower two $J^\pi = \frac{3}{2}^-$ states in ^{59}Ni are given by (see appendix B.7)

$$\Psi(^{59}\text{Ni})_{\substack{J=3/2(1)\\T=3/2}} = +0.535|(1f_{5/2})^2_{01}\, 2p_{3/2}\rangle_{3/2\ 3/2} + 0.772|(2p_{3/2})^3\rangle_{3/2\ 3/2}$$

$$+ 0.254|2p_{3/2}(2p_{1/2})^2_{01}\rangle_{3/2\ 3/2} + |\text{remainder}\rangle , \tag{8.41a}$$

$$\Psi(^{59}\text{Ni})_{\substack{J=3/2\,(2)\\ T=3/2}} = +0.509\,|(1\text{f}_{5/2})^2_{01}\,2\text{p}_{3/2}\rangle_{3/2\;3/2} - 0.200\,|(2\text{p}_{3/2})^3\rangle_{3/2\;3/2}$$

$$+\,0.242\,|2\text{p}_{3/2}\,(2\text{p}_{1/2})^2_{01}\rangle_{3/2\;3/2} + |\text{remainder}\rangle\,. \tag{8.41b}$$

Here the parts $|\text{remainder}\rangle$ contain all components that do not contribute to the spectroscopic factor for the transfer of a $\text{p}_{3/2}$ particle. Application of eq. (8.35) leads to the spectroscopic factor

$$S = 3\left[\sum_{k=1}^{3}\sum_{l=1}^{3} a_k\, b_l\, I_{kl}\right]^2 , \tag{8.42}$$

where a_k and b_l denote the amplitudes of the components in the ^{58}Ni and ^{59}Ni wave functions, respectively. The overlap integrals I_{kl} can be calculated with eqs. (8.12) and (8.33). The values for the nonvanishing integrals are found to be given by

$$I_{11} = +0.577, I_{22} = +0.408 \text{ and } I_{33} = +0.577 \tag{8.43}$$

[the labels k and l are understood to appear in ascending order in eqs. (8.40) and (8.41)]. Insertion of these integrals and the amplitudes of eqs. (8.40) and (8.41) into eq. (8.42) leads to the results

$$S(J^\pi = \tfrac{3}{2}^-(1)) = 3[+0.171 + 0.247 + 0.041]^2 = 0.63\,, \tag{8.44a}$$

$$S(J^\pi = \tfrac{3}{2}^-(2)) = 3[+0.163 - 0.064 + 0.039]^2 = 0.06\,. \tag{8.44b}$$

It is seen that, in this example, the components of the $J^\pi = \frac{3}{2}^-(1)$ state (^{59}Ni ground state) that contribute to the S-factor are all large ($\Sigma_{l=1}^3 b_l^2 = 0.95$) and add constructively. For the $J^\pi = \frac{3}{2}^-(2)$ state the components that contribute form a much smaller fraction of the complete wave function ($\Sigma_{l=1}^3 b_l^2 = 0.36$). Moreover, some cancellation occurs in the latter case. As a result one finds a much smaller S-factor for the second $J^\pi = \frac{3}{2}^-$ state. The experimental S-factors for the ^{58}Ni(d,p)^{59}Ni reaction are $S(J^\pi = \frac{3}{2}^-(1)) = 0.7$ and $S(J^\pi = \frac{3}{2}^-(2)) = 0.08$ [Fulmer, McCarthy, Cohen and Middleton (1964)] in good agreement with our theoretical values.

8.4. Spectroscopic factors for pick-up reactions

The pick-up process is very similar to the process of stripping, i.e. it can be regarded as a stripping reaction in reverse. The projectile picks up a nucleon from the target nucleus and thus again two states are connected that differ one unit in mass number, but this time the initial nucleus is the heavier one. Some examples of pick-up reactions are given in table 8.1. It can be shown that the cross section can be expressed in terms of the function $\sigma_l^{\text{DW}}(\theta)$ (cf. eq. (8.7)) as

$$\sigma_l^{\text{p.u.}}(\theta) = N\sigma_l^{\text{DW}}(\theta)\,\langle C\rangle^2 S \quad \text{with} \quad \langle C\rangle = \langle T_\text{f} T_{\text{f}z}\,\tfrac{1}{2}\,t_z\,|\,T_\text{i} T_{\text{i}z}\rangle\,. \tag{8.45}$$

Table 8.5
Semiempirical values of the normalization factor N for single-particle pick-up reactions

Reaction	N [a]
(p,d)	2.29
(d, ^{3}He)	2.95
(d,t)	3.33
(^{3}He,α)	23
(t,α)	23

a) See e.g. [Bassel (1966); Stock, Bock, David, Duhm and Tamura (1967)].

Here N is a normalization factor depending on the interaction between the incoming projectile and the picked-up particle. Some frequently used values of N are given in table 8.5. The isospin Clebsch-Gordan coefficient corresponds to the one given in eq. (8.7) for a stripping reaction but with initial and final isospin interchanged (see table 8.3). The statistical factor $(2J_\mathrm{f} + 1)/(2J_\mathrm{i} + 1)$ that was present in eq. (8.7) does not occur for a pick-up reaction. The spectroscopic factor for pick-up is defined as

$$S(\rho) = n\,[I(\rho)]^2\,, \tag{8.46}$$

where n denotes the number of active particles in the initial state. Note that this number n refers again to the heavier of the two nuclei involved, as holds also for stripping reactions. The overlap integral is defined by

$$I(\rho) = \langle [\Psi^{\mathrm{as}}_{\Gamma_\mathrm{f}}(1, ..., n-1) \times \rho(n)]_{\Gamma_\mathrm{i}} | \Psi^{\mathrm{as}}_{\Gamma_\mathrm{i}}(1, ..., n)\rangle\,. \tag{8.47}$$

Expression (8.47) is identical to eq. (8.9) if the labels "initial" and "final" of the quantum numbers are interchanged. Therefore the overlap integral (8.47) for a pick-up reaction between two states is the same as the overlap integral (8.9) for a stripping reaction between the same two states.

When initial and final states are given by

$\Phi_\mathrm{i} =$ 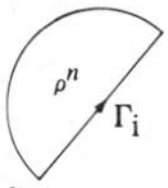

, $\Phi_\mathrm{f} =$ 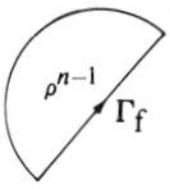

, (8.48)

one obtains in analogy with eq. (8.12) the result

$$I(\rho) = \langle \rho^n \Gamma_\mathrm{i} | \} \rho^{n-1} \Gamma_\mathrm{f} \rangle\,. \tag{8.49}$$

Some pick-up reactions interpreted with one active orbit are listed in table 8.6. It is seen that for the ground-state transitions given, the simple description works out quite well.

For active particles in two orbits with

$$\Phi_\mathrm{i} = |\rho^n_\alpha \lambda^m_\beta\rangle_{\Gamma_\mathrm{i}}\,, \qquad \Phi_\mathrm{f} = |\rho^n_{\alpha'} \lambda^{m-1}_\gamma\rangle_{\Gamma_\mathrm{f}}\,, \tag{8.50}$$

Table 8.6
Some examples of pick-up spectroscopic factors calculated with pure ρ^n configurations of lowest seniority and reduced isospin

Model space	Reaction	n	$(\text{c.f.p.})^2$	Spectroscopic factor S	
				theory [a)]	experiment [b)]
$(d_{5/2})^n$	$^{25}Mg(p,d)^{24}Mg(0)$	9	0.036	0.32	0.37 ± 0.08
	$^{27}Al(n,d)^{26}Mg(0)$	11	0.045	0.50	0.44 ± 0.05
$(d_{3/2})^n$	$^{34}S(p,d)^{33}S(0)$	2	1	2	1.9 ± 0.3
	$^{37}Cl(p,d)^{36}Cl(0)$	5	0.25	1.25	0.95 ± 0.17
$(f_{7/2})^n$	$^{42}Ca(p,d)^{41}Ca(0)$	2	1	2	1.6 ± 0.2
	$^{44}Ca(p,d)^{43}Ca(0)$	4	1	4	3.1 ± 0.3

a) The theoretical spectroscopic factors are given by $S = n \times (\text{c.f.p.})^2$.
b) From the review paper [Endt (1977)].

one obtains

$$I(\lambda) = \sqrt{\frac{m}{n+m}} \langle \lambda^m \beta | \} \lambda^{m-1} \gamma \rangle \; U(\alpha\gamma\Gamma_i\lambda; \Gamma_f\beta) \delta_{\alpha\alpha'} \,. \tag{8.51}$$

When initial and final states are specified by

$$\Phi_i = |\rho_\alpha^n \lambda_\beta^m\rangle_{\Gamma_i} \,, \qquad \Phi_f = |\rho_\gamma^{n-1} \lambda_{\beta'}^m\rangle_{\Gamma_f} \,, \tag{8.52}$$

then the overlap integral is given by

$$I(\rho) = (-1)^{\Gamma_i+\Gamma_f+\alpha+\gamma+m} \sqrt{\frac{n}{n+m}} \langle \rho_\alpha^n | \} \rho^{n-1} \gamma \rangle \; U(\beta\gamma\Gamma_i\rho; \Gamma_f\alpha) \, \delta_{\beta\beta'} \,. \tag{8.53}$$

It is clear that eqs. (8.51) and (8.53) for pick-up reactions are equivalent to those for stripping reactions given in eqs. (8.24) and (8.33), respectively. A comparison

Table 8.7
Spectroscopic factors for the pick-up reaction $^{51}V(d,{}^3He)^{50}Ti$

E_x(MeV)	J^π	Spectroscopic factor S	
		experiment [a)]	theory [b)]
0	0^+	0.73	0.75
1.56	2^+	0.39	0.42
2.67	4^+	0.64	0.75
3.21	6^+	1.05	1.08

a) [Hinterberger, Mairle, Schmidt-Rohr, Turek and Wagner (1968)].
b) Calculated in a $(1f_{7/2})^n$ configuration space.

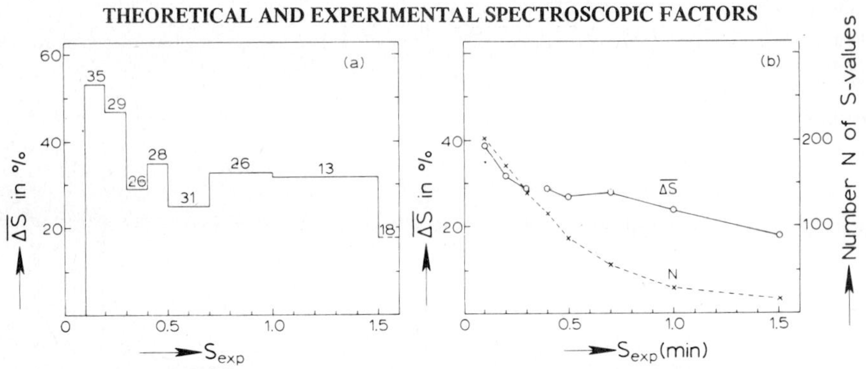

Fig. 8.2. A comparison between theory and experiment for S-factors of single-particle transfer reactions in sd- and fp-shell nuclei. In (a) a histogram is shown of the average deviation $\overline{\Delta S} = \Sigma_k |S_{\rm th}(k) - S_{\rm exp}(k)| / S_{\rm exp}(k)$ given as a percentage with $S_{\rm th}(k)$ and $S_{\rm exp}(k)$ denoting the theoretical and experimental S-value, respectively. The number of S-values is indicated above each block. The values of $\overline{\Delta S}$ for the same data set but plotted as a function of $S_{\rm exp}$(min) are given in (b). Here all values $S_{\rm exp}(k) \geqslant S_{\rm exp}$(min) are taken into account for the evaluation of $\overline{\Delta S}$. For more details about theory and experiment see [Meurders, Glaudemans, Van Hienen and Timmer (1976); Van Hienen (1975); Koops and Glaudemans (1977)].

between S-factors from stripping and pick-up reactions in $A = 21$–44 nuclei is given in [Endt (1977)].

As an illustration of the calculation of pick-up spectroscopic factors we use again the $(1f_{7/2})^n$ wave functions for ^{50}Ti and ^{51}V. From eqs. (8.46) and (8.49) and the c.f.p. listed in table 4.2, one obtains the spectroscopic factors that are given in table 8.7. It is seen that the simple wave functions reproduce the experimental data quite well.

A histogram illustrating the agreement between the theoretical and experimental spectroscopic factors of both stripping and pick-up reactions for over two hundred states in sd- and fp-shell nuclei is given in fig. 8.2a. The comparison is made for the lowest two states of a given spin and isospin in each nucleus. It is seen from the integrated curve of fig. 8.2b that for S-factors larger than 0.3 the average discrepancy between theory and experiment amounts to about 30%; for S-factors larger than 1.5 the average deviation is reduced to only 20%.

8.5. Effects of the configuration space

An example illustrating the sensitivity of calculated S-factors with respect to the model space used for initial and final states will be given for the ^{34}S(^{3}He,α)^{33}S reaction.

The theoretical spectroscopic factors are investigated in three model spaces, to be referred to as (i), (ii) and (iii). In model (i) the wave functions are obtained in a configuration space with three active orbits $1d_{5/2}$, $2s_{1/2}$ and $1d_{3/2}$, but with the

Table 8.8
Some properties of wave functions in ^{33}S and ^{34}S

Nucleus	E_x (MeV)	J^π	$d_{5/2}$ hole admixtures model (i) (%)	Main configuration a)	Intensity of main configuration (%)		
					model (i)	model (ii)	model (iii)
^{34}S	0	0^+	36	$(s^4_{00}\, d^2_{01})_{01}$	37	60	100
^{33}S	0	$\frac{3}{2}^+$	35	$(s^4_{00}\, d_{3/2\,1/2})_{3/2\,1/2}$	36	58	100
	0.84	$\frac{1}{2}^+$	38	$(s^3_{1/2\,1/2}\, d^2_{01})_{1/2\,1/2}$	34	67	100
	1.97	$\frac{5}{2}^+$	43	$(s^3_{1/2\,1/2}\, d^2_{21})_{5/2\,1/2}$	31	62	100
	2.87	$\frac{5}{2}^+$	72	$(s^2_{01}\, d^3_{3/2\,1/2})_{5/2\,1/2}$	18	70	100

a) The orbits $2s_{1/2}$ and $1d_{3/2}$ are denoted by s and d, respectively.

restriction that only up to two holes in the $1d_{5/2}$ orbit are taken into account. Thus no more than two positions in the $1d_{5/2}$ orbit should be unoccupied. In model (ii), for which the configuration space is smaller than for model (i), a closed $1d_{5/2}$ core ($^{28}_{14}Si_{14}$) is assumed with active nucleons in the $2s_{1/2}$ and $1d_{3/2}$ orbits. After the calculation for model (ii) one can construct model (iii). In the latter model space no configuration mixing is taken into account and the configurations assumed for the states involved, are the main components in model (ii). These components are listed in table 8.8. It follows from table 8.9 that the spectroscopic factors calculated for the ground state ($J^\pi = \frac{3}{2}^+$) and first excited state ($J^\pi = \frac{1}{2}^+$) in the model spaces (i), (ii) and (iii) are comparable, although the main configurations (given in table 8.8) occur with quite different intensities. The amount of $1d_{5/2}$ core excitation is very large in space (i), but nevertheless is completely ignored in spaces (ii) and (iii).

Table 8.9
Spectroscopic factors for the reaction $^{34}S(\tau,\alpha)^{33}S$

$J^\pi_i \to J^\pi_f$	Neutron removed from orbit	Spectroscopic factor S			
		theory a)			experiment b)
		(i)	(ii)	(iii)	
$0^+ \to \frac{3}{2}^+(1)$	$1d_{3/2}$	1.8	2.1	2.0	1.9 ± 0.3
$0^+ \to \frac{1}{2}^+(1)$	$2s_{1/2}$	1.0	1.1	1.3	0.68 ± 0.14
$0^+ \to \frac{5}{2}^+(1)$	$1d_{5/2}$	0.05	0	0	0.05 ± 0.02
$0^+ \to \frac{5}{2}^+(2)$	$1d_{5/2}$	0.90	0	0	1.0 ± 0.2

a) See table 8.9.
b) From the compilation [Endt (1977)].

A more sensitive test of the various model assumptions may be expected from a comparison between theory and experiment for pick-up leading to $J^\pi = \frac{5}{2}^+$ states in ^{33}S. For these transitions necessarily a $1d_{5/2}$ neutron must be picked up from the ^{34}S ground state and thus models (ii) and (iii) yield $S = 0$, since they ignore $1d_{5/2}$ holes in ^{33}S. The very small experimental value $S = 0.05$ for the transition to the lowest $\frac{5}{2}^+$ state, however, is not in serious conflict with the assumptions made in models (ii) and (iii). It is remarkable that the large $1d_{5/2}$ hole admixtures with a total intensity of 43% in space (i) do not manifest themselves in a large S-factor. This must be attributed to interference effects (cf. eq. (8.44b)). It turns out to be the second $\frac{5}{2}^+$ state that offers the crucial test of the wave functions. The large experimental spectroscopic factor can be reproduced only if the $1d_{5/2}$ holes are taken into account.

One may conclude that a comparison between theory and experiment for spectroscopic factors provides an essential test of the wave functions despite the rather large uncertainties in the experimental values. Good agreement between experiment and theory does not necessarily guarantee good wave functions, however, since in some cases the calculated values of the spectroscopic factors may not depend strongly on the chosen configuration space, as has been illustrated above.

Important information follows from pick-up reactions that involve particles which occupy orbits that are expected to be only weakly admixed into the ground-state wave function. For example, pick-up from $J^\pi = 0^+$ targets in 2s1d-shell nuclei to $J^\pi = \frac{7}{2}^-$ final states gives information about the amount of $f^n_{7/2}$ admixtures in the 0^+ ground states.

When for a given l-transfer two values of j are allowed (e.g. for $J_i^\pi = \frac{3}{2}^+$ and $J_f^\pi = 2^+$ transfer of both $l_j = d_{3/2}$ and $d_{5/2}$ is possible), one determines theoretically each of the corresponding two spectroscopic factors. In most cases, however, only the sum of the two spectroscopic factors can be compared with the experimental data. When polarized beams and/or targets are used, one can experimentally distinguish the two spectroscopic factors for $j = l + \frac{1}{2}$ and $j = l - \frac{1}{2}$.

8.6. Sum rules for single-particle transfer reactions

From the expression derived in the preceding sections one can derive sum rules for spectroscopic factors. These sum rules can be useful to obtain an upper limit for the experimental spectroscopic factors. Thus they tell whether an observed l_j transfer reaction exhausts most of the expected strength or not.

When initial and final states are assumed to be described by the configurations

$$\Phi_i = |\rho^n\rangle_{\Gamma_i}, \qquad \Phi_f = |\rho^{n-1}\rangle_{\Gamma_f}, \tag{8.54}$$

one obtains from eqs. (8.46) and (8.49) the pick-up spectroscopic factor

$$S^{\text{p.u.}}(\rho) = n\langle \rho^n \Gamma_i | \} \rho^{n-1} \Gamma_f \rangle^2 . \tag{8.55}$$

From the normalization condition of the c.f.p. (see eq. (4.12)) one finds that the sum rule for pick-up reactions is given by

$$\sum_{\Gamma_\mathrm{f}} S^{\mathrm{p.u.}}(\rho) = n \sum_{\Gamma_\mathrm{f}} \langle \rho^n \Gamma_\mathrm{i} | \} \rho^{n-1} \Gamma_\mathrm{f} \rangle^2 = n \,, \tag{8.56}$$

where the summation over Γ_f includes spin and isospin, as well as other labels, for example, seniority and reduced isospin. The number n gives the number of particles in the initial state $|\rho^n\rangle_{\Gamma_\mathrm{i}}$.

For stripping reactions the spectroscopic factor for a single-orbit description is given by (see eq. (8.13))

$$S^{\mathrm{str}}(\rho) = n \langle \rho^n \Gamma_\mathrm{f} | \} \rho^{n-1} \Gamma_\mathrm{i} \rangle^2 \,, \tag{8.57}$$

where n is the number of active particles in the final state. In order to obtain a sum rule for stripping that is equivalent to eq. (8.56) one must sum over initial states Γ_i, which is not feasible experimentally. With a particle-hole relation for c.f.p., however, a more useful sum rule can be derived. This relation is given by [Macfarlane and French (1960)]

$$\langle \rho^n \Gamma_\mathrm{f} | \} \rho^{n-1} \Gamma_\mathrm{i} \rangle^2 = \frac{(N_\rho - n + 1)(2\Gamma_\mathrm{i} + 1)}{n(2\Gamma_\mathrm{f} + 1)} \langle \rho^{N_\rho - n + 1} \Gamma_\mathrm{i} | \} \rho^{N_\rho - n} \Gamma_\mathrm{f} \rangle^2 \,, \tag{8.58}$$

where $N_\rho = 2(2j_\rho + 1)$ denotes the maximum number of nucleons in the orbit ρ. Inserting eq. (8.58) into eq. (8.57) one obtains

$$S^{\mathrm{str}}(\rho) = (N_\rho - n + 1) \frac{2\Gamma_\mathrm{i} + 1}{2\Gamma_\mathrm{f} + 1} \langle \rho^{N_\rho - n + 1} \Gamma_\mathrm{i} | \} \rho^{N_\rho - n} \Gamma_\mathrm{f} \rangle^2 \,. \tag{8.59}$$

For initial and final states given by $\Phi_\mathrm{i} = |\rho^{n-1}\rangle_{\Gamma_\mathrm{i}}$ and $\Phi_\mathrm{f} = |\rho^n\rangle_{\Gamma_\mathrm{f}}$ the normalization condition of the c.f.p. now leads to the sum rule for stripping reactions

$$\sum_{\Gamma_\mathrm{f}} \frac{2\Gamma_\mathrm{f} + 1}{2\Gamma_\mathrm{i} + 1} S^{\mathrm{str}}(\rho) = N_\rho - n + 1 \qquad \text{with } N_\rho = 2(2j_\rho + 1) \,. \tag{8.60}$$

The summation over Γ_f includes all possible values of spin and isospin, as well as other labels, e.g. seniority and reduced isospin for the configuration ρ^n. The right-hand side of eq. (8.60) represents the number of unoccupied places (holes) in the initial state $|\rho^{n-1}\rangle_{\Gamma_\mathrm{i}}$.

It should be remarked that for an application of the sum rules (8.60) and (8.56) it is not necessary to know the spins of the final states. This is because for stripping reactions one determines experimentally the product $(2J_\mathrm{f} + 1)S$ and for pick-up reactions the factor $2J_\mathrm{f} + 1$ is absent (see eqs. (8.7) and (8.45)). The isospins of the final states must be known, however. When the target possesses isospin $T_\mathrm{i} = 0$, one has automatically $T_\mathrm{f} = \frac{1}{2}$. For $T_\mathrm{i} \neq 0$ it follows that one can reach states with $T_\mathrm{f} = T_\mathrm{i} \pm \frac{1}{2}$ and then T_f must be known in order to calculate the Clebsch-Gordan coefficient, $\langle C \rangle$, which enters expressions (8.7) and (8.45) for the measured cross sections. For eq. (8.60), moreover, one needs to know the factor $(2T_\mathrm{f} + 1)/(2T_\mathrm{i} + 1)$.

When the initial and final states are described in a model with active particles in two orbits one can derive similar sum rules.

Suppose that initial and final states are given by

$$\Phi_i = |\rho_\alpha^n \lambda_\beta^m\rangle_{\Gamma_i}\,, \qquad \Phi_f = |\rho_\gamma^{n-1}\lambda_{\beta'}^m\rangle_{\Gamma_f}\,. \tag{8.61}$$

From eq. (8.53) it follows that for the pick-up reaction the spectroscopic factor is given by

$$S^{\text{p.u.}}(\rho) = n\,[\langle\rho^n\alpha|\}\rho^{n-1}\gamma\rangle\; U(\beta\gamma\Gamma_i\rho;\Gamma_f\alpha)]^2\,\delta_{\beta\beta'}\,. \tag{8.62}$$

We show now that a summation over final-state quantum numbers can be performed quite easily. First the orthonormality of the U-coefficients (see eq. (A.1.b6)) is used. This yields

$$\sum_{\Gamma_f} S^{\text{p.u.}}(\rho) = n\langle\rho^n\alpha|\}\rho^{n-1}\gamma\rangle^2\,\delta_{\beta\beta'}\,. \tag{8.63}$$

The summation can also be extended over the intermediate quantum numbers γ and β' that are specified in eq. (8.61). Thus one obtains finally with eq. (8.63)

$$\sum_{\Gamma_f\gamma\beta'} S^{\text{p.u.}}(\rho) = n\,. \tag{8.64}$$

Note that n is the number of particles in the initial state that are equivalent to the transferred particle.

It follows from a comparison of eq. (8.56) with eq. (8.64) that the inactive group λ_β^m does not affect the sum rule. Nonclosed shells, and *a fortiori* closed shells, do not affect the sum when particles in these shells are not transferred in the pick-up reaction.

In order to obtain a useful sum rule for stripping reactions, only a summation over final-state quantum numbers is of practical interest. For initial and final states defined by

$$\Phi_i = |\rho_\alpha^n \lambda_\beta^{m-1}\rangle_{\Gamma_i}\,, \qquad \Phi_f = |\rho_{\alpha'}^n\lambda_\gamma^m\rangle_{\Gamma_f}\,, \tag{8.65}$$

the spectroscopic factor for stripping has been given before as

$$S^{\text{str}}(\lambda) = m\,[\langle\lambda^m\gamma|\}\lambda^{m-1}\beta\rangle\; U(\alpha\beta\Gamma_f\lambda;\Gamma_i\gamma)]^2\,\delta_{\alpha\alpha'}\,. \tag{8.66}$$

To perform the summation over final-state quantum numbers some transformations are necessary. First one can make use of the relation

$$U^2(\alpha\beta\Gamma_f\lambda;\Gamma_i\gamma) = \frac{(2\Gamma_i+1)(2\gamma+1)}{(2\Gamma_f+1)(2\beta+1)}\,U^2(\gamma\alpha\lambda\Gamma_i;\Gamma_f\beta)\,, \tag{8.67}$$

which follows immediately after expressing the U-coefficients in 6-j symbols and using the symmetry properties of 6-j symbols given in appendix A.1. One obtains from eqs. (8.66) and (8.67) and the normalization of the U-coefficients the relation

$$\sum_{\Gamma_f}(2\Gamma_f+1)\,S^{\text{str}}(\lambda) = m\,\frac{(2\Gamma_i+1)(2\gamma+1)}{(2\beta+1)}\,\langle\lambda^m\gamma|\}\lambda^{m-1}\beta\rangle^2\,\delta_{\alpha\alpha'}\,. \tag{8.68}$$

For a summation over all final-state quantum numbers the particle-hole relation for c.f.p., given in eq. (8.58), must be applied. The final result becomes, due to the orthonormality of the c.f.p.,

$$\sum_{\Gamma_f \gamma \alpha'} \frac{2\Gamma_f + 1}{2\Gamma_i + 1} S^{str}(\lambda) = N_\lambda - m + 1 \tag{8.69}$$

with $\Gamma_f \gamma \alpha'$ denoting all final-state quantum numbers. Here $N_\lambda = 2(2j_\lambda + 1)$ denotes the maximum number of particles in shell λ and m is the number of particles in the final state equivalent to the transferred particle λ. The right-hand side of eq. (8.69) thus represents the number of holes in the orbit λ for the target state. Comparison of eq. (8.69) with eq. (8.60) shows that inactive shells (i.e. shells from which no particles are transferred) do not affect the sum.

It is clear from eqs. (8.56), (8.60), (8.64) and (8.69) that the sum rule for stripping as well as for pick-up can never produce a number that is larger than the maximum number of particles that can occupy the orbit involved in the transfer. One thus has

$$\sum_{\Gamma_f} \frac{2\Gamma_f + 1}{2\Gamma_i + 1} S^{str}(\rho) \leqslant 2\rho + 1 , \qquad \sum_{\Gamma_f} S^{p.u.}(\rho) \leqslant 2\rho + 1 , \tag{8.70}$$

where Γ_f denotes *all* final-state quantum numbers. Since $2\rho + 1 \equiv (2j_\rho+1)(2t_\rho+1)$, one has e.g. $2\rho + 1 = 4$, 8 and 12 for $\rho = s_{1/2}$ or $p_{1/2}$, $d_{3/2}$ or $p_{3/2}$ and $d_{5/2}$ or $f_{5/2}$ transfer, respectively. The sum rules given in eqs. (8.64) and (8.69) will be derived again in sect. 15.3 as an application of the second-quantization formalism. The same results can then be obtained without the explicit use of particle-hole relations for c.f.p.

The sum rules derived so far are restricted to initial and final states that are described by pure (unmixed) wave functions. It turns out, however, that the sum rules can be extended to the much more realistic case of wave functions for mixed configurations. In principle one can prove these more general sum rules by writing the spectroscopic factor as in eq. (8.35) and then perform a summation over all final-state quantum numbers. We shall not elaborate on this approach but give instead some of the results obtained in a different way [French and Macfarlane (1961)].

The sum rules so far presented in this chapter can be regarded as applying either to identical particles only or to neutrons and protons simultaneously. In the former case the summations over Γ_f concern the total spin J_f only and for the maximum number of nucleons in one orbit one has $N_\rho = 2j_\rho + 1$. In the latter case the summation over Γ_f includes isospin T_f as well and one has $N_\rho = 2\rho + 1 = (2j_\rho + 1)(2t_\rho + 1) = 2(2j_\rho + 1)$. Unless the target nucleus is characterized by $T_i = 0$, two possibilities exist for the final isospin, i.e. $T_f = T_i \pm \frac{1}{2}$, over which one has to sum also. If final states of only one of these two possible values of T_f are taken into account, however, one can also formulate sum rules for the spectroscopic factors.

Let us define the pick-up strength for one particular l_j value of the transferred particle by

$$G^{\text{p.u.}}(T_{\gtrless}) = \langle C\rangle^2 \sum_{J_\text{f}} S^{\text{p.u.}} , \tag{8.71}$$

where the summation is performed over *all* states of given T_f with $T_\text{f} = T_> = T_i + \frac{1}{2}$ or $T_\text{f} = T_< = T_\text{i} - \frac{1}{2}$. Similarly we define

$$G^{\text{str}}(T_{\gtrless}) = \langle C\rangle^2 \sum_{J_\text{f}} \frac{2J_\text{f}+1}{2J_\text{i}+1} S^{\text{str}} \tag{8.72}$$

for stripping reactions. Denoting with $G_\text{p}^{\text{p.u.}}(T_{\gtrless})$ and $G_\text{p}^{\text{str}}(T_{\gtrless})$ or with $G_\text{n}^{\text{p.u.}}(T_{\gtrless})$ and $G_\text{n}^{\text{str}}(T_{\gtrless})$ a summation that concerns only proton or neutron transfer, respectively, one can derive [French and Macfarlane (1961)] the following sum rules

$$G_{\text{p,n}}^{\text{p.u.}}(T_>) = \frac{T_\text{i} \pm T_{\text{iz}} + 1}{2T_{\text{iz}}(2T_\text{i}+1)} \{-(T_\text{i} - T_{\text{iz}})\langle\text{neutrons}\rangle + (T_\text{i} + T_{\text{iz}})\langle\text{protons}\rangle\} , \tag{8.73a}$$

$$G_{\text{p,n}}^{\text{p.u.}}(T_<) = \frac{T_\text{i} \mp T_{\text{iz}}}{2T_{\text{iz}}(2T_\text{i}+1)} \{(T_\text{i} + T_{\text{iz}} + 1)\langle\text{neutrons}\rangle - (T_\text{i} - T_{\text{iz}} + 1)\langle\text{protons}\rangle\} , \tag{8.73b}$$

$$G_{\text{p,n}}^{\text{str}}(T_>) = \frac{T_\text{i} \mp T_{\text{iz}} + 1}{2T_{\text{iz}}(2T_\text{i}+1)} \{(T_\text{i} + T_{\text{iz}})\langle\text{neutron holes}\rangle - (T_\text{i} - T_{\text{iz}})\langle\text{proton holes}\rangle\} , \tag{8.73c}$$

$$G_{\text{p,n}}^{\text{str}}(T_<) = \frac{T_\text{i} \pm T_{\text{iz}}}{2T_{\text{iz}}(2T_\text{i}+1)} \{-(T_\text{i} - T_{\text{iz}} + 1)\langle\text{neutron holes}\rangle + (T_\text{i} + T_{\text{iz}} + 1)\langle\text{proton holes}\rangle\} , \tag{8.73d}$$

where the upper and lower signs of T_{iz} correspond to proton and neutron transfer, respectively. Here initial (target) isospin and projection are denoted by T_i and T_{iz}. The angular brackets denote average numbers of protons, neutrons, proton holes or neutron holes in the target state that are equivalent to the transferred nucleon. The *average number of nucleons* in a specific orbit ρ is defined as the sum of the numbers of ρ particles in each component of the wave function multiplied by the square of the corresponding amplitude.

It has to be noted that for $T_{\text{iz}} = 0$ the number of neutrons and the number of protons are equal, i.e. $\langle\text{neutrons}\rangle - \langle\text{protons}\rangle = 0$ and $\langle\text{neutron holes}\rangle - \langle\text{proton holes}\rangle = 0$. Substitution of the latter equalities in eqs. (8.73) removes the problem of the seemingly divergent expressions for the case $T_{\text{iz}} = 0$.

Lifting the restriction on the final isospin, i.e. summing over both $T_>$ and $T_<$, one obtains for pick-up reactions

$$G_\text{n}^{\text{p.u.}} = \langle\text{neutrons}\rangle , \qquad G_\text{p}^{\text{p.u.}} = \langle\text{protons}\rangle , \tag{8.74}$$

and for stripping reactions

$$G_\text{n}^{\text{str}} = \langle\text{neutron holes}\rangle , \qquad G_\text{p}^{\text{str}} = \langle\text{proton holes}\rangle . \tag{8.75}$$

Since the maximum number of neutron holes or proton holes in a given orbit j_ρ is equal to $2j_\rho + 1$, one finds from eq. (8.75) for $J_\mathrm{i} = 0$ targets the relation $\Sigma \langle C \rangle^2 S^\mathrm{str} \leqslant 1$; the summation has to be performed over final states $J_\mathrm{f} = j_\rho$. Hence, one observes that for $J_\mathrm{i} = 0$ targets the quantity $\langle C \rangle^2 S$ cannot exceed unity.

Usually one has $T_\mathrm{i} = T_\mathrm{iz}$ for the initial state and then the sum rules can be rewritten for pick-up reactions as

$$G_\mathrm{n}^\mathrm{p.u.}(T_>) = \frac{\langle \text{protons} \rangle}{N - Z + 1}\,, \tag{8.76a}$$

$$G_\mathrm{n}^\mathrm{p.u.}(T_<) = \langle \text{neutrons} \rangle - \frac{\langle \text{protons} \rangle}{N - Z + 1}\,. \tag{8.76b}$$

Similarly one finds for stripping reactions (with $T_\mathrm{i} = T_\mathrm{iz}$)

$$G_\mathrm{p}^\mathrm{str}(T_>) = \frac{\langle \text{neutron holes} \rangle}{N - Z + 1}\,, \tag{8.77a}$$

$$G_\mathrm{p}^\mathrm{str}(T_<) = \langle \text{proton holes} \rangle - \frac{\langle \text{neutron holes} \rangle}{N - Z + 1}\,. \tag{8.77b}$$

Here N and Z represent the number of neutrons and protons in the target nucleus, respectively. In the case of $T_\mathrm{i} = T_\mathrm{iz}$ the proton pick-up and neutron stripping reactions can lead to $T_\mathrm{f} = T_>$ states only and thus one obtains (since there are no contributions from $T_\mathrm{f} = T_<$ states) the same results as in eqs. (8.74) and (8.75)

$$G_\mathrm{p}^\mathrm{p.u.}(T_>) = \langle \text{protons} \rangle\,, \qquad G_\mathrm{n}^\mathrm{str}(T_>) = \langle \text{neutron holes} \rangle\,. \tag{8.78}$$

The average nucleon occupation numbers discussed above and derived from the observed strengths G provide an interesting test of the shell model. It is shown that these numbers can be very easily determined from the model wave functions. Let us take as an example the ground state of ${}^{37}_{17}\mathrm{Cl}_{20}$ in a $2\mathrm{s}_{1/2}$ $1\mathrm{d}_{3/2}$ configuration space, which is given by

$$|\Psi({}^{37}\mathrm{Cl})\rangle_{3/2\;3/2} = a|\mathrm{s}^4\mathrm{d}^5\rangle + b|\mathrm{s}^3\mathrm{d}^6\rangle + c|\mathrm{s}^2\mathrm{d}^7\rangle \qquad \text{with } a^2 + b^2 + c^2 = 1\,, \tag{8.79}$$

where s and d denote the $2\mathrm{s}_{1/2}$ and $1\mathrm{d}_{3/2}$ orbits, respectively. One thus obtains for the average number of nucleons in the $1\mathrm{d}_{3/2}$ orbit $\langle 1\mathrm{d}_{3/2}$ nucleons$\rangle = 5a^2 + 6b^2 + 7c^2$. Similarly for $2\mathrm{s}_{1/2}$ particles $\langle 2\mathrm{s}_{1/2}$ nucleons$\rangle = 4a^2 + 3b^2 + 2c^2$. It is clear that the total number of active particles given by the sum $\langle 1\mathrm{d}_{3/2}$ nucleons$\rangle + \langle 2\mathrm{s}_{1/2}$ nucleons$\rangle = 9$ does not depend on the amplitudes. The average number of holes follows analogously from the relations $\langle 1\mathrm{d}_{3/2}$ holes$\rangle = 3a^2 + 2b^2 + c^2$ and $\langle 2\mathrm{s}_{1/2}$ holes$\rangle = b^2 + 2c^2$.

In order to obtain the average number of particles or holes for protons and neutrons separately, one can write the wave function (8.79) such that for each configuration the numbers of protons and neutrons are specified. One can put at most two identical particles in the $2\mathrm{s}_{1/2}$ orbit and four in the $1\mathrm{d}_{3/2}$ orbit. Thus the wave function of ${}^{37}_{17}Cl_{20}$ in the same model space as used in eq. (8.79) then becomes (since there are three active protons (π) and six active neutrons (ν))

$$|\Psi({}^{37}\mathrm{Cl})\rangle_{J=3/2} = a\,|\pi(\mathrm{s}^2\mathrm{d})\,\nu(\mathrm{s}^2\mathrm{d}^4)\rangle_{3/2} + b\,|\pi(\mathrm{sd}^2)\,\nu(\mathrm{s}^2\mathrm{d}^4)\rangle_{3/2} + c\,|\pi(\mathrm{d}^3)\,\nu(\mathrm{s}^2\mathrm{d}^4)\rangle_{3/2}\,. \tag{8.80}$$

One obtains the average occupation numbers as $\langle 1\mathrm{d}_{3/2}$ protons$\rangle = a^2 + 2b^2 + 3c^2$, $\langle 1\mathrm{d}_{3/2}$ neutrons$\rangle = 4a^2 + 4b^2 + 4c^2 = 4(a^2 + b^2 + c^2) = 4$ and analogously for the other averages. Note that the result for neutrons in this example is independent of the amplitudes of the configurations, since both neutron orbits are completely filled.

8.7. Two-particle transfer reactions

The direct reaction process is not restricted to single-particle transfer. For instance, one may consider any multi-particle transfer reaction such as (^{6}Li,d), where an alpha particle is transferred. In this section only two-nucleon transfer reactions are considered. Some examples are (^{3}He,n), (^{3}He,p), (t,p) and (α,d) for stripping and (p,t), (p,^{3}He) and (d,α) for pick-up of two nucleons.

In analogy with the single-particle transfer process, the cross section can be evaluated in the distorted wave Born approximation. If spin-orbit forces are neglected one obtains the expression [Towner and Hardy (1969)]

$$\sigma(\theta) = \sum_{LL_zSJT} f(S,T)\,|\sum_{\rho\lambda} S^{1/2}(\rho\lambda;JT)B(LL_z\theta EQ)|^2\,. \tag{8.81}$$

Here the kind of reaction enters through the function $f(S,T)$. The kinematical aspects and the mechanism of the reaction are contained in the transfer amplitude $B(LL_z\theta EQ)$, where θ, E and Q denote the scattering angle, the energy of the incident particle and the reaction Q-value, respectively. The nuclear-structure information is contained in the spectroscopic amplitude $S^{1/2}(\rho\lambda;JT)$. There is an incoherent summation over the quantum numbers LL_zSJT of the two transferred nucleons taken as a cluster. The quantum numbers of the transferred pair are defined by $\boldsymbol{L} = \boldsymbol{l}_\rho + \boldsymbol{l}_\lambda$, $\boldsymbol{S} = \boldsymbol{s}_\rho + \boldsymbol{s}_\lambda$, $\boldsymbol{J} = \boldsymbol{j}_\rho + \boldsymbol{j}_\lambda$ and $\boldsymbol{T} = \boldsymbol{t}_\rho + \boldsymbol{t}_\lambda$ with $\boldsymbol{J} = \boldsymbol{L} + \boldsymbol{S}$. There is also a summation (within the absolute-value bars) over ρ and λ, which refers to the individual quantum numbers n, l and j of the two nucleons. It is the latter summation that prevents a complete factorization into a nuclear-structure part $S^{1/2}(\rho\lambda;JT)$ and a nuclear-reaction part $B(LL_z\theta EQ)$. Due to the summation over ρ and λ in eq. (8.81) many different two-nucleon configurations contribute coherently to the cross section and it is not possible to extract the various spectroscopic amplitudes $S^{1/2}(\rho\lambda;JT)$ directly from the measured cross sections.

A separation between nuclear structure and reaction parts is possible for the calculation of the single-nucleon transfer cross section, where the contributions for each individual quantum number ρ of the transferred nucleon do not interfere but add up incoherently. Hence the spectroscopic factors S can be derived from the experimental data and thus can subsequently be compared with theoretical values.

For two-nucleon transfer reactions, theory and experiment must be compared in a different way due to the coherence properties. One has to assume some nuclear model and calculate, after a theoretical evaluation of the spectroscopic amplitudes $S^{1/2}$, the cross section for two-particle transfer. Then the latter can be compared with experiment. It is a disadvantage that no spectroscopic amplitudes can be obtained experimentally in a model-independent way, but it turns out that often the calculated cross section, defined in eq. (8.81), is very sensitive to details of the initial- and final-state wave functions. Thus two-particle transfer reactions can provide a critical test of the calculated wave functions. The spectroscopic amplitude in eq. (8.81) is defined as

$$S^{1/2}(\rho\lambda;\Gamma) = \sqrt{\tfrac{1}{2}A(A-1)} \tag{8.82}$$

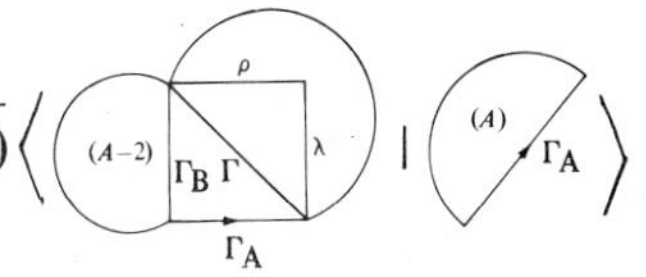

where in the bra function $(A-2)$ represents a configuration of $A-2$ nucleons distributed over one or more single-particle orbits. This group is coupled with the transferred antisymmetric two-particle group $(\rho\lambda)_\Gamma$ to a final spin and isospin Γ_A. Similarly (A) represents a configuration of A nucleons distributed over one or more single-particle orbits.

The square of the spectroscopic amplitude can be considered as the spectroscopic factor for two-particle transfer reactions, but because of the coherence properties of the two-nucleon transfer reaction, the amplitude is always required. A spectroscopic factor thus defined is seen to have the same overall structure as for single-particle transfer reactions, given in eqs. (8.15) and (8.16). The factor $\sqrt{\binom{A}{2}} = \sqrt{\tfrac{1}{2}A(A-1)}$ accounts for the fact that the two transferred nucleons may occupy any two of the A positions of the configuration (A).

Various restrictions are imposed upon the quantum numbers that appear in eq. (8.81). From angular-momentum considerations it follows that for two-particle stripping the spins of initial and final nuclear state are related by

$$\boldsymbol{J}_{\mathrm{f}} = \boldsymbol{J}_{\mathrm{i}} + \boldsymbol{J}\,, \qquad \boldsymbol{J} = \boldsymbol{L} + \boldsymbol{S}\,. \tag{8.83}$$

The connection of J and L with the single-particle states ρ and λ into which the two nucleons are stripped is given by

$$\boldsymbol{J} = \boldsymbol{j}_\rho + \boldsymbol{j}_\lambda\,,$$

$$\boldsymbol{L} = \boldsymbol{l}_\rho + \boldsymbol{l}_\lambda\,,$$

$$\boldsymbol{S} = \boldsymbol{s}_\rho + \boldsymbol{s}_\lambda\,. \tag{8.84}$$

A transferred pair with $S = 0$ is in the singlet state and with $S = 1$ it is in the triplet state. The isospin T, the seniority v and the reduced isospin t of the initial and final nuclear states are related by

$$\boldsymbol{T}_\mathrm{f} = \boldsymbol{T}_\mathrm{i} + \boldsymbol{T} \qquad \text{with } \boldsymbol{T} = \boldsymbol{t}_\rho + \boldsymbol{t}_\lambda \,,$$

$$v_\mathrm{i} - v_\mathrm{f} = 0, \pm 2 \,,$$

$$t_\mathrm{i} - t_\mathrm{f} = 0, \pm 1 \,. \tag{8.85}$$

The summation over the various two-particle configurations is simplified by the assumption of relative S-states only, i.e. their relative orbital angular momenta are equal to zero. This assumption is consistent with the absence of tensor- and velocity-dependent components in the interaction. It is, moreover, in agreement with the observation that the internal wave functions of few-particle systems like ^{2}H, ^{3}H, ^{3}He, ^{4}He are predominantly in a symmetric S-state, in which the relative motion of each nucleon pair is itself in an S-state. The wave function of the transferred pair of particles therefore is spatially symmetric. Due to the required antisymmetry of the total wave function, this implies antisymmetry of the spin-isospin part. For a two-particle system this leads to the restriction (cf. sect. 2.4)

$$S + T = 1 \,. \tag{8.86}$$

The parities of initial and final states are related by the expression

$$\Pi_\mathrm{i}\Pi_\mathrm{f} = (-1)^{l_\rho + l_\lambda} = (-1)^L \,. \tag{8.87}$$

For the latter equality use is made of the assumption that the transferred particles are in a relative S-state.

In reactions where two protons or two neutrons are transferred, such as in (t,p) or (^{3}He,n) reactions, one always has $T = 1$ since $T_z = \pm 1$ and thus $S = 0$. Then for identical-nucleon transfer eq. (8.86) reduces to

$$\boldsymbol{J}_\mathrm{f} = \boldsymbol{J}_\mathrm{i} + \boldsymbol{L} \,. \tag{8.88}$$

From this relation it follows that, when the target spin is given by $J_\mathrm{i} = 0$ and two identical nucleons are transferred, the final spin is given by $J_\mathrm{f} = L$. The final spin thus follows from the observed angular distribution.

More complicated are reactions such as (^{3}He,p) or (t,n) in which an n-p pair is transferred. In this case both $T_\mathrm{np} = 0$ or 1 and thus $S_\mathrm{np} = 1$ or 0, respectively, may contribute. An exception is the (α,d) reaction, where also an n-p pair is transferred. In this case one has only $S_\mathrm{np} = 1$, $T_\mathrm{np} = 0$, since the emitted deuteron and hence the transferred n-p pair is predominantly in a triplet state. A summary of two-nucleon transfer selection rules is given in table 8.10.

Let us now discuss as an example the reaction ^{31}P(^{3}He,p)^{33}S. The ground state of ^{31}P has $J_\mathrm{i}^\pi = \frac{1}{2}^+$ and $T_\mathrm{i} = \frac{1}{2}$. The first excited state of ^{33}S at 0.84 MeV with $J_\mathrm{f}^\pi = \frac{1}{2}^+$ and $T_\mathrm{f} = \frac{1}{2}$ can be reached according to eqs. (8.83), (8.86) and (8.87) with $J = 0$, $T = 1$, $S = 0$ and $L = 0$ but also with $J = 1$, $T = 0$, $S = 1$ and $L = 0$ or 2. Experimentally one observes a pure $L = 0$ distribution. The absence of $L = 2$ transfer can be

Table 8.10
Selection rules for two-nucleon transfer reactions

Reaction [a]	S	T	L = even; $\Pi_i\Pi_f = +1$		L = odd; $\Pi_i\Pi_f = -1$	
			$\rho = \lambda$	$\rho \neq \lambda$	$\rho = \lambda$	$\rho \neq \lambda$
$(^3He,n),(t,p)$	0	1	$J = L$ = even	$J = L$ = even	not allowed	$J = L$ = odd
(α,d)	1	0	$J = L \pm 1$ = odd	$J = L, L \pm 1$	not allowed	$J = L, L \pm 1$

[a] For $(^3He,p)$ and (t,n) reactions no such selection rules exist.

understood from a simple shell-model picture in which one expects a transition from the configuration $(2s_{1/2})^3$ for the ^{31}P ground state to the configuration $|(2s_{1/2})^3_{1/2\,1/2}(1d_{3/2})^2_{01}\rangle_{1/2\,1/2}$ for the ^{33}S excited state. The transferred pair $(1d_{3/2})^2_{01}$ has isospin $T = 1$ and thus must be in the singlet state $S = 0$. From eqs. (8.83) and (8.87) it then follows that only $L = 0$ is allowed.

It should be remarked that when one observes a mixed $L = 0$ and $L = 2$ transition from a $J_i = 0$ target, the transferred pair must be in the triplet $S = 1$ state as follows from eq. (8.83). The value of the final spin is then given by $\boldsymbol{J}_f = \boldsymbol{L} + \boldsymbol{S}$. Thus with $S = 1$ it leads to $J_f = 1$ with a parity that is identical to that of the initial state (since L is even). Similarly one can easily verify that a mixed $L = 1$ and $L = 3$ transition from a $J_i = 0$ target leads to $J_f = 2$ with a parity opposite to that of the initial state. This result can be summarized as follows:

$$\text{for } J_i^\pi = 0^+ \begin{cases} L = 0 \text{ and } 2 \Rightarrow J_f^\pi = 1^+ \\ L = 1 \text{ and } 3 \Rightarrow J_f^\pi = 2^- . \end{cases} \tag{8.89}$$

8.8. Spectroscopic amplitudes

Let us now return to the spectroscopic amplitudes $S^{1/2}$ (see eq. (8.82)), which can be calculated if initial- and final-state wave functions are known. The method will be outlined for two-particle stripping. In case of two-particle pick-up a very similar procedure can be followed.

One active orbit. Suppose that the initial- and final-state wave functions are given by

$\Phi_i =$ 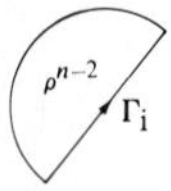

, $\Phi_f =$ 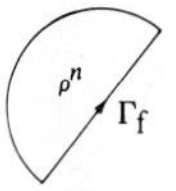

. (8.90)

In order to reach the final state, two nucleons in a configuration ρ^2 must be transferred. The spectroscopic amplitude is defined by (cf. eq. (8.82))

$S^{1/2}(\rho^2;\Gamma) = \sqrt{\tfrac{1}{2}n(n-1)}\,\Big\langle$ 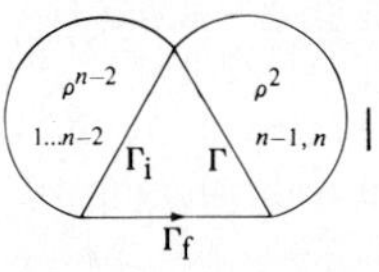

$\Big|$ 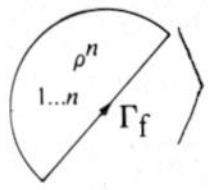

$\Big\rangle$. (8.91)

Expanding the ket wave function of eq. (8.91) with the double-parentage coefficients defined in eq. (4.45), one obtains

$$S^{1/2}(\rho^2;\Gamma) = \sqrt{\tfrac{1}{2}n(n-1)}\sum_{\alpha\beta}\langle\rho^n\Gamma_f|\}\rho^{n-2}\alpha(\rho^2\beta)\rangle\Big\langle$$ 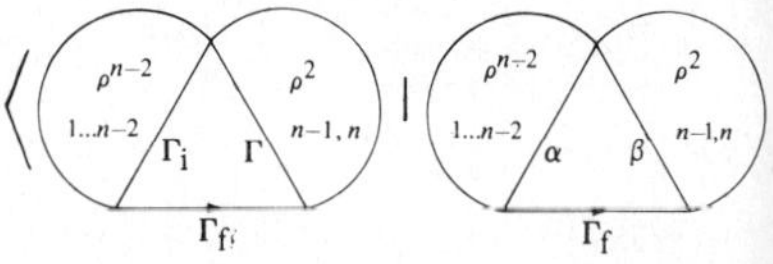 (8.92)

The orthonormality of the wave functions leads to Kronecker deltas $\delta_{\Gamma_i\alpha}\,\delta_{\Gamma\beta}$ and thus one obtains

$$S^{1/2}(\rho^2;\Gamma) = \sqrt{\tfrac{1}{2}n(n-1)}\langle\rho^n\Gamma_f|\}\rho^{n-2}\Gamma_i(\rho^2\Gamma)\rangle\,. \tag{8.93}$$

Two active orbits. Firstly we discuss the case with the two transferred particles being captured in the same orbit. Let initial and final states be given by

$\Phi_i =$ 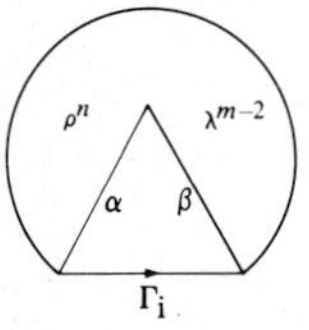 , $\Phi_f =$ 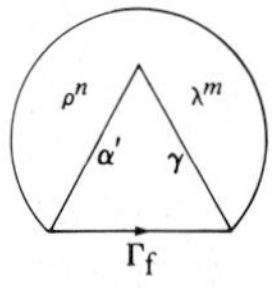 . (8.94)

The spectroscopic amplitude is defined by

$$S^{1/2}(\lambda^2;\Gamma) = \sqrt{\tfrac{1}{2}(n+m)(n+m-1)}$$ 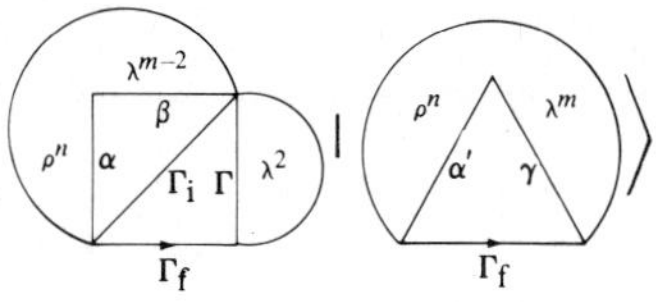 , (8.95)

where the group λ^2 represents the antisymmetric pair of transferred nucleons. We now have to rewrite the bra and ket wave functions such that the overlap can be determined.

The bra function of eq. (8.95) can be expanded with eq. (5.4) in terms of wave functions that are antisymmetric in ρ^n_α, λ^{m-2}_β and λ^2_Γ separately. Since there are $(n+m-2)!/n!(m-2)!$ such terms and each contributes the same amount, one obtains

$$S^{1/2}(\lambda^2;\Gamma) = \sqrt{\frac{(n+m)!}{2n!(m-2)!}}$$ 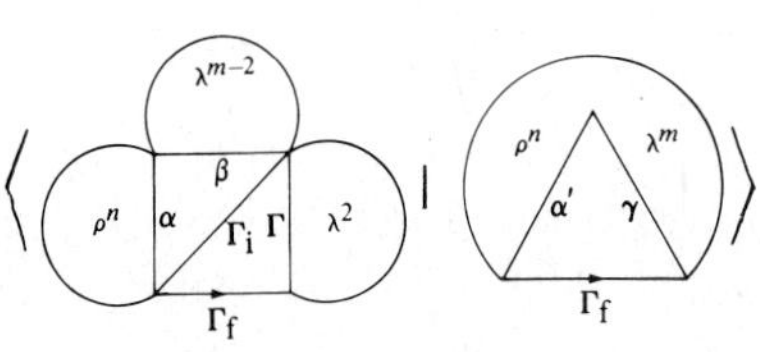 . (8.96)

The ket wave function can now be expanded similarly with eq. (5.4). From orthonormality considerations it follows that only the term $P_r = 1$ contributes. This yields

$$S^{1/2}(\lambda^2;\Gamma)=\sqrt{\tfrac{1}{2}m(m-1)}\Bigg\langle$$ 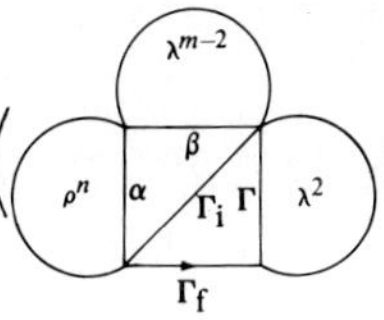 $$\Bigg|$$ 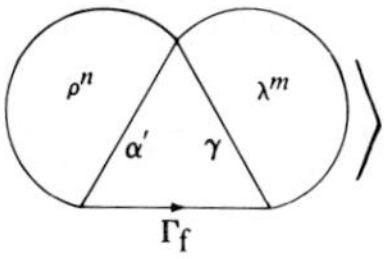 $$\Bigg\rangle\,. \qquad (8.97)$$

The ket wave function can now be expanded further with the aid of double-parentage and recoupling coefficients into

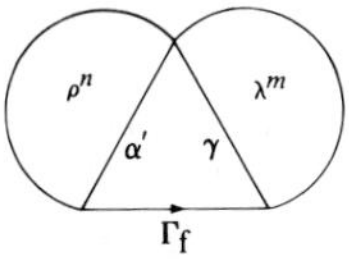 $$=\sum_{\mu\epsilon}\langle\lambda^m\gamma|\}\lambda^{m-2}\mu(\lambda^2\epsilon)\rangle$$ 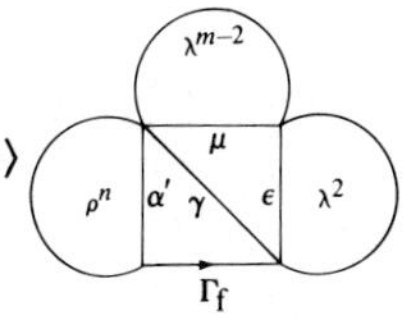

$$=\sum_{\mu\epsilon}\langle\lambda^m\gamma|\}\lambda^{m-2}\mu(\lambda^2\epsilon)\rangle\sum_{\nu}U(\alpha'\mu\Gamma_{\mathrm{f}}\,\epsilon;\nu\gamma)$$ 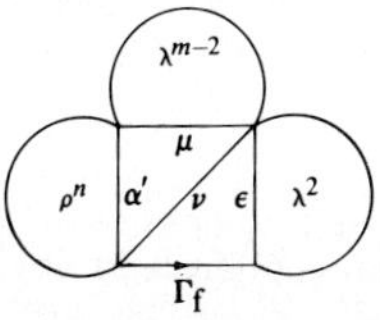 $$. \qquad (8.98)$$

When expression (8.98) is inserted into eq. (8.97) it follows from the orthonormality of the wave functions that one obtains a non-zero contribution only for $\alpha=\alpha'$, $\beta=\mu$, $\epsilon=\Gamma$ and $\nu=\Gamma_{\mathrm{i}}$. Thus the final result is given by

$$S^{1/2}(\lambda^2;\Gamma)=\sqrt{\tfrac{1}{2}m(m-1)}\,\langle\lambda^m\gamma|\}\lambda^{m-2}\beta(\lambda^2\Gamma)\rangle\,U(\alpha\beta\Gamma_{\mathrm{f}}\,\Gamma;\Gamma_{\mathrm{i}}\,\gamma)\,. \qquad (8.99)$$

When initial and final states are described by mixed configurations involving only two active orbits, all cases which are encountered can be summarized rather simply. Let the two transferred particles occupy the orbits σ_{a} and σ_{b}. Then the transition for two-nucleon stripping as well as pick-up can be symbolized by

$$\sum_k a_k$$ 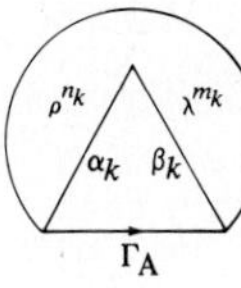 $$\rightleftarrows\sum_l b_l\Bigg[$$ 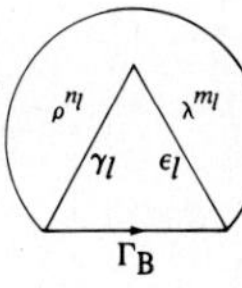 $$\times$$ 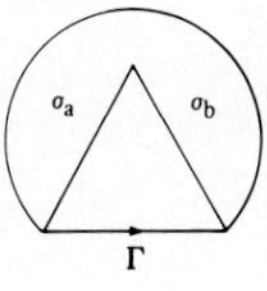 $$\Bigg]^{\Gamma_{\mathrm{A}}}, \qquad (8.100)$$

where a_k and b_l specify the amplitudes and the symbol $\times$ denotes a vector coupling. For $\sigma_{\mathrm{a}}=\sigma_{\mathrm{b}}=\lambda$ one finds immediately from eq. (8.99)

$$S^{1/2}(\lambda^2;\Gamma)=\sum_{kl}a_kb_l\sqrt{\tfrac{1}{2}m_k(m_k-1)}\,\langle\lambda^{m_k}\beta_k|\}\lambda^{m_k-2}\epsilon_l(\lambda^2\,\Gamma)\rangle$$

$$\times\,U(\alpha_k\epsilon_l\Gamma_{\mathrm{A}}\,\Gamma;\Gamma_{\mathrm{B}}\beta_k)\,\delta_{n_kn_l}\,\delta_{m_km_l+2}\,\delta_{\alpha_k\gamma_l}\,. \qquad (8.101)$$

When two particles in the orbit ρ instead of the orbit λ are transferred, one can apply the recoupling (5.13) to both initial- and final-state wave functions to reduce this case to the one discussed above. One then obtains for $\sigma_a = \sigma_b = \rho$ the expression of the spectroscopic amplitude

$$S^{1/2}(\rho^2;\Gamma) = \sum_{k,l} a_k\, b_l \sqrt{\tfrac{1}{2}n_k(n_k-1)}\,\langle \rho^{n_k}\alpha_k | \} \rho^{n_k-2}\gamma_l(\rho^2\Gamma)\rangle$$

$$\times\, U(\beta_k\gamma_l\Gamma_A\Gamma;\Gamma_B\alpha_k)\,(-1)^{\Gamma_A+\Gamma_B-\alpha_k-\gamma_l}\,\delta_{m_k m_l}\,\delta_{n_k,n_l+2}\,\delta_{\beta_k\epsilon_l}, \qquad (8.102)$$

where the extra phase factors derive from the recoupling mentioned above.

The derivation of the spectroscopic amplitude for $\sigma_a = \rho$ and $\sigma_b = \lambda$ is somewhat more complicated. Now one has to separate off one ρ-particle and one λ-particle from the wave function Ψ_{Γ_A} in eq. (8.100) and recouple such that the overlap with Ψ_{Γ_B} can be evaluated immediately. In order to simplify the notation we discuss the procedure for pure configurations such that the indices k and l can be suppressed. The extension to mixed-configuration wave functions is obvious.

From the definition (8.82) and application of the expansion (5.4) one obtains

$$S^{1/2}(\rho\lambda;\Gamma) = \sqrt{\tfrac{1}{2}(n+m)(n+m-1)}$$

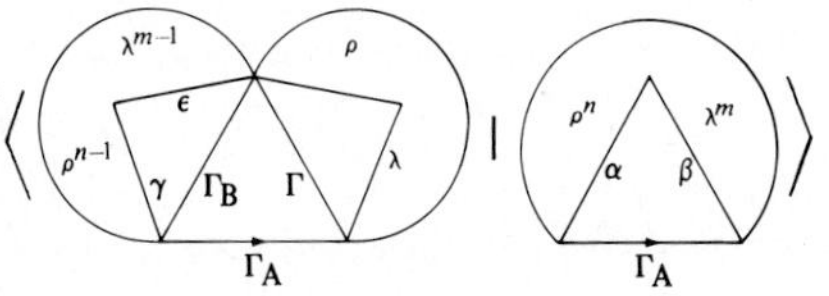

$$= \sqrt{\frac{(n+m)!}{(n-1)!\,(m-1)!}} \qquad (8.103)$$

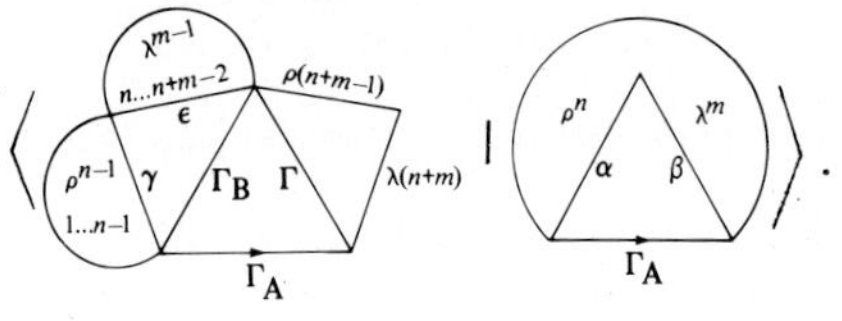

With expansion (5.4) applied to the ket wave function, one arrives at

$$S^{1/2}(\rho\lambda;\Gamma) = (-1)^{m-1}\sqrt{nm} \qquad (8.104)$$

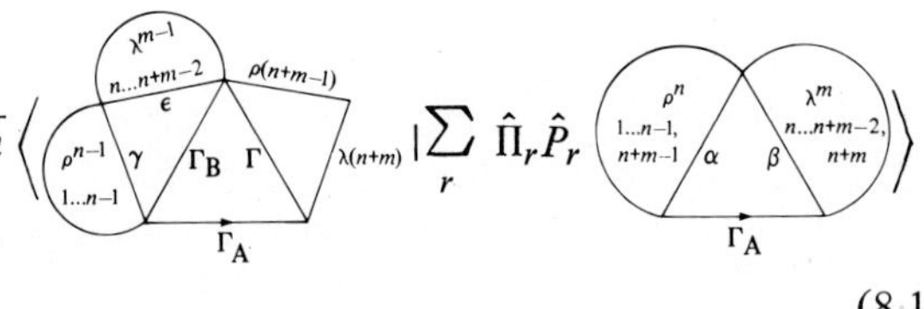

where the phase factor $(-1)^{m-1}$ results from a permutation of the particle labels in the completely antisymmetric ket wave function. After application of the c.f.p. expansion to the groups ρ^n and λ^m one arrives at

$$S^{1/2}(\rho\lambda;\Gamma) = (-1)^{m-1}\sqrt{nm}\sum_{\zeta\theta}\langle \rho^n\alpha | \} \rho^{n-1}\zeta\rangle\langle \lambda^m\beta | \} \lambda^{m-1}\theta\rangle$$

$$\times \qquad (8.105)$$

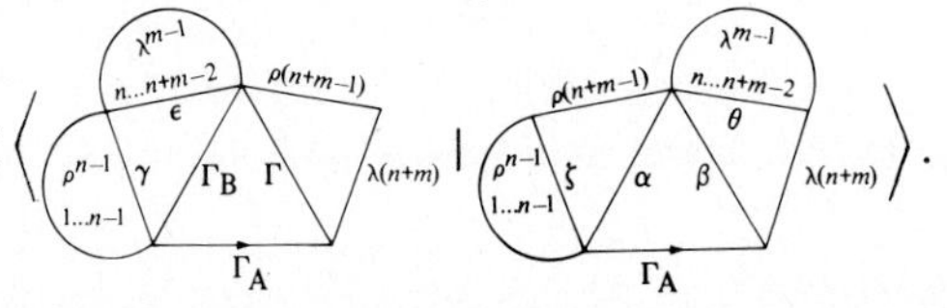

Applying the recoupling (5.21) to the ket wave function, one obtains

$$S^{1/2}(\rho\lambda;\Gamma) = (-1)^{m-1}\sqrt{nm}\sum_{\substack{\zeta\theta\\ \xi\eta}}\langle\rho^n\alpha|\}\rho^{n-1}\zeta\rangle\langle\lambda^m\beta|\}\lambda^{m-1}\theta\rangle$$

$$\times\sqrt{(2\alpha+1)(2\beta+1)(2\xi+1)(2\eta+1)}\begin{Bmatrix}\zeta & \rho & \alpha\\ \theta & \lambda & \beta\\ \xi & \eta & \Gamma_A\end{Bmatrix}$$

$\times\Big\langle$ 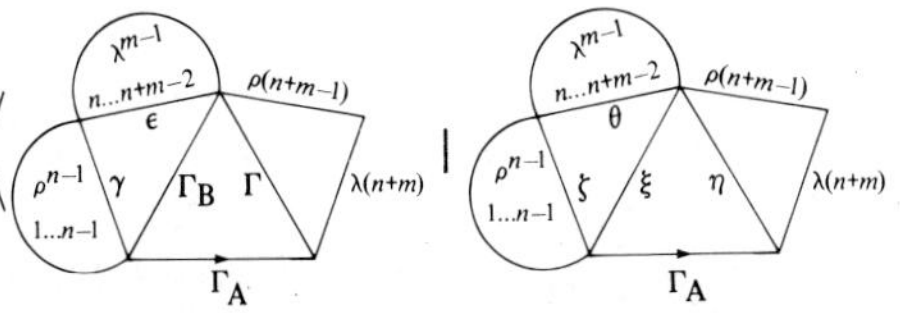 $\Big\rangle$. (8.106)

Due to the orthogonality one obtains a nonvanishing contribution only for $\zeta = \gamma$, $\theta = \epsilon$, $\xi = \Gamma_B$ and $\eta = \Gamma$. The result becomes

$$S^{1/2}(\rho\lambda;\Gamma) = (-1)^{m-1}\sqrt{nm}\,\langle\rho^n\alpha|\}\rho^{n-1}\gamma\rangle\,\langle\lambda^m\beta|\}\lambda^{m-1}\epsilon\rangle$$

$$\times\sqrt{(2\alpha+1)(2\beta+1)(2\Gamma_B+1)(2\Gamma+1)}\begin{Bmatrix}\gamma & \rho & \alpha\\ \epsilon & \lambda & \beta\\ \Gamma_B\Gamma & \Gamma_A\end{Bmatrix}, \qquad (8.107)$$

where the quantum numbers are specified by $\Phi_{\Gamma_B} = |\rho^n_\gamma\lambda^{m-1}_\epsilon\rangle_{\Gamma_B}$ and $\Phi_{\Gamma_A} = |\rho^n_a\lambda^m_\beta\rangle_{\Gamma_A}$. Thus, for mixed configurations, one finds for the case $\sigma_a = \rho$ and $\sigma_b = \lambda$ of eq. (8.100) the result

$$S^{1/2}(\rho\lambda;\Gamma) = \sum_{k,l} a_k\, b_l(-1)^{m_k-1}\sqrt{n_k m_k}\,\langle\rho^{n_k}\alpha_k|\}\rho^{n_k-1}\gamma_l\rangle\langle\lambda^{m_k}\beta_k|\}\lambda^{m_k-1}\epsilon_l\rangle$$

$$\times\sqrt{(2\alpha_k+1)(2\beta_k+1)(2\Gamma_B+1)(2\Gamma+1)}\begin{Bmatrix}\gamma_l & \rho & \alpha_k\\ \epsilon_l & \lambda & \beta_k\\ \Gamma_B & \Gamma & \Gamma_A\end{Bmatrix}\delta_{n_k\, n_l+1}\,\delta_{m_k\, m_l+1}\,. \qquad (8.108)$$

These equations are still rather simple, since for two active orbits no summations over intermediate quantum numbers are involved.

CHAPTER 9

ELECTROMAGNETIC TRANSITION OPERATORS

A large part of the knowledge of nuclei is obtained from the study of electromagnetic transitions, since the electromagnetic interaction is well understood, in contrast with the nuclear forces. It is, for example, the main source of information about the spin assignments of nuclear states. The nuclear multipole moments and the transition rates for the various multipole radiations can be calculated theoretically, once the nuclear wave functions are known.

In this book we shall not give a complete derivation of the required electromagnetic transition operators. Instead only some of the most important steps that lead to explicit expressions for these operators will be summarized. For more details the reader is referred to, for example, [Blatt and Weisskopf (1952); Jackson (1962); Morse and Feshbach (1953) and Roy and Nigam (1967)].

In sect. 9.1 some of the basic equations related to the electromagnetic interaction are summarized. A derivation of the operators that will be used later to calculate electromagnetic transitions and moments is given in sect. 9.2. Centre-of-mass corrections are treated in sect. 9.3. The angular-momentum and parity selection rules are discussed in sect. 9.4. In sect. 9.5 measurable quantities such as reduced transition rates, lifetimes, branching and mixing ratios are defined. The much-used Weisskopf single-particle estimates of transition strengths are derived in sect. 9.6. In sect. 9.7 it is shown that the isospin formalism allows us to express transition strengths in terms of isoscalar and isovector contributions. This separation can be used for example, to correlate transition rates in isobaric mass multiplets. Most applications of the formulas derived in this chapter are discussed in following chapters.

9.1. Basic formulas

The interaction between the nuclear currents and charges on the one hand and the radiation field on the other is given by the coupling term

$$H_{\text{e.m.}} = \frac{1}{c}\int \boldsymbol{j}(\boldsymbol{r},t) \cdot \boldsymbol{A}(\boldsymbol{r},t)\,\mathrm{d}\boldsymbol{r} + \int \rho(\boldsymbol{r},t)\,\varphi(\boldsymbol{r},t)\,\mathrm{d}\boldsymbol{r}\,, \tag{9.1}$$

where $\boldsymbol{j}(\boldsymbol{r},t)$ and $\rho(\boldsymbol{r},t)$ represent the current and charge densities in the nucleus, respectively. The electric and magnetic field strengths of the radiation field are expressed in terms of the vector potential $\boldsymbol{A}(\boldsymbol{r},t)$ and the scalar potential $\varphi(\boldsymbol{r},t)$ by the familiar relations

$$\boldsymbol{E}(\boldsymbol{r},t) = -\boldsymbol{\nabla}\varphi(\boldsymbol{r},t) - \frac{1}{c}\frac{\partial \boldsymbol{A}(\boldsymbol{r},t)}{\partial t}\,, \tag{9.2a}$$

$$B(r,t) = \nabla \times A(r,t) . \tag{9.2b}$$

The fields E and B of the unperturbed radiation field near the nucleus must satisfy the Maxwell equations without source terms, i.e. with vanishing currents and charges,

$$\nabla \times E = -\frac{1}{c}\frac{\partial B}{\partial t}, \qquad \nabla \cdot E = 0 ,$$

$$\nabla \times B = \frac{1}{c}\frac{\partial E}{\partial t}, \qquad \nabla \cdot B = 0 . \tag{9.3}$$

The interaction $H_{\text{e.m.}}$ is considered as a perturbation causing transitions between the stationary states of the nuclear Hamiltonian. The transition amplitudes are determined in perturbation theory by the matrix elements of $H_{\text{e.m.}}$ between the initial and final states considered. The emitted or absorbed gamma radiation can be characterized by its energy, angular momentum and parity. The angular momentum carried away by the gamma quantum determines the multipolarity of the radiation. Angular momentum L corresponds to 2^L pole radiation with its characteristic radiation pattern, i.e. the angular distribution of the intensity of the emitted gamma rays. Two identical intensity distributions for one particular value of L still may correspond to different parities of the fields. The two different possibilities are distinguished as electric 2^L pole radiation and magnetic 2^L pole radiation.

In order to derive the corresponding transition rates it is necessary to make a multipole expansion of the perturbation $H_{\text{e.m.}}$. This requires a decomposition of the potentials into the electric and magnetic multipole parts for the fields they describe. This allows us to investigate the interaction of the nuclear charges and currents with the various multipole fields.

We now discuss some important properties of charges and currents and of the vector Helmholtz equation that are essential for the derivation of the electromagnetic operators. The current and charge densities are connected by the continuity equation that expresses the conservation of charge,

$$\nabla \cdot j(r,t) + \frac{\partial}{\partial t}\rho(r,t) = 0 . \tag{9.4}$$

The description of the process of emission or absorption of gamma radiation by nuclei requires the use of quantum mechanics. Therefore, the current density $j(r,t)$ and the charge density $\rho(r,t)$ are to be considered as operators. The time derivative of an operator $F(t)$ is given by the relation

$$\frac{\partial}{\partial t}F(t) = \frac{\mathrm{i}}{\hbar}\,[H, F(t)] , \tag{9.5}$$

and thus one can write eq. (9.4) as

$$\nabla \cdot j^{\text{op}}(r,t) + \frac{\mathrm{i}}{\hbar}[H, \rho^{\text{op}}(r,t)] = 0 , \tag{9.6}$$

with H representing the total Hamiltonian of the system. Eq. (9.6) relates the charge and the divergence of the current density.

The potentials introduced in eqs. (9.2) are not uniquely determined by the electromagnetic field they describe. This means one may still apply gauge transformations that change the potentials φ and $\boldsymbol{A}$ but that do not affect the fields $\boldsymbol{E}$ and $\boldsymbol{B}$, given in eqs. (9.2). This leaves the possibility of describing the radiation field in terms of a divergence-free vector potential only, obeying

$$\nabla \cdot \boldsymbol{A}(\boldsymbol{r},t) = 0 . \tag{9.7}$$

This condition is referred to as the transverse gauge, the radiation gauge or the Coulomb gauge. Substitution of eqs. (9.2) into the source-free Maxwell equations (9.3) leads to a second-order differential equation for the vector potential, called the wave equation

$$\nabla^2 \boldsymbol{A}(\boldsymbol{r},t) - \frac{1}{c^2}\frac{\partial^2}{\partial t^2}\boldsymbol{A}(\boldsymbol{r},t) = 0 . \tag{9.8}$$

The purely transverse solutions of eqs. (9.7) and (9.8) form a complete basis for the description of the radiation field in the particular gauge.

For gamma radiation of energy $E_\gamma = \hbar\omega$, the wave number is given by

$$q = \frac{\omega}{c} = \frac{\hbar\omega}{\hbar c} = \frac{E_\gamma}{197\,\text{MeV}\cdot\text{fm}} , \tag{9.9}$$

and $\hbar q = E_\gamma/c$ represents the momentum transferred by the gamma radiation. With the harmonic time dependence $\boldsymbol{A}(\boldsymbol{r}, t) \propto \mathrm{e}^{-\mathrm{i}\omega t}$, the wave equation for the vector potential becomes

$$\nabla^2 \boldsymbol{A}(\boldsymbol{r},t) + q^2 \boldsymbol{A}(\boldsymbol{r},t) = 0 , \tag{9.10}$$

which shows that one can write the vector potential as

$$\boldsymbol{A}(\boldsymbol{r},t) = \boldsymbol{A}(q\boldsymbol{r})\, \mathrm{e}^{-\mathrm{i}\omega t} . \tag{9.11}$$

Substitution of eq. (9.11) into eq. (9.10) leads to the *vector Helmholtz equation* [Morse and Feshbach (1953)]

$$\nabla^2 \boldsymbol{A}(q\boldsymbol{r}) + q^2 \boldsymbol{A}(q\boldsymbol{r}) = 0 . \tag{9.12}$$

A complete set of independent solutions, satisfying condition (9.7) and characterized by the angular-momentum quantum numbers L and M of the radiation field, is provided by the Hansen solutions $\mathcal{A}^{\mathcal{M}}_{LM}(q\boldsymbol{r})$ and $\mathcal{A}^{\mathcal{E}}_{LM}(q\boldsymbol{r})$. The former describes magnetic 2^L pole radiation and the latter electric 2^L pole radiation. The condition (9.7) of a divergence-free vector field $\boldsymbol{A}(\boldsymbol{r},t)$ excludes the occurrence of a third independent solution for given L and M. This reflects the fact that for radiation only two independent polarization states are possible. Eq. (9.2b) defines only the curl of the vector potential and thus one does have the freedom to impose a condition on the divergence of the vector potential, as is done in eq. (9.7).

9.2. Electric and magnetic transition operators

The two multipole operators that describe magnetic and electric 2^L pole radiation can be written as (cf. eq. (9.1))

$$O(\mathcal{M}LM) = -\frac{\mathrm{i}}{c}\sqrt{\frac{L}{L+1}}\,\frac{(2L+1)!!}{q^L}\int \boldsymbol{j}^{\mathrm{op}}(\boldsymbol{r})\cdot \mathcal{A}^{\mathcal{M}}_{LM}(q\boldsymbol{r})\,\mathrm{d}\boldsymbol{r}\,, \tag{9.13}$$

$$O(\mathcal{E}LM) = \frac{1}{c}\sqrt{\frac{L}{L+1}}\,\frac{(2L+1)!!}{q^L}\int \boldsymbol{j}^{\mathrm{op}}(\boldsymbol{r})\cdot \mathcal{A}^{\mathcal{E}}_{LM}(q\boldsymbol{r})\,\mathrm{d}\boldsymbol{r}\,, \tag{9.14}$$

where the double factorial is defined by

$$(2L+1)!! = (2L+1)(2L-1)(2L-3)\ldots 3\cdot 1\,. \tag{9.15}$$

Here the normalization is taken such that in the long-wavelength approximation (i.e. $q = \omega/c = 2\pi/\lambda \to 0$) the customary operators are obtained. The *Hansen solutions* are given by

$$\mathcal{A}^{\mathcal{M}}_{LM}(q\boldsymbol{r}) = \frac{\boldsymbol{L}}{\sqrt{L(L+1)}}\,j_L(qr)\,Y_{LM}(\hat{\boldsymbol{r}}) = \frac{1}{q}\,\boldsymbol{\nabla}\times \mathcal{A}^{\mathcal{E}}_{LM}(q\boldsymbol{r})\,, \tag{9.16}$$

$$\mathcal{A}^{\mathcal{E}}_{LM}(q\boldsymbol{r}) = \frac{1}{q\sqrt{L(L+1)}}\,\boldsymbol{\nabla}\times\boldsymbol{L}\,j_L(qr)\,Y_{LM}(\hat{\boldsymbol{r}}) = \frac{1}{q}\,\boldsymbol{\nabla}\times \mathcal{A}^{\mathcal{M}}_{LM}(q\boldsymbol{r})\,. \tag{9.17}$$

Here $\boldsymbol{L} = -\mathrm{i}\boldsymbol{r}\times\boldsymbol{\nabla}$ is the angular-momentum operator and $j_L(qr)$ represents a spherical Bessel function that can be expanded as

$$j_L(qr) = \frac{(qr)^L}{(2L+1)!!}\left(1 - \frac{1}{2}\,\frac{(qr)^2}{2L+3} + \ldots\right). \tag{9.18}$$

It is seen from eqs. (9.16) and (9.17) that the two solutions $\mathcal{A}^{\mathcal{E}}_{LM}(q\boldsymbol{r})$ and $\mathcal{A}^{\mathcal{M}}_{LM}(q\boldsymbol{r})$ are related to each other in a symmetric way. Essentially it is only the parity that distinguishes the two vector fields ★.

A derivation of the Hansen solutions (9.16) and (9.17) is not given here. A solution of the scalar Helmholtz equation (cf. also eq. (9.12))

$$(\nabla^2 + q^2)\,u(q\boldsymbol{r}) = 0 \tag{9.19}$$

with the proper behaviour in the origin (that is, no infinity for $r = 0$) can be writ-

★ The phases of the multipole operators and Hansen solutions have been chosen such that the hermitian conjugates are given by the relations

$$O^{+}(\mathcal{E}LM) = (-1)^{M+1}\,O(\mathcal{E}L-M),\quad O^{\dagger}(\mathcal{M}LM) = (-1)^{M}\,O(\mathcal{M}L-M)\,,$$

$$(\mathcal{A}^{\overline{\omega}}_{LM})^{\dagger} = (-1)^{M+1}\,\mathcal{A}^{\overline{\omega}}_{L-M}\ \text{with}\ \overline{\omega} = \mathcal{E}\ \text{or}\ \mathcal{M}\,.$$

ten as

$$u(qr) = j_L(qr)\, Y_{LM}(\hat{r})\,. \tag{9.20}$$

One can easily show now that the vector fields $\boldsymbol{L}u(qr)$ and $\boldsymbol{\nabla} \times \boldsymbol{L}u(qr)$ must be solutions of the vector Helmholtz equation. Therefore one has to verify only that $\boldsymbol{L}$ and $\boldsymbol{\nabla} \times \boldsymbol{L}$ commute with $\boldsymbol{\nabla}^2 + q^2$ (cf. eq. (A.5.6)).

The second equality of eq. (9.16) can be derived with the identity (cf. eq. (A.5.19))

$$\boldsymbol{\nabla} \times \boldsymbol{\nabla} \times \mathcal{A}^{\mathcal{M}}_{LM} = \boldsymbol{\nabla}\, \boldsymbol{\nabla} \cdot \mathcal{A}^{\mathcal{M}}_{LM} - \boldsymbol{\nabla}^2 \mathcal{A}^{\mathcal{M}}_{LM} \tag{9.21}$$

and eqs. (9.7) and (9.12), obeyed by the Hansen solutions.

In the long-wavelength approximation only the first term of the expansion in eq. (9.18) is retained. Since the operators (9.13) and (9.14) are integrated over the nuclear volume, this approximation is justified if the condition $qR_0 \ll 1$ or $\lambda/2\pi \gg R_0$ is satisfied with $R_0 = 1.2\,A^{1/3}$ fm representing the nuclear radius. Thus the wave length λ of the emitted radiation should be much larger than the nuclear radius. With eq. (9.9) one finds

$$qR_0 = \frac{E_\gamma}{197\ \text{MeV}\cdot\text{fm}} \times 1.2\,A^{1/3}\,\text{fm} = 6 \times 10^{-3}\,\frac{E_\gamma}{\text{MeV}}\,A^{1/3}\,. \tag{9.22}$$

This leads to the condition

$$E_\gamma/\text{MeV} \ll 160\,A^{-1/3}\,. \tag{9.23}$$

Thus for E_γ much lower than 20 MeV the first term of the series expansion (9.18) will suffice. In this long-wavelength approximation the magnetic multipole transition operator (9.13) reduces to

$$O(\mathcal{M}\,LM) = \frac{-1}{c(L+1)} \int \boldsymbol{j}^{\text{op}}(\boldsymbol{r}) \cdot [\boldsymbol{r} \times \boldsymbol{\nabla}\, r^L\, Y_{LM}(\hat{r})]\, \mathrm{d}\boldsymbol{r}\,. \tag{9.24}$$

This expression as well as the original complete expression (9.13), contains the scalar product of the current density and a vector perpendicular to the radius vector $\boldsymbol{r}$. It means that the radial currents in the nucleus do not contribute to the magnetic transitions, but only the currents tangential to a sphere concentric with the origin.

The electric multipole transition operator can be written as the sum of a part depending on the charges and a part depending on the radial currents. Substitution of eq. (9.17) into eq. (9.14) yields

$$O(\mathcal{E}\,LM) = -\frac{\mathrm{i}(2L+1)!!}{c(L+1)q^{L+1}} \int \boldsymbol{j}^{\text{op}}(\boldsymbol{r}) \cdot \boldsymbol{\nabla} \times (\boldsymbol{r} \times \boldsymbol{\nabla})\, j_L(qr)\, Y_{LM}(\hat{r})\, \mathrm{d}\boldsymbol{r}\,. \tag{9.25}$$

With the aid of the operator identity (see eq. (A.5.16))

$$\boldsymbol{\nabla} \times (\boldsymbol{r} \times \boldsymbol{\nabla}) = -\boldsymbol{\nabla} \frac{\partial}{\partial r} r + \boldsymbol{r}\, \boldsymbol{\nabla}^2 \tag{9.26}$$

one can rewrite eq. (9.25). This leads to

$$O(\mathcal{E}LM) = \frac{\mathrm{i}}{c(L+1)} \frac{(2L+1)!!}{q^{L+1}} \left[\int \boldsymbol{j}^{\mathrm{op}}(\boldsymbol{r}) \cdot \boldsymbol{\nabla} \frac{\partial}{\partial r} r j_L(qr)\, Y_{LM}(\hat{\boldsymbol{r}})\,\mathrm{d}\boldsymbol{r} \right.$$

$$\left. + q^2 \int \boldsymbol{j}^{\mathrm{op}}(\boldsymbol{r}) \cdot \boldsymbol{r}\, j_L(qr)\, Y_{LM}(\hat{\boldsymbol{r}})\,\mathrm{d}\boldsymbol{r} \right], \tag{9.27}$$

where use has been made of the fact that spherical Bessel functions obey the equation

$$(\boldsymbol{\nabla}^2 + q^2)\, j_L(qr)\, Y_{LM}(\hat{\boldsymbol{r}}) = 0\,. \tag{9.28}$$

Partial integration of the first term of eq. (9.27) and use of eq. (9.6) then lead to

$$O(\mathcal{E}LM) = \frac{(2L+1)!!}{(L+1)q^L} \left\{ \frac{-1}{\hbar q c} \int [H, \rho^{\mathrm{op}}(\boldsymbol{r})] \frac{\partial}{\partial r} r\, j_L(qr)\, Y_{LM}(\hat{\boldsymbol{r}})\,\mathrm{d}\boldsymbol{r} \right.$$

$$\left. + \frac{\mathrm{i}q}{c} \int \boldsymbol{j}^{\mathrm{op}}(\boldsymbol{r}) \cdot \boldsymbol{r}\, j_L(qr)\, Y_{LM}(\hat{\boldsymbol{r}})\,\mathrm{d}\boldsymbol{r} \right\}. \tag{9.29}$$

It is seen that the electric transition operator consists of two terms of which the first is determined by the time derivative of the charge density according to eq. (9.5) and the second by the radial component of the current. The latter term can be neglected in the long-wavelength limit, i.e. for $q \to 0$.

Retaining only the leading term in the series expansion (9.18) of $j_L(qr)$ one obtains

$$O(\mathcal{E}LM) = \int \frac{-1}{\hbar q c} [H, \rho^{\mathrm{op}}(\boldsymbol{r})]\, r^L\, Y_{LM}(\hat{\boldsymbol{r}})\,\mathrm{d}\boldsymbol{r}\,. \tag{9.30}$$

Let us consider matrix elements of the operator (9.30) taken between nuclear states, i.e. eigenstates of the total Hamiltonian H. Let $|\Psi_\mathrm{i}\rangle$ and $|\Psi_\mathrm{f}\rangle$ represent the initial and final eigenstates of energies E_i and E_f, respectively. The matrix element of the operator in eq. (9.30) then becomes

$$\begin{aligned} \langle \Psi_\mathrm{f} | O(\mathcal{E}LM) | \Psi_\mathrm{i} \rangle &= \frac{-1}{\hbar q c} \int \langle \Psi_\mathrm{f} | [H, \rho^{\mathrm{op}}(\boldsymbol{r})] | \Psi_\mathrm{i} \rangle r^L\, Y_{LM}(\hat{\boldsymbol{r}})\,\mathrm{d}\boldsymbol{r} \\ &= -\frac{E_\mathrm{f} - E_\mathrm{i}}{\hbar q c} \int \langle \Psi_\mathrm{f} | \rho^{\mathrm{op}}(\boldsymbol{r}) | \Psi_\mathrm{i} \rangle r^L\, Y_{LM}(\hat{\boldsymbol{r}})\,\mathrm{d}\boldsymbol{r} \\ &= -\langle \Psi_\mathrm{f} | \int \rho^{\mathrm{op}}(\boldsymbol{r})\, r^L\, Y_{LM}(\hat{\boldsymbol{r}})\,\mathrm{d}\boldsymbol{r} | \Psi_\mathrm{i} \rangle\,. \end{aligned} \tag{9.31}$$

Here the commutator has been worked out by letting H act on the adjacent eigenstate and use has been made of the fact that $E_\mathrm{f} - E_\mathrm{i} = \hbar\omega = \hbar q c$ applies.

For the initial (final) states written at the right-(left-) hand side of the matrix element, the operators O given above describe the absorption of radiation. In order to describe emission one should employ the hermitian conjugates $O^{\dagger}$. However, since summations over the projection quantum numbers $(M_{\rm f}, M_{\rm i}, M)$ are always made to derive the transition probabilities, we do not need to make this distinction and we shall use the same operators regardless of whether they describe absorption or emission of radiation. For electric 2^L pole transitions we shall use the operator ★

$$O(\mathcal{E}LM) = \int \rho^{\rm op}(\boldsymbol{r})\, r^L\, Y_{LM}(\hat{\boldsymbol{r}})\, \mathrm{d}\boldsymbol{r}\, . \tag{9.32}$$

The forms (9.24) and (9.32) for magnetic and electric multipole transition operators, respectively, are valid in the long-wavelength approximation. They are the starting points for the further evaluation of the transition operators to be used throughout this book.

The nucleons are considered as nonrelativistic point particles with charge and/or magnetic moment. Therefore one may write the charge density operator as

$$\rho^{\rm op}(\boldsymbol{r}) = \sum_{k=1}^{A} e(k)\, \delta(\boldsymbol{r} - \boldsymbol{r}(k))\, . \tag{9.33}$$

or the charge density as

$$\rho(\boldsymbol{r}) = \langle \Psi | \rho^{\rm op}(\boldsymbol{r}) | \Psi \rangle$$

$$= \sum_{k=1}^{A} e(k) \int \delta(\boldsymbol{r} - \boldsymbol{r}(k))\, \Psi^*(\boldsymbol{r}(1), \ldots, \boldsymbol{r}(A))\, \Psi(\boldsymbol{r}(1), \ldots, \boldsymbol{r}(A))\, \mathrm{d}\boldsymbol{r}(1) \ldots \mathrm{d}\boldsymbol{r}(A)\, , \tag{9.34}$$

where $e(k)$ denotes the charge of the nucleon numbered k, i.e. $e(k) = 0$ for a neutron and $e(k) = e$ for a proton. Substitution of eq. (9.33) into eq. (9.32) leads to the operator for an electric transition

$$O(\mathcal{E}LM) = \sum_{k=1}^{A} e(k)\, r^L(k)\, Y_{LM}(\hat{\boldsymbol{r}}(k))\, . \tag{9.35}$$

Note that for the evaluation of the electric transition operator it is sufficient to only know the charge distribution. This is a consequence of taking the long-wavelength limit in eq. (9.29), whence the contributions from the radial currents are neglected.

The evaluation of the magnetic transition operator for nonrelativistic point particles is more complicated. In this case one has to calculate the current density

★ It should be noted that, although the operator (9.32) yields the correct matrix elements, its hermitian conjugate is no longer given by the expressions of the preceding footnote but by the relation $O(\mathcal{E}LM)^{\dagger} = (-1)^M O(\mathcal{E}L{-}M)$. This is a consequence of the replacement of the commutator $[H, \rho^{\rm op}]$ by $-[E_{\rm f} - E_{\rm i}]\, \rho^{\rm op}$.

$\boldsymbol{j}(\boldsymbol{r})$ in the nucleus from the expression

$$\boldsymbol{j}(\boldsymbol{r}) = \langle \Psi | \boldsymbol{j}^{\mathrm{op}}(\boldsymbol{r}) | \Psi \rangle$$

$$= \sum_{k=1}^{A} \frac{e(k)}{2M_{\mathrm{p}}} \int \delta(\boldsymbol{r} - \boldsymbol{r}(k)) \, \{\Psi^*(\boldsymbol{r}(1), ..., \boldsymbol{r}(A)\, \boldsymbol{p}(k)\, \Psi(\boldsymbol{r}(1), ..., \boldsymbol{r}(A))$$

$$+ [\boldsymbol{p}(k)\Psi(\boldsymbol{r}(1), ..., \boldsymbol{r}(A))]^* \, \Psi(\boldsymbol{r}(1), ..., \boldsymbol{r}(A))\} \, \mathrm{d}\boldsymbol{r}(1) \, ... \, \mathrm{d}\boldsymbol{r}(A)$$

$$+ \sum_{k=1}^{A} g^s(k) \mu_{\mathrm{N}} \int \delta(\boldsymbol{r} - \boldsymbol{r}(k)) \, \Psi^*(\boldsymbol{r}(1), ..., \boldsymbol{r}(A)) \, (\boldsymbol{\nabla} \times \boldsymbol{s}(k)) \, \Psi(\boldsymbol{r}(1), ..., \boldsymbol{r}(A)) \, \mathrm{d}\boldsymbol{r}(1) \, ... \, \mathrm{d}\boldsymbol{r}(A) \, . \tag{9.36}$$

Here $\frac{1}{2} g^s(k) \mu_{\mathrm{N}}$ represents the magnetic moment of nucleon k with

$$\mu_{\mathrm{N}} = e\hbar / 2M_{\mathrm{p}}c = 1 \text{ n.m.} \tag{9.37}$$

denoting the unit of nuclear magnetic moment, i.e. the nuclear magneton, while M_{p} represents the proton mass. The first sum of terms in eq. (9.36) describes the convection current density, the longitudinal current, while the second sum of terms represents the contribution from the magnetic moments. The latter, divergence-free part of the current is referred to as the transverse current. Substitution of eq. (9.36) into eq. (9.24) leads, after a number of partial integrations, to the operator for a magnetic transition

$$O(\mathcal{M}LM) = \sum_{k=1}^{A} \mu_{\mathrm{N}} \left[g^s(k)\, \boldsymbol{s}(k) + \frac{2g^l(k)}{L+1} \boldsymbol{l}(k) \right] \cdot \boldsymbol{\nabla}(k) r^L(k) \, Y_{LM}(\hat{\boldsymbol{r}}(k)) \, , \tag{9.38}$$

where the orbital g-factors have been introduced as $g^l(k) = 1$ for a proton and $g^l(k) = 0$ for a neutron. For the derivation of the spin contribution term in eq. (9.38) use has been made of the operator identity (9.26).

The second term in eq. (9.38), resulting from the convection current, contains the operator $\boldsymbol{l}(k) = \boldsymbol{r}(k) \times \boldsymbol{p}(k)/\hbar$, which is supposed not to act on $\boldsymbol{\nabla}(k) r^L(k) \, Y_{LM}(\hat{\boldsymbol{r}}(k))$, but only on the nuclear wave functions when the matrix element is taken. Moreover, the gradient operator $\boldsymbol{\nabla}(k)$ acts on $r^L(k) \, Y_{LM}(\hat{\boldsymbol{r}}(k))$ only. Strictly spoken the convection current is determined by the velocity of the particles and not by the momentum as in eq. (9.36). In the presence of velocity-dependent nucleon-nucleon forces, velocity and momentum show a relationship that differs from $\boldsymbol{p} = M\boldsymbol{v}$ and then eq. (9.38) will contain extra terms.

It is pointed out that in this book the electromagnetic properties of the nuclei are evaluated in the impulse approximation, as is conventional. In this approximation the operator that describes the electromagnetic transition or the electromagnetic moment, is a sum of one-body operators each of which describes the interaction of an independent nucleon with the electromagnetic field. Thus all effects associated with the nucleon-nucleon interaction, in particular the mesonic degrees of freedom of the nucleus, e.g. exchange currents, are neglected. This neglect can be viewed as a particular truncation of the configuration space. But also the nucleon wave functions themselves are not evaluated in a complete configuration space. The stratagem to conquer the resulting difficulties consists of the introduction of effective or renormalized operators.

The corrections of the bare operators thus may be traced to two principal sources, not strictly independent. (i) The wave functions used for the calculation are incomplete. This defect may be remedied by the introduction of e.g. core polarization (see chapter 16). (ii) The essentially one-body transition operators do not account for the mesonic degrees of freedom.

The electric transition rates and moments are rather insensitive to interaction effects. Owing to Siegert's theorem [Siegert (1937); Bohr and Mottelson (1969) p. 390] the electric operators that were defined in chapter 9 in the long-wavelength limit for nucleons with point charges, are not affected by the exchange effects. In this approximation it is only the change of the many-body wave function that may affect the value of the electric matrix elements. For the magnetic operators there is no Siegert theorem and mesonic corrections are not negligible. Although we shall treat the first category of corrections in chapter 16, we refrain from a discussion of mesonic effects. For the present it is assumed that effective operators can be meaningfully introduced. Similar remarks apply to the treatment of beta decay in chapter 12.

9.3. Centre-of-mass corrections

The electromagnetic transition operators given above are defined in terms of the nucleon coordinates $\boldsymbol{r}(1), \boldsymbol{r}(2), ..., \boldsymbol{r}(A)$, which refer to some fixed origin in space. The same coordinates are used for the construction of the shell-model wave functions. Since with these $3A$ coordinates all nucleons are treated on the same footing, the required antisymmetrization can be performed in a simple way. However, one wishes to describe intrinsic properties of a nucleus only. Hence it would be more appropriate to separate between the centre-of-mass degrees of freedom and the intrinsic degrees of freedom. Conservation of linear momentum * during the process of excitation or deexcitation of a nucleus through gamma radiation leads to recoil effects. For instance, when gamma radiation is emitted, the nucleus as a whole must recoil with a momentum equal and opposite to that of the emitted photon. The recoiling nucleus gives rise to an additional current that we have ignored sofar. We shall briefly discuss its implication on the electric dipole operator for which this effect is significant. For $\mathcal{M}L$ and $\mathcal{E}L$ operators (the latter for $L \geqslant 2$) the effect is small and hence is usually ignored.

* The use of a shell-model potential that is fixed in space violates the translational invariance of the system. This may result in excitation modes in which the centre-of-mass coordinates perform oscillations. The corresponding states are called *spurious states.* These must be eliminated since they do not describe intrinsic excitations. See sect. 18.4 for a brief discussion.

Let us introduce the centre-of-mass coordinate $\boldsymbol{R}$, which is given by

$$\boldsymbol{R} = \frac{1}{A} \sum_{k=1}^{A} \boldsymbol{r}(k) \,. \tag{9.39}$$

Intrinsic coordinates $\boldsymbol{\rho}(k)$ with respect to the centre of mass can be defined by

$$\boldsymbol{\rho}(k) = \boldsymbol{r}(k) - \boldsymbol{R} \,, \tag{9.40}$$

satisfying the relation

$$\sum_{k=1}^{A} \boldsymbol{\rho}(k) = 0 \,. \tag{9.41}$$

The $\mathcal{E}1$ operator follows from eq. (9.35) and is given by

$$O(\mathcal{E}1M) = \sum_{k=1}^{A} e(k) r\, Y_{1M}(\hat{r}(k)) = \sqrt{\frac{3}{4\pi}} \sum_{k=1}^{A} e(k)\, r_M(k) \,, \tag{9.42}$$

where for the last equality the spherical harmonics Y_{1M} are written explicitly (see appendix A.2). Instead of the coordinates $\boldsymbol{r}(k)$, however, we should use the intrinsic coordinates $\boldsymbol{\rho}(k)$. In terms of the latter coordinates the proper $\mathcal{E}1$ operator is given by

$$O'(\mathcal{E}1M) = \sqrt{\frac{3}{4\pi}} \sum_{k=1}^{A} e(k)\, \rho_M(k) = \sqrt{\frac{3}{4\pi}} \sum_{k=1}^{A} e(k) [r_M(k) - R_M] \,. \tag{9.43}$$

One obtains substituting eq. (9.39) into eq. (9.43)

$$O'(\mathcal{E}1M) = \sqrt{\frac{3}{4\pi}} \left[\sum_{k=1}^{Z} e\, r_M(k) - \frac{Z}{A} \sum_{k=1}^{A} e\, r_M(k) \right]$$

$$= \sqrt{\frac{3}{4\pi}} \left[\sum_{k=1}^{Z} e \left(1 - \frac{Z}{A}\right) r_M(k) - \frac{Z}{A} \sum_{k=Z+1}^{A} e\, r_M(k) \right] . \tag{9.44}$$

The first sum extends over the Z protons and the second one over the $N = A - Z$ neutrons. Rewriting eq. (9.44) one finds

$$O'(\mathcal{E}1M) = \sqrt{\frac{3}{4\pi}} \left[\sum_{k=1}^{Z} e \frac{N}{A} r_M(k) - \sum_{k=Z+1}^{A} e \frac{Z}{A} r_M(k) \right] . \tag{9.45}$$

Comparing eqs. (9.42) and (9.45) one observes that the $\mathcal{E}1$ operator in terms of the coordinates $\boldsymbol{r}(k)$ can still be used if one takes in the former

$$e(k) = \frac{N}{A} e \qquad \text{for protons} \,, \tag{9.46a}$$

$$e(k) = -\frac{Z}{A} e \qquad \text{for neutrons} \,. \tag{9.46b}$$

It is seen that especially for light nuclei these charges deviate strongly from the bare-nucleon values.

For higher-order electric multipole operators and for magnetic multipole operators the correction of the operator due to the centre-of-mass motion cannot be taken into account so easily. One can show that one obtains not only single-particle terms (as for the $\mathcal{E}1$ operator) but also more complicated terms that depend on the coordinates of more than one particle. If one retains the single-particle terms only one finds for the operator with $L \geqslant 2$ the expressions [Eisenberg and Greiner (1970) vol. 2, p. 98]

$$e(k) = e\frac{1}{A^L}[(A-1)^L + (-1)^L (Z-1)] \qquad \text{for protons}, \tag{9.47a}$$

$$e(k) = eZ\left(-\frac{1}{A}\right)^L \qquad \text{for neutrons} \tag{9.47b}$$

For $L = 1$ the expressions (9.46) are recovered.

The reduced proton and neutron charges given in eqs. (9.47) do not differ much from the bare-nucleon charges $e_p = e$ and $e_n = 0$ for $L \geqslant 2$. For example, $\mathcal{E}2$ radiation in a nucleus with $Z = N = 10$ requires $e(k) = 0.925e$ for protons and $e(k) = 0.025e$ for neutrons.

It is noted here that the numerical evaluation of the many-body terms that were neglected to obtain eqs. (9.47), requires the assumption of a particular model. In general one can state that their contribution is not necessarily negligible and their omission cannot be thoroughly justified in a model-independent way.

It should be remarked that the reduced charges discussed above derive from the $\mathcal{E}L$ operator itself. In quite another context one often introduces effective charges, which result from the model wave functions. The consequences of a truncation of the model space can be largely compensated for by the introduction of such effective charges, as will be discussed later. Typical values for $\mathcal{E}2$ effective charges are $e(k) \approx 1.5e$ for protons and $e(k) \approx 0.5e$ for neutrons. Hence these corrections can be much larger than those resulting from the centre-of-mass motion.

Considerations similar to those given above can be applied to the magnetic multipole operators. Since the magnetic operators depend on position coordinates and momentum coordinates, one has to make the replacement (9.40) for the position coordinates as well as the replacement

$$\boldsymbol{p}(k) \Rightarrow \boldsymbol{\pi}(k) \equiv \boldsymbol{p}(k) - \frac{1}{A}\boldsymbol{P} \tag{9.48}$$

for the momenta. Here the centre-of-mass momentum is defined by $\boldsymbol{P} = \Sigma_{k=1}^{A}\boldsymbol{p}(k)$. The resulting correction for the $\mathcal{M}1$ operator is found to be of the order of $1/A$ and thus is usually ignored. For a further discussion the reader is referred to [Gartenhaus and Schwartz (1957)].

9.4. Selection rules

Selection rules are the results of conservation laws. They express certain symmetry conditions that hold for the system under consideration. For instance, the invariance of a nuclear system as a whole under spatial rotations leads to the conservation of the total angular momentum. Thus, when a nucleus emits (absorbs) a photon, the initial (final) total nuclear angular momentum should be equal to the sum of the final (initial) total nuclear angular momentum and the angular momentum carried by the radiation

$$J_i = J_f + L \qquad (J_f = J_i + L)\,. \tag{9.49}$$

This implies that multipole matrix elements $\langle J_f M_f | O(\overline{\omega} LM) | J_i M_i \rangle$, with $\overline{\omega} = \mathcal{E}$ or $\mathcal{M}$ denoting electric or magnetic multipole radiation, can differ from zero only if the selection rule

$$|J_i - J_f| \leqslant L \leqslant J_i + J_f \qquad \text{or} \qquad \Delta(J_i, J_f, L) \tag{9.50}$$

is satisfied. The relation (9.50) is known as the triangle condition, because the three angular momenta must be such that they can form a triangle. One of the consequences of this rule is that gamma transitions $J_i = 0 \rightarrow J_f = 0$ do not occur since monopole radiation ($L = 0$) does not exist. This is obvious as soon as one substitutes $L = 0$ into eqs. (9.16) and (9.17) for the Hansen solutions $\mathcal{A}_{LM}^{\overline{\omega}}(q\boldsymbol{r})$.

Another important selection rule results from the conservation of parity. The parity operator Π^{op} is defined by the relation

$$\Pi^{\text{op}} \Psi(\boldsymbol{r}) = \Psi(-\boldsymbol{r}). \tag{9.51}$$

The parity operator obeys the relation $(\Pi^{\text{op}})^2 = 1$ and therefore only possesses the eigenvalues +1 and −1, corresponding to functions that are even or odd under space reflection,

$$\Pi^{\text{op}} \Psi^+(\boldsymbol{r}) = +\Psi^+(\boldsymbol{r}) \qquad \text{or} \qquad \Pi^{\text{op}} \Psi^-(\boldsymbol{r}) = -\Psi^-(\boldsymbol{r})\,. \tag{9.52}$$

An operator is called even (O^+) or odd (O^-) depending on whether it commutes or anticommutes with the parity operator

$$\Pi^{\text{op}} O^+ = O^+ \Pi^{\text{op}} \qquad \text{or} \qquad \Pi^{\text{op}} O^- = -O^- \Pi^{\text{op}}\,. \tag{9.53}$$

In case eq. (9.52) or (9.53) applies, one can speak of the parity of a function or an operator.

Consider the matrix element of an operator O of parity Π_O between a state $|\text{i}\rangle$ of parity Π_i and a state $|\text{f}\rangle$ of parity Π_f. It follows that one has

$$\langle \text{f} | O | \text{i} \rangle = 0 \qquad \text{for } \Pi_f \, \Pi_O \, \Pi_i = -1\,. \tag{9.54}$$

This relation is referred to as the parity selection rule. For a derivation of this rule a simple change of integration variable from $\boldsymbol{r}$ into $-\boldsymbol{r}$ suffices, because this change on the one hand should leave the value of the matrix element unaltered and on the other hand should multiply the result with $\Pi_f \Pi_O \Pi_i$. The parity selection rule can now be applied to electromagnetic transition matrix elements as soon as the parity of the operator $\boldsymbol{j}^{\mathrm{op}}(\boldsymbol{r}) \cdot \mathcal{A}^{\varpi}_{LM}(\boldsymbol{r})$ is known. The parity of the current density operator is given by $\Pi_j = -1$, since it consists of terms proportional to a velocity and terms $\nabla \times \boldsymbol{s}$ (the spin $\boldsymbol{s}$, being an axial vector, is invariant under the space inversion $\boldsymbol{r} \to -\boldsymbol{r}$). From eqs. (2.29), (9.16) and (9.17) it follows that $\mathcal{A}^{\mathcal{M}}_{LM}(q\boldsymbol{r})$ possesses parity $(-1)^L$ and $\mathcal{A}^{\mathcal{E}}_{LM}(q\boldsymbol{r})$ possesses parity $(-1)^{L+1}$. Summarizing one sees that the electromagnetic 2^L pole transition operators possess the parities

$$\Pi_{O(\mathcal{M}L)} = (-1)^{L+1}\,, \qquad \Pi_{O(\mathcal{E}L)} = (-1)^L\,. \tag{9.55}$$

The parity of electromagnetic radiation is defined as the parity of the magnetic field $\boldsymbol{B}(\boldsymbol{r}) = \nabla \times \boldsymbol{A}(\boldsymbol{r})$ and therefore the parities given in eq. (9.55) can be referred to as the parities of the radiation concerned. The parity selection rule for electromagnetic multipole transitions can now be formulated as

$$\Pi_f \Pi_\gamma \Pi_i = +1\,, \tag{9.56}$$

where Π_γ represents the parity of the emitted or absorbed radiation.

9.5. Transition probabilities and mixing ratios

It can be shown [Blatt and Weisskopf (1952); Roy and Nigam (1967)] that the probability P for emission or absorption of a photon by a nucleus can be expressed in terms of the matrix elements of the corresponding multipole operator as

$$P(\varpi LM; J_iM_i \to J_fM_f) = \frac{8\pi(L+1)}{L[(2L+1)!!]^2}\,\frac{q^{2L+1}}{\hbar}\,\langle J_fM_f|O(\varpi LM)|J_iM_i\rangle^2\,. \tag{9.57}$$

The transition rate T between an initial state J_i and a final state J_f is obtained after averaging over the initial quantum numbers M_i, summation over the unobserved final projection quantum numbers M_f and summation over M. Since the multipole operators are irreducible tensor operators, one may apply Wigner-Eckart's theorem (see appendix A.3a)

$$\langle J_fM_f|O(\varpi LM)|J_iM_i\rangle = \frac{\langle J_iM_iLM|J_fM_f\rangle}{\sqrt{2J_f+1}}\,\langle J_f\|O(\varpi L)\|J_i\rangle\,, \tag{9.58}$$

where the double-bar matrix element denotes the reduced matrix element, which is independent of the projection quantum numbers.

For the transition rate from state J_i to state J_f one then obtains after substitution of eq. (9.58) into eq. (9.57)

$$T(\varpi L; J_i \to J_f) = \frac{1}{2J_i+1}\sum_{M_iMM_f} P(\varpi LM; J_iM_i \to J_fM_f)$$

$$= \frac{8\pi(L+1)}{L[(2L+1)!!]^2}\,\frac{q^{2L+1}}{\hbar}\,\frac{1}{2J_i+1}\sum_{M_iMM_f}\frac{\langle J_iM_iLM|J_fM_f\rangle^2}{2J_f+1}\,\langle J_f\|O(\varpi L)\|J_i\rangle^2$$

$$= \frac{8\pi(L+1)}{L[(2L+1)!!]^2} \frac{q^{2L+1}}{\hbar} \frac{\langle J_f \| O(\varpi L) \| J_i \rangle^2}{2J_i + 1}$$

$$= \frac{8\pi(L+1)}{L[(2L+1)!!]^2} \frac{q^{2L+1}}{\hbar} B(\varpi L; J_i \to J_f) . \tag{9.59}$$

The summation over projection quantum numbers could be performed with the aid of the normalization property of Clebsch-Gordan coefficients. The *reduced transition probabilities*

$$B(\varpi L; J_i \to J_f) = \frac{\langle J_f \| O(\varpi L) \| J_i \rangle^2}{2J_i + 1} \tag{9.60}$$

for electric and magnetic cases have the same dimension, [charge]^2 · [length]^{2L}, as follows from the operators given in eqs. (9.35) and (9.38). Electric transitions are usually expressed in units of $e^2 \cdot \mathrm{fm}^{2L}$ or $e^2 \cdot \mathrm{b}^L$. For magnetic transitions one commonly employs units of $\mathrm{n.m.}^2 \cdot \mathrm{fm}^{2L-2}$ or $\mathrm{n.m.}^2 \cdot \mathrm{b}^{L-1}$, where the nuclear magneton is defined by eq. (9.37). A mean lifetime τ_m corresponds to the transition probability T of the decaying state. The relation is given by

$$\tau_m(\varpi L; J_i \to J_f) = \frac{1}{T(\varpi L; J_i \to J_f)} . \tag{9.61}$$

Using the uncertainty relation $\Delta E \Delta t \approx \hbar$, one can define the width of a level (with the dimension of energy) by

$$\Gamma = \frac{\hbar}{\tau_m} = \hbar T . \tag{9.62}$$

Even in case one considers an initial state that decays to one final state, more than one kind of multipole radiation may occur. It will be explained in sect. 9.6 that there is a strong dependence of the transition probability on the multipole character, however. As a result one usually encounters the mixing of no more than two multipole radiations that differ one unit in angular momentum, say L and $L+1$. To describe the distribution over the two decay modes one introduces the mixing ratio δ, the magnitude of which is defined by the relation

$$\delta^2(\varpi L+1/\varpi' L) = \frac{\Gamma(\varpi L+1; J_i \to J_f)}{\Gamma(\varpi' L; J_i \to J_f)} . \tag{9.63}$$

In order to obey parity conservation one finds from eq. (9.63) that the two competing radiative transitions must be $\mathcal{E}L+1$ and $\mathcal{M}L$ or $\mathcal{M}L+1$ and $\mathcal{E}L$. The angular distribution of mixed gamma radiation, however, depends also on the sign of the mixing ratio δ. This means that from the experimental data on angular distributions one can extract the sign of the mixing ratio.

For the analysis of experimental data the formulas given in [Litherland and

Ferguson (1961); Smith (1962); Poletti and Warburton (1965) ★; Ferguson (1965); Rose and Brink (1967)] unambiguously lead to the same definite sign of the mixing ratio δ. As the sign of δ depends on particular conventions used for wave functions and operators, it is mandatory for a comparison of theory and experiment to fix the sign of the square root of eq. (9.63) such that it is consistent with the assumptions that lead to the formulas used in the experimental analysis.

It is seen in eqs. (9.59) and (9.60) that the transition probability is proportional to the square of the reduced matrix element for the transition involved. The particular phase convention of the mixing ratio that is in agreement with the experimental conventions referred to above, can be given in terms of reduced matrix elements as

$$\delta(\overline{\omega}L+1/\overline{\omega}'L) = \pm\frac{q\sqrt{L(L+2)}}{(L+1)(2L+3)}\frac{\langle J_\mathrm{f}\|\boldsymbol{O}(\overline{\omega}L+1)\|J_\mathrm{i}\rangle}{\langle J_\mathrm{f}\|\boldsymbol{O}(\overline{\omega}'L)\|J_\mathrm{i}\rangle}, \tag{9.64}$$

where (i) the upper sign applies to absorption processes ($E_\mathrm{i} - E_\mathrm{f} < 0$) and the lower sign to emission processes ($E_\mathrm{i} - E_\mathrm{f} > 0$); (ii) the operators are defined in eqs. (9.35) and (9.38); (iii) the reduced matrix elements are defined according to eq. (9.58); (iv) the Condon-Shortley convention [Condon and Shortley (1953)] is used for the angular parts of the wave functions, i.e. each single-particle wave function is a product of a real radial part and a spherical harmonic satisfying

$$Y^*_{LM}(\hat{r}) = (-1)^M\, Y_{L-M}(\hat{r})\,. \tag{9.65}$$

The Condon-Shortley convention guarantees that the matrix elements of electromagnetic transition operators are real. It is remarked here that reality of the matrix elements can also be reached in another convention [Biedenharn and Rose (1953)], where factors i are inserted in the angular parts of wave functions and operators. This will affect, however, the expression giving δ in terms of the reduced matrix elements.

In this book we shall use the Condon-Shortley phase convention. For the most common cases of $\mathcal{E}2/\mathcal{M}1$ and $\mathcal{M}2/\mathcal{E}1$ mixing the mixing ratios are defined by

$$\delta(\mathcal{E}2/\mathcal{M}1) = \pm\tfrac{1}{10}q\sqrt{3}\,\frac{\langle J_\mathrm{f}\|\boldsymbol{O}(\mathcal{E}2)\|J_\mathrm{i}\rangle}{\langle J_\mathrm{f}\|\boldsymbol{O}(\mathcal{M}1)\|J_\mathrm{i}\rangle}, \tag{9.66a}$$

$$\delta(\mathcal{M}2/\mathcal{E}1) = \pm\tfrac{1}{10}q\sqrt{3}\,\frac{\langle J_\mathrm{f}\|\boldsymbol{O}(\mathcal{M}2)\|J_\mathrm{i}\rangle}{\langle J_\mathrm{f}\|\boldsymbol{O}(\mathcal{E}1)\|J_\mathrm{i}\rangle}, \tag{9.66b}$$

with the upper and lower signs again referring to absorption and emission, respectively. The comparison of the calculated mixing ratios with the experimental values constitutes an essential test of the theoretical wave functions.

★ It is emphasized that here we refer to eq. (11) of [Poletti and Warburton (1965)] with $\sigma = 0$ for mixtures $\mathcal{M}L/\mathcal{E}L+1$ and $\sigma = 1$ for mixtures $\mathcal{E}L/\mathcal{M}L+1$. Numerical values in that reference are presented for $\sigma = 0$, regardless of the nature of the transition.

So far it has been assumed that a given state decays to only one lower-lying state. When more than one final state is involved, one obtains the total width Γ_t, corresponding to the lifetime of the level considered, by summing the partial widths $\Gamma(\varpi L; J_i \to J_{f_k})$ for the decay modes to all final states f_k. One can then define branching ratios P_k, usually normalized to one hundred,

$$P_k = \frac{\sum_{\varpi L} \Gamma(\varpi L; J_i \to J_{f_k})}{\Gamma_t} \times 100 \,, \tag{9.67}$$

where the total width for gamma decay is given by

$$\Gamma_t = \sum_{\varpi, L, J_{f_k}} \Gamma(\varpi L; J_i \to J_{f_k}) \,. \tag{9.68}$$

9.6. Single-particle estimates

In order to obtain some idea of the orders of magnitude involved, a very crude estimate of the transition matrix elements will be given. Let us assume that the wave functions for initial and final states are constant over the nuclear volume of radius R and zero for $r > R$. With the normalization condition $\int |\Psi_i|^2 \, d\boldsymbol{r}(1) \ldots d\boldsymbol{r}(A) = \int |\Psi_f|^2 \, d\boldsymbol{r}(1) \ldots d\boldsymbol{r}(A) = 1$ and with the approximation $Y_{LM}(\hat{\boldsymbol{r}}) \approx 1$, one obtains from eq. (9.35) the order-of-magnitude estimate for electric multipole transitions given by

$$|\langle f | O(\mathcal{E} LM) | i \rangle| \approx ZeR^L \,. \tag{9.69}$$

Similarly one derives for the contribution of the convection current to the magnetic transition matrix element, i.e. the term containing the angular momentum $\boldsymbol{l}$ in eq. (9.38),

$$|\langle f | O_{\mathrm{orb}}(\mathcal{M} LM) | i \rangle|$$

$$= |\sum_k \frac{2g^l(k)}{L+1} \mu_N \int \Psi^*(\boldsymbol{r}(1), \ldots, \boldsymbol{r}(A)) \boldsymbol{l}(k) \Psi(\boldsymbol{r}(1), \ldots, \boldsymbol{r}(A)) \cdot \boldsymbol{\nabla}(k) r^L(k) Y_{LM}(\hat{\boldsymbol{r}}(k)) d\boldsymbol{r}(1) \ldots d\boldsymbol{r}(A)|$$

$$= |\sum_k \frac{2g^l(k)}{L+1} \mu_N \int \Psi^*(\boldsymbol{r}(1), \ldots, \boldsymbol{r}(A)) \boldsymbol{\nabla}(k) \Psi(\boldsymbol{r}(1), \ldots, \boldsymbol{r}(A)) \cdot \boldsymbol{l}(k) r^L(k) Y_{LM}(\hat{\boldsymbol{r}}(k)) \, d\boldsymbol{r}(1) \ldots d\boldsymbol{r}(A)|$$

$$\approx Ze \frac{v}{c} R^L \,, \tag{9.70}$$

where for the latter estimate it is assumed that $\hbar \boldsymbol{\nabla}/iM$ yields a factor v, and $l(k)$ a factor L. (Remember the definition $\mu_N = e\hbar/2M_p c$.) The lengths of the vectors of spin and orbital angular momentum can be given in a semiclassical picture as $|\boldsymbol{s}| = \sqrt{\frac{3}{4}}$ and $|\boldsymbol{l}|/(L+1) = \sqrt{L/(L+1)}$, respectively, and hence are of the same order of magnitude. Thus the spin contribution to the magnetic transition matrix element can be estimated by taking

$$g^s s = \frac{5l}{L+1} = 2.5 \times \frac{2l}{L+1} , \tag{9.71}$$

where the factor 5 is obtained as an average of the absolute values of proton and neutron g^s factors, which are given by 5.6 and −3.8, respectively. Thus one reaches the very approximate relation

$$\langle \mathrm{f} | O(\mathcal{M}LM) | \mathrm{i} \rangle^2 \approx 10 \left(\frac{v}{c} \right)^2 \langle \mathrm{f} | O(\mathcal{E}LM) | \mathrm{i} \rangle^2 \approx 10 \left(\frac{\hbar}{M_\mathrm{p} Rc} \right)^2 \langle \mathrm{f} | O(\mathcal{E}LM) | \mathrm{i} \rangle^2 , \tag{9.72}$$

where the order of magnitude of the ratio v/c is obtained from the uncertainty relation for a nucleon in a box of size R, i.e.

$$M_\mathrm{p} v R \approx \hbar \qquad \text{or} \ \frac{v}{c} \approx \frac{\hbar}{M_\mathrm{p} Rc} . \tag{9.73}$$

The same estimate is obtained when in eq. (9.38) the operator $\boldsymbol{\nabla}$ is replaced by $1/R$. Substituting numerical values one finds for nuclei near the mass number $A = 40$ the estimate

$$\frac{v}{c} = \frac{\hbar}{M_\mathrm{p} Rc} \approx 0.05 . \tag{9.74}$$

It should be noted, however, that in eq. (9.72) either the magnetic or the electric multipole matrix elements must vanish for given initial and final states, because of conservation of parity. Therefore eq. (9.72) should be interpreted as to hold for transitions between states that do differ in parity change, but that are otherwise similar.

For an exact evaluation of the transition rates between nuclear states, complete wave functions should be known. Since the transitions are described by single-particle operators, it follows that the transition matrix elements vanish except when they are taken between states differing in the quantum numbers of not more than one nucleon.

A useful and very frequently employed approximation is the Weisskopf estimate. Then it is assumed that initial and final states are described by one and the same $J = 0$ core (that does not change during the transition) and a single active nucleon that makes the transition. For the total wave functions one can then write, ignoring antisymmetrization between core and extra nucleon, the product wave function

$$\Psi = \Phi_\mathrm{core} \, \phi , \tag{9.75}$$

where both Φ_core and ϕ are normalized. The transition probability can be calculated after substitution of the reduced matrix element of the relevant operator between the initial and final single-particle states ϕ_i and ϕ_f into eq. (9.60).

Let the wave function of the extra particle in the initial state be given by

$$\phi_{n_i l_i \frac{1}{2} j_i m_i}(\boldsymbol{r}) = u_{n_i l_i}(r)\, \psi_{l_i \frac{1}{2} j_i m_i}(\hat{\boldsymbol{r}}) \,, \tag{9.76}$$

where the radial part, $u_{n_i l_i}(r)$, is determined by the single-particle potential caused by the presence of the core and the angular part $\psi_{l_i \frac{1}{2} j_i m_i}(\hat{\boldsymbol{r}})$ is defined by eq. (2.14). If now the initial and final radial wave functions are taken to be constant over the nuclear volume of radius R and equal to zero for $r > R$, then the normalization condition

$$\int_0^\infty u^2 r^2 \,\mathrm{d}r = 1 \tag{9.77}$$

leads to

$$\begin{aligned} u(r) &= \sqrt{\frac{3}{R^3}} \qquad \text{for } r \leqslant R \,, \\ &= 0 \qquad \text{for } r > R \,. \end{aligned} \tag{9.78}$$

The reduced matrix element of the electric 2^L pole transition operator given in eq. (9.35) can now be rewritten (cf. eqs. (6.32) and (6.33))

$$\langle j_f \| O(\mathcal{E}L) \| j_i \rangle^2 = \frac{e^2 \langle r^L \rangle^2 (2j_f+1)(2L+1)(2j_i+1)}{4\pi} \begin{pmatrix} j_f & L & j_i \\ -\frac{1}{2} & 0 & \frac{1}{2} \end{pmatrix}^2 \frac{1+(-1)^{l_f+L+l_i}}{2} \,, \tag{9.79}$$

where one has, because of eq. (9.78),

$$\langle r^L \rangle \equiv \int_{r=0}^{\infty} u_f(r)\, r^L\, u_i(r)\, r^2 \,\mathrm{d}r = \frac{3}{L+3} R^L \,. \tag{9.80}$$

For the order-of-magnitude estimate we evaluate the transition between states $j_i = L \pm \frac{1}{2}$ and $j_f = \frac{1}{2}$ for which we need the explicit values (see eq. A.1.a13)

$$\begin{pmatrix} \frac{1}{2} & L & L \pm \frac{1}{2} \\ -\frac{1}{2} & 0 & \frac{1}{2} \end{pmatrix}^2 = \frac{1}{2(2L+1)} \,. \tag{9.81}$$

From eqs. (9.59), (9.79), (9.80) and (9.81) one obtains for the transition probability

$$T(\mathcal{E}L; J_i = L \pm \tfrac{1}{2} \rightarrow J_f = \tfrac{1}{2}) = \frac{2(L+1)}{L[(2L+1)!!]^2} \left(\frac{3}{L+3}\right)^2 \frac{e^2}{\hbar c}\, \omega (qR)^{2L} \,. \tag{9.82}$$

With the numerical value $e^2/\hbar c = 1/137$ and the relation

$$\omega q^{2L} = \omega \left(\frac{\omega}{c}\right)^{2L} = c \left(\frac{\hbar\omega}{\hbar c}\right)^{2L+1} = 3 \times 10^{23} \mathrm{fm} \cdot \mathrm{s}^{-1} \left(\frac{\hbar\omega}{197\ \mathrm{MeV} \cdot \mathrm{fm}}\right)^{2L+1} \,, \tag{9.83}$$

one finds that eq. (9.82) assumes the convenient form

$$T(\mathcal{E}L; J_i = L \pm \tfrac{1}{2} \to J_f = \tfrac{1}{2}) = \frac{4 \cdot 4(L+1)}{L[(2L+1)!!]^2} \left(\frac{3}{L+3}\right)^2 \left(\frac{\hbar\omega}{197\ \text{MeV}}\right)^{2L+1} \left(\frac{R}{\text{fm}}\right)^{2L} 10^{21}\,\text{s}^{-1} \tag{9.84}$$

From eqs. (9.72) and (9.82) one obtains for the magnetic multipole transition rates

$$T(\mathcal{M}L; J_i = L \pm \tfrac{1}{2} \to J_f = \tfrac{1}{2}) = \frac{20(L+1)}{L[(2L+1)!!]^2} \left(\frac{3}{L+3}\right)^2 \frac{e^2}{\hbar c} \left(\frac{\hbar}{M_p R c}\right)^2 \omega (qR)^{2L}. \tag{9.85}$$

With the numerical value

$$20 \frac{e^2}{\hbar c} \left(\frac{\hbar}{M_p R c}\right)^2 \omega (qR)^{2L} = \frac{20}{137} \left(\frac{\hbar}{M_p c}\right)^2 \left(\frac{\omega}{c}\right)^{2L+1} c R^{2L-2}$$

$$= \frac{20}{137} (0.21\ \text{fm})^2 \left(\frac{\hbar\omega}{197\ \text{MeV} \cdot \text{fm}}\right)^{2L+1} 3 \times 10^{23} \text{fm} \cdot \text{s}^{-1}\, R^{2L-2}$$

$$= 1.9 \left(\frac{\hbar\omega}{197\ \text{MeV}}\right)^{2L+1} \left(\frac{R}{\text{fm}}\right)^{2L-2} 10^{21}\ \text{s}^{-1} \tag{9.86}$$

inserted into eq. (9.85) one obtains

$$T(\mathcal{M}L; J_i = L \pm \tfrac{1}{2} \to J_f = \tfrac{1}{2}) = \frac{1.9(L+1)}{L[(2L+1)!!]^2} \left(\frac{3}{L+3}\right)^2 \left(\frac{\hbar\omega}{197\ \text{MeV}}\right)^{2L+1} \left(\frac{R}{\text{fm}}\right)^{2L-2} 10^{21}\,\text{s}^{-1} \tag{9.87}$$

Substituting $R = 1.20 \times A^{1/3}$ fm into eqs. (9.84) and (9.87), one obtains the Weisskopf estimates.

According to eq. (9.62) a width Γ_W can be introduced that corresponds with the Weisskopf estimate. The explicit expressions for Γ_W for the lower-order multipole transitions are given in the following chapter. It should be noted that the actual widths may deviate strongly from these estimates that are made for constant radial wave functions in the extreme single-particle model. Nevertheless the Weisskopf estimates are quite useful, as they provide a standard against which to compare experimentally observed widths. These estimates thus yield a first indication whether the transition under consideration is of single-particle character or of collective nature.

It is quite customary to quote calculated or experimentally determined electromagnetic transition strengths in Weisskopf units, i.e. as the dimensionless quotient

$$M_W^2 = \frac{\Gamma}{\Gamma_W}, \qquad \text{or} \qquad \Gamma = M_W^2\ \text{W.u.}\,. \tag{9.88}$$

In this ratio the strong energy dependence of the width that varies with multipolarity, has been divided out. The quotient M_W^2 is a measure for the intrinsic transition rate.

For a comparison with experiment one has also to take into account the possibility of internal conversion. When internal conversion takes place, the energy released in the transition is used to eject an atomic, bound electron. The total width then becomes

$$\Gamma(\varpi L; J_\mathrm{i} \to J_\mathrm{f}) = \Gamma_\gamma(\varpi L; J_\mathrm{i} \to J_\mathrm{f}) + \Gamma_\mathrm{conv}(\varpi L; J_\mathrm{i} \to J_\mathrm{f})$$

$$= \Gamma_\gamma(\varpi L; J_\mathrm{i} \to J_\mathrm{f})(1+\alpha)\,, \qquad (9.89)$$

where the dimensionless internal-conversion ratio

$$\alpha = \Gamma_\mathrm{conv}/\Gamma_\gamma \qquad (9.90)$$

is introduced. For nuclei of high Z-value this ratio can be large for low transition energies ($\lesssim 100$ keV). This holds in particular for high values of the multipolarity, where the gamma-transition probability becomes small as explained below.

In order to estimate the influence of multipolarity L on the transition probability, we compare two transitions that differ by one unit in multipole order. When both transitions are electric or magnetic one obtains from eq. (9.82) or (9.85)

$$\frac{T(\varpi L+1)}{T(\varpi L)} = \frac{L(L+2)(L+3)^2}{(L+1)^2(L+4)^2(2L+3)^2}(qR)^2 \approx \left(\frac{qR}{2L+3}\right)^2 . \qquad (9.91)$$

For a transition energy $E_\gamma = \hbar\omega = 1$ MeV (and thus $q = \hbar\omega/\hbar c \approx 0.005\ \mathrm{fm}^{-1}$) and a nuclear radius $R = 1.2\,A^{1/3}$ fm, this leads to

$$\frac{T(\varpi L+1)}{T(\varpi L)} \approx \frac{4\times 10^{-5}}{(2L+3)^2} A^{2/3} . \qquad (9.92)$$

The ratio between quadrupole and dipole radiation for example is of the order 10^{-3} to 10^{-5}. Comparison of electric and magnetic radiation of the same multipolarity yields, as was derived in eqs. (9.72) and (9.74),

$$\frac{T(\mathcal{M}L)}{T(\mathcal{E}L)} \approx 10\left(\frac{\hbar}{M_\mathrm{p}Rc}\right)^2 \approx 0.3\,A^{-2/3} . \qquad (9.93)$$

It should be pointed out that relations (9.92) and (9.93) have been calculated for the sake of numerical comparison only, since the parity selection rule prevents the two radiations compared from occurring simultaneously. Therefore a comparison of electric and magnetic multipole radiation of order L and $L \pm 1$, respectively, is more realistic. From eqs. (9.92) and (9.93) one obtains

$$\frac{T(\mathcal{E}L+1)}{T(\mathcal{M}L)} = \frac{T(\mathcal{E}L+1)}{T(\mathcal{E}L)}\,\frac{T(\mathcal{E}L)}{T(\mathcal{M}L)} \approx \frac{10^{-4}}{(2L+3)^2} A^{4/3} \approx 10^{-4} . \qquad (9.94)$$

Similarly one obtains the estimate

$$\frac{T(\mathcal{M}L+1)}{T(\mathcal{E}L)} \approx \frac{10^{-5}}{(2L+3)^2} \approx 10^{-7} . \qquad (9.95)$$

These results can be summarized by the sequence of multipolarities listed according to decreasing transition rate as

$$T(\mathcal{E}1) > T(\mathcal{M}1) > T(\mathcal{E}2) > T(\mathcal{M}2) > T(\mathcal{E}3) > T(\mathcal{M}3) \ldots . \tag{9.96}$$

It has been mentioned before that the actual transition rates may deviate appreciably from the estimates given above, since a very rough nuclear model has been used.

9.7. Transition operators and isospin

This section will be devoted to some general features of electromagnetic transition rates and especially to the significance of the isoscalar and isovector parts of the transition operators. The operators given in eqs. (9.35) and (9.38) are defined such that one sums over all A nucleons ($k = 1, \ldots, A$). One should realize, however, that the nucleon charges $e(k)$ and gyromagnetic ratios $g(k)$ are different for protons and neutrons. We shall show that one can use the isospin formalism to rewrite these operators such that all terms are treated on the same footing. This is achieved with the operators $\frac{1}{2}(1 \pm \tau_z)$. Repeating the results that were given in eq. (2.50), one has

$$\tfrac{1}{2}(1+\tau_z)\phi_\mathrm{p} = 0\,, \qquad \tfrac{1}{2}(1+\tau_z)\phi_\mathrm{n} = \phi_\mathrm{n}\,,$$

$$\tfrac{1}{2}(1-\tau_z)\phi_\mathrm{p} = \phi_\mathrm{p}\,, \qquad \tfrac{1}{2}(1-\tau_z)\phi_\mathrm{n} = 0\,. \tag{9.97}$$

One can thus rewrite the operator for an electric multipole transition, given in eq. (9.35), as

$$O(\mathcal{E}LM) = \sum_{k=1}^{A} [\tfrac{1}{2}(1-\tau_z(k))e_\mathrm{p} + \tfrac{1}{2}(1+\tau_z(k))e_\mathrm{n}]\, r^L(k)\, Y_{LM}(\hat{r}(k))\,. \tag{9.98}$$

Analogously one can rewrite the operator given in eq. (9.38) for a magnetic multipole transition as

$$O(\mathcal{M}LM) = \sum_{k=1}^{A} \mu_\mathrm{N} \Big\{ [\tfrac{1}{2}(1-\tau_z(k))\, g_\mathrm{p}^s + \tfrac{1}{2}(1+\tau_z(k))\, g_\mathrm{n}^s]\, \boldsymbol{s}(k)$$

$$+ [\tfrac{1}{2}(1-\tau_z(k))\, g_\mathrm{p}^l + \tfrac{1}{2}(1+\tau_z(k))\, g_\mathrm{n}^l]\, \frac{2\boldsymbol{l}(k)}{L+1} \Big\} \cdot \boldsymbol{\nabla}(k)\, r^L\, Y_{LM}(\hat{r}(k))\,. \tag{9.99}$$

After a separation of the τ_z independent terms from the τ_z dependent terms, eqs. (9.98) and (9.99) assume the form

$$O(\overline{\omega}LM) = \sum_{k=1}^{A} S(\overline{\omega}LM, k)\, 1 - \sum_{k=1}^{A} V(\overline{\omega}LM, k)\, \tau_z(k)\,. \tag{9.100}$$

For electric transitions it follows from eq. (9.98) that

$$S(\mathcal{E}LM, k) = \tfrac{1}{2}(e_\mathrm{p} + e_\mathrm{n})\, r^L(k)\, Y_{LM}(\hat{r}(k)). \tag{9.101}$$

$$V(\mathcal{E}LM,k) = \tfrac{1}{2}(e_\mathrm{p} - e_\mathrm{n})\, r^L(k)\, Y_{LM}(\hat{r}(k)) \,. \tag{9.102}$$

For magnetic transitions one obtains from eq. (9.99)

$$S(\mathcal{M}LM,k) = \mu_\mathrm{N}\left\{\tfrac{1}{2}(g_\mathrm{p}^s + g_\mathrm{n}^s)\, \boldsymbol{s}(k) + (g_\mathrm{p}^l + g_\mathrm{n}^l)\frac{\boldsymbol{l}(k)}{L+1}\right\} \cdot \boldsymbol{\nabla}(k)\, r^L(k)\, Y_{LM}(\hat{\boldsymbol{r}}(k)) \,, \tag{9.103}$$

$$V(\mathcal{M}LM,k) = \mu_\mathrm{N}\left\{\tfrac{1}{2}(g_\mathrm{p}^s - g_\mathrm{n}^s)\, \boldsymbol{s}(k) + (g_\mathrm{p}^l - g_\mathrm{n}^l)\frac{\boldsymbol{l}(k)}{L+1}\right\} \cdot \boldsymbol{\nabla}(k)\, r^L(k)\, Y_{LM}(\hat{\boldsymbol{r}}(k)) \,. \tag{9.104}$$

It is seen from eq. (9.100) that a transition operator contains a part that is proportional to the unit operator in isospace. This is called the *isoscalar part.* The other part in eq. (9.100) is vectorial in isospace and is called the *isovector part.*

The matrix elements of these operators in the isospin formalism can be reduced as well in coordinate space as in isospace, i.e. the Wigner-Eckart theorem is applied twice. The reduced transition probability was defined in eq. (9.60) as

$$B(\varpi L; J_\mathrm{i} T_\mathrm{i} T_z \to J_\mathrm{f} T_\mathrm{f} T_z) = \frac{\langle J_\mathrm{f} T_\mathrm{f} T_z \| \boldsymbol{O}(\varpi L) \| J_\mathrm{i} T_\mathrm{i} T_z\rangle^2}{2J_\mathrm{i}+1} \,. \tag{9.105}$$

Here the isospin labels T_i and T_f as well as their projection T_z are given, since the double bars still refer to reduction in coordinate space only. However, the dependence on the projection T_z can also be factored out by application of the Wigner-Eckart theorem to the isoscalar and isovector parts separately. Using triple-bar matrix elements to indicate reduction in coordinate space as well as in isospace, one obtains after substitution of eq. (9.100) into eq. (9.105)

$$\begin{aligned}
&B(\varpi L; J_\mathrm{i} T_\mathrm{i} T_z \to J_\mathrm{f} T_\mathrm{f} T_z) \\
&= \frac{1}{2J_\mathrm{i}+1}\left[\frac{\langle T_\mathrm{i} T_z 00 | T_\mathrm{f} T_z\rangle}{\sqrt{2T_\mathrm{f}+1}} \langle J_\mathrm{f} T_\mathrm{f} ||| \sum_{k=1}^{A} \boldsymbol{S}(\varpi L,k)\boldsymbol{1} ||| J_\mathrm{i} T_\mathrm{i}\rangle\right. \\
&\quad \left. - \frac{\langle T_\mathrm{i} T_z 10 | T_\mathrm{f} T_z\rangle}{\sqrt{2T_\mathrm{f}+1}} \langle J_\mathrm{f} T_\mathrm{f} ||| \sum_{k=1}^{A} \boldsymbol{V}(\varpi L,k)\, \boldsymbol{\tau}(k) ||| J_\mathrm{i} T_\mathrm{i}\rangle\right]^2 \\
&= \frac{1}{(2J_\mathrm{i}+1)(2T_\mathrm{f}+1)} [\delta_{T_\mathrm{i} T_\mathrm{f}} \langle J_\mathrm{f} T_\mathrm{f} ||| \sum_{k=1}^{A} \boldsymbol{S}(\varpi L,k)\boldsymbol{1} ||| J_\mathrm{i} T_\mathrm{i}\rangle \\
&\quad - \langle T_\mathrm{i} T_z 10 | T_\mathrm{f} T_z\rangle \langle J_\mathrm{f} T_\mathrm{f} ||| \sum_{k=1}^{A} \boldsymbol{V}(\varpi L,k)\, \boldsymbol{\tau}(k) ||| J_\mathrm{i} T_\mathrm{i}\rangle]^2 \,.
\end{aligned} \tag{9.106}$$

The triple-bar matrix elements for many-particle states can be expressed in terms of single-particle reduced matrix elements. The Racah algebra that is required to achieve this will be treated in chapter 10.

Note that as a result of the Kronecker delta $\delta_{T_\mathrm{i} T_\mathrm{f}}$ in the isoscalar part and the Clebsch-Gordan coefficient in the isovector part of eq. (9.106) no transition occurs

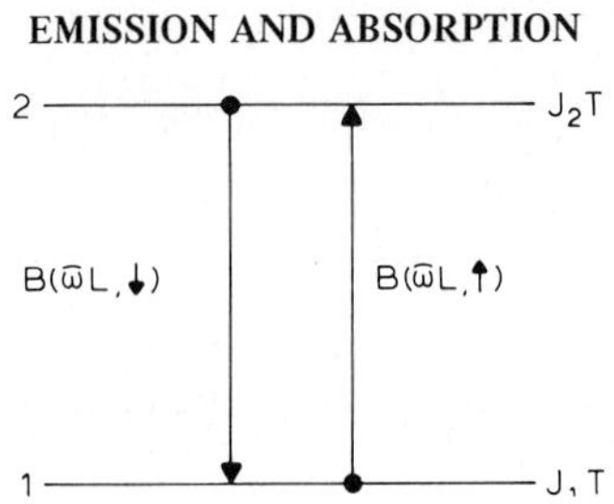

Fig. 9.1. For $J_1 \neq J_2$ the reduced transition rates for emission and absorption differ by a statistical factor.

between states that differ more than one unit in isospin, i.e. the selection rule $\Delta T \equiv |T_i - T_f| \leqslant 1$ applies. It is clear also that the isoscalar part does not contribute to $\Delta T \neq 0$ transitions and this affects, e.g. $\mathcal{E}2$, $\Delta T = 1$ transitions, as will be shown in chapter 10. For $\Delta T = 0$ transitions, i.e. $T_i = T_f = T$, one can directly evaluate the Clebsch-Gordan coefficient in expression (9.106) as

$$\langle TT_z 10 | TT_z \rangle = T_z / \sqrt{T(T+1)} \,. \tag{9.107}$$

The resulting T_z dependence of the isovector part has important consequences when electromagnetic transition rates are correlated in isospin multiplets such as mirror nuclei. It follows directly from eqs. (9.106) and (9.107) that for $\Delta T = 0$ transitions in self-conjugate nuclei (i.e. $T_z = 0$ nuclei) the isovector part does not contribute. For example, this affects strongly $\mathcal{M}1$ transition rates in such nuclei.

Finally we give the relation between the $B(\overline{\omega}L)$ values for the emission and absorption process. Suppose we have two states labelled 1 and 2 (see fig. 9.1). The relation between the reduced transition probabilities $B(\overline{\omega}L\downarrow) = B(\overline{\omega}L; 2 \to 1)$ and $B(\overline{\omega}L\uparrow) = B(\overline{\omega}L; 1 \to 2)$ is given by

$$B(\overline{\omega}L\downarrow) = \frac{2J_1 + 1}{2J_2 + 1} B(\overline{\omega}L\uparrow) \,. \tag{9.108}$$

This relation follows directly from eq. (9.105), since the absolute value of the reduced matrix element is not affected by the interchange of initial and final states. Eq. (9.108) follows also from eq. (9.106), of course, but then symmetry properties of the Clebsch-Gordan coefficients must be used.

CHAPTER 10

ELECTROMAGNETIC TRANSITION RATES

In this chapter we discuss the methods to calculate electromagnetic transition rates, once the corresponding operators and wave functions are given.

In sect. 10.1 the Weisskopf estimates, derived in the previous chapter, are treated in more detail and are related to observable quantities. Estimated ratios of isoscalar and isovector contributions are used in sect. 10.2 to correlate $\mathcal{M}1$ and $\mathcal{E}2$ transition rates for corresponding states in isospin multiplets. Expressions for the single-particle matrix elements of electric and magnetic multipole transition operators are derived in sects. 10.3 and 10.4, respectively. In sect. 10.5 the expansion of many-particle single-shell matrix elements is given in terms of single-particle matrix elements. This expansion is applied to the calculation of transition rates in ^{51}V. In this section it is also shown that for identical particles in a single orbit no $\mathcal{M}1$ transitions are possible. The evaluation of transition matrix elements for wave functions in which two active orbits are involved is given in sect. 10.6. The effect of configuration mixing on transition rates is discussed briefly in sect. 10.7. The evaluation of empirical single-particle matrix elements is treated in sect. 10.8.

10.1. Weisskopf estimates

It is explained in chapter 9 that two different types of multipole transitions can be distinguished, i.e. electric and magnetic, depending upon the parity change between initial and final states. Electromagnetic transition rates show a rather strong dependence on the transition energy. This dependence increases with the multiplicity of the transition, as can be seen from eq. (9.59). The Weisskopf estimates (see sect. 9.6) give a rough idea about the expected magnitudes of the radiation widths. These estimates for radiation of multipolarity 2^L are based on a very simple model with the assumptions:

(i) The nucleus consists of an inert core plus one active particle.

(ii) The transition takes place between states $j_{\mathrm{i}} = L \pm \frac{1}{2}$ and $j_{\mathrm{f}} = \frac{1}{2}$.

(iii) The radial parts of the initial- and final-state wave functions are both given by $u(r)$ = constant for $r \leqslant R$ and $u(r) = 0$ for $r > R$, where R denotes the nuclear radius.

Expressions for the rates of electric and magnetic multipole transitions calculated with these assumptions are given in eqs. (9.84) and (9.87).

It is common practice to compare an experimentally determined transition strength with the corresponding Weisskopf estimate, the Weisskopf unit. The main reason for expressing transition rates in these units is the removal of the strong dependence on the transition energy. This way a measure is obtained for the intrinsic transition probability, which is determined by the wave functions of the nuclear states only. Alternatively one may quote instead of the width $\Gamma(\overline{\omega}L)$ the reduced transition probability $B(\overline{\omega}L; J_i \to J_f)$, defined in eq. (9.60), with $\overline{\omega}$ denoting the magnetic or electric character of the transition. The probability $B(\overline{\omega}L)$ still contains an overall dependence on the nuclear radius R or mass number A. In order to facilitate conversion of the various quantities we now give some of the pertinent formulas relating them.

The quotient of transition rate and Weisskopf estimate, denoted by the symbol $M_W^2(\overline{\omega}L)$, was introduced in eq. (9.88) as

$$M_W^2(\overline{\omega}L) \equiv \frac{\Gamma(\overline{\omega}L)}{\Gamma_W(\overline{\omega}L)} = \frac{B(\overline{\omega}L)}{B_W(\overline{\omega}L)} . \tag{10.1}$$

Here $\Gamma_W(\overline{\omega}L)$ and $B_W(\overline{\omega}L)$ represent Weisskopf estimates of the width and reduced transition probability, respectively. For the relation between the dimensionless number $M_W^2(\overline{\omega}L)$ and the reduced transition strength $B(\overline{\omega}L)$, one must first evaluate the Weisskopf estimate $B_W(\overline{\omega}L)$.

For electric radiation $\mathcal{E}L$ one finds, after substitution of eqs. (9.79), (9.80) and (9.81) into eq. (9.60),

$$B_W(\mathcal{E}L) = \frac{1}{4\pi}\left(\frac{3}{L+3}\right)^2 e^2 R^{2L} . \tag{10.2}$$

Using the estimate (9.72) one obtains for magnetic radiation $\mathcal{M}L$

$$B_W(\mathcal{M}L) \approx \left(\frac{e\hbar}{2M_p c}\right)^2 \frac{40}{e^2 R^2} B_W(\mathcal{E}L) . \tag{10.3}$$

Substitution of eq. (10.2) leads to

$$B_W(\mathcal{M}L) = \frac{10}{\pi}\left(\frac{3}{L+3}\right)^2 R^{2L-2} \mu_N^2 . \tag{10.4}$$

Here

$$\mu_N = \frac{e\hbar}{2M_p c} = 1 \text{ n.m.} = 0.105\ e\cdot\text{fm} \tag{10.5}$$

represents the nuclear magneton. According to eq. (10.1) now the following two relations result

$$M_W^2(\mathcal{E}L) = 4\pi\left(\frac{L+3}{3}\right)^2 \frac{B(\mathcal{E}L)}{e^2 R^{2L}} , \tag{10.6}$$

$$M_W^2(\mathcal{M}L) = \tfrac{1}{10}\pi\left(\frac{L+3}{3}\right)^2 \frac{B(\mathcal{M}L)}{\mu_N^2 R^{2L-2}} . \tag{10.7}$$

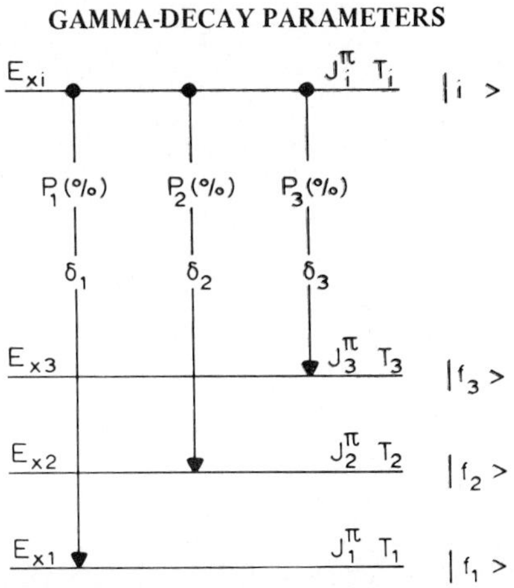

Fig. 10.1. The γ decay of an initial state $|i\rangle$ to the final states $|f_k\rangle$. The branching ratios P_k give the relative intensity of each branch as a percentage of the total intensity and the symbols δ_k denote the multipole mixing ratios.

Inserting the commonly used value $R = 1.20 \times A^{1/3}$ fm into eqs. (10.6) and (10.7) one obtains for electric dipole and quadrupole transitions the relations

$$M_{\mathrm{W}}^2(\mathcal{E}1) = \frac{15.5}{A^{2/3}} \frac{B(\mathcal{E}1)}{e^2 \cdot \mathrm{fm}^2} = \frac{1550}{A^{2/3}} \frac{B(\mathcal{E}1)}{e^2 \cdot \mathrm{b}}, \tag{10.8a}$$

$$M_{\mathrm{W}}^2(\mathcal{E}2) = \frac{16.8}{A^{4/3}} \frac{B(\mathcal{E}2)}{e^2 \cdot \mathrm{fm}^4} = \frac{16.8 \times 10^4}{A^{4/3}} \frac{B(\mathcal{E}2)}{e^2 \cdot \mathrm{b}^2}, \tag{10.8b}$$

where e.g. the notation $B(\mathcal{E}1)/e^2 \cdot \mathrm{fm}^2$ denotes the value of $B(\mathcal{E}1)$ expressed in units of $e^2 \cdot \mathrm{fm}^2$. For magnetic dipole and quadrupole transitions one finds

$$M_{\mathrm{W}}^2(\mathcal{M}1) = 0.559 \frac{B(\mathcal{M}1)}{\mu_{\mathrm{N}}^2}, \tag{10.9a}$$

$$M_{\mathrm{W}}^2(\mathcal{M}2) = \frac{0.606}{A^{2/3}} \frac{B(\mathcal{M}2)}{\mu_{\mathrm{N}}^2 \cdot \mathrm{fm}^2} = \frac{60.6}{A^{2/3}} \frac{B(\mathcal{M}2)}{\mu_{\mathrm{N}}^2 \cdot \mathrm{b}}, \tag{10.9b}$$

where e.g. the notation $B(\mathcal{M}1)/\mu_{\mathrm{N}}^2$ denotes the value of $B(\mathcal{M}1)$ expressed in units of $(\mathrm{n.m.})^2$.

An initial state $|i\rangle$ may decay to several final states $|f_k\rangle$. For a detailed comparison between experiment and theory it is necessary to determine the experimental transition probabilities for the decay of the state $|i\rangle$ to each state $|f_k\rangle$ separately (see fig. 10.1). The total width Γ_t of the initial state can be expressed in terms of partial widths Γ_k that each correspond to the decay to a final state f_k, as

$$\Gamma_t = \sum_k \Gamma_k . \tag{10.10}$$

Assuming that the initial state decays only by gamma emission, one determines the partials widths Γ_k from the measured branching ratios P_k, where the latter are as usual normalized to one hundred, i.e. $\Sigma_k P_k = 100$. One thus obtains

$$\Gamma_k = \frac{P_k}{100} \Gamma_t . \tag{10.11}$$

The width for gamma decay to a final state $|f_k\rangle$ often results from electromagnetic radiation of more than one multipolarity. In most practical cases not more than two L-values compete significantly (cf. eq. (9.96)). Assuming that angular momenta $L + 1$ and L contribute, one has for the width due to the decay to the state $|f_k\rangle$

$$\Gamma_k(\overline{\omega}L + 1; \overline{\omega}'L) = \Gamma_k(\overline{\omega}L + 1) + \Gamma_k(\overline{\omega}'L) . \tag{10.12}$$

Note that in this sum no phases of the contributing multipole radiations are involved.

The ratio of the partial widths $\Gamma_k(\overline{\omega}L + 1)$ and $\Gamma_k(\overline{\omega}'L)$ for two competing multipolarities can be measured experimentally. It is expressed usually in terms of the mixing ratio δ_k by the relation

$$\delta_k^2 = \frac{\Gamma_k(\overline{\omega}L + 1)}{\Gamma_k(\overline{\omega}'L)} = \frac{\text{intensity of } 2^{L+1} \text{ pole radiation}}{\text{intensity of } 2^L \text{ pole radiation}} . \tag{10.13}$$

From eqs. (10.12) and (10.13) one finds

$$\Gamma_k(\overline{\omega}'L) = \frac{\Gamma_k(\overline{\omega}L + 1; \overline{\omega}'L)}{1 + \delta_k^2} ,$$

$$\Gamma_k(\overline{\omega}L + 1) = \frac{\delta_k^2}{1 + \delta_k^2} \Gamma_k(\overline{\omega}L + 1; \overline{\omega}'L) . \tag{10.14}$$

Combining eqs. (10.11) and (10.14) one can express the widths $\Gamma_k(\overline{\omega}'L)$ and $\Gamma_k(\overline{\omega}L + 1)$ in terms of the total width Γ_t as

$$\Gamma_k(\overline{\omega}'L) = \frac{1}{1 + \delta_k^2} \frac{P_k}{100} \Gamma_t ,$$

$$\Gamma_k(\overline{\omega}L + 1) = \frac{\delta_k^2}{1 + \delta_k^2} \frac{P_k}{100} \Gamma_t . \tag{10.15}$$

The mean lifetime τ_m is related to the total gamma width Γ_t as

$$\Gamma_t = \frac{\hbar}{\tau_m} = \frac{658 \text{ fs}}{\tau_m} \text{ meV} , \tag{10.16}$$

where the value $\hbar = 658 \times 10^{-15}$ meV · s is inserted and femtoseconds (1 fs = 10^{-15} s) are used as units of time. (Instead of the mean lifetime τ_m one also uses the half life $\tau_{1/2}$, related by $\tau_m = \tau_{1/2}/\ln 2 = 1.44\,\tau_{1/2}$.) For the partial widths one now finds the relations

$$\Gamma_k(\bar{\omega}'L) = 6.58 \frac{P_k}{1+\delta_k^2} \frac{\text{fs}}{\tau_m} \text{meV} , \tag{10.17}$$

$$\Gamma_k(\bar{\omega}L+1) = 6.58 \frac{\delta_k^2}{1+\delta_k^2} P_k \frac{\text{fs}}{\tau_m} \text{meV} . \tag{10.18}$$

In order to compare the widths given in eqs. (10.17) and (10.18) with the Weisskopf estimates, one must evaluate

$$M_W^2(\bar{\omega}'L) = \frac{\Gamma_k(\bar{\omega}'L)}{\Gamma_W(\bar{\omega}'L)} = 6.58 \frac{P_k}{1+\delta_k^2} \frac{\text{fs}}{\tau_m} \frac{\text{meV}}{\Gamma_W(\bar{\omega}'L)} , \tag{10.19}$$

$$M_W^2(\bar{\omega}L+1) = \frac{\Gamma_k(\bar{\omega}L+1)}{\Gamma_W(\bar{\omega}L+1)} = 6.58 \frac{\delta_k^2}{1+\delta_k^2} P_k \frac{\text{fs}}{\tau_m} \frac{\text{meV}}{\Gamma_W(\bar{\omega}L+1)} . \tag{10.20}$$

The Weisskopf estimates for lower-order multipole transitions, derived from eqs. (9.85) and (9.87), are given in table 10.1.

Let us apply eqs. (10.19) and (10.20) to cases that involve mixed $\mathcal{M}1$ and $\mathcal{E}2$

Table 10.1
The Weisskopf single-particle widths Γ_W (W.u.) in meV

Electric a)	Magnetic a)
$\Gamma_W(\mathcal{E}1) = 68\, A^{2/3} E_\gamma^3$	$\Gamma_W(\mathcal{M}1) = 21\, E_\gamma^3$
$\Gamma_W(\mathcal{E}2) = 4.9 \times 10^{-5}\, A^{4/3} E_\gamma^5$	$\Gamma_W(\mathcal{M}2) = 1.5 \times 10^{-5}\, A^{2/3} E_\gamma^5$
$\Gamma_W(\mathcal{E}3) = 2.3 \times 10^{-11}\, A^2 E_\gamma^7$	$\Gamma_W(\mathcal{M}3) = 6.8 \times 10^{-12}\, A^{4/3} E_\gamma^7$
$\Gamma_W(\mathcal{E}4) = 6.8 \times 10^{-18}\, A^{8/3} E_\gamma^9$	$\Gamma_W(\mathcal{M}4) = 2.1 \times 10^{-18}\, A^2 E_\gamma^9$
$\Gamma_W(\mathcal{E}5) = 1.6 \times 10^{-24}\, A^{10/3} E_\gamma^{11}$	$\Gamma_W(\mathcal{M}5) = 4.9 \times 10^{-25}\, A^{8/3} E_\gamma^{11}$

a) The symbol A denotes the mass number and E_γ the transition energy in MeV.

transitions. With the Weisskopf estimates given in table 10.1 one finds

$$M_{\mathrm{W}}^2(\mathcal{M}1) = 0.313 \frac{1}{1+\delta_k^2} P_k \frac{\mathrm{fs}}{\tau_{\mathrm{m}}} \left(\frac{E_\gamma}{\mathrm{MeV}}\right)^{-3}, \tag{10.21}$$

$$M_{\mathrm{W}}^2(\mathcal{E}2) = 1.34 \times 10^5 \frac{\delta_k^2}{1+\delta_k^2} P_k \frac{\mathrm{fs}}{\tau_{\mathrm{m}}} \left(\frac{E_\gamma}{\mathrm{MeV}}\right)^{-5} A^{-4/3}, \tag{10.22}$$

where δ_k denotes the $\mathcal{E}2/\mathcal{M}1$ mixing ratio and P_k the branching ratio as a percentage for the transition to the final state $|\mathrm{f}_k\rangle$. Similarly one obtains for a transition involving mixed $\mathcal{M}2$ and $\mathcal{E}1$ radiation

$$M_{\mathrm{W}}^2(\mathcal{E}1) = 0.0968 \frac{1}{1+\delta_k^2} P_k \frac{\mathrm{fs}}{\tau_{\mathrm{m}}} \left(\frac{E_\gamma}{\mathrm{MeV}}\right)^{-3} A^{-2/3}, \tag{10.23}$$

$$M_{\mathrm{W}}^2(\mathcal{M}2) = 4.39 \times 10^5 \frac{\delta_k^2}{1+\delta_k^2} P_k \frac{\mathrm{fs}}{\tau_{\mathrm{m}}} \left(\frac{E_\gamma}{\mathrm{MeV}}\right)^{-5} A^{-2/3}, \tag{10.24}$$

where δ_k denotes the $\mathcal{M}2/\mathcal{E}1$ mixing ratio.

10.2. Isoscalar and isovector contributions

It is shown in sect. 9.7 that a transition probability is determined by an isoscalar and an isovector contribution. Both parts can be calculated, once the wave functions of the initial and final state are known. In this section it is shown that rough estimates of the relative magnitudes of the isoscalar and isovector parts can be made, without having to perform a detailed calculation. These estimates lead to correlations between transition rates of corresponding states in conjugate nuclei. Since most experimental information on this subject in lighter nuclei stems from transitions between states of equal parity, only $\mathcal{M}1$ and $\mathcal{E}2$ transitions will be discussed.

Magnetic dipole transitions. Inserting the isoscalar and isovector operators for an $\mathcal{M}1$ transition given in eqs. (9.103) and (9.104) into the expression for the transition strength given in eq. (9.106) one finds

$$B(\mathcal{M}1) = \frac{1}{(2J_{\mathrm{i}}+1)(2T_{\mathrm{f}}+1)} \{\delta_{T_{\mathrm{i}}T_{\mathrm{f}}}[\beta_1(g_{\mathrm{p}}^l + g_{\mathrm{n}}^l) + \beta_2(g_{\mathrm{p}}^s + g_{\mathrm{n}}^s)]$$
$$- \langle T_{\mathrm{i}}T_z 10|T_{\mathrm{f}}T_z\rangle [\beta_3(g_{\mathrm{p}}^l - g_{\mathrm{n}}^l) + \beta_4(g_{\mathrm{p}}^s - g_{\mathrm{n}}^s)]\}^2, \tag{10.25}$$

where β_1 and β_2 specify matrix elements that contribute to the isoscalar part and similarly β_3 and β_4 for the isovector part. Using eq. (A.2.23) one derives (see also sect. 10.4) for the coefficients β_k the explicit relations

$$\beta_1 = \frac{1}{2}\sqrt{\frac{3}{4\pi}}\langle J_\mathrm{f}\| \sum_{k=1}^{A} l(k) \| J_\mathrm{i}\rangle \langle T_\mathrm{f} \| 1 \| T_\mathrm{i}\rangle \mu_\mathrm{N} , \tag{10.26a}$$

$$\beta_2 = \frac{1}{2}\sqrt{\frac{3}{4\pi}}\langle J_\mathrm{f}\| \sum_{k=1}^{A} s(k) \| J_\mathrm{i}\rangle \langle T_\mathrm{f} \| 1 \| T_\mathrm{i}\rangle \mu_\mathrm{N} , \tag{10.26b}$$

$$\beta_3 = \frac{1}{2}\sqrt{\frac{3}{4\pi}}\langle J_\mathrm{f} T_\mathrm{f} \||| \sum_{k=1}^{A} l(k)\tau(k) \||| J_\mathrm{i} T_\mathrm{i}\rangle \mu_\mathrm{N} , \tag{10.26c}$$

$$\beta_4 = \frac{1}{2}\sqrt{\frac{3}{4\pi}}\langle J_\mathrm{f} T_\mathrm{f} \||| \sum_{k=1}^{A} s(k)\tau(k) \||| J_\mathrm{i} T_\mathrm{i}\rangle \hat{\mu}_\mathrm{N} . \tag{10.26d}$$

For the initial and final states being orthogonal eigenstates of the total Hamiltonian and eigenstates of the total angular momentum J one has the condition

$$\langle J_\mathrm{f} \| J \| J_\mathrm{i}\rangle = 0 . \tag{10.27}$$

From the relation

$$J = \sum_{k=1}^{A} j(k) = \sum_{k=1}^{A} [l(k) + s(k)] \tag{10.28}$$

one thus obtains

$$\langle J_\mathrm{f} \| J \| J_\mathrm{i}\rangle = \langle J_\mathrm{f} \| \sum_{k=1}^{A} l(k) \| J_\mathrm{i}\rangle + \langle J_\mathrm{f} \| \sum_{k=1}^{A} s(k) \| J_\mathrm{i}\rangle = 0 . \tag{10.29}$$

From a comparison of eqs. (10.26a) and (10.26b) with eq. (10.29) one finds the relation $\beta_1 = -\beta_2$, since the unit operator in isospace contributes the same factor to both β_1 and β_2. Insertion of the nucleon g-factors $g_\mathrm{p}^l = 1$, $g_\mathrm{n}^l = 0$, $g_\mathrm{p}^s = 5.6$ and $g_\mathrm{n}^s = -3.8$ into eq. (10.25) leads to the expression

$$B(\mathcal{M}1) = \frac{1}{(2J_\mathrm{i}+1)(2T_\mathrm{f}+1)} [-0.8\beta_1 \delta_{T_\mathrm{i}T_\mathrm{f}} - \langle T_\mathrm{i} T_z 10 | T_\mathrm{f} T_z\rangle (\beta_3 + 9.4\beta_4)]^2 \mu_\mathrm{N}^2 . \tag{10.30}$$

Due to the large coefficient of the β_4 term in eq. (10.30) one expects the isovector part generally to be much larger than the isoscalar part. For a $\Delta T = 0$ ($T_\mathrm{i} = T_\mathrm{f}$) transition one obtains from eq. (10.30) and the explicit value $\langle T T_z 10 | T T_z\rangle = T_z [T(T+1)]^{-1/2}$ the relation

$$B(\mathcal{M}1) = [M_\mathrm{is}(\mathcal{M}1) + T_z M_\mathrm{iv}(\mathcal{M}1)]^2 \quad \text{with } |M_\mathrm{is}(\mathcal{M}1)| < |M_\mathrm{iv}(\mathcal{M}1)| . \tag{10.31}$$

In this equation $M_{is}(\mathcal{M}1)$ and $M_{iv}(\mathcal{M}1)$ denote the isoscalar and isovector matrix elements, respectively, with the inclusion of the numerical factors that are given explicitly in eq. (10.30). It thus follows that $\Delta T = 0$ transitions of $\mathcal{M}1$ character in selfconjugate nuclei ($T_z = 0$) should be weak compared to average $\mathcal{M}1$ strengths, which is confirmed by the experimental data [Endt and Van der Leun (1974b)].

Histograms of experimentally determined strengths of magnetic multipole transitions in $A < 45$ nuclei are presented in fig. 10.2. In this figure the strengths are expressed in units of the single-particle Weisskopf estimate Γ_W, given in table 10.1. The isoscalar and isovector strengths can be determined separately (i) from transitions with $\Delta T \neq 0$ (only the isovector part contributes), (ii) from transitions with $\Delta T = 0$ in $T_z = 0$ nuclei (only the isoscalar part contributes) and (iii) from corresponding transitions in isospin multiplets, i.e. for states differing only in the value of T_z.

Electric quadrupole transitions. With the isoscalar and isovector operators given in eqs. (9.101) and (9.102) one can write the transition strength given in eq. (9.106) as

MAGNETIC TRANSITION STRENGTHS IN $A < 45$ NUCLEI (NOT RETARDED)

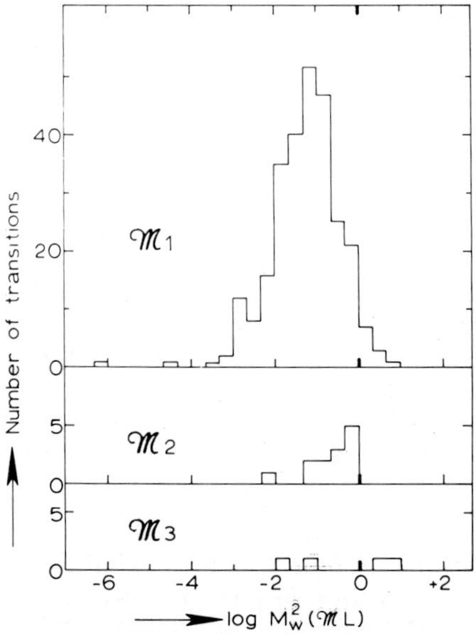

Fig. 10.2. Histograms of experimental γ-ray strengths (W.u.) of magnetic transitions in $A < 45$ nuclei. The strengths, ordered according to multipolarity, are given for transitions that are not retarded because of isospin selection rules.

$$B(\mathcal{E}2) = \frac{1}{4(2J_i+1)(2T_f+1)} [\delta_{T_iT_f}\beta_1'(e_p+e_n) - \langle T_iT_z10|T_fT_z\rangle \beta_2'(e_p-e_n)]^2 , \tag{10.32}$$

where the reduced matrix elements

$$\beta_1' = \langle J_f \| \sum_{k=1}^{A} r^2(k) Y_2(\hat{r}(k)) \| J_i\rangle \langle T_f \| 1 \| T_i\rangle , \tag{10.33a}$$

$$\beta_2' = \langle J_f T_f ||| \sum_{k=1}^{A} r^2(k) Y_2(\hat{r}(k)) \tau(k) ||| J_i T_i\rangle \tag{10.33b}$$

contribute to the isoscalar and isovector parts, respectively.

It turns out that shell-model calculations often underestimate $\mathcal{E}2$ transition strengths. This can be traced back to too small a configuration space being taken into account, i.e. significant contributions to the $\mathcal{E}2$ transition strength that derive from configurations outside the model space, are simply ignored. This loss of $\mathcal{E}2$ strength can be largely compensated for by the introduction of effective proton and neutron charges. Thus one employs for protons the effective charge $e + \Delta e_p$ and for neutrons the effective charge Δe_n, with $\Delta e_p/e$ and $\Delta e_n/e$ both being positive. The additional charges Δe_p and Δe_n usually are found to depend not too strongly on the initial and final single-particle states involved. For simplicity then one often takes these charges for proton and neutron equal and state independent. This means that for a calculation of transition rates in a certain mass region, one frequently makes the assumption $\Delta e_p = \Delta e_n = \Delta e$. The good results obtained with the latter approach have made it an accepted procedure in many applications.

The use of an effective charge will affect the ratio between a calculated isoscalar and isovector contribution. According to eq. (10.32) the isoscalar part is proportional to the sum of proton and neutron charge. An effective charge thus leads to an increase in the isoscalar contribution given by the factor $1 + (\Delta e_p + \Delta e_n)/e$. The isovector part is proportional to the difference of the proton and neutron charge and thus changes by a factor $1 + (\Delta e_p - \Delta e_n)/e$.

A phenomenological determination of the correlation between the configuration space used in a calculation and the effective charge needed will be illustrated by some transition rates in ${}^{33}_{16}S_{17}$. The levels considered in this example are given in fig. 10.3 and they refer to the lowest level for each spin $J^\pi = \frac{1}{2}^+, \frac{3}{2}^+, \frac{5}{2}^+$ and $\frac{7}{2}^+$. Only the $\mathcal{E}2$ decay to the $J^\pi = \frac{3}{2}^+$ ground state is discussed. The transition rates are calculated in three different model spaces.

(i) With the pure configurations listed in table 10.2. In this model each wave function has one component only.

(ii) A two-orbit calculation for an inert core of ${}^{28}_{14}Si_{14}$ and the remaining nucleons

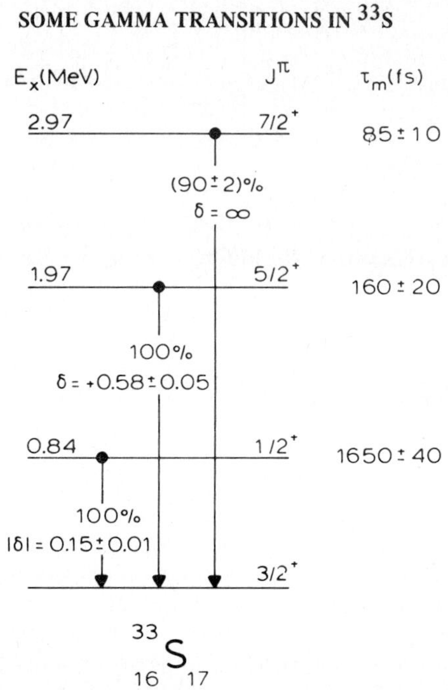

Fig. 10.3. The decay properties of some of the lower states in ^{33}S, taken from the review paper [Endt and Van der Leun (1973)]. The mixing ratios δ refer to $\mathcal{E}2/\mathcal{M}1$ radiation.

distributed over the orbits $2s_{1/2}$ and $1d_{3/2}$. In this model each wave function has approximately ten components.

(iii) A three-orbit calculation with at least ten particles in the $1d_{5/2}$ orbit and no further restrictions on the nucleon distributions over the $2s_{1/2}$ and $1d_{3/2}$ orbits. This leads to states described by approximately 200 components.

It is clear from table 10.3 that the wave functions with a small number of components reproduce the experimental data only if a large value of Δe is employed. Note that in this example a single value of Δe suffices to reproduce several transition rates rather well. It is this feature which has made the use of an effective charge so successful.

Let us now return to the influence of effective charges on the ratio of isoscalar and isovector contributions to $\mathcal{E}2$ transition rates. For a $\Delta T = 0$ transition one obtains from eq. (10.32)

$$B(\mathcal{E}2) = |M_{is}(\mathcal{E}2) + T_z M_{iv}(\mathcal{E}2)|^2 \qquad \text{with } |M_{is}(\mathcal{E}2)| > |M_{iv}(\mathcal{E}2)|\,, \tag{10.34}$$

where $M_{is}(\mathcal{E}2)$ and $M_{iv}(\mathcal{E}2)$ denote the isoscalar and isovector contributions, res-

Table 10.2
The pure configurations in ^{33}S used in model (i)

E_x (MeV)	J^π	Configuration
		$(2s_{1/2})^n_{J_1T_1}(1d_{3/2})^m_{J_2T_2}$
0	$\frac{3}{2}^+$	$(2s_{1/2})^4_{00}(1d_{3/2})^1_{3/2\ 1/2}$
0.84	$\frac{1}{2}^+$	$(2s_{1/2})^3_{1/2\ 1/2}(1d_{3/2})^2_{01}$
1.97	$\frac{5}{2}^+$	$(2s_{1/2})^3_{1/2\ 1/2}(1d_{3/2})^2_{21}$
2.97	$\frac{7}{2}^+$	$(2s_{1/2})^3_{1/2\ 1/2}(1d_{3/2})^2_{30}$

pectively, and the inequality is found to hold in most cases.

Let us illustrate the influence of the configuration space and the effective charge on the isoscalar and isovector contributions. The average ratio of the isoscalar and isovector contributions for the three transitions in ^{33}S, shown in fig. 10.3, are plotted in fig. 10.4. In one case no effective charge is assumed, i.e. $\Delta e = 0$. It is seen that the ratio $M_{is}(\mathcal{E}2)/M_{iv}(\mathcal{E}2)$ increases with increasing size of the model space. Thus one finds the largest ratio for the most realistic model space. The other case shows the same ratio with the effective charge Δe in each model space chosen such that optimum agreement with the experimental data is obtained. It follows that in the latter case the relation $M_{is}(\mathcal{E}2) \gg M_{iv}(\mathcal{E}2)$ is obtained also for the small configuration space. This is due to the effective charge Δe, which increases the isoscalar contribution as explained before but leaves the isovector part unaffected.

Table 10.3
Strengths of $\mathcal{E}2$ transitions in ^{33}S (expressed in W.u.) as a function of the model space and of the effective charge

Transition	Calculated $\mathcal{E}2$ strengths						Experimental values [a]
	model (i)		model (ii)		model (iii)		
$J_i \to J_f$	$\Delta e = 0$	$\Delta e = 1.1e$	$\Delta e = 0$	$\Delta e = 0.6e$	$\Delta e = 0$	$\Delta e = 0.5e$	
$\frac{1}{2}^+ \to \frac{3}{2}^+$	0.2	4.3	1.6	5.9	1.4	4.5	4.0 ± 0.2
$\frac{5}{2}^+ \to \frac{3}{2}^+$	0.3	6.0	0.9	5.6	1.8	7.3	6.7 ± 1.2
$\frac{7}{2}^+ \to \frac{3}{2}^+$	1.1	4.9	1.8	5.7	1.7	4.8	5.8 ± 0.7

[a] [Schwalm (1973); Endt and Van der Leun (1973)].

CALCULATED ISOSCALAR AND ISOVECTOR $\mathcal{E}2$ CONTRIBUTIONS IN ^{33}S

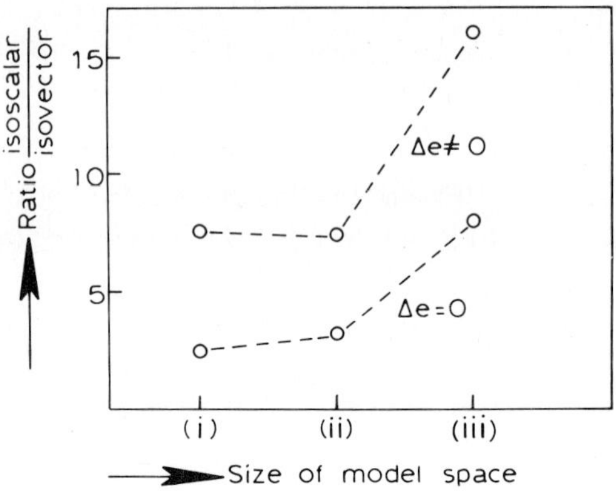

Fig. 10.4. The average ratio of the calculated isoscalar and isovector parts of some $\mathcal{E}2$ transitions in ^{33}S. This ratio is plotted for the model spaces (i), (ii) and (iii) discussed in the text and for the effective charges given in table 10.3.

Wave functions of corresponding states in mirror nuclei are identical when effects of charge-dependent forces are assumed to be negligible. Thus when dealing with two corresponding transitions in such nuclei one has identical contributions from the isoscalar parts as well as from the isovector parts. The only difference in the transition strengths results from the sign of T_z (cf. eqs. (10.31) and (10.34)). This means that the isoscalar and isovector contributions can be extracted separately from experimentally known transition rates between corresponding states in mirror nuclei.

The fact that the isoscalar contribution is considerably larger than the isovector

THE A = 30 ISOSPIN TRIPLET

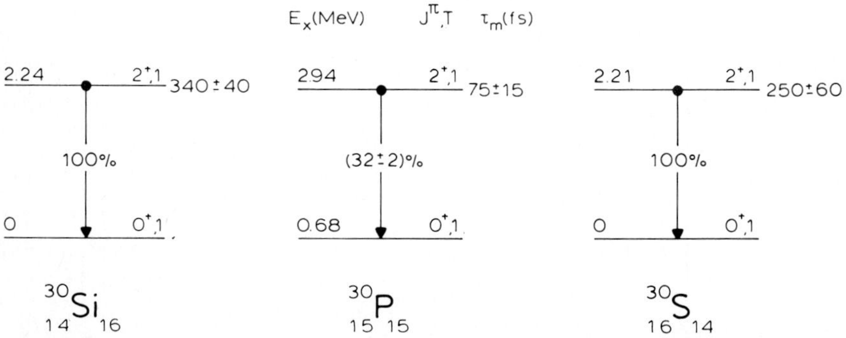

Fig. 10.5. Summary of the experimental data on $\mathcal{E}2$ transition rates for the lower two T = 1 states in the A = 30 isospin triplet. The data are taken from the review paper [Endt and Van der Leun (1974a)].

contribution turns out to be quite general for $\mathcal{E}2$ transitions. Hence it is a useful property to correlate experimental data in isospin multiplets.

A direct determination of the isoscalar and isovector contributions follows e.g. from a comparison of corresponding $\Delta T = 0$ transitions between $T = 1$ states in isospin triplets ($T_z = -1, 0$ and $+1$). For the nucleus with $T_z = 0$ only the isoscalar part contributes, since the isovector part vanishes. The different transition strength in either the $T_z = +1$ or -1 nucleus then gives the information necessary to determine the isovector part. This way the strength in one of the latter two $T = 1$ nuclei determines the other one.

An example is the triplet ${}^{30}_{14}Si_{16}$, ${}^{30}_{15}P_{15}$ and ${}^{30}_{16}S_{14}$. The reduced transition rates of the corresponding $\mathcal{E}2$ transitions from the lowest $J^\pi = 2^+, T = 1$ state to the $J^\pi = 0^+, T = 1$ state are known experimentally (see fig. 10.5). The strengths obtained from the data [Endt and Van der Leun (1974a)] with eq. (10.22) can be written with expression (10.34) as

$$^{30}\mathrm{Si}:\ M_\mathrm{W}^2(\mathcal{E}2) = \frac{B(\mathcal{E}2)}{B_\mathrm{W}(\mathcal{E}2)} = \frac{[M_\mathrm{is}(\mathcal{E}2) + M_\mathrm{iv}(\mathcal{E}2)]^2}{B_\mathrm{W}(\mathcal{E}2)} = 7.3 \pm 0.9\,, \tag{10.35}$$

$$^{30}\mathrm{P}:\ M_\mathrm{W}^2(\mathcal{E}2) = \frac{B(\mathcal{E}2)}{B_\mathrm{W}(\mathcal{E}2)} = \frac{[M_\mathrm{is}(\mathcal{E}2)]^2}{B_\mathrm{W}(\mathcal{E}2)} = 11 \pm 2\,, \tag{10.36}$$

$$^{30}\mathrm{S}:\ M_\mathrm{W}^2(\mathcal{E}2) = \frac{B(\mathcal{E}2)}{B_\mathrm{W}(\mathcal{E}2)} = \frac{[M_\mathrm{is}(\mathcal{E}2) - M_\mathrm{iv}(\mathcal{E}2)]^2}{B_\mathrm{W}(\mathcal{E}2)} = 11 \pm 3\,. \tag{10.37}$$

From these equations one derives a ratio $|M_\mathrm{is}(\mathcal{E}2)/M_\mathrm{iv}(\mathcal{E}2)| \gtrsim 5$.

A summary of the experimentally determined strengths of electric multipole transitions for $A < 45$ nuclei is presented in fig. 10.6. The strengths are expressed in Weisskop units, given in table 10.1.

A further experimental test of the relative magnitudes of isoscalar and isovector contributions for magnetic dipole as well as electric quadrupole transitions is obtained from the $\mathcal{E}2/\mathcal{M}1$ mixing ratios for corresponding $\Delta T = 0$ transitions in mirror nuclei. From eqs. (9.64), (9.60), (10.31) and (10.34) one immediately derives the proportionality

$$\delta(\mathcal{E}2/\mathcal{M}1) \propto E_\gamma \frac{M_\mathrm{is}(\mathcal{E}2) + T_z M_\mathrm{iv}(\mathcal{E}2)}{M_\mathrm{is}(\mathcal{M}1) + T_z M_\mathrm{iv}(\mathcal{M}1)}\,. \tag{10.38}$$

This leads with the inequalities (see eqs. (10.31) and (10.34))

$$|M_\mathrm{is}(\mathcal{E}2)| > |M_\mathrm{iv}(\mathcal{E}2)|\,, \qquad |M_\mathrm{is}(\mathcal{M}1)| < |M_\mathrm{iv}(\mathcal{M}1)|\,, \tag{10.39}$$

to the approximate relation for $T_z \neq 0$ nuclei

$$\delta(\mathcal{E}2/\mathcal{M}1) \propto E_\gamma \frac{M_\mathrm{is}(\mathcal{E}2)}{T_z M_\mathrm{iv}(\mathcal{M}1)}\,. \tag{10.40}$$

When one replaces T_z by its opposite value, it follows that the mixing ratio changes sign. The absolute value of the mixing ratio should not change much, when (i) cor-

ELECTRIC TRANSITION STRENGTHS IN $A < 45$ NUCLEI (NOT RETARDED)

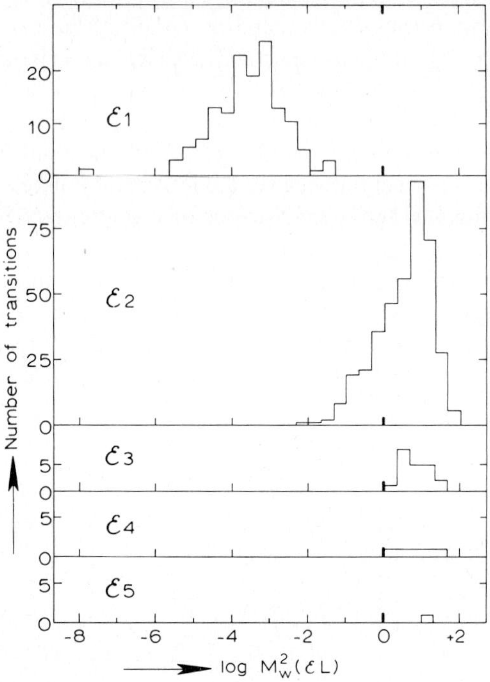

Fig. 10.6. Histograms of experimental γ-ray strengths (in W.u.) of electric transitions in $A < 45$ nuclei. The strengths, ordered according to multipolarity, are given for transitions that are not retarded due to isospin selection rules.

responding transition energies E_γ in mirror nuclei are comparable, (ii) the inequalities (10.39) are well-satisfied and (iii) charge effects on nuclear wave functions are negligible. The last assumption is expected to hold mainly for strong transitions, since the latter then result from large components in the wave functions or from constructive interference of many small components. Very weak transitions derive, however, either from small components in the wave functions of initial and/or final states or from a cancellation of strong contributions. In the latter case the transitions rates may be more affected by small changes in the wave functions that are caused by charge dependent forces.

The presently available experimental information on mixing ratios in mirror nuclei for the mass region $23 \leqslant A \leqslant 39$ is shown in fig. 10.7. The most striking feature is the experimental result, that not only the sign flip of T_z is observed in all cases, but that also the absolute values of $\delta(\mathcal{E}2/\mathcal{M}1)$ for corresponding transitions are equal within the experimental errors. In fact the average ratio of corresponding δ-values shown in fig. 10.7 is equal to -0.97 ± 0.04, which confirms the close analogy between corresponding mixing ratios.

It should be remarked that the experimentally determined ratio of corresponding

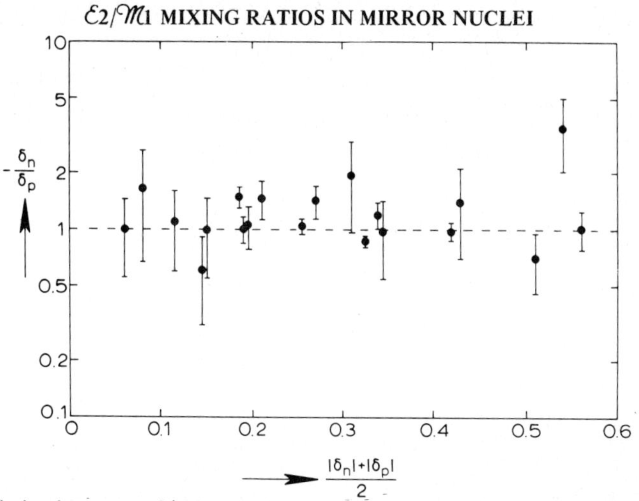

Fig. 10.7. Relation between $\mathcal{E}2/\mathcal{M}1$ mixing ratios δ_n and δ_p of mirror transitions in sd-shell nuclei. The symbols δ_n and δ_p denote the measured mixing ratios of corresponding transitions in the mirror nuclei $_ZA_{N+1}$ and $_{Z+1}A_N$, respectively [Glaudemans and Van der Leun (1971)].

δ-values doet not seem to depend on the strength of the transitions, since the transitions used in fig. 10.7 include $\mathcal{M}1$ strengths in the range 0.001–0.2 W.u. and $\mathcal{E}2$ strengths of 0.6–30 W.u. A complication in comparing signs of mixing ratios is the existence of different conventions for extracting mixing ratios from angular distribution and correlation measurements (see sect. 9.5).

Summarizing one may say that, at least for lighter nuclei and for transitions that are not too weak, presently available experimental data lead to the approximate inequalities.

$$|M_{\text{iv}}(\mathcal{M}1)| \gtrsim 5\,|M_{\text{is}}(\mathcal{M}1)|\,, \tag{10.41}$$

$$|M_{\text{is}}(\mathcal{E}2)| \gtrsim 5\,|M_{\text{iv}}(\mathcal{E}2)|\,. \tag{10.42}$$

These relations are expected to hold in most cases.

10.3. Single-particle matrix elements for $\mathcal{E}L$ transitions

The expression for the reduced transition rate $B(\overline{\omega}L; \Gamma_i \to \Gamma_f)$, given in eq. (9.105), contains the reduced matrix elements $\langle \Gamma_f ||| \Sigma_{k=1}^{A} O_\Lambda(k) ||| \Gamma_i \rangle$, where $|\Gamma_i\rangle$ and $|\Gamma_f\rangle$ denote many-particle wave functions with the symbol Γ denoting as usual both J and T and where $O_\Lambda(k)$ is a tensor operator of rank L_Λ in coordinate space and T_Λ in isospace. Since $O_\Lambda(k)$ is a single-particle operator, it is possible to express the many-particle matrix elements in terms of single-particle matrix elements. The necessary Racah algebra needed to perform this reduction is outlined in sect. 10.5. In this section the single-particle matrix elements for electric multipole operators are discussed first.

The initial and final single-particle wave functions denoted by $|\rho\rangle$ and $|\lambda\rangle$, respectively, can be written as a product of a radial, an angular and an isospin dependent part

$$|nljt\rangle = |nl\rangle\,|ljm\rangle\,|tt_z\rangle\,. \tag{10.43}$$

With the isoscalar operator given in eq. (9.101) one can now write the single-particle matrix element, reduced in coordinate space and isospace, as

$$\langle\lambda\,|||\boldsymbol{S}(\mathcal{E}L)\mathbf{1}|||\,\rho\rangle = \tfrac{1}{2}(e_\mathrm{p}+e_\mathrm{n})\langle n_\lambda l_\lambda|r^L|n_\rho l_\rho\rangle\,\langle l_\lambda j_\lambda\|\boldsymbol{Y}_L(\hat{\boldsymbol{r}})\|l_\rho j_\rho\rangle\,\langle t_\lambda\|\mathbf{1}\|t_\rho\rangle\,. \tag{10.44}$$

For the isovector operator (9.102) one obtains similarly the matrix element

$$\langle\lambda\,|||\boldsymbol{V}(\mathcal{E}L)\boldsymbol{\tau}|||\,\rho\rangle = \tfrac{1}{2}(e_\mathrm{p}-e_\mathrm{n})\langle n_\lambda l_\lambda|r^L|n_\rho l_\rho\rangle\,\langle l_\lambda j_\lambda\|\boldsymbol{Y}_L(\hat{\boldsymbol{r}})\|l_\rho j_\rho\rangle\,\langle t_\lambda\|\boldsymbol{\tau}\|t_\rho\rangle\,. \tag{10.45}$$

The radial matrix elements in these equations are defined by (cf. eq. (2.17))

$$\langle n_\lambda l_\lambda|r^L|n_\rho l_\rho\rangle = \int_{r=0}^{\infty} R_{n_\lambda l_\lambda}(r)r^L R_{n_\rho l_\rho}(r)r^2\,\mathrm{d}r\,. \tag{10.46}$$

For the evaluation of this radial integral usually harmonic-oscillator wave functions are used. Their explicit form is given in eq. (2.21). Focusing attention on the dependence on the size parameter (cf. eq. (2.36))

$$b = \sqrt{\frac{\hbar}{M_\mathrm{p}\omega}} = 1.00\,A^{1/6}\ \mathrm{fm}\,, \tag{10.47}$$

one can write the radial wave function as

$$R_{nl}(r) = C_{nl}b^{-3/2}\left(\frac{r}{b}\right)^l \mathrm{e}^{-r^2/2b^2}\,{}_1F_1\!\left(1-n, l+\tfrac{3}{2}; \frac{r^2}{b^2}\right)\,. \tag{10.48}$$

In this expression C_{nl} contains all b-independent constants not shown explicitly. The b-dependence of the matrix element (10.46) can be easily factored out after introduction of the new integration variable $r' = r/b$ into the integral (10.46). One thus obtains, using eqs. (10.47) and (10.48),

$$\langle n_\lambda l_\lambda|r^L|n_\rho l_\rho\rangle_b = \left(\frac{b}{\mathrm{fm}}\right)^L \langle n_\lambda l_\lambda|r^L|n_\rho l_\rho\rangle_{b=1\,\mathrm{fm}} = (1.00\,A^{1/6})^L\langle n_\lambda l_\lambda|r^L|n_\rho l_\rho\rangle_{b=1\,\mathrm{fm}}\,, \tag{10.49}$$

where the integral at the right-hand side is evaluated for $b = 1$ fm. Numerical values of the radial integrals calculated for $b = 1$ fm with the sign of the radial wave functions positive near the origin are given in appendix B.5. These radial integrals for

$b = 1$ fm can be converted for any value of b, i.e. for any mass number A, by application of relation (10.49).

The reduced angular matrix element in eqs. (10.44) and (10.45) can be evaluated by the use of eq. (A.3.e5) (with the coupling order $\boldsymbol{j} = \boldsymbol{l} + \boldsymbol{s}$) as

$$\langle l_\lambda j_\lambda \| Y_L(\hat{r}) \| l_\rho j_\rho \rangle = (-1)^{j_\lambda + 1/2} \sqrt{\frac{(2j_\lambda + 1)(2j_\rho + 1)(2L + 1)}{4\pi}} \begin{pmatrix} j_\lambda & L & j_\rho \\ \frac{1}{2} & 0 & -\frac{1}{2} \end{pmatrix}$$

$$\times \tfrac{1}{2}(1 + (-1)^{l_\lambda + L + l_\rho}) . \tag{10.50}$$

The last matrix element of eq. (10.44) is obtained from eq. (A.3.c1) after substitution of the isospin $t = \frac{1}{2}$, which leads to

$$\langle t = \tfrac{1}{2} \| \mathbf{1} \| t = \tfrac{1}{2} \rangle = \sqrt{2} . \tag{10.51}$$

Similarly the last matrix element of eq. (10.45) follows from eq. (A.3.c7) if moreover one takes into account $\boldsymbol{\tau} = 2\boldsymbol{t}$. One obtains

$$\langle t = \tfrac{1}{2} \| \boldsymbol{\tau} \| t = \tfrac{1}{2} \rangle = \sqrt{6} . \tag{10.52}$$

In order to comprise the final results for eqs. (10.44) and (10.45) in one expression, we use the label $I = 0$ to denote matrix elements of the isoscalar part and $I = 1$ for the isovector part,

$$\langle \lambda \| \| O(\mathcal{E}L) \| \| \rho \rangle_{I=0} \equiv \langle \lambda \| \| S(\mathcal{E}L) \mathbf{1} \| \| \rho \rangle , \tag{10.53}$$

$$\langle \lambda \| \| O(\mathcal{E}L) \| \| \rho \rangle_{I=1} \equiv \langle \lambda \| \| V(\mathcal{E}L) \boldsymbol{\tau} \| \| \rho \rangle . \tag{10.54}$$

Now we can give the matrix elements as

$$\langle \lambda \| \| O(\mathcal{E}L) \| \| \rho \rangle_I = (e_\mathrm{p} + (-1)^I e_\mathrm{n}) \langle n_\lambda l_\lambda | r^L | n_\rho l_\rho \rangle f_I^{(\mathcal{E}L)}(\lambda; \rho) \tag{10.55}$$

with

$$f_I^{(\mathcal{E}L)}(\lambda; \rho) = (-1)^{j_\lambda + 1/2} \tfrac{1}{4} \sqrt{\frac{(2j_\lambda + 1)(2j_\rho + 1)(2L + 1)}{2\pi}} \begin{pmatrix} j_\rho & L & j_\lambda \\ \frac{1}{2} & 0 & -\frac{1}{2} \end{pmatrix}$$

$$\times [1 + (-1)^{l_\rho + l_\lambda + L}] \sqrt{2I + 1} . \tag{10.56}$$

Values of $f_I^{(\mathcal{E}L)}(\lambda; \rho)$ for $L = 1, 2$ and 3 and various single-particle orbits λ and ρ are listed in appendix B.6 (see appendix B.5 for the values of $\langle n_\lambda l_\lambda | r^L | n_\rho l_\rho \rangle$).

The single-particle matrix elements vanish when the triangle condition $\Delta(j_\rho j_\lambda L)$ is not satisfied or when $l_\rho + l_\lambda + L$ assumes an odd value. The latter condition is a direct consequence of the parity selection rule for electric transitions given in eq. (9.56).

Table 10.4
Some examples illustrating the calculation of isoscalar reduced single-particle matrix elements for $\mathcal{E}\,2$ transitions [a)]

$\langle\lambda \| O(\mathcal{E}2) \| \rho\rangle_{I=0}$	$\langle r^2\rangle_b = 1$ fm (fm^2)	$f_{I=0}^{(\mathcal{E}2)}(\rho;\lambda)$	Value ($(e_\mathrm{p}+e_\mathrm{n})\mathrm{fm}^2$)
$\langle 1\mathrm{d}_{5/2} \| O(\mathcal{E}2) \| 1\mathrm{d}_{5/2}\rangle_{I=0}$	3.50	−0.522	−1.827
$\langle 1\mathrm{d}_{5/2} \| O(\mathcal{E}2) \| 1\mathrm{d}_{3/2}\rangle_{I=0}$	3.50	−0.261	−0.914
$\langle 1\mathrm{f}_{5/2} \| O(\mathcal{E}2) \| 1\mathrm{p}_{3/2}\rangle_{I=0}$	2.96	−0.261	−0.772
$\langle 1\mathrm{f}_{5/2} \| O(\mathcal{E}2) \| 2\mathrm{p}_{3/2}\rangle_{I=0}$	−3.74	−0.261	0.976

a) The values are calculated for the coupling order $j = l + s$ and for radial wave functions that are positive near $r = 0$.

For the derivation of matrix element (10.50) the coupling order $j = l + s$ is assumed. One could take also the order $j = s + l$, but this leads to a different phase factor. It is stressed again that once a coupling order is chosen, this order must be used consistently in all expressions including, e.g. those of two-body interaction matrix elements. A similar remark holds for the phases of the radial wave functions $R_{nl}(r)$. The radial matrix elements, listed in appendix B.5, are calculated for radial wave functions that are taken with a positive sign near $r = 0$. Therefore this convention must be used also for the derivation of two-body matrix elements.

Often one needs, for a calculation of transition rates involving particles in the orbits ρ and λ, the matrix elements for single-particle transitions $\rho \to \lambda$ as well as $\lambda \to \rho$. The relation connecting the corresponding reduced single-particle matrix elements of a 2^L pole operator is given by

$$\langle\lambda \| O(\overline{\omega}L) \| \rho\rangle = (-1)^{\lambda-\rho}\langle\rho \| O(\overline{\omega}L) \| \lambda\rangle\,. \tag{10.57}$$

This expression follows immediately from eq. (A.3.b5), but can for this specific case also be obtained from eq. (10.56) by interchange of j_λ and j_ρ.

Some typical examples illustrating the construction of reduced single-particle matrix elements for $\mathcal{E}2$ transitions are given in table 10.4.

10.4. Single-particle matrix elements for $\mathcal{M}L$ transitions

We now turn to the derivation of single-particle matrix elements for magnetic multipole transitions. The relevant operator is given in eq. (9.38) or, after separation into isoscalar and isovector parts, in eqs. (9.103) and (9.104). Because of the presence of the scalar product of $\boldsymbol{l}$ or $\boldsymbol{s}$ and the gradient operator $\boldsymbol{\nabla}$, these operators are not yet in a form to which the standard techniques for evaluation of the matrix elements can be applied. In appendix A.2 it is shown that for any vector $\mathbf{\upsilon}$ we have the relation

$$(\nabla r^L Y_{LM}(\hat{r}))\cdot \mathbf{\upsilon} = \sqrt{L(2L+1)}\, r^{L-1}\, [\mathbf{Y}_{L-1}(\hat{r}) \times \mathbf{\upsilon}]^L_M\,. \tag{10.58}$$

It is to be noted here again that in the magnetic 2^L pole operator the operators $\mathbf{l}$ or $\mathbf{s}$ do not act on $\nabla r^L Y_{LM}(\hat{r})$ and that the gradient operator ∇ acts on $r^L Y_{LM}(\hat{r})$ only. Hence the ordering of $\mathbf{l}$ or $\mathbf{s}$ and $\mathbf{\upsilon}\, r^L Y_{LM}(\hat{r})$ may be inverted without consequences. The square brackets in eq. (10.58) denote the tensor coupling of the spherical harmonic $Y_{L-1,M}(\hat{r})$ and the vector $\mathbf{\upsilon}$ to a tensor of rank L, which is in fact the kind of tensor one expects for a 2^L pole transition.

The reduced single-particle matrix elements of the isoscalar part of the operator, given in eq. (9.103), can now be written as

$$\langle\lambda|||S(\mathcal{M}L)|||\rho\rangle = \sqrt{L(2L+1)}\,\mu_N \left\{\frac{g^l_p + g^l_n}{L+1}\langle l_\lambda j_\lambda\| r^{L-1}[\mathbf{Y}_{L-1}\times \mathbf{l}]^L\| l_\rho j_\rho\rangle\right.$$

$$\left. + \tfrac{1}{2}(g^s_p + g^s_n)\langle l_\lambda j_\lambda\| r^{L-1}[\mathbf{Y}_{L-1}\times \mathbf{s}]^L\| l_\rho j_\rho\rangle\right\}\langle t_\lambda\|1\|t_\rho\rangle\,. \tag{10.59}$$

Similarly the isovector operator (9.104) yields

$$\langle\lambda|||V(\mathcal{M}L)|||\rho\rangle = \sqrt{L(2L+1)}\,\mu_N \left\{\frac{g^l_p - g^l_n}{L+1}\langle l_\lambda j_\lambda\| r^{L-1}[\mathbf{Y}_{L-1}\times \mathbf{l}]^L\| l_\rho j_\rho\rangle\right.$$

$$\left. + \tfrac{1}{2}(g^s_p - g^s_n)\langle l_\lambda j_\lambda\| r^{L-1}[\mathbf{Y}_{L-1}\times \mathbf{s}]^L\| l_\rho j_\rho\rangle\right\}\langle t_\lambda\|\boldsymbol{\tau}\|t_\rho\rangle\,. \tag{10.60}$$

The reduced matrix elements in isospace have been calculated already (cf. eqs. (10.51) and (10.52)). The evaluation of the other reduced matrix elements in eqs. (10.59) and (10.60) is somewhat more complex, especially for $L > 1$. We now have to deal with tensor-coupled operators that either both operate in the same space of the orbital coordinates or each operate in different spaces, i.e. of orbital and spin coordinates. In the former case one can employ eq. (A.3.d9) for the reduction. For the coupling order $\mathbf{l}+\mathbf{s}=\mathbf{j}$ one obtains

$$\langle n_\lambda l_\lambda j_\lambda\| r^{L-1}[\mathbf{Y}_{L-1}\times \mathbf{l}]^L\| n_\rho l_\rho j_\rho\rangle$$

$$= (-1)^{l_\lambda+1/2+j_\rho+L}\sqrt{(2j_\lambda+1)(2j_\rho+1)}\begin{Bmatrix} l_\lambda & l_\rho & L\\ j_\rho & j_\lambda & \tfrac{1}{2}\end{Bmatrix}\langle n_\lambda l_\lambda\| r^{L-1}[\mathbf{Y}_{L-1}\times \mathbf{l}]^L\| n_\rho l_\rho\rangle\,. \tag{10.61}$$

The evaluation of the reduced matrix element given above is simplified considerably for $L = 1$. We therefore treat this particular case first. With the spherical harmonic of rank zero given by $Y_{00}(\hat{r}) = (4\pi)^{-1/2}$ one obtains from eq. (10.61)

$$\langle n_\lambda l_\lambda j_\lambda \| r^{L-1} [Y_{L-1} \times l]^L \| n_\rho l_\rho j_\rho \rangle_{L=1} = \frac{1}{\sqrt{4\pi}} \langle l_\lambda j_\lambda \| l \| l_\rho j_\rho \rangle \delta_{n_\lambda n_\rho}$$

$$= (-1)^{l_\lambda + j_\rho + 3/2} \sqrt{\frac{(2j_\lambda + 1)(2j_\rho + 1)}{4\pi}} \begin{Bmatrix} l_\lambda & l_\rho & 1 \\ j_\rho & j_\lambda & \frac{1}{2} \end{Bmatrix} \langle l_\lambda \| l \| l_\rho \rangle \delta_{n_\lambda n_\rho}$$

$$= (-1)^{l_\lambda + j_\rho + 3/2} \sqrt{\frac{l_\lambda(l_\lambda + 1)(2l_\lambda + 1)(2j_\lambda + 1)(2j_\rho + 1)}{4\pi}} \begin{Bmatrix} l_\lambda & l_\rho & 1 \\ j_\rho & j_\lambda & \frac{1}{2} \end{Bmatrix} \delta_{l_\lambda l_\rho} \delta_{n_\lambda n_\rho}, \tag{10.62}$$

where for the last equality use is made of eq. (A.3.c5). Note that the matrix element vanishes for $l_\lambda \neq l_\rho$ or $n_\lambda \neq n_\rho$.

The evaluation of the other contributions to the magnetic single-particle matrix elements given in eqs. (10.59) and (10.60) also simplifies for $L = 1$. Its reduction can be performed quite analogously with eq. (A.3.d8) and is given by

$$\langle n_\lambda l_\lambda j_\lambda \| r^{L-1} [Y_{L-1} \times s]^{(L)} \| n_\rho l_\rho j_\rho \rangle_{L=1} = \frac{1}{\sqrt{4\pi}} \langle l_\lambda j_\lambda \| s \| l_\rho j_\rho \rangle \delta_{n_\lambda n_\rho}$$

$$= (-1)^{l_\lambda + j_\lambda + 3/2} \sqrt{\frac{(2j_\lambda + 1)(2j_\rho + 1)}{4\pi}} \begin{Bmatrix} \frac{1}{2} & \frac{1}{2} & 1 \\ j_\rho & j_\lambda & l_\lambda \end{Bmatrix} \langle \tfrac{1}{2} \| s \| \tfrac{1}{2} \rangle \, \delta_{l_\lambda l_\rho} \delta_{n_\lambda n_\rho}$$

$$= (-1)^{l_\lambda + j_\lambda + 3/2} \sqrt{\frac{3(2j_\lambda + 1)(2j_\rho + 1)}{8\pi}} \begin{Bmatrix} \frac{1}{2} & \frac{1}{2} & 1 \\ j_\rho & j_\lambda & l_\lambda \end{Bmatrix} \delta_{l_\lambda l_\rho} \delta_{n_\lambda n_\rho}, \tag{10.63}$$

where for the last equality use has been made of eq. (A.3.c6). Insertion of the matrix elements (10.62) and (10.63) into eqs. (10.59) and (10.60) leads to the final expression for an $\mathcal{M}1$ reduced single-particle matrix element given by

$$\langle \lambda ||| O(\mathcal{M}1) ||| \rho \rangle_I = (-1)^{l_\lambda} \sqrt{\frac{3(2I + 1)(2j_\lambda + 1)(2j_\rho + 1)}{4\pi}} \, \mu_{\mathrm{N}}$$

$$\times \Bigg[\tfrac{1}{2} \{g_{\mathrm{p}}^l + (-1)^I g_{\mathrm{n}}^l\} (-1)^{j_\rho + 3/2} \sqrt{2l_\lambda(l_\lambda + 1)(2l_\lambda + 1)} \begin{Bmatrix} l_\lambda & l_\rho & 1 \\ j_\rho & j_\lambda & \frac{1}{2} \end{Bmatrix}$$

$$+ \tfrac{1}{2} \{g_{\mathrm{p}}^s + (-1)^I g_{\mathrm{n}}^s\} (-1)^{j_\lambda + 3/2} \sqrt{3} \begin{Bmatrix} \frac{1}{2} & \frac{1}{2} & 1 \\ j_\rho & j_\lambda & l_\lambda \end{Bmatrix} \Bigg] \delta_{l_\lambda l_\rho} \delta_{n_\lambda n_\rho}, \tag{10.64}$$

where the matrix elements of the isoscalar and isovector parts are defined by

$$\langle\lambda \parallel\!| O(\mathcal{M}1) |\!\parallel \rho\rangle_{I=0} \equiv \langle\lambda \parallel\!| \boldsymbol{S}(\mathcal{M}1)\mathbf{1} |\!\parallel \rho\rangle ,$$

$$\langle\lambda \parallel\!| O(\mathcal{M}1) |\!\parallel \rho\rangle_{I=1} \equiv \langle\lambda \parallel\!| \boldsymbol{V}(\mathcal{M}1)\boldsymbol{\tau} |\!\parallel \rho\rangle . \tag{10.65}$$

Note that the matrix elements vanish for $l_\lambda \neq l_\rho$. The spin and orbital g-factors g^s and g^l, respectively, taken from the compilation [Chaloupka et al. (1974)] are given by

$$g^s_{\rm p} = 5.5857 , \qquad g^l_{\rm p} = 1 \qquad \text{for protons} , \tag{10.66}$$

$$g^s_{\rm n} = -3.8263 , \qquad g^l_{\rm n} = 0 \qquad \text{for neutrons} . \tag{10.67}$$

Some values of reduced single-particle $\mathcal{M}1$ matrix elements are given in table 10.5.

We still must evaluate the reduced single-particle matrix elements for $\mathcal{M}L$ transitions with $L > 1$. Let us start with the matrix element given in the right-hand side of eq. (10.61). The operator contains a product of two tensors both operating on the orbital part of the single-nucleon wave function. Application of eq. (A.3.d13) leads to a product of two reduced matrix elements given by

$$\langle n_\lambda l_\lambda \| r^{L-1} [Y_{L-1} \times l]^L \| n_\rho l_\rho\rangle$$

$$= (-1)^{L+l_\lambda+l_\rho} \sqrt{2L+1} \sum_{n'l'} \begin{Bmatrix} L-1 & 1 & L \\ l_\rho & l_\lambda & l' \end{Bmatrix} \langle n_\lambda l_\lambda \| r^{L-1} Y_{L-1} \| n'l'\rangle\langle n'l' \| l \| n_\rho l_\rho\rangle . \tag{10.68}$$

The last matrix element in this equation is given in eq. (A.3.c5) from which it fol-

Table 10.5
Some examples illustrating the calculation a) of isovector reduced single-particle matrix elements for $\mathcal{M}1$ transitions

$\langle\lambda \parallel\!| O(\mathcal{M}1) |\!\parallel \rho\rangle_{I=1}$	Value in n.m.
$\langle 1d_{5/2} \parallel\!| O(\mathcal{M}1) |\!\parallel 1d_{5/2}\rangle_{I=1}$	$3.469(g^l_{\rm p} - g^l_{\rm n}) + 0.867(g^s_{\rm p} - g^s_{\rm n}) = 11.63$
$\langle 2s_{1/2} \parallel\!| O(\mathcal{M}1) |\!\parallel 2s_{1/2}\rangle_{I=1}$	$0.733(g^s_{\rm p} - g^s_{\rm n}) = 6.90$
$\langle 1d_{3/2} \parallel\!| O(\mathcal{M}1) |\!\parallel 1d_{3/2}\rangle_{I=1}$	$2.782(g^l_{\rm p} - g^l_{\rm n}) - 0.464(g^s_{\rm p} - g^s_{\rm n}) = -1.58$
$\langle 1d_{5/2} \parallel\!| O(\mathcal{M}1) |\!\parallel 1d_{3/2}\rangle_{I=1}$	$0.927(g^l_{\rm p} - g^l_{\rm n}) - 0.927(g^s_{\rm p} - g^s_{\rm n}) = -7.80$

a) The values are given for the coupling order $j = l + s$.

lows that only $l' = l_\rho$ and $n' = n_\rho$ contribute to the summation. The first matrix element can be written with the use of eq. (A.3.e3) as

$$\langle n_\lambda l_\lambda \| r^{L-1} Y_{L-1} \| n_\rho l_\rho \rangle = \langle n_\lambda l_\lambda | r^{L-1} | n_\rho l_\rho \rangle \langle l_\lambda \| Y_{L-1} \| l_\rho \rangle$$

$$= \langle n_\lambda l_\lambda | r^{L-1} | n_\rho l_\rho \rangle (-1)^{l_\lambda} \sqrt{\frac{(2l_\lambda + 1)(2L-1)(2l_\rho + 1)}{4\pi}} \begin{pmatrix} l_\lambda & L-1 & l_\rho \\ 0 & 0 & 0 \end{pmatrix} . \tag{10.69}$$

Substituting eq. (10.69) into eq. (10.68) one finds

$$\langle n_\lambda l_\lambda j_\lambda \| r^{L-1} [Y_{L-1} \times l]^L \| n_\rho l_\rho j_\rho \rangle = (-1)^{l_\lambda + l_\rho + j_\rho + 1/2} \langle n_\lambda l_\lambda | r^{L-1} | n_\rho l_\rho \rangle (2l_\rho + 1)$$

$$\times \sqrt{\frac{(2L-1)(2L+1)(2l_\lambda + 1) l_\rho (l_\rho + 1)(2j_\lambda + 1)(2j_\rho + 1)}{4\pi}}$$

$$\times \begin{Bmatrix} l_\lambda & l_\rho & L \\ j_\rho & j_\lambda & \frac{1}{2} \end{Bmatrix} \begin{Bmatrix} L-1 & 1 & L \\ l_\rho & l_\lambda & l_\rho \end{Bmatrix} \begin{pmatrix} l_\lambda & L-1 & l_\rho \\ 0 & 0 & 0 \end{pmatrix} . \tag{10.70}$$

The last matrix element to be evaluated in eqs. (10.59) and (10.60) for $L > 1$ is that for the operator $r^{L-1} [Y_{L-1} \times s]^L$. In this case the operator acts on both the orbital and intrinsic spin coordinates. With eq. (A.3.d4) one can write

$$\langle n_\lambda l_\lambda j_\lambda \| r^{L-1} [Y_{L-1} \times s]^L \| n_\rho l_\rho j_\rho \rangle$$

$$= \sqrt{(2j_\lambda + 1)(2L+1)(2j_\rho + 1)} \begin{Bmatrix} l_\lambda & \frac{1}{2} & j_\lambda \\ l_\rho & \frac{1}{2} & j_\rho \\ L-1 & 1 & L \end{Bmatrix} \langle n_\lambda l_\lambda \| r^{L-1} Y_{L-1} \| n_\rho l_\rho \rangle \langle s \| s \| s \rangle . \tag{10.71}$$

The value of the first reduced matrix element in this expression is given in eq. (10.69), while the second one follows from eq. (A.3.c5) with $s = \frac{1}{2}$. Taking together all contributions one obtains

$$\langle n_\lambda l_\lambda j_\lambda \| r^{L-1} [Y_{L-1} \times s]^L \| n_\rho l_\rho j_\rho \rangle$$

$$= (-1)^{l_\lambda} \langle n_\lambda l_\lambda | r^{L-1} | n_\rho l_\rho \rangle \sqrt{\frac{3(2L+1)(2L-1)(2l_\lambda + 1)(2l_\rho + 1)(2j_\lambda + 1)(2j_\rho + 1)}{8\pi}}$$

$$\times \begin{Bmatrix} l_\lambda & \frac{1}{2} & j_\lambda \\ l_\rho & \frac{1}{2} & j_\rho \\ L-1 & 1 & L \end{Bmatrix} \cdot \begin{pmatrix} l_\lambda & L-1 & l_\rho \\ 0 & 0 & 0 \end{pmatrix} . \tag{10.72}$$

The complete expression of a reduced single-particle matrix element for a magnetic multipole transition is obtained by substituting eqs. (10.70) and (10.72) into eqs. (10.59) and (10.60). This leads finally to the expression

$$\langle\lambda|||O(\mathcal{M}L)|||\rho\rangle_I = \langle n_\lambda l_\lambda|r^{L-1}|n_\rho l_\rho\rangle f_I^{(\mathcal{M}L)}(\lambda;\rho) \tag{10.73a}$$

with

$$f_I^{(\mathcal{M}L)}(\lambda;\rho) = (-1)^{l_\lambda}(2L+1)\sqrt{\frac{L(2L-1)(2l_\lambda+1)(2l_\rho+1)(2j_\lambda+1)(2j_\rho+1)}{4\pi}}$$
$$\times\begin{pmatrix} l_\lambda & L-1 & l_\rho \\ 0 & 0 & 0 \end{pmatrix}\sqrt{2I+1}\left[\frac{g_\mathrm{p}^l+(-1)^I g_\mathrm{n}^l}{L+1}(-1)^{l_\rho+j_\rho+1/2}\sqrt{2l_\rho(l_\rho+1)(2l_\rho+1)}\right.$$
$$\left.\times\begin{Bmatrix} l_\lambda & l_\rho & L \\ j_\rho & j_\lambda & \frac{1}{2} \end{Bmatrix}\begin{Bmatrix} L-1 & 1 & L \\ l_\rho & l_\lambda & l_\rho \end{Bmatrix} + \tfrac{1}{2}\{g_\mathrm{p}^s+(-1)^I g_\mathrm{n}^s\}\sqrt{3}\begin{Bmatrix} l_\lambda & \frac{1}{2} & j_\lambda \\ l_\rho & \frac{1}{2} & j_\rho \\ L-1 & 1 & L \end{Bmatrix}\right]\mu_\mathrm{N}\,, \tag{10.73b}$$

and $I = 0$ and 1 labelling the isoscalar and isovector matrix elements, respectively (cf. eq. (10.65)). The g-factors are given in eqs. (10.66) and (10.67). The radial integrals are defined in eq. (10.46) and listed in appendix B.5. Values of the functions $f_I^{(\mathcal{M}L)}(\lambda;\rho)$ for various orbits and multipolarities L are listed in appendix B.6. Note that the 9-j symbol occurring in eq. (10.73b) reduces to a 6-j symbol for $L = 1$, when one of its arguments vanishes (cf. eq. (10.64)).

10.5. Transitions within a single-orbit configuration

After the derivation of the single-particle matrix elements for electromagnetic transitions in the preceding sections, we now turn to the evaluation of matrix elements for many-particle wave functions.

Let us assume that the initial- and final-state wave functions are simply described by configurations with n particles in one orbit ρ outside a closed-shell core. The reduced transition matrix element can then be written with the diagrammatic notation for the states $|\rho^n\rangle_\Gamma$ as

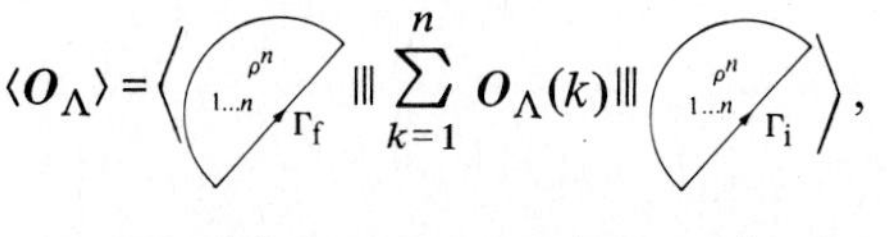

(10.74)

where $O_\Lambda(k)$ denotes a single-particle electromagnetic transition operator (of rank L_Λ in coordinate space and rank I_Λ in isospace) that acts on the coordinates of a particle labelled k. Again $I_\Lambda = 0$ denotes the isoscalar contribution and $I_\Lambda = 1$ the isovector contribution. Since the initial- and final-state wave functions are both antisymmetric in the n equivalent particles, all contributions of the summation over

k in eq. (10.74) are equal. Thus one may write, taking $k = n$,

$\langle O_\Lambda \rangle = n \Big\langle$ 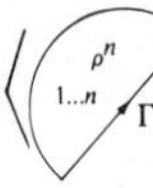 $|||O_\Lambda(n)|||$ 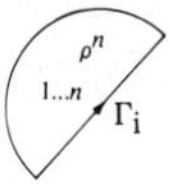 $\Big\rangle$. (10.75)

With the c.f.p. expansion of eq. (5.3) one can isolate particle n from both wave functions, so that one obtains

$\langle O_\Lambda \rangle = n \sum_{\epsilon} \langle \rho^n \Gamma_f | \} \rho^{n-1} \epsilon \rangle \sum_{\epsilon'} \langle \rho^n \Gamma_i | \} \rho^{n-1} \epsilon' \rangle \Big\langle$ 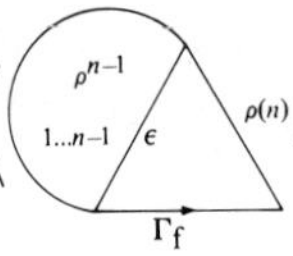 $|||O_\Lambda(n)|||$ 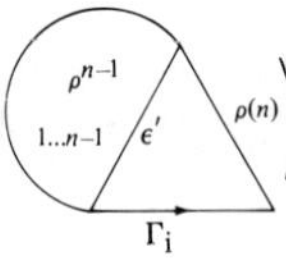 $\Big\rangle$

(10.76)

The operator $O_\Lambda(n)$ acts only on the variables of particle n and thus application of eq. (A.3.d8) leads to the final result

$\Big\langle$ 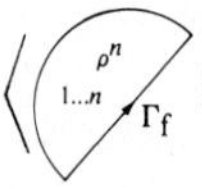 $||| \sum_{k=1}^{n} O_\Lambda(k) |||$ 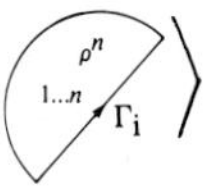 $\Big\rangle$

$$= n \sum_{\epsilon} \langle \rho^n \Gamma_f | \} \rho^{n-1} \epsilon \rangle \langle \rho^n \Gamma_i | \} \rho^{n-1} \epsilon \rangle (-1)^{\epsilon + \rho + \Gamma_f + \Lambda} \sqrt{(2\Gamma_f + 1)(2\Gamma_i + 1)}$$

$$\times \begin{Bmatrix} \rho & \rho & \Lambda \\ \Gamma_i & \Gamma_f & \epsilon \end{Bmatrix} \langle \rho(n) ||| O_\Lambda(n) ||| \rho(n) \rangle \,. \tag{10.77}$$

The evaluation of the reduced single-particle matrix element on the right-hand side of eq. (10.77) has been discussed in preceding sections.

Application. Eq. (10.77) can be used to evaluate $\mathcal{M}1$ and $\mathcal{E}2$ strengths in the nucleus ${}^{51}_{23}V_{28}$. The level scheme of this nucleus has been calculated already in sect. 4.6 in a configuration space with three protons in the $(1f_{7/2})^3_{JT}$ configuration. The neutrons are assumed to form a closed $(1f_{7/2})^8_{00}$ shell. The transitions to be discussed are shown in fig. 10.8.

The calculation will be applied first to the decay of the first excited state $J^\pi = \frac{5}{2}^-$ at $E_x = 0.32$ MeV to the $J^\pi = \frac{7}{2}^-$ ground state. Since both states have the same isospin T we are dealing with a $\Delta T = 0$ transition. The reduced $\mathcal{E}2$ transition rate can be written according to eqs. (9.106) and (9.107) as

$$B(\mathcal{E}2) = \frac{1}{(2J_i + 1)(2T_f + 1)} \Bigg[\langle J_f T_f ||| \sum_{k=1}^{3} S(\mathcal{E}2, k) \mathbf{1} ||| J_i T_i \rangle$$

$$- \frac{T_z}{\sqrt{T(T+1)}} \langle J_f T_f ||| \sum_{k=1}^{3} V(\mathcal{E}2, k) \boldsymbol{\tau}(k) ||| J_i T_i \rangle \Bigg]^2 \,. \tag{10.78}$$

The matrix element in this expression must be evaluated for the three-proton states $|J_f T_f\rangle$ and $|J_i T_i\rangle$. Note that in this calculation only three protons are taken into ac-

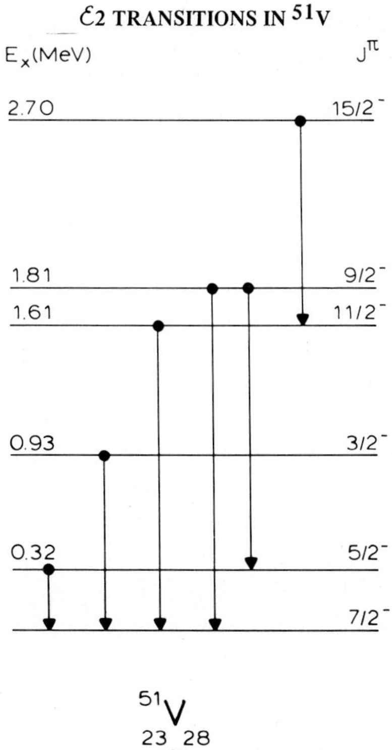

Fig. 10.8. The ℰ2 transitions in ^{51}V which are interpreted in terms of a $(1f_{7/2})^3$ model.

count, since it is assumed that the other protons and also the neutrons form completely inactive groups, each coupled to $J = 0$. The isospins T_f and T_i in eq. (10.78) are thus given by $T_i = T_f = \frac{3}{2}$ of the active three-proton system and not by the total isospin $T = \frac{5}{2}$ of the nucleus $^{51}_{23}V_{28}$.

The reduced matrix elements in eq. (10.78) can be expanded in terms of reduced single-particle matrix elements according to eq. (10.77). Inserting the numerical values for the quantum numbers in the (J, T) product notation, one obtains

$$\langle \rho^n J_f T_f ||| \sum_{k=1}^{3} O_\Lambda(k) ||| \rho^n J_i T_i \rangle = \langle (1f_{7/2})^3 \tfrac{7}{2} \tfrac{3}{2} ||| \sum_{k=1}^{3} O_\Lambda(k) ||| (1f_{7/2})^3 \tfrac{5}{2} \tfrac{3}{2} \rangle$$

$$= 3 \sum_{J_\epsilon T_\epsilon} \langle f^3_{7/2} \tfrac{7}{2} \tfrac{3}{2} |\} f^2_{7/2} J_\epsilon T_\epsilon \rangle \langle f^3_{7/2} \tfrac{5}{2} \tfrac{3}{2} |\} f^2_{7/2} J_\epsilon T_\epsilon \rangle (-1)^{(J_\epsilon + T_\epsilon) + (7/2 + 1/2) + (7/2 + 3/2) + (2 + I_\Lambda)}$$

$$\times \sqrt{(8 \cdot 4)(6 \cdot 4)} \begin{Bmatrix} \tfrac{7}{2} & \tfrac{7}{2} & 2 \\ \tfrac{5}{2} & \tfrac{7}{2} & J_\epsilon \end{Bmatrix} \begin{Bmatrix} \tfrac{1}{2} & \tfrac{1}{2} & I_\Lambda \\ \tfrac{3}{2} & \tfrac{3}{2} & T_\epsilon \end{Bmatrix} \langle 1f_{7/2} ||| O_\Lambda ||| 1f_{7/2} \rangle . \qquad (10.79)$$

The summation over (J_ϵ, T_ϵ) is restricted to the pairs (0, 1), (2, 1), (4, 1) and (6, 1) due to the antisymmetry of the $(1f_{7/2})^2_{J_\epsilon T_\epsilon}$ states. The c.f.p. can be obtained from table 4.2, from which it follows that the pair $(J_\epsilon, T_\epsilon) = (0, 1)$ does not contribute, due to a vanishing c.f.p. The required spin dependent 6-j symbols in eq. (10.79) are given by

$$\begin{Bmatrix} \frac{7}{2} & \frac{7}{2} & 2 \\ \frac{5}{2} & \frac{7}{2} & J_\epsilon \end{Bmatrix} = \begin{cases} +\frac{1}{12} & \text{for } J_\epsilon = 2 \\ +\dfrac{1}{6\sqrt{15}} & \text{for } J_\epsilon = 4 \\ -\frac{1}{12} & \text{for } J_\epsilon = 6\ , \end{cases} \tag{10.80}$$

and the isospin dependent 6-j symbols for $T_\epsilon = 1$ by

$$\begin{Bmatrix} \frac{1}{2} & \frac{1}{2} & I_\Lambda \\ \frac{3}{2} & \frac{3}{2} & 1 \end{Bmatrix} = \begin{cases} -\dfrac{1}{2\sqrt{2}} & \text{for } I_\Lambda = 0 \quad \text{(isoscalar part)} \\ +\frac{1}{3}\sqrt{\frac{5}{8}} & \text{for } I_\Lambda = 1 \quad \text{(isovector part)}\ . \end{cases} \tag{10.81}$$

Inserting these values into eq. (10.79) one derives that the isoscalar matrix element $(I_\Lambda = 0)$ is given by

$$\langle(1f_{7/2})^3\ \tfrac{7}{2}\ \tfrac{3}{2} ||| \sum_{k=1}^{3} \boldsymbol{S}(\mathcal{E}2, k)\mathbf{1} ||| (1f_{7/2})^3\ \tfrac{5}{2}\ \tfrac{3}{2}\rangle = -1.71\langle 1f_{7/2} ||| \boldsymbol{S}(\mathcal{E}2)\mathbf{1} ||| 1f_{7/2}\rangle\ . \tag{10.82}$$

Similarly one obtains an expression for the isovector matrix element $(I_\Lambda = 1)$, given by

$$\langle(1f_{7/2})^3\ \tfrac{7}{2}\ \tfrac{3}{2} ||| \sum_{k=1}^{3} \boldsymbol{V}(\mathcal{E}2, k)\boldsymbol{\tau}(k) ||| (1f_{7/2})^3\ \tfrac{5}{2}\ \tfrac{3}{2}\rangle = -1.29\langle 1f_{7/2} ||| \boldsymbol{V}(\mathcal{E}2)\boldsymbol{\tau} ||| 1f_{7/2}\rangle\ . \tag{10.83}$$

The numerical values of the reduced single-particle matrix elements from expression eqs. (10.49), (10.55) and (10.56) as

$$\begin{aligned} &\langle 1f_{7/2} ||| \boldsymbol{S}(\mathcal{E}2)\mathbf{1} ||| 1f_{7/2}\rangle = -10.3(e_p + e_n)\ \text{fm}^2\ , \\ &\langle 1f_{7/2} ||| \boldsymbol{V}(\mathcal{E}2)\boldsymbol{\tau} ||| 1f_{7/2}\rangle = -17.8(e_p - e_n)\ \text{fm}^2\ . \end{aligned} \tag{10.84}$$

Inserting these values in eqs. (10.82) and (10.83) one obtains from expression (10.78)

$$B(\mathcal{E}2; \tfrac{5}{2}^- \to \tfrac{7}{2}^-) = \tfrac{1}{24}\ [-17.6(e_p + e_n) - 17.6(e_p - e_n)]^2 \text{fm}^4 = 52 e_p^2 \cdot \text{fm}^4\ . \tag{10.85}$$

It should be remarked that in this particular example dealing with active protons only, the transition strength should not depend of course on the neutron charge e_n.

Table 10.6
A comparison of theory and experiment for the $\mathcal{E}2$ strengths in ^{51}V with $(1f_{7/2})^3$ wave functions

$J_i^\pi \to J_f^\pi$	$B(\mathcal{E}2)$ $(e^2 \cdot fm^4)$			$M_W^2(\mathcal{E}2)$
	theory		experiment a)	experiment
	$e_p = e$	$e_p = 1.7e$		
$\frac{5}{2}^- \to \frac{7}{2}^-$	52	150	154 ± 8	14 ± 1
$\frac{3}{2}^- \to \frac{7}{2}^-$	18	53	72 ± 13	6.4 ± 1.2
$\frac{11}{2}^- \to \frac{7}{2}^-$	24	68	78 ± 14	6.9 ± 1.2
$\frac{9}{2}^- \to \frac{7}{2}^-$	9	26	28 ± 6	2.4 ± 0.6
$\frac{9}{2}^- \to \frac{5}{2}^-$	9	24	28 ± 7	2.4 ± 0.6
$\frac{15}{2}^- \to \frac{11}{2}^-$	17	49	66 ± 5	5.9 ± 0.4

a) From the review [Brown, Fossan, McDonald and Snover (1974)].

Therefore the coefficients of $(e_p + e_n)$ and $(e_p - e_n)$ in eq. (10.85) must be equal. The appearance of the neutron charge e_n could have been avoided by working in the proton-neutron formalism instead of in the isospin formalism.

The $\mathcal{E}2$ transition strengths indicated in fig. 10.8 and calculated with the procedure outlined above in a $(1f_{7/2})^3$ proton configuration are listed in table 10.6. The experimental strengths are given both as $B(\mathcal{E}2)$ in $e^2 \cdot fm^4$ and as $M_W^2(\mathcal{E}2)$ (see eq. (10.8b)).

It is seen that with the bare-proton charge $e_p = e$, the resulting $\mathcal{E}2$ strengths are too small compared to the experimental data. It was mentioned before that this is a common feature in shell-model calculations. Especially with the simple configuration space employed here, one cannot expect that the use of an effective proton charge can be avoided. This means that an additional proton charge, the polarization charge Δe_p, is introduced to compensate for the incompleteness of the model space. Thus the proton is assumed to carry a charge given by $e_p = e + \Delta e_p$. From comparison with experiment it follows that a reasonable effective charge is given by $e_p = 1.7e$, i.e. $\Delta e_p = 0.7e$.

It should be remarked that a polarization charge with an approximate value $\Delta e \approx 0.5e - 1.5e$ is quite typical for many shell-model calculations. It is gratifying to observe that the $\mathcal{E}2$ data in ^{51}V can be nicely correlated this way, as is shown in the third column of table 10.6. Note that in this simple case of a description in terms of a pure ρ'' configuration the ratios of the $\mathcal{E}2$ strengths are determined by the coefficients of the reduced single-particle matrix elements in eq. (10.79) and hence are not affected by the value of the effective charge.

A calculation of the magnetic dipole transition rates can be performed in complete analogy with the calculation of electric quadrupole transition strengths. However, such a calculation for ^{51}V in a pure $(1f_{7/2})^3$ proton configuration space will lead to vanishing $\mathcal{M}1$ strengths. This is the result of the selection rule that within a j^n configuration of identical particles, no dipole transitions occur. This rule can be proved as follows. As we are dealing with identical particles there is no need to use the isospin formalism. Let the relevant operator be given by $\Sigma_{k=1}^{n} O_{L=1}(k)$, then the transition matrix element under consideration can be expressed in terms of a single-particle matrix element as in eq. (10.77) by

$$\langle j^n J_f \| \sum_{k=1}^{n} O_{L=1}(k) \| j^n J_i \rangle = \langle j \| O_{L=1} \| j \rangle \sum_{\epsilon} C(\epsilon) \, . \tag{10.86}$$

Here $C(\epsilon)$ comprises all expansion coefficients that have been lumped together for brevity. The generalized Landé formula (see eq. (A.4.6)) can be applied to the reduced single-particle matrix element to yield

$$\langle j \| O_{L=1} \| j \rangle = \langle j \| \boldsymbol{j} \| j \rangle \frac{\langle jm | \boldsymbol{j} \cdot \boldsymbol{O}_{L=1} | jm \rangle}{j(j+1)} \, . \tag{10.87}$$

The expectation value of the operator $\boldsymbol{j} \cdot \boldsymbol{O}_{L=1}$ is independent of the quantum number m, since the operator is a scalar. In a semiclassical picture eq. (10.87) expresses the fact that the expectation value of any vector operator $\boldsymbol{O}_{L=1}$ in the state $|jm\rangle$ is given by the expectation value of the projection of $\boldsymbol{O}_{L=1}$ onto the angular momentum operator $\boldsymbol{j}$. The operator $\boldsymbol{O}_{L=1}$ enters the coefficients $C(\epsilon)$ only through its vector property ($L = 1$), as follows from eq. (10.77). Let us consider now eq. (10.86) applied to the operator $\boldsymbol{J} = \Sigma_{k=1}^{n} \boldsymbol{j}(k)$ and multiply both sides with the factor $\langle jm | \boldsymbol{j} \cdot \boldsymbol{O}_{L=1} | jm \rangle / j(j+1)$, which is independent of J_i, J_f and m. It then follows from eq. (10.87) that the reduced matrix element of the operator $\Sigma_{k=1}^{n} O_{L=1}(k)$ differs only by a constant factor from that of the operator $\boldsymbol{J}$. The operator $\boldsymbol{J}$ vanishes between the orthogonal states $|j^n J_f\rangle$ and $|j^n J_i\rangle$. Thus one concludes that indeed no dipole transitions can take place within single-orbit configurations. For $\mathcal{E}1$ transitions one could have reached this conclusion immediately from parity considerations, since all j^n states have the same parity.

10.6. Particles in two orbits

A calculation of electromagnetic transition matrix elements becomes less simple when more than one active orbit is involved. As a consequence one has to deal with two types of matrix elements:

(i) Transitions where initial and final state differ in a recoupling of the angular momenta only with no change in the distribution of the particles over the various orbits.

(ii) Transitions in which one particle changes orbit. We shall discuss both types of matrix elements separately.

No particles change orbit. Let us consider a nucleus described by a number of particles in two active orbits and all other nucleons forming an inert closed-shell core. It will be shown that the corresponding elements can be expressed in terms of the single-orbit matrix elements, which are discussed in sect. 10.5.

For two active orbits both initial and final states are assumed to be described by configurations with n particles in orbit ρ and m particles in orbit λ. The reduced matrix element of the transition operator can be written as (see also eq. (10.74))

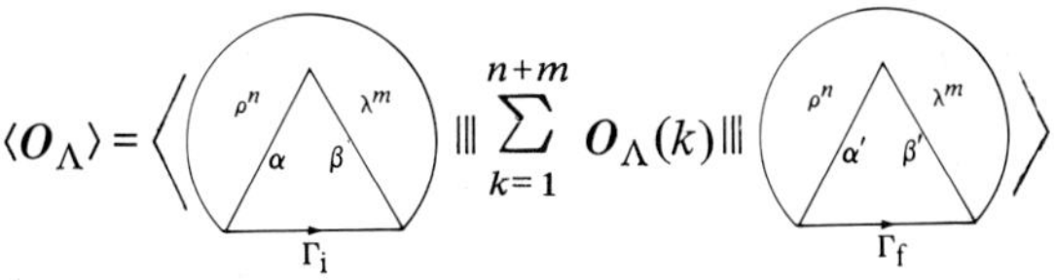

$$\langle O_\Lambda \rangle = \left\langle \; \left(\begin{smallmatrix} \rho^n & & \lambda^m \\ & \alpha & \beta \end{smallmatrix} \right)_{r_i} \; \right\| \sum_{k=1}^{n+m} O_\Lambda(k) \left\| \; \left(\begin{smallmatrix} \rho^n & & \lambda^m \\ & \alpha' & \beta' \end{smallmatrix} \right)_{r_f} \; \right\rangle . \tag{10.88}$$

Application of eq. (5.4) to the bra wave function yields

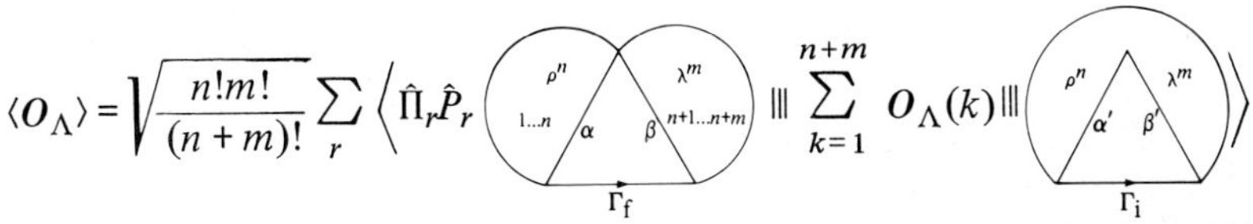

$$\langle O_\Lambda \rangle = \sqrt{\frac{n!\,m!}{(n+m)!}} \sum_r \left\langle \hat{\Pi}_r \hat{P}_r \left(\begin{smallmatrix} \rho^n & & \lambda^m \\ 1..n\ \alpha & & \beta\ n+1..n+m \end{smallmatrix} \right)_{r_f} \right\| \sum_{k=1}^{n+m} O_\Lambda(k) \left\| \left(\begin{smallmatrix} \rho^n & & \lambda^m \\ & \alpha' & \beta' \end{smallmatrix} \right)_{r_i} \right\rangle . \tag{10.89}$$

Each term in the sum over r has the same magnitude and sign, as follows from a derivation analogous to that used to obtain eq. (5.26). There are $(n+m)!/n!\,m!$ terms in the summation over r in eq. (10.89) and thus one obtains after application of the expansion (5.4) also to the ket wave function

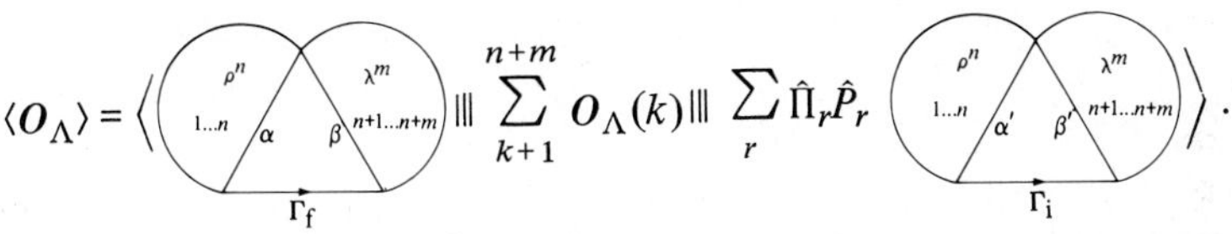

$$\langle O_\Lambda \rangle = \left\langle \left(\begin{smallmatrix} \rho^n & & \lambda^m \\ 1..n\ \alpha & & \beta\ n+1..n+m \end{smallmatrix} \right)_{r_f} \right\| \sum_{k+1}^{n+m} O_\Lambda(k) \left\| \sum_r \hat{\Pi}_r \hat{P}_r \left(\begin{smallmatrix} \rho^n & & \lambda^m \\ 1..n\ \alpha' & & \beta'\ n+1..n+m \end{smallmatrix} \right)_{r_i} \right\rangle . \tag{10.90}$$

The operator $O_\Lambda(k)$ is a single-particle operator and all order-preserving permutations $\hat{P}_r$ with the exception of $P_r = 1$ always interchange at least two particles belonging to different orbits. Thus it is only $P_r = 1$ that yields a nonvanishing contribution. Performing separate summations for particles in the orbits ρ and λ, one obtains

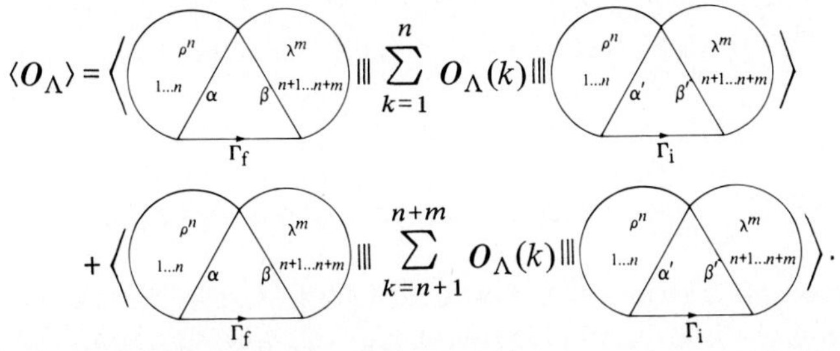

$$\langle O_\Lambda \rangle = \left\langle \left(\begin{smallmatrix} \rho^n & & \lambda^m \\ 1..n\ \alpha & & \beta\ n+1..n+m \end{smallmatrix} \right)_{r_f} \right\| \sum_{k=1}^{n} O_\Lambda(k) \left\| \left(\begin{smallmatrix} \rho^n & & \lambda^m \\ 1..n\ \alpha' & & \beta'\ n+1..n+m \end{smallmatrix} \right)_{r_i} \right\rangle$$

$$+ \left\langle \left(\begin{smallmatrix} \rho^n & & \lambda^m \\ 1..n\ \alpha & & \beta\ n+1..n+m \end{smallmatrix} \right)_{r_f} \right\| \sum_{k=n+1}^{n+m} O_\Lambda(k) \left\| \left(\begin{smallmatrix} \rho^n & & \lambda^m \\ 1..n\ \alpha' & & \beta'\ n+1..n+m \end{smallmatrix} \right)_{r_i} \right\rangle . \tag{10.91}$$

Note that in the first term of eq. (10.91) each operator $O_\Lambda(k)$ acts only on the particles in the group ρ^n whereas in the second term it operates on the group λ^m.

Therefore eqs. (A.3.d8) and (A.3.d9) can be used for a further reduction of the first and second term in eq. (10.91), respectively. This leads to the final expression

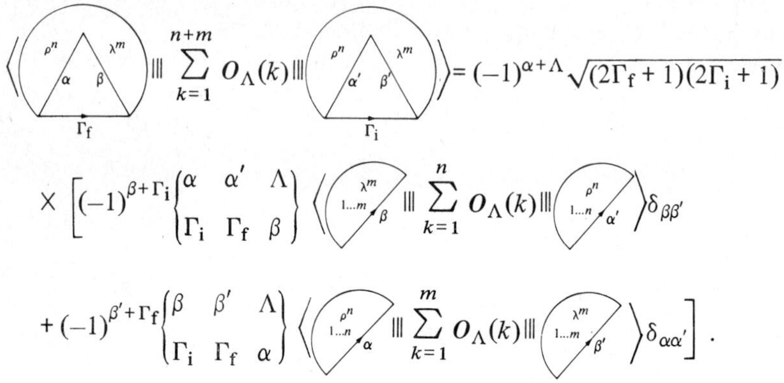

$$
\left\langle \left(\triangle \right)^{n+m} \left\| \sum_{k=1}^{n+m} O_\Lambda(k) \right\| \left(\triangle \right) \right\rangle = (-1)^{\alpha+\Lambda} \sqrt{(2\Gamma_f + 1)(2\Gamma_i + 1)}
$$

$$
\times \left[(-1)^{\beta+\Gamma_i} \begin{Bmatrix} \alpha & \alpha' & \Lambda \\ \Gamma_i & \Gamma_f & \beta \end{Bmatrix} \left\langle \left(\right)_{\beta}^{\lambda^m} \left\| \sum_{k=1}^{n} O_\Lambda(k) \right\| \left(\right)_{\alpha'}^{\rho^n} \right\rangle \delta_{\beta\beta'} \right.
$$

$$
\left. + (-1)^{\beta'+\Gamma_f} \begin{Bmatrix} \beta & \beta' & \Lambda \\ \Gamma_i & \Gamma_f & \alpha \end{Bmatrix} \left\langle \left(\right)_{\alpha}^{\rho^n} \left\| \sum_{k=1}^{m} O_\Lambda(k) \right\| \left(\right)_{\beta'}^{\lambda^m} \right\rangle \delta_{\alpha\alpha'} \right]. \tag{10.92}
$$

The reduced single-orbit transition matrix elements can be evaluated as given in eq. (10.77). It is clear from the Kronecker deltas in eq. (10.92) that no transitions occur between states with both $\alpha \neq \alpha'$ and $\beta \neq \beta'$. From the 6-j symbols it follows that the intermediate spins and isospins denoted by α and β must obey the triangle conditions

$$
|\alpha - \alpha'| \leqslant \Lambda \leqslant \alpha + \alpha' \qquad \text{for} \quad \beta = \beta'
$$

or

$$
|\beta - \beta'| \leqslant \Lambda \leqslant \beta + \beta' \qquad \text{for} \quad \alpha = \alpha'. \tag{10.93}
$$

From eq. (10.93) one concludes that for $\alpha = \alpha' = 0$ (i.e. $J_\alpha = T_\alpha = J_{\alpha'} = T_{\alpha'} = 0$) the first term in eq. (10.92) cannot contribute, since monopole radiation does not exist. For $\alpha = \alpha' = 0$ the coefficients multiplying the reduced matrix element in the second term of eq. (10.92) are equal to unity, as follows directly from the explicit value of the 6-j symbol, which is given by

$$
\begin{Bmatrix} \beta & \beta' & \Lambda \\ \Gamma_i & \Gamma_f & 0 \end{Bmatrix} = (-1)^{\Gamma_f + \Gamma_i + \Lambda} [(2\Gamma_f + 1)(2\Gamma_i + 1)]^{-1/2} \quad \text{for } \beta = \Gamma_f \text{ and } \beta' = \Gamma_i. \tag{10.94}
$$

Hence we have the rule: *zero-coupled groups, such as closed shells, do not contribute to the transition strength.* Thus these groups may be ignored as being completely inactive.

One particle changes orbit. Consider the case where a particle performs an electromagnetic transition from one orbit to another. Since one deals with single-particle operators for electromagnetic transitions, it is only one nucleon that can change orbit. The corresponding reduced matrix elements for two active orbits ρ and λ are given by

$\langle O_\Lambda \rangle = \Big\langle$ 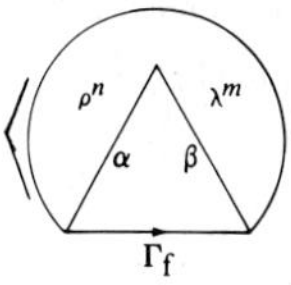

$\Big|\Big|\Big| \sum_{k=1}^{n+m} o_\Lambda(k) \Big|\Big|\Big|$ 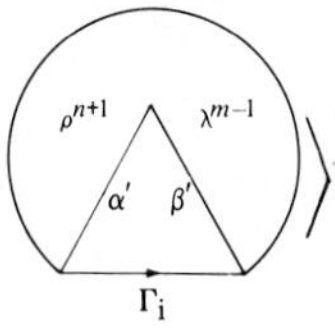

$\Big\rangle$, (10.95)

$\langle O_\Lambda \rangle' = \Big\langle$ 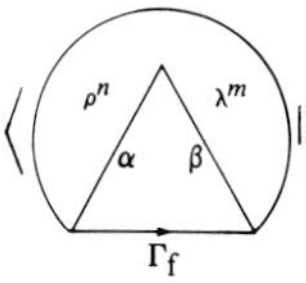

$\Big|\Big|\Big| \sum_{k=1}^{n+m} o_\Lambda(k) \Big|\Big|\Big|$ 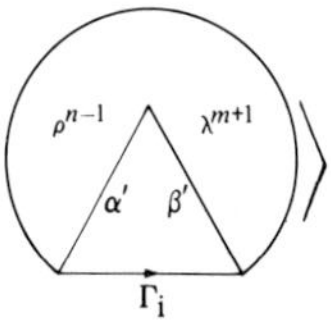

$\Big\rangle$. (10.96)

The reduced matrix element (10.96) can be treated as the one given in eq. (10.95) by exchanging in the former the bra and ket wave function with the aid of the relation

$$\langle \psi_{\Gamma_i} ||| O_\Lambda ||| \psi_{\Gamma_f} \rangle = (-1)^{\Gamma_i - \Gamma_f} \langle \psi_{\Gamma_f} ||| O_\Lambda ||| \psi_{\Gamma_i} \rangle , \tag{10.97}$$

that is derived in appendix A.3.b. The reduction of the matrix element (10.95) can be performed by applying eq. (5.4) to the bra wave function first

$\langle O_\Lambda \rangle = \sqrt{\dfrac{n!m!}{(n+m)!}} \sum_r \Big\langle \hat{\Pi}_r \hat{P}_r$ 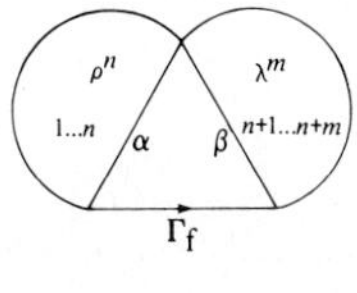

$\Big|\Big|\Big| \sum_{k=1}^{n+m} o_\Lambda(k) \Big|\Big|\Big|$ 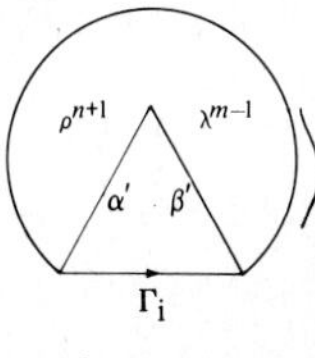

$\Big\rangle$. (10.98)

Each term in the sum over the order-preserving permutations $\hat{P}_r$ leads to the same contribution. Thus one obtains, taking the contribution for $P_r = 1$ and multiplying with the number of order-preserving permutations $(n+m)!/n!m!$, the result

$\langle O_\Lambda \rangle = \sqrt{\dfrac{(n+m)!}{n!m!}} \Big\langle$ 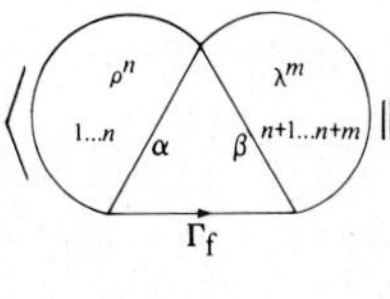

$\Big|\Big|\Big| \sum_{k=1}^{n+m} o_\Lambda(k) \Big|\Big|\Big|$ 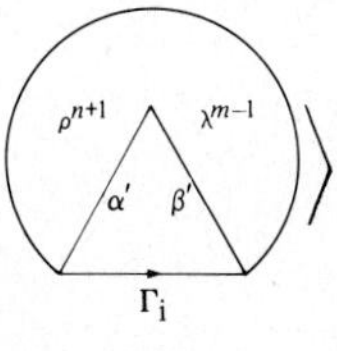

$\Big\rangle$. (10.99)

Application of expansion (5.4) to the ket wave function yields

$\langle O_\Lambda \rangle = \sqrt{\dfrac{n+1}{m}} \Big\langle$ 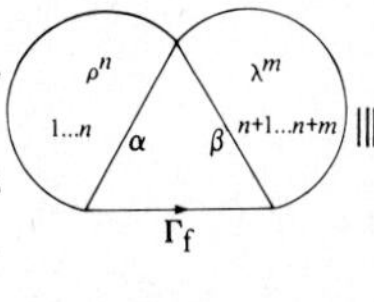

$\Big|\Big|\Big| \sum_{k=1}^{n+m} o_\Lambda(k) \Big|\Big|\Big| \sum_r \hat{\Pi}_r \hat{P}_r$ 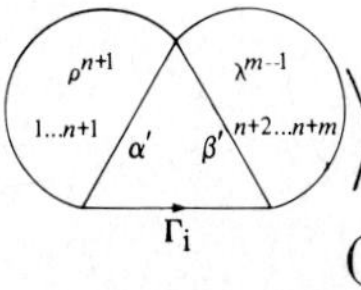

$\Big\rangle$. (10.100)

Remember that the order-preserving permutations $\hat{P}_r$ always interchange two or more particles in different orbits except for the identity $P_r = 1$. When the action of $\hat{P}_r$ involves a particle labelled k with $k = 1, ..., n-1$ or n, one is left with a matrix element with at least two particles (labelled k and $n+1$) in different orbits for initial and final state in eq. (10.100). This leads for the single-particle operator $O_\Lambda(k)$ to a vanishing contribution. Thus anyway $\hat{P}_r$ should leave the particles $1, ..., n$ unaffected. Then the only nonvanishing contributions derive from the terms $O_\Lambda(k)\hat{\Pi}_{n+1,k}\hat{P}_{n+1,k}$ with $k = n+1, n+2, ..., n+m$, which includes the operator $\hat{P}_{n+1,n+1} = 1$. Again the resulting contributions are all equal in magnitude and sign. One obtains, taking the contribution for $P_r = 1$ and consequently $k = n+1$, the result

$\langle O_\Lambda \rangle = \sqrt{(n+1)m}\,\Big\langle$ 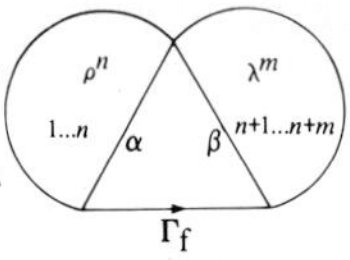

$\|| O_\Lambda(n+1) \||$ 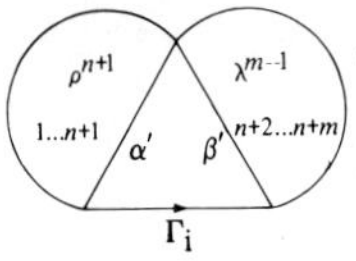

$\Big\rangle .$ (10.101)

For a further reduction of the matrix element we must single out the particle labelled $n+1$ on which the operator acts.

The phases of the c.f.p. expansion of eq. (5.3) are defined for the removal of the last particle in an antisymmetric group of equivalent particles. It requires $m-1$ transpositions in the group λ_β^m to change the sequence from $n+1, n+2, ..., n+m$ to $n+2, ..., n+m, n+1$, which introduces a sign $(-1)^{m-1}$. Application of the c.f.p. expansion to the bra and ket function of eq. (10.101) then yields

$$\langle O_\Lambda \rangle = \sqrt{(n+1)m}\,(-1)^{m-1} \sum_{\epsilon\epsilon'} \langle \lambda^m \beta | \} \lambda^{m-1} \epsilon \rangle \langle \rho^{n+1} \alpha' | \} \rho^n \epsilon' \rangle$$

$\times \Big\langle$ 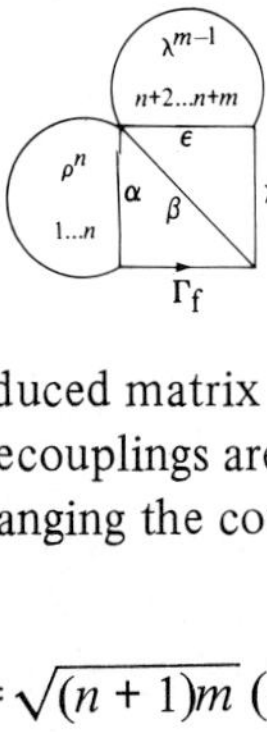

$\lambda(n+1)\ \|| O_\Lambda(n+1) \||$ 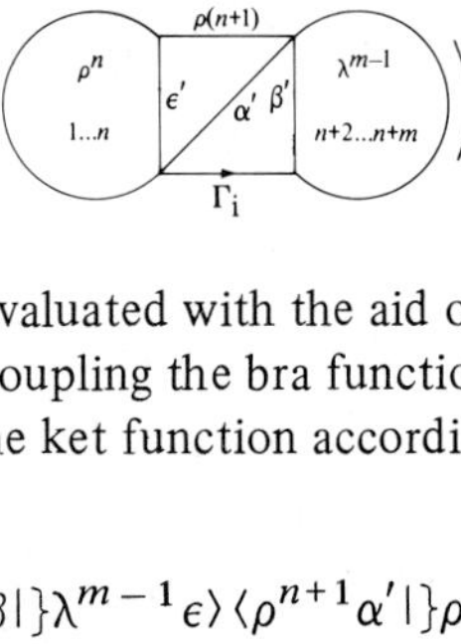

$\Big\rangle .$ (10.102)

The reduced matrix element can be evaluated with the aid of eq. (A.3.d8), if first some recouplings are performed. Recoupling the bra function according to eq. (5.19) and changing the coupling order in the ket function according to eq. (5.10), one finds

$$\langle O_\Lambda \rangle = \sqrt{(n+1)m}\,(-1)^{m-1} \sum_{\epsilon\epsilon'} \langle \lambda^m \beta | \} \lambda^{m-1} \epsilon \rangle \langle \rho^{n+1} \alpha' | \} \rho^n \epsilon' \rangle$$

$\times \sum_\nu U(\alpha\epsilon\Gamma_f\lambda; \nu\beta) \Big\langle$ 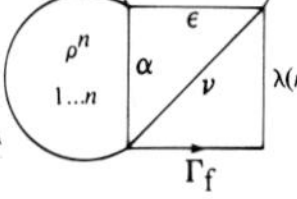

$\lambda(n+1)\ \|| O_\Lambda(n+1) \|| (-1)^{\Gamma_i - \alpha' - \beta'}$ 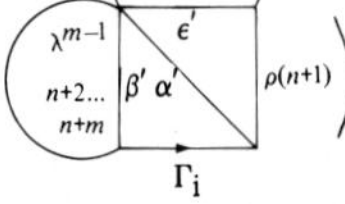

$\Big\rangle .$

(10.103)

After a recoupling of the ket with eq. (5.19) and a change in the coupling sequence of the groups $\rho^n_{\epsilon'}$ and $\lambda^{m-1}_{\beta'}$ with eq. (5.10), one arrives at

$$\langle O_\Lambda \rangle = (-1)^{m+\Gamma_i-\alpha'-\beta'-1}\sqrt{(n+1)m}\sum_{\epsilon\epsilon'}\langle\lambda^m\beta|\}\lambda^{m-1}\epsilon\rangle\langle\rho^{n+1}\alpha'|\}\rho^n\epsilon'\rangle\sum_{\nu\mu}U(\alpha\epsilon\Gamma_f\lambda;\nu\beta)$$

$$\times\, U(\beta'\epsilon'\Gamma_i\rho;\mu\alpha')(-1)^{\mu-\beta'-\epsilon'}\Big\langle$$

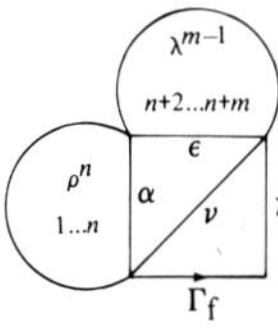

$$|||O_\Lambda(n+1)|||$$

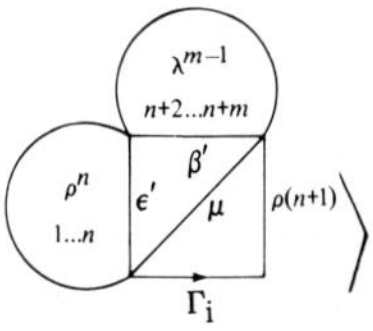

$$\Big\rangle. \qquad (10.104)$$

Since the operator $O_\Lambda(n+1)$ acts only on the particle labelled $n+1$, one can now use eq. (A.3.d8) for a further reduction. This leads to the final result

$$\Big\langle$$

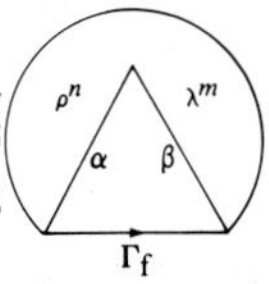

$$|||\sum_{k=1}^{n+m} O_\Lambda(k)|||$$

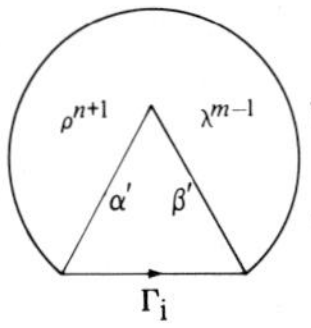

$$\Big\rangle$$

$$= (-1)^{m+\Gamma_i+\Gamma_f+\alpha+\alpha'+\rho+\Lambda-1}\sqrt{(n+1)m(2\Gamma_f+1)(2\Gamma_i+1)}$$

$$\times\,\langle\lambda^m\beta|\}\lambda^{m-1}\beta'\rangle\langle\rho^{n+1}\alpha'|\}\rho^n\alpha\rangle\sum_{\nu}U(\alpha\beta'\Gamma_f\lambda;\nu\beta)U(\beta'\alpha\Gamma_i\rho;\nu\alpha')$$

$$\times\begin{Bmatrix}\lambda & \rho & \Lambda\\ \Gamma_i & \Gamma_f & \nu\end{Bmatrix}\langle\lambda|||O_\Lambda|||\rho\rangle, \qquad (10.105)$$

where it has been used that in a (J, T) product notation one has $(-1)^{2\beta'} = (-1)^{2\nu} = +1$. From the U-coefficients and 6-j symbol in eq. (10.105) it follows that the sum over ν is restricted by the triangle conditions $\Delta(\alpha\beta'\nu)$, $\Delta(\Gamma_i\rho\nu)$ and $\Delta(\Gamma_f\lambda\nu)$. The evaluation of the reduced single-particle matrix elements is discussed in sects. 10.3 and 10.4.

It may become clear from the derivations given above that, when more than two active orbits are involved, the reduction formulas become quite complex. In such cases the second-quantization formalism is more convenient. The principles of this formalism are discussed in chapters 13, 14 and 15.

10.7. Configuration mixing

Up till here it has been assumed that initial and final states are described by pure configurations. Let us now suppose that the initial and final state are given by mixed configurations

$$\Psi_{\mathrm{i}} = \sum_k a_k^{(\mathrm{i})} \Phi_k \, , \tag{10.106}$$

$$\Psi_{\mathrm{f}} = \sum_l a_l^{(\mathrm{f})} \Phi_l \, , \tag{10.107}$$

with Φ_k representing shell-model basis states and $a_k^{(\mathrm{i})}$ and $a_l^{(\mathrm{f})}$ denoting the amplitudes. One then obtains the transition strength by evaluating

$$B(\bar{\omega}L; \mathrm{i} \to \mathrm{f}) = \frac{1}{(2J_{\mathrm{i}}+1)(2T_{\mathrm{f}}+1)} \Big[\sum_{kl} a_k^{(\mathrm{i})} a_l^{(\mathrm{f})} \langle \Phi_k \,|||\, O_\Lambda(\bar{\omega}L) \,|||\, \Phi_l \rangle\Big]^2 \, . \tag{10.108}$$

The evaluation of the reduced matrix elements $\langle \Phi_k \,|||\, O_\Lambda(\bar{\omega}L) \,|||\, \Phi_l \rangle$ is discussed in sects. 10.5 and 10.6 for states Φ described by one- and two-orbit configurations.

It is clear that depending upon the signs of the reduced matrix elements as well as of the amplitudes $a_k^{(\mathrm{i})}$ and $a_l^{(\mathrm{f})}$, constructive or destructive interference will occur. This is illustrated with some typical examples. Let us introduce a truncation amplitude a_{trunc} and take into account all components with amplitudes a_k that satisfy the condition $|a_k| \geqslant a_{\mathrm{trunc}}$. In fig. 10.9 values of $M_{\mathrm{W}}^2(\mathcal{M}1)$ and $M_{\mathrm{W}}^2(\mathcal{E}2)$ are given for some transitions in $27 \leqslant A \leqslant 29$ nuclei as a function of a_{trunc}. Note that the $\mathcal{E}2$ strengths derive mainly from constructive interference of many contributions, whereas for the $\mathcal{M}1$ strengths strong cancellations occur. This is a typical feature observed in many calculations of $\mathcal{M}1$ and $\mathcal{E}2$ strengths with the shell model.

CONTRIBUTIONS OF SMALL COMPONENTS IN WAVE FUNCTIONS

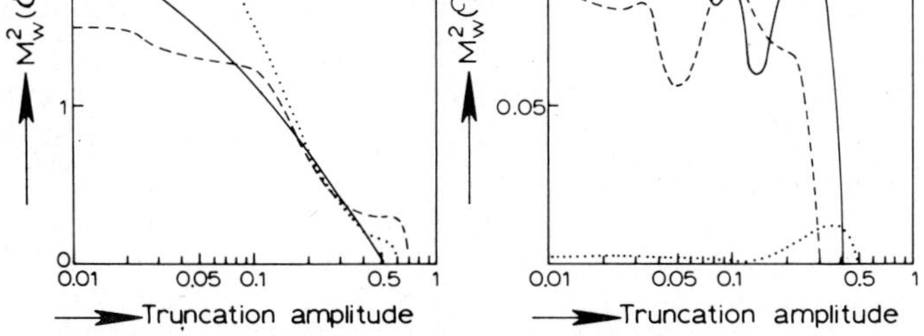

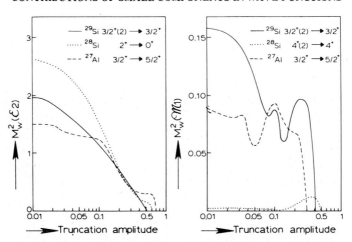

Fig. 10.9. The influence of amplitude truncation on the calculated $\mathcal{E}2$ and $\mathcal{M}1$ transition strengths. Given are typical examples of transitions in $A = 27$, 28 and 29 nuclei [De Voigt, Glaudemans, De Boer and Wildenthal (1972)].

RELATION BETWEEN THE NORM AND THE NUMBER OF COMPONENTS

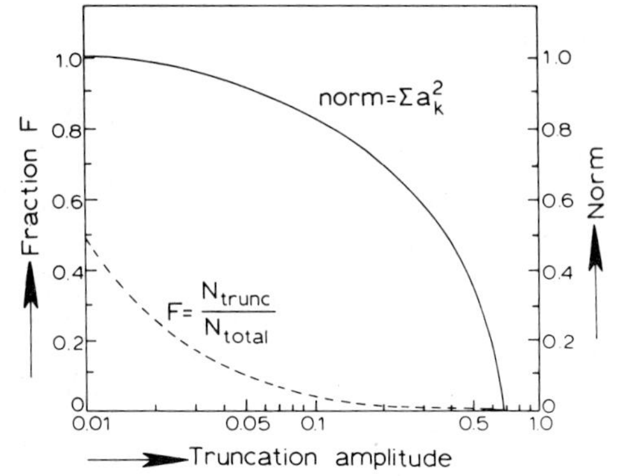

Fig. 10.10. The norm $\Sigma_{k=1}^{N_{\text{trunc}}} a_k^2$ and the fraction $F = N_{\text{trunc}}/N_{\text{total}}$ plotted as a function of the truncation amplitude a_{trunc}. The two quantities plotted represent an average for the wave functions used for the transitions indicated in fig. 10.9.

We shall now consider the contributions from the small components in more detail. For the truncated wave functions one can plot the norm $\Sigma_k a_k^2$ with $|a_k| > a_{\text{trunc}}$ against the amplitude a_{trunc}, as is done in fig. 10.10. The norm is equal to unity, of course, when all amplitudes are taken into account, i.e. $a_{\text{trunc}} = 0$. It is interesting to determine the number of components of the wave function, N_{trunc}, that corresponds to each value of a_{trunc}. In fig. 10.10 the fraction $N_{\text{trunc}}/N_{\text{total}}$ is plotted as a function of a_{trunc}. It is seen that for $a_{\text{trunc}} = 0.01$ half the number of components make up 99% of the norm. In this example all components each with an amplitude less than 0.05 (i.e. less than 0.25% intensity) contribute approximately 10% to the norm. Their effect on the $\mathcal{M}1$ and $\mathcal{E}2$ strengths, however, is usually considerably larger (see fig. 10.9). The contribution from the components of the wave functions with amplitudes less than 0.01, are not shown. These very weak terms are found not to contribute significantly to the transition rates.

10.8. Effective matrix elements from experimental data

The reduced transition probability can be expressed in terms of a reduced matrix element as (cf. eq. (9.60))

$$B(\varpi L; J_{\text{i}} \to J_{\text{f}}) = \frac{\langle \Psi_{\text{f}} \| O(\varpi L) \| \Psi_{\text{i}} \rangle^2}{2J_{\text{i}} + 1} \, . \qquad (10.109)$$

It has been pointed out in chapter 1 that in many cases effective operators are to be used in a truncated shell-model space. This means that one tries to find an effective operator $O'(\varpi L)$ such that for the truncated wave functions Ψ' the relation

$$\langle \Psi_f' \| O'(\varpi L) \| \Psi_i' \rangle = \langle \Psi_f \| O(\varpi L) \| \Psi_i \rangle \,, \tag{10.110}$$

is satisfied, when O and Ψ denote the true operator and wave functions.

There are two methods to obtain effective operators, i.e. (i) use of perturbation theory and (ii) parametrization. We will restrict this discussion to the latter method and postpone the approach with perturbation theory to chapter 16.

It has been explained in the previous sections that the matrix element in eq. (10.109) for the many-particle wave functions Ψ_i and Ψ_f can be expressed linearly in terms of single-particle matrix elements x_k. Thus one can write

$$B(\varpi L; J_i \to J_f) = \left(\sum_{k=1}^{N_x} \alpha_k x_k\right)^2 \,, \tag{10.111}$$

where N_x denotes the number of single-particle matrix elements x_k and the expansion coefficients resulting from Racah algebra and configuration mixing are given by α_k.

Let us now consider the matrix elements x_k as parameters to be determined from experimental data. This approach is only useful of course, when a small number of parameters x_k is sufficient to correlate a large body of electromagnetic transition data. One obtains from eq. (10.111) a linear equation in the parameters when the square root of the experimental transition strength, rather than the strength itself, is compared with the calculated value, i.e.

$$\pm\sqrt{B(\varpi L; J_i \to J_f)} = \sum_{k=1}^{N_x} \alpha_k x_k \,. \tag{10.112}$$

This approach, however, requires knowledge of the proper sign of the square root. The sign cannot be determined experimentally, but theoretically it depends on the conventional overall phase of the initial- and final-state wave functions. It is found empirically, however, that the sign of the right-hand side of eq. (10.112) is insensitive to rather small variations in the parameters x_k. Therefore it is not unrealistic to expect that the signs obtained from the reduced single-particle matrix elements x_k calculated for the bare operators can be used. Fortunately, there is a very nice check on the phases employed. It is provided by a comparison of signs of calculated multipole-mixing ratios with those determined experimentally. This approach is not affected by the freedom of phase mentioned above, since a change of the overall phase of e.g. the initial state results in a sign flip of the matrix elements of both electric and magnetic radiation, but it leaves the sign of their ratio unaffected.

Some additional equations in the parameters can be obtained from a comparison of calculated multipole moments with experimental data. The calculation of a multipole moment requires the evaluation of the reduced matrix elements $\langle \Psi_f \| O(\varpi L) \| \Psi_i \rangle$

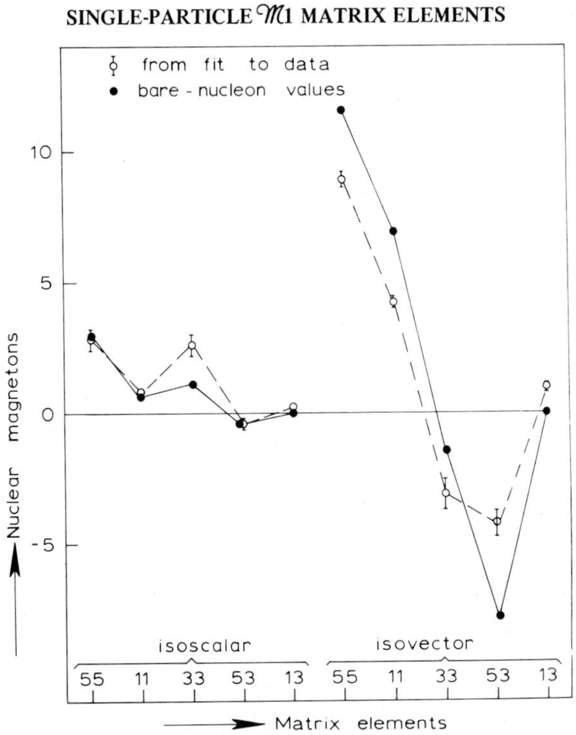

Fig. 10.11. The ten values of the single-particle 𝔐1 matrix elements obtained from a fit to 48 observed 𝔐1 transition strengths and three dipole moments in A = 27–29 nuclei [De Voigt, Glaudemans, De Boer and Wildenthal (1972)] are compared with the bare-nucleon values derived from eq. (10.64). The single-particle states are labelled 1 for $2s_{1/2}$, 3 for $1d_{3/2}$ and 5 for $1d_{5/2}$.

for $\Psi_i = \Psi_f$ (cf. eq. (10.109)), as will be shown in chapter 11. Therefore multipole moments are very useful for a search on the parameters x_k since (i) the sign of the reduced matrix element $\langle\Psi\|O\|\Psi\rangle$ is known from experiment and (ii) multipole moments are often known with great accuracy.

The least-squares fitting procedure is straightforward (see chapter 7), once the equations for the parameters x_k have been linearized and the proper phases have been determined for the square root of the measured transition rates. The weighting factor in the least-squares fitting of each equation may be derived from the errors assigned to the experimental data.

An example of a fit of matrix elements is shown in fig. 10.11. The effective reduced single-particle matrix elements of the 𝔐1 operator are determined from a fit to experimental data in A = 27–29 nuclei. The wave functions are calculated with the assumption of an inert ^{16}O core and active nucleons in the $1d_{5/2}$, $2s_{1/2}$ and $1d_{3/2}$ orbits with the MSDI as an effective interaction. In order to keep the diagonalization of the matrices feasible, restrictions are imposed on the number of particles that can be excited out of the $1d_{5/2}$ orbit. In this model space one needs five isoscalar and five isovector single-particle reduced matrix elements which are all treated as parameters. It is seen from fig. 10.11 that the ten parameters are all well-determined by the experimental data. Moreover, one sees that the effective values do not deviate more than a factor of two from the values calculated with eq. (10.64), which are shown also for comparison. Exceptions are the isoscalar and isovector parts of the matrix elements $\langle 2s_{1/2} ||| O(\mathcal{M}\, 1) ||| 1d_{3/2} \rangle$, which should vanish owing to the l-selection rule (see eq. (10.64)). The value determined from the fit turns out to be different from zero. This, however, can be justified in terms of perturbation theory as will be discussed in chapter 16.

For $\mathcal{E}2$ transitions the number of parameters x_k in eq. (10.112) can be reduced considerably, when it is assumed that the effective proton and neutron charges of the electric operator are orbit independent. This way one can express all electric single-particle matrix elements in terms of only two effective-charge parameters e_{p} and e_{n}. Many experimental data have been reproduced reasonably well with this approach. A similar assumption can be made about the g-factors entering the magnetic operators. The magnetic single-particle matrix elements can then be expressed in terms of the four effective g-factors $g^l_{\text{p}}, g^l_{\text{n}}, g^s_{\text{p}}$ and g^s_{n}.

Finally it should be remarked that the determination of reduced single-particle matrix elements from experimental data is a useful method to correlate electromagnetic properties, especially where the approach with perturbation theory is still of insufficient accuracy.

CHAPTER 11

ELECTRIC AND MAGNETIC MULTIPOLE MOMENTS

To each nuclear state corresponds a particular distribution of charges and currents. One can introduce the static multipole moments to describe the interaction of these charges and currents with an external electric or magnetic field. These fields may derive, for example, from the electrons in the atom or from another external source. A multipole moment calculated from a nuclear model serves as a particular interesting test of the theory since, in contrast to spectroscopic factors and transition rates, the wave function of only one nuclear state is involved.

A derivation of the operators for electric and magnetic multipoles is given in sects. 11.1 and 11.2, respectively. It is shown that these operators are very similar to those for the electromagnetic transitions that have been discussed in the previous chapters. Some selection rules are mentioned in sect. 11.3. The difference between an intrinsic and a spectroscopic quadrupole moment is discussed in sect. 11.4. Expressions for the electric quadrupole moments and magnetic dipole moments, derived from an extreme single-particle model, are given in sects. 11.5 and 11.6, respectively. In sect. 11.7 a procedure is outlined to calculate multipole moments from many-particle, multishell wave functions. Results of some calculations are compared with experimental data in sect. 11.8. It is shown in sect. 11.9 that very simple expressions can be used sometimes to correlate magnetic dipole moments in mirror nuclei or in neighbouring nuclei.

11.1. Electric multipole moments

When $\rho^{(e)}(\boldsymbol{r})$ describes the nuclear charge distribution, then the electrostatic energy of a nucleus in an external potential $\phi(\boldsymbol{r})$ is given by

$$U = \int \rho^{(e)}(\boldsymbol{r})\phi(\boldsymbol{r})\, \mathrm{d}\boldsymbol{r}\,. \tag{11.1}$$

When the potential $\phi(\boldsymbol{r})$ is only slowly varying over the dimensions of the nucleus it makes sense to replace $\phi(\boldsymbol{r})$ in eq. (11.1) by the Taylor expansion

$$\phi(\boldsymbol{r}) = \phi(0) + \boldsymbol{r}\cdot\boldsymbol{\nabla}\phi(0) + \tfrac{1}{2}\sum_{i,j=1}^{3} r_i r_j \frac{\partial^2\phi(0)}{\partial r_i r_j} + \text{higher-order terms}\,. \tag{11.2}$$

In this expression the three cartesian components x, y and z of $\boldsymbol{r}$ are denoted by r_1, r_2 and r_3, respectively. The origin $r = 0$ may be chosen somewhere in the charge-current system, e.g. in the centre of mass of the nucleus.

With the well-known relation between the potential and the electric field

$$E(\boldsymbol{r}) = -\boldsymbol{\nabla}\phi(\boldsymbol{r}) \tag{11.3}$$

one can rewrite eq. (11.2) as

$$\phi(\boldsymbol{r}) = \phi(0) - \boldsymbol{r}\cdot E(0) - \tfrac{1}{6}\sum_{ij} 3r_i r_j \frac{\partial E_j(0)}{\partial r_i} + \text{higher-order terms}\,. \tag{11.4}$$

The external field satisfies Poisson's equation

$$\boldsymbol{\nabla}\cdot E(\boldsymbol{r}) = -4\pi\rho^{\text{ext}}(\boldsymbol{r}) = 0 \tag{11.5}$$

inside the nucleus, i.e. away from the sources $\rho^{\text{ext}}(\boldsymbol{r})$ of the external field. Hence an extra term $r^2\,\boldsymbol{\nabla}\cdot E(0) \equiv r^2\,\Sigma_i \partial E_i(0)/\partial r_i$ in eq. (11.4) does not contribute to the integral (11.1). Thus substitution of the expression

$$\phi(\boldsymbol{r}) = \phi(0) - \boldsymbol{r}\cdot E(0) - \tfrac{1}{6}\sum_{ij} (3r_i r_j - r^2\delta_{ij}) \frac{\partial E_j(0)}{\partial r_i} + \ldots \tag{11.6}$$

into eq. (11.1) leads to the same energy U as substitution of eq. (11.4).

The introduction of the extra term in eq. (11.6) may seem rather arbitrary, but it has as a consequence that the tensor multiplying $\partial E_j(0)/\partial r_i$ is traceless, i.e. $\Sigma_{i=j}(3r_i r_j - r^2\delta_{ij}) = 0$ (and hence also $\Sigma_i Q_{ii} = 0$, see eq. (11.10) below). The expression (11.1) for the energy now takes the form

$$U = q\phi(0) - \boldsymbol{d}\cdot E(0) - \tfrac{1}{6}\sum_{ij} Q_{ij} \frac{\partial E_j(0)}{\partial r_i} + \ldots.\,, \tag{11.7}$$

where the total charge or monopole moment is given by

$$q = \int \rho^{(\text{e})}(\boldsymbol{r})\,\mathrm{d}\boldsymbol{r}\,, \tag{11.8}$$

the dipole moment vector by

$$\boldsymbol{d} = \int \boldsymbol{r}\rho^{(\text{e})}(\boldsymbol{r})\,\mathrm{d}\boldsymbol{r}\,, \tag{11.9}$$

and the quadrupole moment tensor by

$$Q_{ij} = \int (3r_i r_j - r^2\delta_{ij})\,\rho^{(\text{e})}(\boldsymbol{r})\,\mathrm{d}\boldsymbol{r}\,. \tag{11.10}$$

The tensor

$$T_{ij} \equiv 3r_i r_j - r^2\delta_{ij} \tag{11.11}$$

has nine components but, since it is traceless ($\Sigma_i T_{ii} = 0$) and symmetric ($T_{ij} = T_{ji}$), the components must obey 1 + 3 = 4 conditions. It can be shown [DeShalit and Talmi (1963) ch. 10] that the remaining five components are equivalent to $r^2 Y_{2M}(\hat{\boldsymbol{r}})$, with $M = -2, -1, 0, +1, +2$, where $Y_{2M}(\hat{\boldsymbol{r}})$ is a spherical harmonic for angular momentum $L = 2$. This means that under rotations of the coordinate frame these five components transform among themselves, i.e. each component can, after rotation, always be expressed as a linear combination of the original set of five. It is clear now why the tensor T_{ij} had to be made traceless, since the trace being a scalar quantity transforms as a tensor of angular momentum $L = 0$. Thus the presence of a nonvanishing trace leads to a mixed $L = 0$ and $L = 2$ transformation character.

It is seen from eq. (11.7) that (i) the monopole moment (a scalar) combines with the potential, (ii) the dipole moment (a vector) combines with the electric field and (iii) the quadrupole moment (a traceless symmetric second-rank tensor) combines with the vector gradient of the electric field.

Continuation of the Taylor expansion leads to higher multipole moments, but this description in cartesian coordinates soon becomes rather cumbersome. This is in particular so since the construction of tensors of transformation behaviour corresponding to a pure angular momentum L then gets increasingly complicated. Therefore we now turn to a description that is tailored to the use of angular momentum, since it is given in terms of spherical harmonics.

For the monopole moment (11.8) this leads immediately to

$$q = \sqrt{4\pi} \int \rho^{(e)}(\boldsymbol{r}) Y_{00}(\hat{\boldsymbol{r}}) \mathrm{d}\boldsymbol{r} = \sum_k e(k) , \tag{11.12}$$

since one has $Y_{00}(\hat{\boldsymbol{r}}) = (4\pi)^{-1/2}$.

Writing the dipole moment (11.9) in terms of spherical components (see eq. (A.2.9)) one obtains for the M-component

$$d_M = \int \rho^{(e)}(\boldsymbol{r}) r_M \mathrm{d}\boldsymbol{r} = \sqrt{\frac{4\pi}{3}} \int \rho^{(e)}(\boldsymbol{r}) r Y_{1M}(\hat{\boldsymbol{r}}) \mathrm{d}\boldsymbol{r} . \tag{11.13}$$

The numerical factor $\sqrt{4\pi/3}$ occurs for historical reasons, because the dipole moment is defined conventionally as $e\boldsymbol{r}$.

Let us now turn to the discussion of the quadrupole moment of a nuclear state $|JM\rangle$. The quadrupole moment tensor Q_{ij}, defined in eq. (11.10), is traceless. Thus we have in cartesian coordinates the relation

$$Q_{xx} + Q_{yy} + Q_{zz} = 0 . \tag{11.14}$$

The nuclear charge distribution in a state $|JM\rangle$ is given by

$$\rho^{(e)}_{JM}(\boldsymbol{r}) = \langle JM | \sum_{k=1}^{A} e(k) \delta(\boldsymbol{r} - \boldsymbol{r}(k)) | JM\rangle \tag{11.15}$$

and is axially symmetric about the z-axis. Therefore one has also the relation

$$Q_{xx} = Q_{yy} . \tag{11.16}$$

From the conditions (11.14) and (11.16) one obtains

$$Q_{zz} = -2Q_{xx} = -2Q_{yy} \,. \tag{11.17}$$

Further, because of the axial symmetry about the z-axis, it follows that the three integrals in eq. (11.10) with the cross terms xy, xz and yz vanish. This results in the equalities

$$Q_{xy} = Q_{xz} = Q_{yz} = 0 \,. \tag{11.18}$$

Hence, due to eq. (11.17), only one independent quadrupole component, i.e. Q_{zz}, remains, which can be represented by

$$Q(JM) = \int \rho_{JM}^{(e)}(r)(3z^2 - r^2)\mathrm{d}\boldsymbol{r} \,. \tag{11.19}$$

When alternatively the quadrupole moment is written in terms of the five spherical harmonics $Y_{2M}(\hat{r})$ with $M = 0, \pm 1, \pm 2$, then, due to the axial symmetry of the charge distribution, the components with $M \neq 0$ vanish. The connection between $Y_{20}(\hat{r})$ and cartesian coordinates is given by (see table A.2.1)

$$r^2 Y_{20}(\hat{r}) = \sqrt{\frac{5}{16\pi}}(2z^2 - x^2 - y^2) = \sqrt{\frac{5}{16\pi}}(3z^2 - r^2) \,. \tag{11.20}$$

Combining eqs. (11.15), (11.19) and (11.20) one obtains

$$Q(JM) = \int \rho_{JM}^{(e)}(r)(3z^2 - r^2)\mathrm{d}\boldsymbol{r} = \sqrt{\frac{16\pi}{5}} \int \rho_{JM}^{(e)}(r) r^2 Y_{20}(\hat{r})\mathrm{d}\boldsymbol{r}$$

$$= \sqrt{\frac{16\pi}{5}} \sum_{k=1}^{A} e(k)\langle JM | r^2(k) Y_{20}(\hat{r}(k)) | JM\rangle \,. \tag{11.21}$$

Here also for historical reasons a numerical factor $\sqrt{16\pi/5}$ occurs, because the quadrupole moment of an axially symmetric body is conventionally defined as $\langle 3z^2 - r^2 \rangle$.

The expectation value in eq. (11.21) still depends on the projection quantum number M. For given J the moments for different values M are not independent, however, since they are related by Clebsch-Gordan coefficients according to the Wigner-Eckart theorem. In nuclear physics the quadrupole moment of a state of angular momentum J is defined as the expectation value in the state $M = J$. This leads to the largest observable quadrupole moment for J, as is shown later. It is referred to as the *spectroscopic* or *static* quadrupole moment, which must not be confused with the *intrinsic* quadrupole moment that will be discussed in sect. 11.4 in terms of a model.

Summarizing one has for the spectroscopic quadrupole moment the definition

$$Q \equiv Q(J, M=J) = \sum_k e(k)\langle JJ|3z^2(k) - r^2(k)|JJ\rangle$$

$$= \sqrt{\frac{16\pi}{5}} \sum_{k=1}^{A} e(k)\langle JJ|r^2(k)Y_{20}(\hat{r}(k))|JJ\rangle = \sqrt{\frac{16\pi}{5}} \langle JJ20|JJ\rangle \frac{\langle J\|O(\mathcal{E}2)\|J\rangle}{\sqrt{2J+1}}$$

$$= \sqrt{\frac{16\pi}{5}} \sqrt{\frac{J(2J-1)}{(J+1)(2J+1)(2J+3)}} \langle J\|O(\mathcal{E}2)\|J\rangle , \tag{11.22}$$

which follows after application of the Wigner-Eckart theorem (A.3.a14) and substitution of the operator $O(\mathcal{E}2)$ defined in eq. (9.35). The calculation of the reduced matrix element $\langle J\|O(\mathcal{E}2)\|J\rangle$ is completely analogous to the one entering the reduced transition rate $B(\mathcal{E}2)$, which has been discussed in the preceding chapters. For the calculation of a quadrupole moment initial- and final-state wave function must be taken identical. It thus follows that a computer program written to calculate $B(\mathcal{E}2)$ values can be used directly to obtain quadrupole moments.

It is seen from eq. (11.22) that the quadrupole moment of a spherical charge distribution vanishes, since then $\langle r^2\rangle = \langle x^2+y^2+z^2\rangle = 3\langle z^2\rangle$. As will be discussed later the converse is not true, i.e. a vanishing spectroscopic quadrupole moment not necessarily implies that a nucleus is spherical. It follows also that a prolate charge distribution (i.e. stretched along the z-axis) possesses a positive quadrupole moment ($\langle r^2\rangle < 3\langle z^2\rangle$) and an oblate distribution yields a negative quadrupole moment ($\langle r^2\rangle > 3\langle z^2\rangle$).

In general an electric 2^L pole moment with $L \geqslant 3$ of a state of total angular momentum J can be defined as

$$Q^{(L)} = \int \rho^{(e)}_{JJ}(r) r^L\, Y_{L0}(\hat{r})\mathrm{d}r$$

$$= \sum_{k=1}^{A} e(k)\langle JJ|r^L(k)Y_{L0}(\hat{r}(k))|JJ\rangle . \tag{11.23}$$

Of course this definition could have been used for all L values, but it is convention in quoting experimental values for $L = 2$ to use eq. (11.22), i.e. with the factor $\sqrt{16\pi/5}$.

The electric 2^L pole operator $r^L Y_{LM}(\hat{r})$ possesses parity $(-1)^L$, and hence the electric 2^L pole moments must vanish for odd values of L. This is a direct consequence of parity conservation in the matrix elements of eq. (11.23) for nuclear states possessing well-defined parity.

11.2. Magnetic multipole moments

The introduction of magnetic moments is somewhat less immediate then that of electric multipole moments. It is shown first that for the steady state a magnetic charge density $\rho^{(m)}$ can be introduced such that an expression for magnetic multipole moments can be given that is analogous to the one for electric multipole moments.

The magnetization density $\boldsymbol{m}(\boldsymbol{r})$ of a nucleus derives from two sources: (i) the orbital motion of the charged particles, i.e. the convection currents in the nucleus, and (ii) the magnetic moments associated with the spins of the individual nucleons. Thus one can write in an obvious notation

$$\boldsymbol{m}(\boldsymbol{r}) = \boldsymbol{m}_{\mathrm{c}}(\boldsymbol{r}) + \boldsymbol{m}_{\mathrm{s}}(\boldsymbol{r}) . \tag{11.24}$$

The convection current density corresponding to the magnetization density $\boldsymbol{m}_{\mathrm{c}}(\boldsymbol{r})$ is given by

$$\frac{1}{c}\boldsymbol{j}_{\mathrm{c}}(\boldsymbol{r}) = \boldsymbol{\nabla} \times \boldsymbol{m}_{\mathrm{c}}(\boldsymbol{r}) . \tag{11.25}$$

Being the curl of another vector field $\boldsymbol{m}_{\mathrm{c}}(\boldsymbol{r})$, the current density $\boldsymbol{j}_{\mathrm{c}}(\boldsymbol{r})$ is seen to be divergence free, i.e. $\boldsymbol{\nabla}\cdot\boldsymbol{j}_{\mathrm{c}}(\boldsymbol{r}) = 0$. This agrees with the continuity equation (conservation of charge)

$$0 = \boldsymbol{\nabla}\cdot\boldsymbol{j}_{\mathrm{c}} + \frac{\partial\rho^{(\mathrm{e})}}{\partial t} = \boldsymbol{\nabla}\cdot\boldsymbol{j}_{\mathrm{c}} , \tag{11.26}$$

since one has $\partial\rho^{(\mathrm{e})}/\partial t = 0$ in the case of static fields and stationary currents. From Maxwell's equations (Ampère's law of induction) one obtains with eq. (11.25)

$$\boldsymbol{\nabla} \times \boldsymbol{H} = \frac{4\pi}{c}\boldsymbol{j}_{\mathrm{c}} = 4\pi\,\boldsymbol{\nabla} \times \boldsymbol{m}_{\mathrm{c}} . \tag{11.27}$$

With the spin magnetization density being given by $\boldsymbol{m}_{\mathrm{s}}(\boldsymbol{r})$, the magnetic induction in the nucleus is given by

$$\boldsymbol{B} = \boldsymbol{H} + 4\pi\boldsymbol{m}_{\mathrm{s}} . \tag{11.28}$$

Using eq. (11.24) one can now rewrite eq. (11.27) as

$$\boldsymbol{\nabla} \times (\boldsymbol{B} - 4\pi\,\boldsymbol{m}) = 0 . \tag{11.29}$$

Since the vector field $\boldsymbol{B} - 4\pi\,\boldsymbol{m}$ is seen to be irrotational, it can be written as the gradient of a scalar field

$$\boldsymbol{B} - 4\pi\,\boldsymbol{m} = -\boldsymbol{\nabla}\phi^{(\mathrm{m})} \tag{11.30}$$

With the Maxwell equation

$$\boldsymbol{\nabla}\cdot\boldsymbol{B} = 0 \tag{11.31}$$

one now derives from eq. (11.30)

$$\boldsymbol{\nabla}^2\phi^{(\mathrm{m})} = 4\pi\boldsymbol{\nabla}\cdot\boldsymbol{m} \equiv -4\pi\rho^{(\mathrm{m})} . \tag{11.32}$$

The introduction of a *magnetic charge density* $\rho^{(\mathrm{m})} \equiv -\boldsymbol{\nabla}\cdot\boldsymbol{m}$ thus has led to an equation for a magnetic potential $\phi^{(\mathrm{m})}$ of exactly the same shape as the Poisson equation governing the electric potential $\phi^{(\mathrm{e})}$, i.e.

$$\nabla^2 \phi^{(\mathrm{e})} = -4\pi\rho^{(\mathrm{e})} . \tag{11.33}$$

Now with the magnetic charge density $\rho^{(\mathrm{m})}$ we can define magnetic multipole moments in exact analogy with the electric multipole moments.

The magnetic multipole moments describe the interaction of a nucleus in an external magnetic field. In analogy with eq. (11.23) one can define magnetic multipoles as

$$\mu^{(L)} = \int \rho^{(\mathrm{m})}(\boldsymbol{r}) r^L Y_{L0}(\hat{\boldsymbol{r}}) \mathrm{d}\boldsymbol{r}$$

$$= \int \langle JM = J | -\nabla \cdot (\boldsymbol{m}_{\mathrm{c}}^{\mathrm{op}}(\boldsymbol{r}) + \boldsymbol{m}_{\mathrm{s}}^{\mathrm{op}}(\boldsymbol{r})) | JM = J \rangle r^L Y_{L0}(\hat{\boldsymbol{r}}) \mathrm{d}\boldsymbol{r}$$

$$= \langle JM = J | \int \mathrm{d}\boldsymbol{r} [-\nabla \cdot (\boldsymbol{m}_{\mathrm{c}}^{\mathrm{op}}(\boldsymbol{r}) + \boldsymbol{m}_{\mathrm{s}}^{\mathrm{op}}(\boldsymbol{r}))] r^L Y_{L0}(\boldsymbol{r}) | JM = J \rangle , \tag{11.34}$$

where for the latter equality the integration over the nucleon coordinates $\boldsymbol{r}(1), ..., \boldsymbol{r}(A)$ (implied in the matrix elements) and over $\boldsymbol{r}$ are interchanged. The operators $\boldsymbol{m}^{\mathrm{op}}(\boldsymbol{r})$, $\boldsymbol{m}_{\mathrm{c}}^{\mathrm{op}}(\boldsymbol{r})$ and $\boldsymbol{m}_{\mathrm{s}}^{\mathrm{op}}(\boldsymbol{r})$ are all three defined by

$$\boldsymbol{m}(\boldsymbol{r}) = \langle JJ | \boldsymbol{m}^{\mathrm{op}}(\boldsymbol{r}) | JJ \rangle . \tag{11.35}$$

For the lowest-order multipole moment $L = 0$ one obtains with $Y_{00}(\hat{\boldsymbol{r}}) = (4\pi)^{-1/2}$

$$\mu^{(0)} = -\frac{1}{\sqrt{4\pi}} \int \nabla \cdot \boldsymbol{m}(\boldsymbol{r}) \mathrm{d}\boldsymbol{r} = -\frac{1}{\sqrt{4\pi}} \oint \boldsymbol{m} \cdot \mathrm{d}\boldsymbol{S} = 0 , \tag{11.36}$$

where, according to the definition of divergence, the volume integration of $\nabla \cdot \boldsymbol{m}(\boldsymbol{r})$ is replaced by the integration of $\boldsymbol{m}(\boldsymbol{r})$ over a surface enclosing the nucleus. When the radius of this surface is chosen large enough, the integral vanishes due to the vanishing of $\boldsymbol{m}(\boldsymbol{r})$. Thus in contrast to the electric case, magnetic monopoles do not exist. This conclusion can also be made directly from the Maxwell equations. The electric monopole charge density, i.e. the density of free charge, follows from Poisson's equation (cf. eq. (11.5)). The corresponding equation (11.31) for the magnetic case then implies the absence of magnetic monopoles. Representing the electric or magnetic fields in terms of field lines, one always has to draw the $\boldsymbol{B}$-lines as closed curves, while the $\boldsymbol{E}$-lines originate from and vanish on electric monopoles.

Let us now focus attention on magnetic multipoles with $L \neq 0$. We make use of the identity (see eq. (A.5.16)).

$$\mathrm{i}\,\nabla \times \boldsymbol{l} = \boldsymbol{r}\nabla^2 - \nabla \frac{\partial}{\partial r} r \tag{11.37}$$

and the equation

$$\nabla^2 r^L Y_{L0}(\hat{r}) = 0 . \tag{11.38}$$

Rewriting the part of eq. (11.34) that depends on the magnetization density $\boldsymbol{m}_c(\boldsymbol{r})$ and performing partial integrations, one obtains

$$-\int \nabla \cdot \boldsymbol{m}_c(\boldsymbol{r}) r^L Y_{L0}(\hat{r}) \mathrm{d}\boldsymbol{r} = \int \boldsymbol{m}_c(\boldsymbol{r}) \cdot \nabla r^L Y_{L0}(\hat{r}) \mathrm{d}\boldsymbol{r}$$

$$= \frac{1}{L+1} \int \boldsymbol{m}_c(\boldsymbol{r}) \cdot \nabla \frac{\partial}{\partial r} r^{L+1} Y_{L0}(\hat{r}) \mathrm{d}\boldsymbol{r} = \frac{-\mathrm{i}}{L+1} \int \boldsymbol{m}_c(\boldsymbol{r}) \cdot \nabla \times \boldsymbol{l}\, r^L Y_{L0}(\hat{r}) \mathrm{d}\boldsymbol{r}$$

$$= \frac{-\mathrm{i}}{L+1} \int (\nabla \times \boldsymbol{m}_c(\boldsymbol{r})) \cdot \boldsymbol{l}\, r^L Y_{L0}(\hat{r}) \mathrm{d}\boldsymbol{r} = \frac{-\mathrm{i}}{(L+1)c} \int \boldsymbol{j}_c(\boldsymbol{r}) \cdot \boldsymbol{l}\, r^L Y_{L0}(\hat{r}) \mathrm{d}\boldsymbol{r} , \tag{11.39}$$

where for the last step eq. (11.25) is used.

According to standard quantum mechanics the current density for a particle in a state ϕ is given by the expression [Messiah (1965)]

$$\boldsymbol{j}_c(\boldsymbol{r}) = \frac{e\hbar}{2M\mathrm{i}} \{\phi^*(\boldsymbol{r}) \nabla \phi(\boldsymbol{r}) - \phi(\boldsymbol{r}) \nabla \phi^*(\boldsymbol{r})\} . \tag{11.40}$$

This corresponds to the classical expression

$$\boldsymbol{j}_c = e\boldsymbol{v} = e \frac{\boldsymbol{p}}{M} \tag{11.41}$$

with the momentum $\boldsymbol{p}$ replaced by the operator $\hbar\nabla/\mathrm{i}$. The current density for an A-particle system is then given by

$$\boldsymbol{j}_c(\boldsymbol{r}) = \frac{\hbar}{2M\mathrm{i}} \sum_{k=1}^{A} e(k) \int \mathrm{d}\boldsymbol{r}(1) \ldots \mathrm{d}\boldsymbol{r}(A)$$

$$\times \{\psi^*(\boldsymbol{r}(1), \ldots, \boldsymbol{r}(A)) \delta(\boldsymbol{r} - \boldsymbol{r}(k)) \nabla(k) \psi(\boldsymbol{r}(1), \ldots, \boldsymbol{r}(A))$$

$$- \psi(\boldsymbol{r}(1), \ldots, \boldsymbol{r}(A)) \delta(\boldsymbol{r} - \boldsymbol{r}(k)) \nabla(k) \psi^*(\boldsymbol{r}(1), \ldots, \boldsymbol{r}(A))\} . \tag{11.42}$$

Substitution of eq. (11.42) into eq. (11.39) leads to

$$-\int \nabla \cdot \boldsymbol{m}_c(\boldsymbol{r}) r^L Y_{L0}(\hat{r}) \mathrm{d}\boldsymbol{r} = \frac{-\hbar}{2(L+1)Mc} \sum_{k=1}^{A} e(k) \int \mathrm{d}\boldsymbol{r}(1) \ldots \mathrm{d}\boldsymbol{r}(A)$$

$$\times \{(\psi^* \nabla(k) \psi) \cdot \boldsymbol{l}(k) r^L(k) Y_{L0}(\hat{r}(k)) - (\psi \nabla(k) \psi^*) \cdot \boldsymbol{l}(k) r^L(k) Y_{L0}(\hat{r}(k))\} . \tag{11.43}$$

Partial integration yields

$$-\int (\psi \nabla \psi^*) \cdot (l r^L Y_{L0}) \mathrm{d}\boldsymbol{r} = \int \psi^* (\nabla \cdot (l r^L Y_{L0}) \psi) \mathrm{d}\boldsymbol{r} = \int \psi^* (l r^L Y_{L0}) \cdot \nabla \psi \mathrm{d}\boldsymbol{r} \,, \tag{11.44}$$

where use is made of the operator identity (see eq. (A.5.9))

$$\nabla \cdot \boldsymbol{l} = 0 \,. \tag{11.45}$$

It is seen that the two terms in eq. (11.43) yield the same contribution, which can be evaluated further as

$$\int \psi^* (l r^L Y_{L0}) \cdot \nabla \psi \mathrm{d}\boldsymbol{r} = -\mathrm{i} \int \psi^* (\boldsymbol{r} \times \nabla r^L Y_{L0}) \cdot \nabla \psi \mathrm{d}\boldsymbol{r}$$

$$= \mathrm{i} \int \psi^* (\nabla r^L Y_{L0}) \cdot (\boldsymbol{r} \times \nabla \psi) \mathrm{d}\boldsymbol{r} = -\int \psi^* (\nabla r^L Y_{L0}) \cdot (\boldsymbol{l} \psi) \mathrm{d}\boldsymbol{r} \,, \tag{11.46}$$

where the vector identity

$$(\boldsymbol{r} \times \boldsymbol{a}) \cdot \boldsymbol{b} = -\boldsymbol{a} \cdot (\boldsymbol{r} \times \boldsymbol{b}) \tag{11.47}$$

has been used.

We still must evaluate the part in eq. (11.34) that depends on the spin magnetization density $\boldsymbol{m}_{\mathrm{s}}$ given by

$$\boldsymbol{m}_{\mathrm{s}}(\boldsymbol{r}) = \sum_{k=1}^{A} \mu_{\mathrm{N}} g^{\mathrm{s}}(k) \int \mathrm{d}\boldsymbol{r}(1) \ldots \mathrm{d}\boldsymbol{r}(A)\, \psi^*(\boldsymbol{r}(1), \ldots, \boldsymbol{r}(A)) \delta(\boldsymbol{r} - \boldsymbol{r}(k)) \boldsymbol{s}(k)\, \psi(\boldsymbol{r}(1), \ldots, \boldsymbol{r}(A)) \,, \tag{11.48}$$

where $\frac{1}{2} g^s(k) \mu_{\mathrm{N}}$ denotes the spin magnetic moment of nucleon k and μ_{N} the nuclear magneton (c.f. eq. (9.37)). One partial integration now yields

$$-\int \nabla \cdot \boldsymbol{m}_{\mathrm{s}}(\boldsymbol{r}) r^L Y_{L0}(\hat{\boldsymbol{r}}) \mathrm{d}\boldsymbol{r} = \int \boldsymbol{m}_{\mathrm{s}}(\boldsymbol{r}) \cdot \nabla r^L Y_{L0}(\hat{\boldsymbol{r}}) \mathrm{d}\boldsymbol{r}$$

$$= \sum_{k=1}^{A} \mu_{\mathrm{N}} g^s(k) \int \mathrm{d}\boldsymbol{r}(1) \ldots \mathrm{d}\boldsymbol{r}(A)\, \psi^*(\boldsymbol{r}(1), \ldots, \boldsymbol{r}(A)) \boldsymbol{s}(k) \cdot [\nabla(k) r^L Y_{L0}(\hat{\boldsymbol{r}}(k))]$$

$$\times\, \psi(\boldsymbol{r}(1), \ldots, \boldsymbol{r}(A)) \,. \tag{11.49}$$

As a result we now have after substitution of eqs. (11.43), (11.44), (11.46) and (11.49) into eq. (11.34) the final expression for the magnetic 2^L pole moment

$$\mu^{(L)} = \langle JJ | \sum_{k=1}^{A} \mu_{\mathrm{N}} \{\nabla(k) r^L(k) Y_{L0}(\hat{\boldsymbol{r}}(k))\} \cdot \left\{ \frac{2g^l(k)}{L+1} \boldsymbol{l}(k) + g^s(k) \boldsymbol{s}(k) \right\} | JJ \rangle \,, \tag{11.50}$$

where the orbital g-factor $g^l(k) = 1$ for a proton and $g^l(k) = 0$ for a neutron is used.

The most important magnetic multipole moment is the magnetic dipole moment. For this case of $L = 1$ eq. (11.50) assumes a particularly simple form after substitution of $[\nabla r Y_{10}(\hat{r})] \cdot \boldsymbol{l} = \sqrt{3/4\pi}\, l_z$ (see eq. (A.2.23)). For historical reasons the magnetic dipole moment is normalized differently than in eq. (11.50), i.e. an overall factor of $(\frac{4}{3}\pi)^{1/2}$ must be added. Thus the magnetic dipole moment μ of a state of total angular momentum J assumes the form

$$\mu^{(1)} \equiv \mu = \langle JJ | \sum_{k=1}^{A} \{g^l(k) l_z(k) + g^s(k) s_z(k)\} | JJ \rangle \mu_N$$

$$= \sqrt{\frac{4\pi}{3}} \langle JJ10 | JJ \rangle \frac{\langle J \| O(\mathcal{M}1) \| J \rangle}{\sqrt{2J+1}} \mu_N$$

$$= \sqrt{\frac{4\pi}{3}} \sqrt{\frac{J}{(J+1)(2J+1)}} \langle J \| O(\mathcal{M}1) \| J \rangle \mu_N \,, \tag{11.51}$$

which follows after application of the Wigner-Eckart theorem (see the derivation of eq. (11.22)). Thus the calculation of a magnetic dipole moment is quite similar to that of an $\mathcal{M}1$ transition (see eq. (9.38)).

Summarizing we can say that the operators for electric and magnetic multipole moments are identical to those for multipole transitions, except for the mentioned normalization factors for magnetic dipole and electric quadrupole operators. Thus for the evaluation of multipole moments of many-particle states one can use exactly the same methods as for the transition rates that have been discussed in chapter 10.

11.3. Selection rules

From the parity selection rule for electromagnetic multipole operators (see eq. (9.54)) and the parities given in eqs. (9.55) one finds that for all quantum mechanical systems of well-defined parity (i) all odd electric multipoles vanish and (ii) all even magnetic multipoles vanish. Conservation of angular momentum also leads to selection rules. A 2^L pole moment in a state of angular momentum J is proportional to the matrix element $\langle JJ | O_{L0} | JJ \rangle$, where O_{LM} denotes a tensor operator of angular momentum L and projection M. According to the Wigner-Eckart theorem this matrix element is proportional to the Clebsch-Gordan coefficient $\langle JJL0 | JJ \rangle$, which vanishes if the condition $L \leqslant 2J$ is not satisfied.

It follows that for nuclear states with spin $J = 0$ or $\frac{1}{2}$ the electric quadrupole moment as well as all higher-order moments vanish. But it should not be concluded that these states possess a spherical intrinsic shape. This can be clarified by a discussion of the connection between spectroscopic and intrinsic quadrupole moments given below.

11.4. Intrinsic and spectroscopic quadrupole moments

Consider a classical, axially symmetric charge distribution $\rho_\beta^{(e)}(\boldsymbol{r})$. Let the symmetry axis z' of the charge distribution make an angle β with the laboratory z-axis (see fig. 11.1). We shall use two coordinate systems with the origins coinciding:

(i) polar coordinates r, θ, ϕ with respect to the laboratory frame;

(ii) polar coordinates r, θ', ϕ' with respect to a frame fixed in the charge distribution, having z' along the symmetry axis.

With the z'-axis possessing polar angles β and γ in the laboratory system one has the relation

$$\cos\theta = \cos\theta' \cos\beta + \sin\theta' \sin\beta \cos(\phi' - \gamma) \,. \tag{11.52}$$

The spectroscopic quadrupole moment is defined in the laboratory system, according to eq. (11.21), by

$$Q(\beta) = \int \rho_\beta^{(e)}(\boldsymbol{r})[3z^2 - r^2]\,\mathrm{d}\boldsymbol{r} = \int \rho_\beta^{(e)}(\boldsymbol{r}) r^2 [3\cos^2\theta - 1]\,\mathrm{d}\boldsymbol{r} \,, \tag{11.53}$$

where the quantum mechanical labels J, M are replaced by the angle β in the classical description. (It is seen below that the quadrupole moment does not depend on the angle γ.) Since the charge distribution is assumed to be axially symmetric about the z'-axis and therefore independent of the azimuthal angle ϕ' one may, after substitution of eq. (11.52) into eq. (11.53), perform an averaging over the angle ϕ'. One finds

$$\frac{1}{2\pi}\int_0^{2\pi} \mathrm{d}\phi' [3\cos^2\theta - 1] = \tfrac{1}{2}[3\cos^2\beta - 1]\,[3\cos^2\theta' - 1] \,, \tag{11.54}$$

INTRINSIC AND LABORATORY COORDINATE SYSTEMS

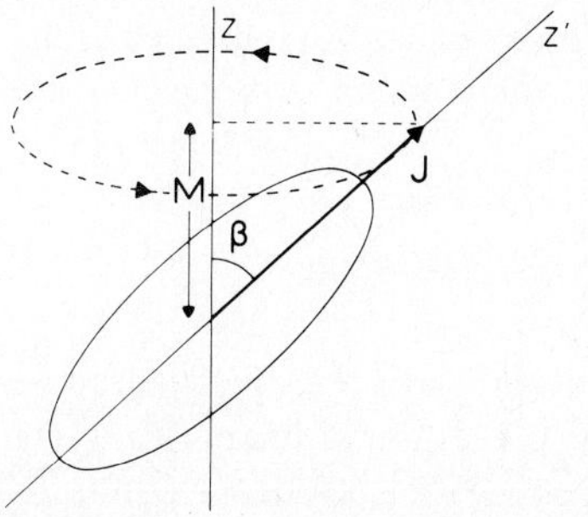

Fig. 11.1. The spectroscopic quadrupole moment is obtained by the semiclassical procedure of averaging the intrinsic quadrupole moment over the precession of J about the laboratory z-axis.

as results immediately from the relations

$$\frac{1}{2\pi}\int_0^{2\pi} \mathrm{d}\phi' \cos^2\phi' = \tfrac{1}{2}\,, \qquad \frac{1}{2\pi}\int_0^{2\pi} \mathrm{d}\phi' \cos\phi' = 0\,. \tag{11.55}$$

Let us denote the original charge denstiy distribution $\rho_\beta^{(e)}(\boldsymbol{r})$ in the coordinates r, θ', ϕ' by $\rho^{(e)}(\boldsymbol{r}')$. Eq. (11.53) then becomes

$$Q(\beta) = \tfrac{1}{2}[3\cos^2\beta - 1] \int \rho^{(e)}(\boldsymbol{r}')\,[3\cos^2\theta' - 1]\,r^2\,\mathrm{d}\boldsymbol{r}'$$

$$= \tfrac{1}{2}[3\cos^2\beta - 1] \int \rho^{(e)}(\boldsymbol{r}')(3z' - r^2)\,\mathrm{d}\boldsymbol{r}' = \tfrac{1}{2}[3\cos^2\beta - 1]\,Q'\,, \tag{11.56}$$

where Q' represents the *intrinsic quadrupole moment*, i.e. defined with respect to the axis of symmetry of the charge distribution.

Eq. (11.56) shows that the magnitude of $Q(\beta)$ is largest when the positive angle β is smallest. Classically one can put $\beta = 0$ to obtain the largest value $Q(\beta = 0) = Q'$, but quantally one must substitute

$$\cos\beta = \frac{M}{\sqrt{J(J+1)}}\,, \tag{11.57}$$

and thus one finds

$$Q(JM) = \frac{3M^2 - J(J+1)}{2J(J+1)}\,Q'\,. \tag{11.58}$$

From eq. (11.58) it follows that the quadrupole moment in the state $|JM\rangle$ is related to the one in the state $|JM = J\rangle$ as

$$\frac{Q(JM)}{Q(JM = J)} = \frac{Q(JM)}{Q} = \frac{3M^2 - J(J+1)}{J(2J-1)}\,. \tag{11.59}$$

The *spectroscopic quadrupole moment* Q is defined as the moment in the state $M = J$. It is the maximum value of the moment that one can observe in the laboratory system. It follows from eq. (11.58) that for $J \neq 0$ one has

$$Q = \frac{2J-1}{2(J+1)}\,Q'\,. \tag{11.60}$$

The semiclassical derivation shows that the quadrupole moment is partially smeared out ($Q < Q'$) due to the precession of the nuclear system about the laboratory z-axis. For $J = \frac{1}{2}$ it is seen from eq. (11.60) that even for maximal line-up of the nuclear system, i.e. $M = J$, the spectroscopic quadrupole moment vanishes completely, although the system may possess an intrinsic quadrupole moment. It requires a quantal description of the precessing nucleus to show that also for $J = 0$ the spectroscopic quadrupole moment vanishes. Instead of eq. (11.58) one finds a slightly different and more appropriate result.

In a more rigorous discussion of the spectroscopic multipole moments, one should employ the Wigner-Eckart theorem. The expectation value of the quadrupole moment operator, defined in eq. (11.22), can be expressed as a reduced matrix element by

$$Q(JM) = \sqrt{\frac{16\pi}{5}} \langle JM | \sum_{k=1}^{A} e(k) r^2(k) Y_{20}(\hat{r}(k)) | JM \rangle$$

$$= \sqrt{\frac{16\pi}{5}} \frac{\langle JM20|JM\rangle}{\sqrt{2J+1}} \langle J \| \sum_{k=1}^{A} e(k) r^2(k) Y_2(\hat{r}(k)) \| J \rangle . \tag{11.61}$$

Inserting the explicit value of the Clebsch-Gordan coefficient (see eq. (A.1.a12)) one obtains

$$Q(JM) = \sqrt{\frac{16\pi}{5}} \frac{3M^2 - J(J+1)}{\sqrt{J(J+1)(2J-1)(2J+1)(2J+3)}} \langle J \| \sum_{k=1}^{A} e(k) r^2(k) Y_2(\hat{r}(k)) \| J \rangle . \tag{11.62}$$

The spectroscopic quadrupole moment ($M = J$) thus assumes the form

$$Q = \sqrt{\frac{16\pi}{5}} \sqrt{\frac{J(2J-1)}{(J+1)(2J+1)(2J+3)}} \langle J \| \sum_{k=1}^{A} e(k) r^2(k) Y_2(\hat{r}(k)) \| J \rangle , \tag{11.63}$$

which vanishes for $J = 0$ and $J = \frac{1}{2}$.

Eq. (11.62) shows that the relation (11.59), although derived semiclassically, is a rigorous result.

11.5. Single-particle electric quadrupole moments

The nuclear quadrupole moments vary widely in magnitude. In particular the nuclei in the mass regions $150 < A < 190$ and $A > 225$ possess large permanent deformations. Light nuclei usually can be considered as to consist of a spherical core with a small number of extra nucleons. In such a picture the nuclear quadrupole moment derives completely from the extra nucleons. The extra nucleons may be coupled to pairs j^2 with $J = 0$ and then, in this extreme single-particle model, the quadrupole moment is due to the last odd proton.

Let us derive the expression for the quadrupole moment of a single proton in a particular shell-model orbit $|nljm\rangle$. According to eq. (11.22) the quadrupole moment for a charged particle is given by

$$Q_{\text{s.p.}} = \sqrt{\frac{16\pi}{5}} \langle nlj\, m{=}j|er^2 Y_{20}(\hat{r})|nlj\, m{=}j\rangle . \tag{11.64}$$

First we write the single-particle wave function as $|nlj\rangle = |nl\rangle\,|ljm\rangle$, i.e. as a product of a radial part and a spin-angle part. The integration over the spin-angle coordinates can be achieved with the Wigner-Eckart theorem (A.3.a15). The radial integral is kept as a separate factor $\langle nl|r^2|nl\rangle$ (cf. eq. (10.46)). Thus one finds, using eq. (A.3.e5),

$$Q_{\text{s.p.}} = e\sqrt{\frac{16\pi}{5}} \langle nl|r^2|nl\rangle \begin{pmatrix} j & 2 & j \\ -j & 0 & j \end{pmatrix} \langle l\tfrac{1}{2}j\|Y_2\|l\tfrac{1}{2}j\rangle$$

$$= -e\langle nl|r^2|nl\rangle \frac{2j-1}{2(j+1)} . \tag{11.65}$$

The minus sign in eq. (11.65) reflects the fact that the density of a state $|jm=j\rangle$ is concentrated along the equator. For such a distribution one has the inequality $\langle 3z^2\rangle < \langle r^2\rangle$, which results in a negative quadrupole moment (cf. eq. (11.19)). The radial integral in eq. (11.65) can be evaluated for harmonic-oscillator wave functions with eq. (2.32).

Comparison of these single-particle values with the experimental data on quadrupole moments shows that the single-particle values are far too small. Moreover, the majority of the measured quadrupole moments turn out to be positive rather than negative. This indicates that not only one but at least several nucleons contribute to the quadrupole moment.

11.6. Single-particle magnetic dipole moments

From eq. (11.51) it is seen that the vector operator for the magnetic dipole moment is given by

$$\boldsymbol{\mu}^{\text{op}} = \sum_{k=1}^{A} [g^l(k)\boldsymbol{l}(k) + g^s(k)\boldsymbol{s}(k)]\,\mu_{\text{N}} . \tag{11.66}$$

The total angular momentum is given by

$$\boldsymbol{J} = \sum_{k=1}^{A} [\boldsymbol{l}(k) + \boldsymbol{s}(k)] . \tag{11.67}$$

Both vector operators are linear combinations of the orbital angular momenta $\boldsymbol{l}(k)$ and spins $\boldsymbol{s}(k)$, but with different coefficients, since one has $g^l \neq g^s$ for protons as well as for neutrons. Thus the two vector operators $\boldsymbol{\mu}$ and $\boldsymbol{J}$ are not "parallel". However, the expectation values of these operators in a state $|JM = J\rangle$ can be compared. Application of the Landé formula (see eq. (A.4.6)) to the expression for the single-particle magnetic moment yields

$$\mu = \langle jm = j|\mu_z^{\text{op}}|jm = j\rangle = \langle jj|g^l l_z + g^s s_z|jj\rangle \mu_N$$

$$= \frac{\langle jj|g^l(\boldsymbol{l}\cdot\boldsymbol{j}) + g^s(\boldsymbol{s}\cdot\boldsymbol{j})|jj\rangle}{j(j+1)} \langle jj|j_z|jj\rangle \mu_N \equiv g^j j \mu_N \,. \tag{11.68}$$

The g-factor g^j introduced in eq. (11.68) as the ratio of the magnetic dipole moment μ (in units of μ_N) and the value of j is thus given by

$$g^j = \frac{\langle jj|g^l(\boldsymbol{l}\cdot\boldsymbol{j}) + g^s(\boldsymbol{s}\cdot\boldsymbol{j})|jj\rangle}{j(j+1)}$$

$$= \frac{g^l[j(j+1) + l(l+1) - s(s+1)] + g^s[j(j+1) + s(s+1) - l(l+1)]}{2j(j+1)} \,. \tag{11.69}$$

The last step is obtained by noting that from $\boldsymbol{j} = \boldsymbol{l} + \boldsymbol{s}$ it follows that one has $\boldsymbol{s} = \boldsymbol{j} - \boldsymbol{l}$ and hence $s^2 = j^2 + l^2 - 2(\boldsymbol{j}\cdot\boldsymbol{l})$ or $(\boldsymbol{l}\cdot\boldsymbol{j}) = \frac{1}{2}[j^2 + l^2 - s^2]$.

From this equation one obtains with $j = l \pm \frac{1}{2}$ for a single-particle state the well-known Schmidt values for the g-factor given by

$$g^j = \frac{(2j-1)g^l + g^s}{2j} \qquad \text{for} \quad j = l + \tfrac{1}{2} \,, \tag{11.70a}$$

$$g^j = \frac{(2j+3)g^l - g^s}{2(j+1)} \qquad \text{for} \quad j = l - \tfrac{1}{2} \,. \tag{11.70b}$$

Thus with eq. (11.68) one can write the single-particle magnetic dipole moment as

$$\mu_{\text{s.p.}} = g^j j \mu_N = [l g^l + \tfrac{1}{2} g^s]\,\mu_N \qquad \text{for} \quad j = l + \tfrac{1}{2} \,, \tag{11.71a}$$

$$\mu_{\text{s.p.}} = \frac{j}{j+1}\,[(l+1)g^l - \tfrac{1}{2} g^s]\,\mu_N \qquad \text{for} \quad j = l - \tfrac{1}{2} \,, \tag{11.71b}$$

where the orbital and spin g-factors are given in eqs. (10.66) and (10.67).

11.7. Moments in a multiorbit configuration space

It has been pointed out already in sect. 11.2 that the operators for electric and magnetic multipole moments are identical to those of $\mathcal{E}L$ and $\mathcal{M}L$ radiation apart from an extra factor for multipolarity $L \leqslant 2$. Consequently the evaluation of matrix elements involving states described by many active particles in one or more orbits can be performed in complete analogy with that of reduced transition rates $B(\overline{\omega}L)$.

The evaluation of $B(\overline{\omega}L)$ is discussed in detail in chapters 9 and 10. Let us write the electric or magnetic multipole operator O as the sum of two parts (cf. eq. (9.100) for the transition operator)

$$O(\overline{\omega}LM) = C(\overline{\omega}L)\Big[\sum_{k=1}^{A} S(\overline{\omega}LM, k)1 - \sum_{k=1}^{A} V(\overline{\omega}LM, k)\tau_z(k)\Big] \,, \tag{11.72}$$

where S and $V\tau_z$ denote the isoscalar and isovector parts, respectively, defined in eqs. (9.101)–(9.104). The constants $C(\overline{\omega}L)$ are defined as (cf. sects. 11.1 and 11.2)

$$C(\overline{\omega}L) = L\sqrt{\frac{4\pi}{2L+1}} \qquad \text{for } L \leqslant 2\,,$$

$$C(\overline{\omega}L) = 1 \qquad \text{for } L \geqslant 3\,. \tag{11.73}$$

The electric or magnetic multipole moment $\mathfrak{M}(\overline{\omega}L)$ in the state $|JJTT_z\rangle$ is thus given by the expectation value

$$\begin{aligned}\mathfrak{M}(\overline{\omega}L) &= \langle JJTT_z|O(\overline{\omega}L0)|JJTT_z\rangle \\ &= C(\overline{\omega}L)\Big[\langle JJTT_z|\sum_{k=1}^{A} S(\overline{\omega}L0, k)1|JJTT_z\rangle - \langle JJTT_z|\sum_{k=1}^{A} V(\overline{\omega}L0, k)\tau_z(k)|JJTT_z\rangle\Big]\,.\end{aligned} \tag{11.74}$$

Application of the Wigner-Eckart theorem (A.3.a17) to coordinate space and isospace leads to

$$\begin{aligned}\mathfrak{M}(\overline{\omega}L) &= C(\overline{\omega}L)\frac{\langle JJL0|JJ\rangle}{\sqrt{2J+1}}\left\{\frac{\langle TT_z00|TT_z\rangle}{\sqrt{2T+1}}\langle JT|||\sum_{k=1}^{A} S(\overline{\omega}L, k)1|||JT\rangle\right. \\ &\quad \left. - \frac{\langle TT_z10|TT_z\rangle}{\sqrt{2T+1}}\langle JT|||\sum_{k=1}^{A} V(\overline{\omega}L, k)\boldsymbol{\tau}(k)|||JT\rangle\right\} \\ &= C(\overline{\omega}L)\frac{\langle JJL0|JJ\rangle}{\sqrt{(2J+1)(2T+1)}}\left\{\langle JT|||\sum_{k=1}^{A} S(\overline{\omega}L, k)1|||JT\rangle\right. \\ &\quad \left. - \frac{T_z}{\sqrt{T(T+1)}}\langle JT|||\sum_{k=1}^{A} V(\overline{\omega}L, k)\boldsymbol{\tau}(k)|||JT\rangle\right\}\,.\end{aligned} \tag{11.75}$$

The evaluation of the reduced matrix elements in this expression has already been discussed in chapter 10. Comparison of the general expression (11.75) for a multipole moment with that of the reduced transition rate $B(\bar{\omega}L)$, given in eq. (9.106), leads to the relation

$$\mathfrak{M}^2(\bar{\omega}L) = C^2(\bar{\omega}L)\langle JJL0|JJ\rangle^2 B(\bar{\omega}L; JTT_z \to JTT_z)\,. \tag{11.76}$$

The coefficients $C(\bar{\omega}L)$ are given in eq. (11.73) and the evaluation of $B(\bar{\omega}L; JTT_z \to JTT_z)$ has been discussed in chapter 10. The presence of the Clebsch-Gordan coefficient $\langle JJL0|JJ\rangle$ leads to the selection rule $L \leqslant 2J$, mentioned before in sect. 11.3.

11.8. Illustrations

In this section some results are given of shell-model calculations on electric quadrupole moments and magnetic dipole moments in light nuclei. The calculated spectroscopic quadrupole moments of the lowest $J^\pi = 2^+$ states of doubly even nuclei in the mass region $20 \leqslant A \leqslant 38$ are shown in fig. 11.2 together with the presently known experimental data. The theoretical results are obtained from shell-model calculations for an inert ^{16}O core and active $1d_{5/2}$, $2s_{1/2}$ and $1d_{3/2}$ orbits. It is seen that the shell model correctly reproduces the sign alternations that are observed experimentally as a function of the mass number. This corresponds, from the collective point of view, with changes in shape from prolate to oblate or *vice versa,* as explained in sect. 11.1.

A magnetic dipole moment μ can be written according to eq. (11.75) as a sum of two terms

$$\mu = \mu_0 + \mu_1\,, \tag{11.77}$$

where μ_0 and μ_1 denote the isoscalar and isovector contribution, respectively, with the isovector part μ_1 being proportional to T_z.

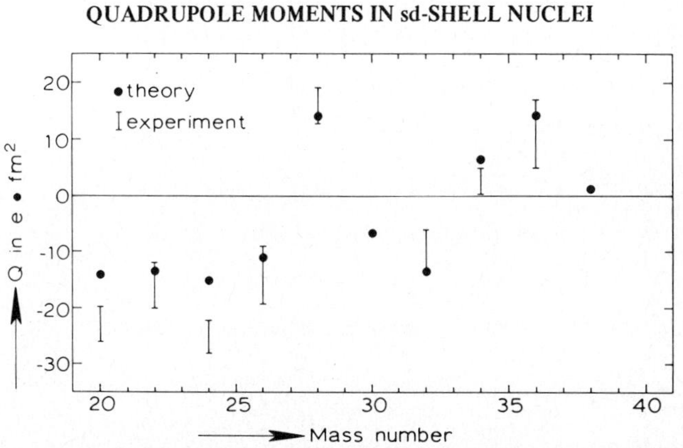

Fig. 11.2. A comparison between experimental and theoretical quadrupole moments of the first excited $J^\pi = 2^+$ states in doubly even sd-shell nuclei. The experimental data are taken from [Endt and Van der Leun (1973); Olin, Häusser, Alexander, Ferguson and Witthuhn (1974)]. The shell-model calculations are taken from [Wildenthal, McGrory and Glaudemans (1971)] except for the value of ^{26}Mg [Glaudemans, Koops, Meurders and Cole (1974)].

Let us restrict the discussion of the isoscalar part μ_0, since it shows a particularly simple behaviour as a function of the mass number. One can obtain μ_0 directly from experimentally determined magnetic dipole moments in $T_z = 0$ nuclei or, summing the dipole moments of corresponding states in mirror nuclei from the relation

$$\mu_0 = \tfrac{1}{2}[\mu(A, T_z) + \mu(A, -T_z)] \ . \tag{11.78}$$

It follows from eqs. (11.72), (9.103) and (A.2.23) that the isoscalar part for the state $|JJTT_z\rangle$ is given by

$$\mu_0 = \tfrac{1}{2}\langle JJTT_z| \sum_{k=1}^{A} [(g_p^l + g_n^l)l_z(k) + (g_p^s + g_n^s)s_z(k)] \, |JJTT_z\rangle \mu_N \ . \tag{11.79}$$

Inserting the values $g_p^l = 1$ and $g_n^l = 0$ and using $j(k) = l(k) + s(k)$ one obtains

$$\mu_0 = \tfrac{1}{2}\langle JJTT_z| \sum_{k=1}^{A} j_z(k) + (g_p^s + g_n^s - 1) \sum_{k=1}^{A} s_z(k)|JJTT_z\rangle \mu_N$$

$$= [\tfrac{1}{2}J + 0.38\langle JJTT_z| \sum_{k=1}^{A} s_z(k)|JJTT_z\rangle] \, \mu_N \ , \tag{11.80}$$

where the last step follows after substitution of the numerical values $g_p^s = 5.59$ and $g_n^s = -3.83$.

Let us assume that the configuration considered can be described as an inert core plus N active nucleons in one and the same orbit j. This will allow us to evaluate the matrix element of $\Sigma_k s_z(k)$ in eq. (11.80) rather simply, since now it can be expressed in one single-particle matrix element $\langle jm|s_z|jm\rangle$ (cf. eq. (10.77)). The latter diagonal matrix element can be rewritten by the use of Landé's formula (A.4.6) as

$$\langle jm|s_z|jm\rangle = \frac{\langle jm|\boldsymbol{s}\cdot\boldsymbol{j}|jm\rangle}{j(j+1)} \langle jm|j_z|jm\rangle \ . \tag{11.81}$$

As we have the relation

$$\boldsymbol{l}^2 = (\boldsymbol{j} - \boldsymbol{s})^2 = \boldsymbol{j}^2 + \boldsymbol{s}^2 - 2\boldsymbol{s}\cdot\boldsymbol{j} \ , \tag{11.82}$$

the matrix element of $\boldsymbol{s}\cdot\boldsymbol{j}$ can be evaluated immediately and we obtain

$$\langle jm|s_z|jm\rangle = \frac{j(j+1) + s(s+1) - l(l+1)}{2j(j+1)} \langle jm|j_z|jm\rangle \ . \tag{11.83}$$

This implies that in eq. (11.80) the operator $\Sigma_k s_z(k)$ can be replaced by $J_z = \Sigma_{k=1}^{N} j_z(k)$ multiplied by the factor given in eq. (11.83). Note that this factor is the same for all particles in the orbit j. Thus we obtain, substituting $s = \tfrac{1}{2}$, and $\langle JJTT_z|J_z|JJTT_z\rangle = J$, the final result for the isoscalar part of the magnetic dipole

ISOSCALAR g-FACTORS

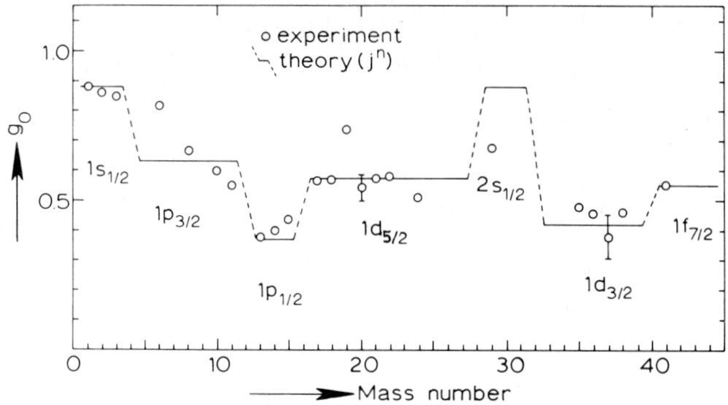

Fig. 11.3. The isoscalar g-factor, g_0, obtained from the experimental data for the lowest state with $J \neq 0$ in mirror nuclei and selfconjugate nuclei [Shirley and Lederer (1975)] is compared with the value calculated with the assumption of a pure j^n configuration.

moment

$$\mu_0 = g_0 J \mu_N = \left(\frac{1}{2} \pm \frac{0.38}{2l+1}\right) J \mu_N \qquad \text{for} \quad j = l \pm \frac{1}{2}\,, \tag{11.84}$$

where an isoscalar g-factor g_0 is introduced.

GROUND STATE g-FACTORS OF PROTON-RICH NUCLEI

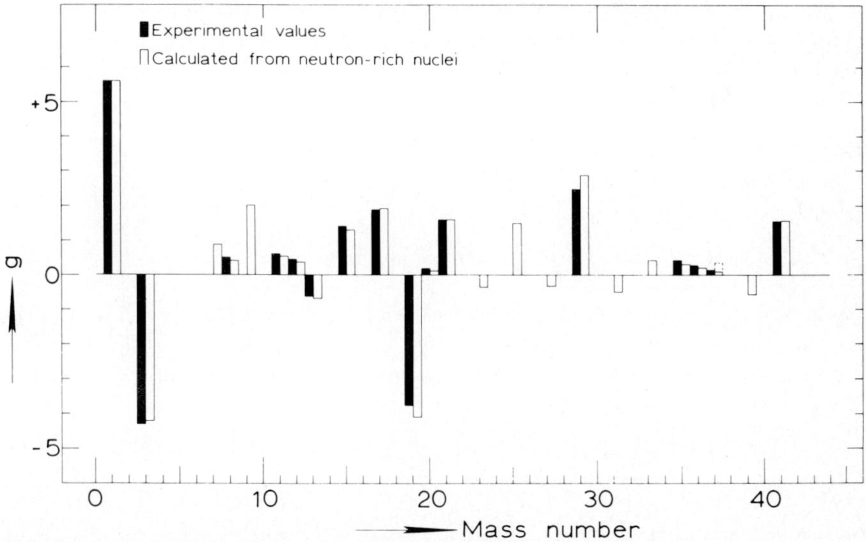

Fig. 11.4. A comparison between experimental g-factors for nuclei with $T_z < 0$ and those calculated from g-factors of the corresponding nuclei with $T_z > 0$ in isospin doublets. An error larger than 0.05 n.m. is indicated by a dotted line.

In fig. 11.3 the values of g_0 calculated from eq. (11.84) are compared with experimental values derived with eq. (11.78) for nuclei with $A \leqslant 41$. Data from mirror nuclei and self-conjugate nuclei are used. It is seen that the values of g_0 obtained from the very simple expression (11.84) agree well with experiment. Deviations from the pure j^n predictions can be explained rather well by taking into account more active orbits [Van Hienen and Glaudemans (1972)].

It may thus be concluded that the experimentally determined isoscalar contribution to the magnetic dipole moments of light nuclei can be reproduced rather accurately with a simple j^n configuration. Much more complex wave functions do not seem to produce considerably different results in most cases. The factor g_0 obtained for a j^n configuration may be useful for an estimate of the g-factors in $T_z = 0$ nuclei. In the second place it allows the determination of one of the g-factors of corresponding states in mirror nuclei when the other of the two is known. This is illustrated in fig. 11.4.

11.9. The additivity relation

Let us discuss finally a simple relation that may be useful to correlate magnetic dipole moments in neighbouring nuclei. If a nucleus with total angular momentum J is assumed to consist of three groups of nucleons: the core with $J_{\text{core}} = 0$ and two groups labelled A and B with angular momenta J_A and J_B, one has the relation

$$J_\text{A} + J_\text{B} = J\,. \tag{11.85}$$

In principle such a partition into three different groups can always be made, for any number of particles. One can write the magnetic moment in the state $|JM = J\rangle$ as

$$\mu = gJ\mu_\text{N} = \langle JM = J|gJ_z|JM = J\rangle\mu_\text{N}\,, \tag{11.86}$$

where the nuclear g-factor represents the ratio of μ and $J\mu_\text{N}$.

If we now assign g-factors g_A and g_B to the groups A and B, respectively, the magnetic moment of the system can be written as

$$\mu = gJ\mu_\text{N} = \langle JM = J|g_\text{A}J_{\text{A}z} + g_\text{B}J_{\text{B}z}|JM = J\rangle\mu_\text{N}\,. \tag{11.87}$$

The factors g_A and g_B depend each on the structure of the groups A and B, which includes a possible interaction with the core. The effects of the interaction between groups A and B are ignored. The right-hand side of eq. (11.87) can now be expanded further with the aid of the generalized Landé formula as

$$\mu = \frac{\langle JJ|g_\text{A}\boldsymbol{J}_\text{A}\cdot\boldsymbol{J} + g_\text{B}\boldsymbol{J}_\text{B}\cdot\boldsymbol{J}|JJ\rangle}{J(J+1)}\langle JJ|J_z|JJ\rangle\mu_\text{N}\,. \tag{11.88}$$

The g-factor is thus given by the expression

$$g = \frac{\langle JJ|g_\text{A}\boldsymbol{J}_\text{A}\cdot\boldsymbol{J} + g_\text{B}\boldsymbol{J}_\text{B}\cdot\boldsymbol{J}|JJ\rangle}{J(J+1)}\,. \tag{11.89}$$

Table 11.1
A comparison between some experimental g-factors [a] and those obtained with the additivity relation

Nucleus	J^π	nucleus A	config. [b]	g_A	nucleus B	config. [b]	g_B	g_{add}	g_{exp}
$^{28}_{13}Al_{15}$	3^+	$^{27}_{13}Al_{14}$	$\pi(1d_{5/2})$	+1.457	$^{29}_{14}Si_{15}$	$\nu(2s_{1/2})$	−1.111	+1.029	+0.930
$^{36}_{19}K_{17}$	2^+	$^{37}_{19}K_{18}$	$\pi(1d_{3/2})$	+0.135	$^{35}_{18}Ar_{17}$	$\nu(1d_{3/2})$	+0.422	+0.279	+0.274
$^{50}_{23}V_{27}$	6^+	$^{51}_{23}V_{28}$	$\pi(1f_{7/2})$	+1.472	$^{51}_{24}Cr_{27}$	$\nu(1f_{7/2})$	−0.267	+0.603	+0.558
$^{58}_{27}Co_{31}$	2^+	$^{57}_{27}Co_{30}$	$\pi(1f_{7/2})$	+1.350(3)	$^{57}_{26}Fe_{31}$	$\nu(2p_{3/2})$	−0.103	+2.077(5)	+2.021(3)
$^{86}_{37}Rb_{49}$	2^-	$^{85}_{37}Rb_{48}$	$\pi(1f_{5/2})$	+0.541	$^{87}_{38}Sr_{49}$	$\nu(1g_{9/2})$	−0.243	−0.896	−0.846
$^{130}_{53}I_{77}$	5^-	$^{129}_{53}I_{76}$	$\pi(1g_{7/2})$	+0.749	$^{129}_{52}Te_{77}$	$\nu(1h_{11/2})$	−0.21	−0.050(8)	−0.025(3)
$^{138}_{57}La_{81}$	5^+	$^{137}_{57}La_{80}$	$\pi(1g_{7/2})$	+0.770(2)	$^{137}_{56}Ba_{81}$	$\nu(2d_{3/2})$	+0.625	+0.727	+0.743
$^{170}_{69}Tm_{101}$	1^-	$^{169}_{69}Tm_{100}$	$\pi(3s_{1/2})$	−0.463(3)	$^{169}_{68}Er_{101}$	$\nu(3p_{1/2})$	+1.03(5)	+0.28(3)	+0.248(4)
$^{206}_{83}Bi_{123}$	10^-	$^{209}_{83}Bi_{126}$	$\pi(1h_{9/2})$	+0.913	$^{205}_{82}Pb_{123}$	$\nu(1i_{13/2})$	−0.150(6)	+0.266(4)	±0.263(2)

[a] Taken from the compilation [Shirley and Lederer (1975)]. Errors in the last digit larger than unity are given in brackets.
[b] The configuration assumed for the last odd proton (π) or odd neutron (ν).

For an evaluation of the matrix elements of $J_A \cdot J$ and $J_B \cdot J$ we start from the equality $J = J_A + J_B$ and write

$$J_A \cdot J = J_A \cdot (J_A + J_B) = J_A^2 + J_A \cdot J_B , \tag{11.90}$$

$$J^2 = (J_A + J_B)^2 = J_A^2 + J_B^2 + 2J_A \cdot J_B \tag{11.91}$$

or

$$J_A \cdot J_B = \tfrac{1}{2}(J^2 - J_A^2 - J_B^2) . \tag{11.92}$$

Inserting eq. (11.92) into eq. (11.90) we find immediately

$$J_A \cdot J = \tfrac{1}{2}(J^2 + J_A^2 - J_B^2) \tag{11.93}$$

and similarly

$$J_B \cdot J = \tfrac{1}{2}(J^2 + J_B^2 - J_A^2) . \tag{11.94}$$

Insertion of eqs. (11.93) and (11.94) into eq. (11.89) now yields the desired expression

$$g = \frac{g_A [J(J+1) + J_A(J_A+1) - J_B(J_B+1)] + g_B [J(J+1) + J_B(J_B+1) - J_A(J_A+1)]}{J(J+1)}$$

$$= \tfrac{1}{2}(g_A + g_B) + \tfrac{1}{2}(g_A - g_B) \frac{J_A(J_A+1) - J_B(J_B+1)}{J(J+1)} . \tag{11.95}$$

Eq. (11.95) is called the *additivity relation*.

The additivity relation simplifies considerably when $J_A = 0$ and hence $g = g_B$ with, of course, $J = J_B$. This implies that the magnetic moment remains unchanged upon adding a group of nucleons coupled to $J_A = 0$, as long as the structure of group B is not altered. It is found experimentally that the magnetic moments of states with the same J value in nuclei that differ in Z and/or N by an even, small number of nucleons indeed are often almost identical.

The additivity relation (11.95) may be useful for an estimate of one of the g-factors g_A, g_B or g if the other two are known. Assuming that the interaction between the groups A and B can be neglected, we may take for g_A and g_B the experimental g-factors of nuclei with only group A or group B coupled to a core with $J_{core} = 0$. For the application of eq. (11.95) it is not necessary that the cores are the same in the two nuclei. As an illustration some experimental g-factors and those obtained with the additivity relation are compared in table 11.1. It is seen that in these examples the semiempirical values agree very well with the experimental data.

CHAPTER 12

ALLOWED BETA DECAY

The phenomenon of nuclear beta decay is associated with an interaction that we have not yet considered in the previous chapters. The strength of this interaction is many orders of magnitude smaller than the electromagnetic interaction and is referred to as the weak interaction. Among the large number of elementary particles quite many processes caused by the weak interaction are known at present. Here we consider only the process of nuclear beta decay, which involves the proton, neutron, electron and neutrino.

Some introductory remarks on the theory of allowed beta decay, leading to Fermi and Gamow-Teller contributions, are made in sect. 12.1. The *J*, *T* and parity-selection rules for an allowed beta transition are derived in sect. 12.2. The evaluation of the matrix elements, which correspond to Fermi and Gamow-Teller contributions is given in sects. 12.3 and 12.4, respectively. The theoretical evaluation of log *ft* values is treated in sect. 12.5. Approximate relations between log *ft* values and magnetic dipole transition rates and moments are derived and illustrated with some examples in sect. 12.6.

12.1. Beta transition rates

The measured mean life of the free neutron that decays under the influence of the weak interaction into a proton, electron and antineutrino is given by $\tau_m \cong 16$ min. This long mean life of the neutron shows that the interaction causing beta emission is very weak indeed since, for example, magnetic dipole radiation of the same energy (0.78 MeV) and a strength of 1 W.u. would lead according to eq. (10.21) to a value of $\tau_m \approx 10^{-13}$ sec. A summary of the possible weak-interaction processes that involve electrons in a nucleus ${}_Z X_N$ is given in table 12.1.

An example of the first three reactions listed in table 12.1 is given in fig. 12.1. It is seen that ${}^{64}_{29}\mathrm{Cu}_{35}$ decays into ${}^{64}_{30}\mathrm{Zn}_{34} + \mathrm{e}^- + \bar{\nu}$ by β^- decay, into ${}^{64}_{28}\mathrm{Ni}_{36} + \mathrm{e}^+ + \nu$ by β^+ decay and into ${}^{64}_{28}\mathrm{Ni}_{36} + \nu$ by electron capture. When the electron is captured from the atomic K-shell, the process is referred to as K-capture. Neutrino capture is observed, e.g., in the reaction ${}^{37}_{17}\mathrm{Cl}_{20} + \nu \to {}^{37}_{18}\mathrm{Ar}_{19} + \mathrm{e}^-$. The latter reaction has been used for the detection of solar neutrinos. Antineutrinos (e.g. those produced by a reactor) can be captured by protons in the reaction $\mathrm{p} + \bar{\nu} \to \mathrm{e}^+ + \mathrm{n}$.

The electron and the neutrino are leptons, i.e. particles not partaking in the strong interaction. When, as is customary, a lepton number of +1 is assigned to the leptons (e^- and ν) and a lepton number of -1 to the antileptons (e^+ and $\bar{\nu}$) then the total lepton number in a reaction is conserved. This conservation law determines whether

Table 12.1
Weak interaction processes in nuclei

${}_Z X_N \rightarrow {}_{Z+1}X_{N-1} + e^- + \bar{\nu}$	β^- decay
${}_Z X_N \rightarrow {}_{Z-1}X_{N+1} + e^+ + \nu$	β^+ decay
${}_Z X_N + e^- \rightarrow {}_{Z-1}X_{N+1} + \nu$	electron capture
${}_Z X_N + \nu \rightarrow {}_{Z+1}X_{N-1} + e^-$; ${}_Z X_N + \bar{\nu} \rightarrow {}_{Z-1}X_{N+1} + e^+$	neutrino capture or inverse β-decay

in the reactions listed in table 12.1 a neutrino or antineutrino occurs. Since the relevant interaction is very weak, it is quite justified to use first-order perturbation theory for the calculation of transition rates.

The foundations of the theory of beta decay were laid down originally by Fermi [Fermi (1934)]. The description of nuclear beta decay has not changed essentially, except for the modifications necessary since the discovery of parity non-conservation for the weak interaction in 1957. The theory is based on the formal analogy which one can establish with the description of the electromagnetic interaction, i.e. the product of the nuclear charge-current density and the electromagnetic potentials, as given in eq. (9.1).

The data on the weak interaction can adequately be described by a Hamiltonian that is composed of a nucleon charge-current and a lepton charge-current [Wu and

DECAY MODES OF THE ^{64}Cu GROUND STATE

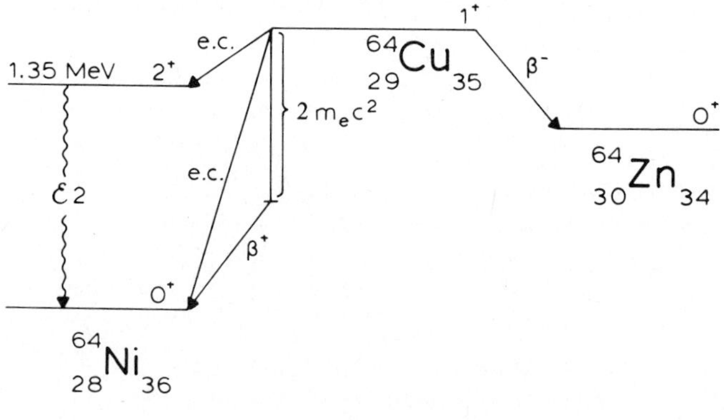

Fig. 12.1. The decay of the $J^\pi = 1^+$ ground state of ^{64}Cu takes place via each of the first three weak-interaction processes listed in table 12.1. One has observed β^- decay to the $J^\pi = 0^+$ ground state of ^{64}Zn, β^+ decay and electron capture (e.c.) to the $J^\pi = 0^+$ ground state of ^{64}Ni and electron capture to the first excited state in ^{64}Ni.

Moszkowski (1966); Roy and Nigam (1967)]. The interaction Hamiltonian thus constructed still contains a number of coefficients measuring the relative strengths of the various forms of coupling. From the requirements of relativistic invariance and parity nonconservation one can deduce that in fact there are ten complex coefficients. This number is reduced appreciably as soon as one requires the theory to be invariant under the operation of time reflection and when one takes into account the experimental electron-neutrino angular correlations as well as the observed polarization of the electrons emitted in beta-decay. Then it turns out that the theory of beta-decay needs only two real coupling constants, i.e. G_V associated with the vector part of the charge-current and G_A associated with the axial-vector part of the charge-current. The constants G_V and G_A must be evaluated empirically from experimental data on beta decay. The procedures to evaluate these constants are discussed in sect. 12.5.

In lowest order of approximation the nucleons are considered to be nonrelativistic particles and the lepton wave functions are evaluated at the origin $r = 0$. The resulting expressions describe the so-called allowed beta transitions. They are characterized by the selection rules that are discussed in the next section. If the assumption of nonrelativistic nucleons is dropped (i.e. also the small components of the wave functions are considered) and the variation of the lepton wave functions over the nuclear volume is taken into account, one obtains the so-called forbidden transition amplitudes. The strengths for forbidden transitions are considerably smaller than for the allowed transitions. One can show that in the approximation of allowed transitions the vector part of the interaction reduces to the nuclear matrix element of the unit operator **1** and the axial-vector part to the nuclear matrix element of the Pauli spin operator $\boldsymbol{\sigma}$. This concerns the coordinate space part of the operator only, which is thus seen to be independent of the position coordinates. For the forbidden transitions, though, the operators are not so simple and, moreover, one has to evaluate radial matrix elements.

As in a beta transition a neutron is converted into a proton (or *vice versa*) an isospin raising or lowering operator must also be present. It has been shown in sect. 2.3 that the operators $t_{\pm} = \frac{1}{2}(\tau_x \pm i\tau_y)$ bring about these conversions. Thus one has

$$t_+\phi_p = \phi_n\,, \qquad t_+\phi_n = 0\,, \qquad t_-\phi_p = 0\,, \qquad t_-\phi_n = \phi_p\,, \tag{12.1}$$

where ϕ_p and ϕ_n denote single-proton and single-neutron states, respectively. The operator t_- describes β^- decay and t_+ describes β^+ decay, since customarily the initial wave function is written on the right-hand side in a matrix element.

Both the vector and the axial-vector interaction may contribute simultaneously. Hence the beta transition probability $T(\beta)$ depends on two different nuclear matrix elements and can be written as

$$T(\beta) \propto G_V^2 \langle M_F \rangle^2 + G_A^2 \langle M_{GT} \rangle^2\,, \tag{12.2}$$

where G_V and G_A are the coupling constants mentioned before. The matrix elements

$\langle M_\mathrm{F}\rangle$ (also denoted as $\int 1$ or $\langle 1\rangle$) and $\langle M_\mathrm{GT}\rangle$ (also denoted as $\int \boldsymbol{\sigma}$ or $\langle\boldsymbol{\sigma}\rangle$) are referred to as the Fermi and Gamow-Teller matrix elements, respectively, after the physicists who first suggested them. It can be shown that no interference term between vector and axial-vector interaction occurs.

When the initial nucleus is unpolarized one should in eq. (12.2) average $\langle M_\mathrm{F}\rangle^2$ and $\langle M_\mathrm{GT}\rangle^2$ over the different possible orientations of the initial nucleus. Similarly one must sum over the unobserved magnetic quantum numbers of the final nucleus. The square of the Fermi matrix element is then defined by

$$\langle M_\mathrm{F}\rangle^2 = \frac{1}{2J_\mathrm{i}+1}\sum_{M_\mathrm{i}M_\mathrm{f}} \langle J_\mathrm{f}M_\mathrm{f}T_\mathrm{f}T_\mathrm{fz}|1\sum_{k=1}^{A} t_\pm(k)|J_\mathrm{i}M_\mathrm{i}T_\mathrm{i}T_\mathrm{iz}\rangle^2$$

$$= \langle J_\mathrm{f}MT_\mathrm{f}T_\mathrm{fz}|1\sum_{k=1}^{A} t_\pm(k)|J_\mathrm{i}MT_iT_\mathrm{iz}\rangle^2 \qquad (12.3)$$

with f and i labelling final and initial states, respectively. The operation $(2J_\mathrm{i}+1)^{-1}$ $\Sigma_{M_\mathrm{i}M_\mathrm{f}}$ does not affect the Fermi matrix element in eq. (12.3), because the coordinate space operator 1 is a scalar, thus yielding nonvanishing contributions only for $M = M_\mathrm{i} = M_\mathrm{f}$ independent of M.

The square of the Gamow-Teller matrix element is defined by

$$\langle M_\mathrm{GT}\rangle^2 = \frac{1}{2J_\mathrm{i}+1}\sum_{qM_\mathrm{i}M_\mathrm{f}} |\langle J_\mathrm{f}M_\mathrm{f}T_\mathrm{f}T_\mathrm{fz}|\sum_{k=1}^{A} \sigma_q(k)t_\pm(k)|J_\mathrm{i}M_\mathrm{i}T_\mathrm{i}T_\mathrm{iz}\rangle|^2 . \qquad (12.4)$$

Since the spin operator appears in eq. (12.4) in its cartesian components $\sigma_q = \{\sigma_x, \sigma_y, \sigma_z\}$, this expression is not convenient for further reduction with the Wigner-Eckart theorem. After substitution of the spherical components $\sigma_m = \{\sigma_{-1}, \sigma_0, \sigma_{+1}\}$ with (cf. eq. (A.2.8))

$$\sigma_x = \sqrt{\tfrac{1}{2}}(\sigma_{-1} - \sigma_{+1}) , \qquad \sigma_y = \mathrm{i}\sqrt{\tfrac{1}{2}}(\sigma_{-1} + \sigma_{+1}) , \qquad \sigma_z = \sigma_0 , \qquad (12.5)$$

one finds the equivalent expression

$$\langle M_\mathrm{GT}\rangle^2 = \frac{1}{2J_\mathrm{i}+1}\sum_{mM_\mathrm{i}M_\mathrm{f}} |\langle J_\mathrm{f}M_\mathrm{f}T_\mathrm{f}T_\mathrm{fz}|\sum_{k=1}^{A} \sigma_m(k)t_\pm(k)|J_\mathrm{i}M_\mathrm{i}T_\mathrm{i}T_\mathrm{iz}\rangle|^2 . \qquad (12.6)$$

12.2. Selection rules

The coordinate space part of the Fermi transition operator in the matrix element (12.3) is the unit operator and thus does not change the spin. Moreover, a scalar operator does not change sign under the parity operation. Hence the operator for a

Fermi transition, given by $\Sigma_k t_\pm(k) = T_\pm$, affects only the orientation (i.e. the projection T_z) of the isospin (cf. eq. (2.63)) and consequently one obtains the selection rules

$$\Delta J = 0\,, \qquad \Delta T = 0\,, \qquad \Pi_\mathrm{i} = \Pi_\mathrm{f}\,, \qquad \text{for a Fermi transition}\,, \tag{12.7}$$

where Π_i and Π_f denote the parity of initial and final state, respectively.

The coordinate space part of the Gamow-Teller transition operator in the matrix element (12.6) is the spin operator $\boldsymbol{\sigma}$, which does not change sign under the parity operation. The spin and isospin selection rules for a Gamow-Teller transition follow directly after application of the Wigner-Eckart theorem to both coordinate space and isospace parts of the matrix elements. Therefore it is necessary to employ the spherical components $\tau_{\pm 1} = 2t_{\pm 1} = \mp\sqrt{2}t_\pm$ (see eqs. (2.53), (2.54) and (A.2.8)). One thus rewrites eq. (12.6) as

$$\langle M_\mathrm{GT}\rangle^2 = \frac{1}{2J_\mathrm{i}+1}\sum_{M_\mathrm{i}M_\mathrm{f}m} \langle J_\mathrm{f}M_\mathrm{f}T_\mathrm{f}T_\mathrm{fz}|\sum_{k=1}^{A} \sigma_m(k)t_\pm(k)|J_\mathrm{i}M_\mathrm{i}T_\mathrm{i}T_\mathrm{iz}\rangle^2$$

$$= \frac{1}{2(2J_\mathrm{i}+1)}\sum_{M_\mathrm{i}M_\mathrm{f}m}\left\{\frac{\langle J_\mathrm{i}M_\mathrm{i}1m|J_\mathrm{f}M_\mathrm{f}\rangle}{\sqrt{2J_\mathrm{f}+1}}\,\frac{\langle T_\mathrm{i}T_\mathrm{iz}1\pm 1|T_\mathrm{f}T_\mathrm{fz}\rangle}{\sqrt{2T_\mathrm{f}+1}}\langle J_\mathrm{f}T_\mathrm{f}|||\sum_{k=1}^{A}\boldsymbol{\sigma}(k)\boldsymbol{\tau}(k)|||J_\mathrm{i}T_\mathrm{i}\rangle\right\}^2$$

$$= \frac{\langle T_\mathrm{i}T_\mathrm{iz}1\pm 1|T_\mathrm{f}T_\mathrm{fz}\rangle^2}{2(2J_\mathrm{i}+1)(2T_\mathrm{f}+1)}\langle J_\mathrm{f}T_\mathrm{f}|||\sum_{k=1}^{A}\boldsymbol{\sigma}(k)\boldsymbol{\tau}(k)|||J_\mathrm{i}T_\mathrm{i}\rangle^2\,. \tag{12.8}$$

From the Clebsch-Gordan coefficients in this expression and conservation of parity one obtains the selection rules

$$\Delta J = 0 \text{ or } 1 \; (\text{no } J_\mathrm{i} = 0 \to J_\mathrm{f} = 0)\,,$$

$$\Delta T = 0 \text{ or } 1 \text{ and } \Pi_\mathrm{i} = \Pi_\mathrm{f}\,, \qquad \text{for a Gamow-Teller transition.} \tag{12.9}$$

The J-selection rules given in eqs. (12.7) and (12.9) can also be obtained when one thinks of the beta-decay process as a reaction in which an electron and a neutrino are emitted. The conservation of angular momentum is then given by

$$\boldsymbol{J}_\mathrm{i} = \boldsymbol{J}_\mathrm{f} + \boldsymbol{L}_{\mathrm{e}\nu} + \boldsymbol{S}_{\mathrm{e}\nu}\,, \tag{12.10}$$

where $\boldsymbol{J}_\mathrm{i}$ and $\boldsymbol{J}_\mathrm{f}$ denote the nuclear initial and final spin, respectively. The symbols $\boldsymbol{L}_{\mathrm{e}\nu}$ and $\boldsymbol{S}_{\mathrm{e}\nu}$ denote the total orbital angular momentum and spin, respectively, of the emitted electron-neutrino pair. In allowed beta decay only $L_{\mathrm{e}\nu} = 0$ appears. Since both leptons possess intrinsic spin $s = \frac{1}{2}$, one has either $S_{\mathrm{e}\nu} = 0$ or 1. A Fermi transition corresponds to the situation, where the spins of the leptons are antiparallel and thus are in a singlet state ($S_{\mathrm{e}\nu} = 0$). This leads to the selection rule $\Delta J = 0$. For a Gamow-Teller transition the intrinsic spins of the emitted leptons are parallel. They are thus in a triplet state ($S_{e\nu} = 1$) from which the relation $J_i = J_f + 1$ follows, which leads to the selection rules given above.

Since the orbital angular momenta of the nucleons are not affected in allowed beta decay, it follows that no nucleon can make the single-particle transition $l_i j_i \to l_f j_f$ with $l_i \neq l_f$. Thus e.g. a $2s_{1/2} \to 1d_{3/2}$ transition is forbidden, whereas a $1d_{5/2} \to 1d_{3/2}$ transition is possible.

12.3. Fermi matrix elements

It was seen in eq. (12.3) that the Fermi transitions are described by the operator

$$1 \sum_{k=1}^{A} t_\pm(k) = 1T_\pm = 1(T_x \pm iT_y)\,, \tag{12.11}$$

i.e. the unit operator in coordinate space and the raising or lowering operator for the total isospin. As the nuclear wave functions are assumed to be eigenfunctions of the isospin, the nonvanishing many-body Fermi matrix element can be evaluated with the use of eq. (2.69)

$$\begin{aligned}\langle JMTT_{fz}|1 \sum_{k=1}^{A} t_\pm(k)|JMTT_{iz}\rangle &= \sqrt{(T \mp T_{iz})(T \pm T_{iz}+1)}\\ &= \sqrt{T(T+1) - T_{iz}T_{fz}} \qquad \text{for } \beta^\pm \text{ decay}\,.\end{aligned} \tag{12.12}$$

Thus the square of the Fermi matrix element is found to be given by

$$\langle M_F\rangle^2 = T(T+1) - T_{iz}T_{fz}\,, \tag{12.13}$$

provided that the initial and final states are *analogue states* with $J_f = J_i$, $T_f = T_i$ and $T_{fz} = T_{iz} \pm 1$. Otherwise the Fermi matrix element vanishes. Note that expression (12.13) is completely independent of the coordinate space part of the initial- and final-state wave functions and thus is model independent as long as isospin is a good quantum number.

Application of eq. (12.13) to the decay of the free neutron leads to the value

$$\langle M_F\rangle^2_{\text{free neutron}} = 1\,. \tag{12.14}$$

12.4. Gamow-Teller matrix elements

The Gamow-Teller matrix element (12.6) cannot be expressed directly in terms of the total isospin T, as could be done with the Fermi matrix element (see eq. (12.13)). This is a consequence of the fact that the summation over the particle label

k in $t_\pm(k)$ cannot be performed because of the combination of two operators, $t_\pm(k)$ and $\boldsymbol{\sigma}(k)$. Except in the case of the decay of the free neutron, where only one nucleon is involved, one finds as a simple application of the general expression (12.8) by the aid of eq. (A.3.c9) with $\boldsymbol{\sigma} = 2\mathbf{s}$

$$\langle M_{\rm GT}\rangle^2_{\rm free\,neutron} = \tfrac{1}{2}\langle \tfrac{1}{2}\,\tfrac{1}{2}1 - 1|\tfrac{1}{2} - \tfrac{1}{2}\rangle^2 \langle \tfrac{1}{2}\,\tfrac{1}{2}|||\mathbf{s}\boldsymbol{\tau}|||\tfrac{1}{2}\,\tfrac{1}{2}\rangle^2 = 3\,. \tag{12.15}$$

For the evaluation of the Gamow-Teller matrix element (12.8) for many-particle states in general, the same methods should be employed that were used in sects. 10.5 and 10.6 for the matrix elements of electromagnetic transition operators. Thus, for instance, when initial and final states are described by n active particles in only one orbit ρ, one finds with the same methods as used for the derivation of eq. (10.77),

$$\langle \rho^n \Gamma_{\rm f} ||| \sum_{k=1}^{n} \boldsymbol{\sigma}(k)\boldsymbol{\tau}(k) ||| \rho^n \Gamma_{\rm i}\rangle$$

$$= n\sum_{\epsilon} \langle \rho^n \Gamma_{\rm f}|\}\rho^{n-1}\epsilon\rangle\langle \rho^n \Gamma_{\rm i}|\}\rho^{n-1}\epsilon\rangle(-1)^{\epsilon+\rho+\Gamma_{\rm f}}\sqrt{(2\Gamma_{\rm f}+1)(2\Gamma_{\rm i}+1)}\begin{Bmatrix}\rho & \rho & 1\\ \Gamma_{\rm i} & \Gamma_{\rm f} & \epsilon\end{Bmatrix}$$

$$\times\, \langle \rho |||\boldsymbol{\sigma\tau}||| \rho\rangle\,. \tag{12.16}$$

Note that the operator $\boldsymbol{\sigma\tau}$ is of rank one in coordinate space and in isospace.

We are now left with a discussion of the reduced single-particle matrix elements

$$\langle l_{\rm f} j_{\rm f} t = \tfrac{1}{2} |||\boldsymbol{\sigma\tau}||| l_{\rm i} j_{\rm i} t = \tfrac{1}{2}\rangle = \langle l_{\rm f} j_{\rm f} \|\boldsymbol{\sigma}\| l_{\rm i} j_{\rm i}\rangle \langle t = \tfrac{1}{2} \|\boldsymbol{\tau}\| t = \tfrac{1}{2}\rangle\,.$$

The values of the reduced matrix elements given above follow from eqs. (10.52) and (10.63) and the result is given by

$$\langle l_{\rm f} j_{\rm f} t = \tfrac{1}{2} |||\boldsymbol{\sigma\tau}||| l_{\rm i} j_{\rm i} t = \tfrac{1}{2}\rangle =$$

$$= (-1)^{l_{\rm f}+j_{\rm f}+3/2}\, 6\sqrt{(2j_{\rm f}+1)(2j_{\rm i}+1)}\begin{Bmatrix}\tfrac{1}{2} & \tfrac{1}{2} & 1\\ j_{\rm i} & j_{\rm f} & l_{\rm f}\end{Bmatrix}\delta_{l_{\rm i} l_{\rm f}}\,. \tag{12.17}$$

Insertion of this single-particle matrix element into expression (12.16) thus leads to the matrix element of $\boldsymbol{\sigma\tau}$ for a ρ^n configuration. Similarly eqs. (10.92) and (10.105) can be used for two-orbit configurations.

One can use expression (12.17) also to derive a simple expression for $\langle M_{\rm GT}\rangle^2$ in case one considers an inert core with $J = 0$, $T = 0$ and a single active nucleon. We then assume that in the beta-decay process the single nucleon makes a transition $lj_{\rm i} \to lj_{\rm f}$. Inserting eq. (12.17) into eq. (12.8) one obtains the extreme single-particle

Table 12.2
Values of $\langle M_{\mathrm{GT}}\rangle^2$ in the extreme single-particle description for $lj_{\mathrm{i}} \xrightarrow{\beta} lj_{\mathrm{f}}$

j_{f} \ j_{i}	$l+\frac{1}{2}$	$l-\frac{1}{2}$
$l+\frac{1}{2}$	$\dfrac{j_{\mathrm{f}}+1}{j_{\mathrm{f}}}$	$\dfrac{2j_{\mathrm{f}}+1}{j_{\mathrm{f}}}$
$l-\frac{1}{2}$	$\dfrac{2j_{\mathrm{f}}+1}{j_{\mathrm{f}}+1}$	$\dfrac{j_{\mathrm{f}}}{j_{\mathrm{f}}+1}$

estimate

$$\langle M_{\mathrm{GT}}\rangle^2_{\mathrm{s.p.}} = 6(2j_{\mathrm{f}}+1)\begin{Bmatrix} \frac{1}{2} & \frac{1}{2} & 1 \\ j_{\mathrm{i}} & j_{\mathrm{f}} & l \end{Bmatrix}^2 , \tag{12.18}$$

since the square of the Clebsch-Gordan coefficient in eq. (12.8) assumes the value $\frac{2}{3}$. The explicit values for this single-particle estimate with the value of the 6-j symbol given in eq. (A.1.b14) are summarized in table 12.2. These values may deviate considerably from the observed values, since the assumption of only one active particle being responsible for the beta transition is quite naive.

12.5. Log *ft* values

Beta-transition probabilities are calculated, just like electromagnetic transition probabilities, in terms of perturbation theory. For given momenta of the emitted leptons the transition probability is proportional to the volume of the available phase space. This determines the shape of the beta spectrum. The total beta-decay rate of one nuclear state into another is obtained after integration over the spectrum of the electron energy. This results in the dependence of the transition strength on the maximum available energy for the decay process, i.e. the energy difference between initial and final nuclear states. As a result one obtains for the decay rate

$$T(\beta^{\pm}) = \frac{m^5c^4}{2\pi^3\hbar^7} f^{\pm}(Z, W_0)[G_{\mathrm{V}}^2\langle M_{\mathrm{F}}\rangle^2 + G_{\mathrm{A}}^2\langle M_{\mathrm{GT}}\rangle^2] , \tag{12.19}$$

where the dimensionless function $f^{\pm}(Z, W_0)$ describes the dependence on the nuclear charge Ze and the available energy W_0. The coupling constants G_{V} and G_{A} determine the strength of the weak interaction. Beta-decay rates are usually quoted in terms of their log ft value, rather than as the transition probability $T(\beta)$. From eq. (12.19) one finds for the comparative half life, i.e. the product of the statistical function $f^{\pm}(Z, W_0)$ (the ± sign is omitted from now on) and the actual half life t with

$t = \tau_m \ln 2$, the expression

$$f(Z, W_0)t = f(Z, W_0)\frac{\ln 2}{T(\beta)} = \frac{K}{G_V^2\langle M_F\rangle^2 + G_A^2\langle M_{GT}\rangle^2}, \qquad (12.20)$$

where the constant factor is given by

$$K = 2\pi^3\hbar^7 \ln 2/m^5c^4 = 1.231 \times 10^{-94}\ \mathrm{erg}^2\cdot\mathrm{cm}^6\cdot\mathrm{sec}\,. \qquad (12.21)$$

As the comparative half lives ft vary over several orders of magnitude, it is customary to quote the ^{10} logarithm of ft (expressed in seconds). For the allowed transitions the log ft values are mostly in the range 3 to 6, while higher values correspond to the forbidden transitions. The dependence of the latter on the nuclear wave functions involves the matrix elements of operators more complicated than 1 and $\boldsymbol{\sigma}$. The statistical function $f(Z, W_0)$ has been computed [Wilkinson and Macefield (1974)] with corrections applied for finite nuclear size and screening by the atomic electrons.

The coupling constants G_V and G_A can be obtained from the experimental data as follows. The Gamow-Teller matrix element does not contribute to $J_i = 0 \to J_f = 0$ transitions. Eq. (12.20) can then be written as

$$ft = \frac{K}{G_V^2\langle M_F\rangle^2} \qquad \text{for} \qquad J_i = J_f = 0\,. \qquad (12.22)$$

Eq. (12.22) leads to a determination of G_V^2 from $J^\pi = 0^+ \to J^\pi = 0^+$ transitions between members of a $T = 1$ multiplet with $\langle M_F\rangle^2 = 2$ according to eq. (12.13). The ft-value that can be derived from the experimental data after application of several corrections is given as [Hardy and Towner (1975)]

$$ft = 3081.7 \pm 1.9\ \mathrm{sec} \qquad \text{for} \qquad J_i^\pi = J_f^\pi = 0^+ \text{ and } T_i = T_f = 1\,. \qquad (12.23)$$

A slightly different value is given in [Raman, Walkiewicz and Behrens (1975)]. The difference is due to another choice for the Coulomb correction. Inserting the experimental ft-value given in eq. (12.23) and the model independent matrix element $\langle M_F\rangle^2 = 2$ into eq. (12.22) one obtains

$$\frac{K}{G_V^2} = 2ft(0^+ \to 0^+) = 6163\ \mathrm{sec}\,. \qquad (12.24)$$

Thus eq. (12.20) can be rewritten as

$$ft = \frac{6163}{\langle M_F\rangle^2 + \left(\dfrac{G_A}{G_V}\right)^2 \langle M_{GT}\rangle^2}\ \mathrm{sec}\,. \qquad (12.25)$$

The ratio $(G_A/G_V)^2$ can now be obtained, for example, from the experimentally determined ft-values for the neutron decay. In this case one finds from eq. (12.14) the value $\langle M_F \rangle^2 = 1$ and from eq. (12.15) the value $\langle M_{GT} \rangle^2 = 3$. Together with the experimentally determined ft-value for neutron decay given by $ft = 1098 \pm 16$ sec. this leads to $(G_A/G_V)^2 = 1.54$. An estimate of $(G_A/G_V)^2$ from odd-mass nuclei with $11 \leqslant A \leqslant 21$ [Wilkinson (1973)] leads to a ratio of the coupling constants given by $(G_A/G_V)^2 \approx 1.27$, which is considerably smaller than the value obtained from the neutron decay.

This reduction of the ratio G_A/G_V, applied to obtain an effective value for the coupling constants for a many-nucleon system, is another example of a renormalization of transition operators. In chapter 9 we have discussed that, because of the nucleon-nucleon interaction, the impulse approximation may not be strictly valid for the electromagnetic transition operators. Similarly here for beta transitions one may expect that the exchange of mesons in a many-nucleon system will affect the coupling constants compared to their value for free nucleons. According to the theory of the weak interaction the hypothesis of the conserved vector current (see e.g., [Wu and Moskowski (1966)]) implies that the coupling constant for the vector current G_V is not changed. The axial current, though, is not conserved and thus the Gamow-Teller decay rates are expected to be affected. If it is assumed that this change can be described adequately by a renormalized coupling constant, one is led to such a reduced value of $(G_A/G_V)^2$. We shall adopt the value

$$(G_A/G_V)^2 = 1.4 , \tag{12.26}$$

which is the average of the values $(G_A/G_V)^2 = 1.54$ and 1.27 discussed above.

It should be remarked that the value given in eq. (12.26) is usually good enough in view of the accuracy in present experimental ft-values and theoretically calculated Gamow-Teller contributions. Substitution of eq. (12.26) into eq. (12.25) thus leads to the final expression

$$ft = \frac{6163}{\langle M_F \rangle^2 + 1.4 \langle M_{GT} \rangle^2} \text{ sec} . \tag{12.27}$$

12.6. Beta decay and the magnetic dipole interaction

Consider states of the nuclei ${}_Z A_N$ and ${}_{Z\pm 1}A_{N\mp 1}$ that are members of an isobaric multiplet. Let $\Psi_1(J_1T_1)$ and $\Psi_1'(J_1T_1)$ denote the corresponding wave functions, i.e. they are analogue states, and let $\Psi_2(J_2T_2)$ be the wave function of another state in the nucleus ${}_Z A_N$ (see fig. 12.2). In this section we derive some approximate relations between the ft-value for the decay $\Psi_1' \xrightarrow{\beta} \Psi_2$ and the $\mathcal{M}1$ strength for the decay $\Psi_2 \xrightarrow{\gamma} \Psi_1$.

The relation between the ft-value and the $\mathcal{M}1$ strength results from the fact that both involve the reduced matrix elements of the operator $\boldsymbol{\sigma}$. For pure Gamow-Tel-

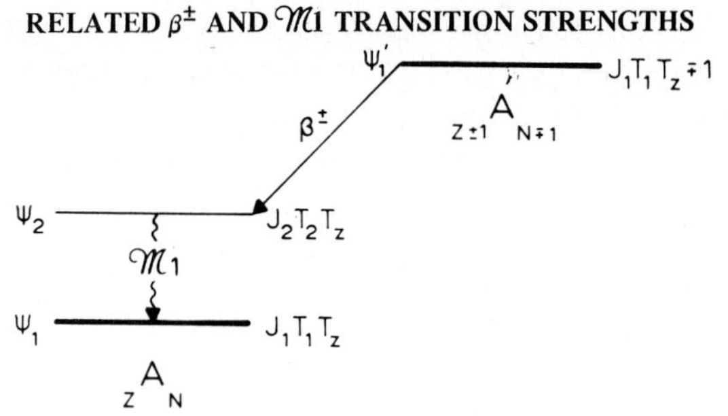

Fig. 12.2. The states Ψ_1 and Ψ'_1 (indicated by bold lines) are assumed to be analogue states. The lifetime of the state Ψ_2 and the ft-value for the β^+ transition $\Psi'_1 \to \Psi_2$ are roughly related by eq. (12.34a), if the lifetime is assumed to be determined mainly by the $\mathcal{M}1$ transition strength.

ler transitions one obtains, according to eqs. (12.8) and (12.27),

$$ft = \frac{6163 \text{ sec}}{1.4\langle M_{\text{GT}}\rangle^2} = \frac{8.8 \times 10^3 (2J_1+1)(2T_2+1)}{\left[\langle T_1 T'_z 1 \pm 1 | T_2 T_z\rangle \langle \Psi_2 ||| \sum_{k=1}^{A} \boldsymbol{\sigma}(k)\boldsymbol{\tau}(k) ||| \Psi'_1\rangle\right]^2} \text{ sec}. \tag{12.28}$$

One can thus express the reduced matrix element in terms of an ft-value (substituting $\boldsymbol{\sigma} = 2\boldsymbol{s}$) as

$$\langle \Psi_2 ||| \sum_{k=1}^{A} \boldsymbol{s}(k)\boldsymbol{\tau}(k) ||| \Psi'_1\rangle^2 = \frac{(2J_1+1)(2T_2+1)}{\langle T_1 T'_z 1 \pm 1 | T_2 T_z\rangle^2} \frac{2.2 \times 10^3 \text{ sec}}{ft}. \tag{12.29}$$

The reduced transition rate $B(\overline{\omega}L)$ given in eq. (9.106) contains an isoscalar and an isovector part. For $\mathcal{M}1$ transitions the latter is expected to be most important (cf. eq. (10.31)). Making the assumption that the isoscalar contribution may be neglected completely, one obtains (see e.g. eqs. (10.25) and (10.26)), inserting the g-factors given in eqs. (10.66) and (10.67),

$$B(\mathcal{M}1) \approx \frac{3}{4\pi} \frac{\langle T_2 T_z 1 0 | T_1 T_z\rangle^2}{(2J_2+1)(2T_1+1)}$$

$$\times \left[\tfrac{1}{2}(g_{\text{p}}^{l} - g_{\text{n}}^{l})\langle \Psi_1 ||| \sum_{k=1}^{A} \boldsymbol{l}(k)\boldsymbol{\tau}(k) ||| \Psi_2\rangle + \tfrac{1}{2}(g_{\text{p}}^{s} - g_{\text{n}}^{s})\langle \Psi_1 ||| \sum_{k=1}^{A} \boldsymbol{s}(k)\boldsymbol{\tau}(k) ||| \Psi_2\rangle\right]^2 \mu_{\text{N}}^2$$

$$\approx \frac{5.3\langle T_2 T_z 1 0 | T_1 T_z\rangle^2}{(2J_2+1)(2T_1+1)} \langle \Psi_1 ||| \sum_{k=1}^{A} \boldsymbol{s}(k)\boldsymbol{\tau}(k) ||| \Psi_2\rangle^2 \mu_{\text{N}}^2 . \tag{12.30}$$

For the last step an additional approximation is made by assuming that, due to the smallness of the ratio $(g_\mathrm{p}^l - g_\mathrm{n}^l)/(g_\mathrm{p}^s - g_\mathrm{n}^s) \approx 0.1$, the contribution of the orbital matrix element $\langle l\tau\rangle$ can be ignored in this crude estimate.

Since $\Psi_1(J_1T_1)$ and $\Psi_1'(J_1, T_1)$ are taken to be analogue states one has the relation

$$\langle\Psi_2 ||| \sum_{k=1}^{A} s(k)\tau(k) ||| \Psi_1'\rangle^2 = \langle\Psi_2 ||| \sum_{k=1}^{A} s(k)\tau(k) ||| \Psi_1\rangle^2 = \langle\Psi_1 ||| \sum_{k=1}^{A} s(k)\tau(k) ||| \Psi_2\rangle^2 , \tag{12.31}$$

where for the last step eq. (A.3.b5) has been used. From eqs. (12.29), (12.30) and (12.31) one obtains the desired relation

$$\frac{B(\mathcal{M}1)}{\mu_\mathrm{N}^2} \approx 1.17 \times 10^4 \frac{(2J_1+1)(2T_2+1)}{(2J_2+1)(2T_1+1)} \frac{\langle T_2T_z10|T_1T_z\rangle^2}{\langle T_1T_z'1 \pm 1|T_2T_z\rangle^2} \frac{\mathrm{sec}}{ft} , \tag{12.32}$$

where $B(\mathcal{M}1)/\mu_\mathrm{N}^2$ denotes the reduced $\mathcal{M}1$ transition rate expressed in (nuclear magneton)^2 and similarly ft/sec the ft-value expressed in seconds.

Let us assume that the lifetime of the state Ψ_2 is completely determined by the $\mathcal{M}1$ transition strength to the state Ψ_1 (see fig. 12.2). One then finds from eqs. (10.21) and (10.9a) the relation between the lifetime τ_m and the reduced transition rate $B(\mathcal{M}1)$

$$\frac{\tau_\mathrm{m}}{\mathrm{fs}} = 56\left(\frac{\mathrm{MeV}}{E_\gamma}\right)^3 \frac{\mu_\mathrm{N}^2}{B(\mathcal{M}1)} . \tag{12.33}$$

Combining eqs. (12.32) and (12.33) one obtains an approximate relation between the lifetime of the state Ψ_2 and the ft-value for the decay $\Psi_1' \to \Psi_2$ (see fig. 12.2)

$$\frac{\tau_\mathrm{m}}{\mathrm{fs}} \approx 4.8 \times 10^{-3} \frac{(2J_2+1)(2T_1+1)}{(2J_1+1)(2T_2+1)} \left(\frac{\langle T_1T_{1z}'1 \pm 1|T_2T_{2z}\rangle}{\langle T_2T_{2z}10|T_1T_{1z}\rangle}\right)^2 \left(\frac{\mathrm{MeV}}{E_\gamma}\right)^3 \frac{ft}{\mathrm{sec}} . \tag{12.34a}$$

When the initial states for both beta and gamma decay are the analogue states $\Psi_1(J_1T_1)$ and $\Psi_1'(J_1T_1)$, which decay to the same final state $\Psi_2(J_2T_2)$, one derives along the same lines (see fig. 12.3)

$$\frac{\tau_\mathrm{m}}{\mathrm{fs}} \approx 4.8 \times 10^{-3} \left(\frac{\langle T_1T_{1z}'1 \pm 1|T_2T_{2z}\rangle}{\langle T_1T_{1z}10|T_2T_{2z}\rangle}\right)^2 \left(\frac{\mathrm{MeV}}{E_\gamma}\right)^3 \frac{ft}{\mathrm{sec}} . \tag{12.34b}$$

Note that the spin and isospin weighting factors appearing in eq. (12.34a) are absent from eq. (12.34b), since in the latter case the initial as well as the final spins are the same for both beta and gamma decay.

Summarizing the conditions that led to the relations (12.34), one has

RELATED $\beta^{\pm}$ AND $\mathcal{M}1$ TRANSITION STRENGTHS

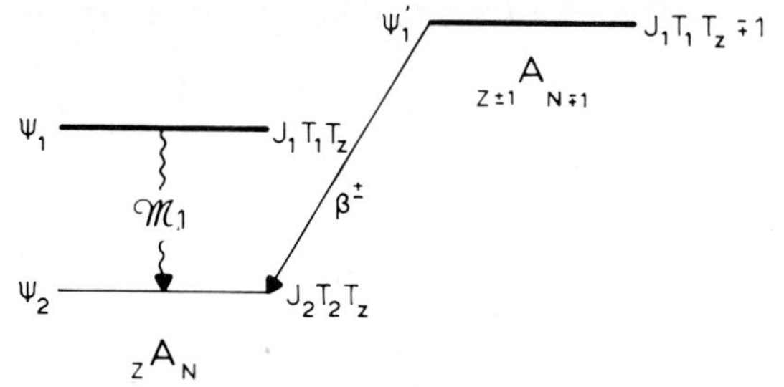

Fig. 12.3. The initial states for β-decay and $\mathcal{M}1$ radiation, i.e. Ψ'_1 and Ψ_1, respectively, are assumed to be analogue states (bold lines). The lifetime of the state Ψ_1 and the *ft*-value for the $\beta^{\pm}$ transition $\Psi'_1 \to \Psi_2$ are roughly related by eq. (12.34b), if the lifetime is assumed to be determined mainly by the $\mathcal{M}1$ transition strength.

(i) The beta and $\mathcal{M}1$ transitions involve two analogue states (see figs. 12.2 and 12.3).

(ii) The Fermi matrix element does not contribute.

(iii) The gamma decay proceeds via a pure $\mathcal{M}1$ transition.

(iv) The only contribution to the $\mathcal{M}1$ strength derives from the matrix element $\langle \boldsymbol{\sigma\tau} \rangle$, i.e. the isoscalar contributions as well as the isovector orbital contributions are neglected.

Let us illustrate relation (12.34b) by applying it to the $A = 30$ situation shown in fig. 12.4. In this example all the conditions mentioned above are met exactly, except for the neglect of the isovector orbital contribution to the $\mathcal{M}1$ strength. The β^+ decay of ${}^{30}_{16}S_{14}$ to the ${}^{30}_{15}P_{15}$ ground state corresponds with the $\mathcal{M}1$ decay of the $J^{\pi} = 0^+$, $T = 1$ state at $E_x = 0.68$ MeV. Application of eq. (12.34b) with the values

RELATED β^+ AND $\mathcal{M}1$ TRANSITION STRENGTHS IN $A = 30$ NUCLEI

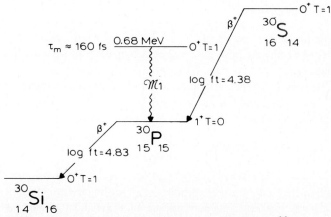

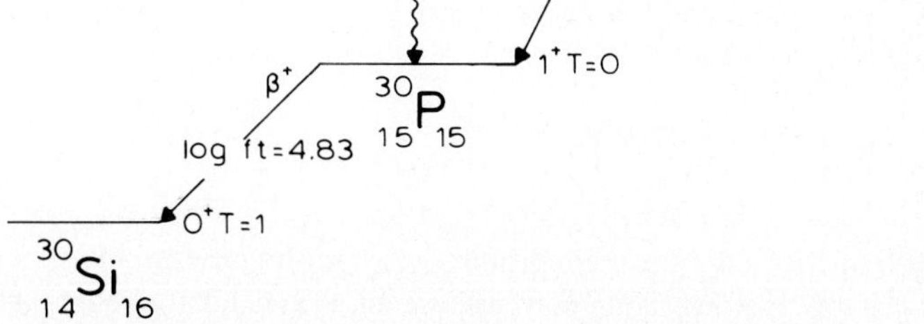

Fig. 12.4. An estimate of the lifetime of the state at $E_x = 0.68$ MeV in ${}^{30}P$ can be obtained with eq. (12.35) from the *ft*-values of the β^+ decay of ${}^{30}S$ and ${}^{30}P$.

$T_1 = 1, T_2 = T_{2z} = T_{1z} = 0$ and $T'_{1z} = -1$ and substitution of the vector coupling coefficients $\langle 1\ -1\ 1+1|00\rangle^2 = \frac{1}{3}$ and $\langle 1010|00\rangle^2 = \frac{1}{3}$ lead to the relation

$$\frac{\tau_m}{\text{fs}} \approx 4.8 \times 10^{-3} \left(\frac{\text{MeV}}{E_\gamma}\right)^3 \frac{ft}{\text{sec}} . \tag{12.35}$$

From the measured value $\log ft = 4.38 \pm 0.02$, one obtains the estimated lifetime given by $\tau_m = (366 \pm 18)$fs. This value should be compared with the experimental value $\tau_m = (157 \pm 25)$fs. The discrepancy between the estimated and experimental value of τ_m shows that the orbital contribution to the $\mathcal{M}1$ strength can be rather important.

It is interesting to remark that a check on the ft-value for the beta-decay process $^{30}S \to {}^{30}P$ can be obtained from the measured ft-value of the corresponding $^{30}P \to {}^{30}Si$ decay, since the ^{30}S and ^{30}Si ground states are analogue states ($J^\pi = 0^+, T = 1$) (see fig. 12.4). From eq. (12.8) one finds for the decay $^{30}S \to {}^{30}P$

$$\langle M_{GT}\rangle^2_{S\to P} = \tfrac{1}{2}\langle 1\ -1\ 1 \pm 1|00\rangle^2 \langle \boldsymbol{\sigma\tau}\rangle^2 = \tfrac{1}{6}\langle \boldsymbol{\sigma\tau}\rangle^2 , \tag{12.36}$$

and similarly for the $^{30}P \to {}^{30}Si$ decay

$$\langle M_{GT}\rangle^2_{P\to Si} = \tfrac{1}{18}\langle 0\,0\,1+1|1+1\rangle^2\ \langle \boldsymbol{\sigma\tau}\rangle^2 = \tfrac{1}{18}\langle \boldsymbol{\sigma\tau}\rangle^2 . \tag{12.37}$$

The squared reduced matrix elements $\langle \boldsymbol{\sigma\tau}\rangle^2$ are identical in the two cases, since without Coulomb effects the wave functions of ^{30}S and ^{30}Si are identical. The ratio of the ft-values for the two transitions follows from eqs. (12.28), (12.36) and (12.37) as

$$\frac{ft(^{30}P \to {}^{30}Si)}{ft(^{30}S \to {}^{30}P)} = \frac{\langle M_{GT}\rangle^2_{S\to P}}{\langle M_{GT}\rangle^2_{P\to Si}} = 3 . \tag{12.38}$$

With the experimental values $\log ft(^{30}P \to {}^{30}Si) = 4.83 \pm 0.02$ and $\log ft(^{30}S \to {}^{30}P) = 4.38 \pm 0.02$ one finds the ratio 2.8 ± 0.2, which agrees well with the theoretical value given above.

Eq. (12.34a) can be applied also to e.g. $\Delta T = 0$ transitions in mirror nuclei. Substitution of $T_1 = T_2 = \frac{1}{2}$ and the values $\langle \frac{1}{2} \mp \frac{1}{2}\ 1 \pm 1|\frac{1}{2} \pm \frac{1}{2}\rangle^2 = \frac{2}{3}$ and $\langle \frac{1}{2} \pm \frac{1}{2}\ 1\,0|\frac{1}{2} \pm \frac{1}{2}\rangle^2 = \frac{1}{3}$ into eq. (12.34a) leads to

$$\frac{\tau_m}{\text{fs}} \approx 9.6 \times 10^{-3}\, \frac{2J_2+1}{2J_1+1} \left(\frac{\text{MeV}}{E_\gamma}\right)^3 \frac{ft}{\text{sec}} . \tag{12.39}$$

For $\Delta T = 0$ transitions only one condition, i.e. a vanishing Fermi matrix element, is fulfilled in general. However, one may still use eq. (12.39), based on eq. (12.34a), to obtain a very crude estimate of the lifetime from a known ft-value (or *vice versa*). Some applications of eq. (12.39) are given in table 12.3, from which it follows that

Table 12.3
Some examples illustrating the approximate relation between log ft values and lifetimes

Beta decay	log ft [a]	Gamma decay E_x (MeV)	J_2	J_1	τ_m^{th}(fs) [b]	τ_m^{exp}(fs) [c]
$^{23}Mg \xrightarrow{\beta^+} {}^{23}Na(1)$	4.39 ± 0.02	0.44	$\frac{5}{2}^+$	$\frac{3}{2}^+$	4150 ± 200	1600 ± 80
$^{31}S \xrightarrow{\beta^+} {}^{31}P(1)$	4.99 ± 0.04	1.27	$\frac{3}{2}^+$	$\frac{1}{2}^+$	915 ± 90	735 ± 50
$^{33}Cl \xrightarrow{\beta^+} {}^{33}S(1)$	5.61 ± 0.08	0.84	$\frac{1}{2}^+$	$\frac{3}{2}^+$	3300 ± 700	1700 ± 150
$^{33}S(2)$	4.89 ± 0.05	1.97	$\frac{5}{2}^+$	$\frac{3}{2}^+$	146 ± 20	160 ± 20
$^{35}Ar \xrightarrow{\beta^+} {}^{35}Cl(1)$	5.09 ± 0.02	1.22	$\frac{1}{2}^+$	$\frac{3}{2}^+$	325 ± 15	180 ± 20
$^{35}Cl(2)$	5.51 ± 0.02	1.76	$\frac{5}{2}^+$	$\frac{3}{2}^+$	855 ± 50	460 ± 50
$^{35}Cl(4)$	4.92 ± 0.04	2.69	$\frac{3}{2}^+$	$\frac{3}{2}^+$	41 ± 4	50 ± 15

a) Taken from the compilation [Endt and Van der Leun (1973)].
b) Calculated with eq. (12.39).
c) Taken from the compilation [Endt and Van der Leun (1974a)].

in these examples the estimated lifetimes differ less than a factor of three from the observed values.

In a similar way one can derive an approximate relation between ft-values and magnetic dipole moments of mirror nuclei. The relation derives again from the occurrence of the operator $\boldsymbol{\sigma}\boldsymbol{\tau}$ in the Gamow-Teller matrix element and in the isovector part of the magnetic moment. The isovector contribution μ_1 can be evaluated from the magnetic dipole moments μ_A and μ_B of the corresponding states A and B in mirror nuclei as follows from eq. (11.77)

$$\mu_1 = \tfrac{1}{2}(\mu_A - \mu_B) . \tag{12.40}$$

From eqs. (11.75), (11.73), (9.104) and (A.2.23) one finds, ignoring the orbital contribution to the isovector part (cf. eq. (12.30)), the approximate relation

$$\mu_1 \approx -\frac{\langle J\,J\,1\,0|J\,J\rangle}{\sqrt{(2J+1)(2T+1)}}\frac{T_z}{\sqrt{T(T+1)}}\langle J\,T\|\|\sum_{k=1}^{A}\boldsymbol{\sigma}(k)\boldsymbol{\tau}(k)\|\|J\,T\rangle\,\tfrac{1}{4}(g_p^s - g_n^s)\mu_N , \tag{12.41}$$

where μ_N denotes the nuclear magneton. Inserting the Gamow-Teller matrix element (12.8) into the expression (12.27) for the ft-value one obtains

$$ft = 6163\ \text{sec}/[\langle M_F\rangle^2 + 1.4\frac{\langle T_i T_{iz}\,1 \pm 1|T_f T_{fz}\rangle^2}{2(2J_i+1)(2T_f+1)}\langle J_f T_f\|\|\sum_{k=1}^{A}\boldsymbol{\sigma}(k)\boldsymbol{\tau}(k)\|\|J_i T_i\rangle^2] . \tag{12.42}$$

Table 12.4
Related magnetic moments μ (in n.m.) and ft-values in some mirror nuclei

Mirror nuclei A	B	Magn. moments [a)] μ_A	μ_B	J^π	ft-value × 10^{-3} sec^{-1} theory [b)]	experiment [c)]
^{17}O	^{17}F	−1.89	+4.72	$\frac{5}{2}^+$	1.3	2.3
^{19}F	^{19}Ne	+2.63	−1.89	$\frac{1}{2}^+$	1.3	1.7
^{21}Ne	^{21}Na	−0.66	+2.39	$\frac{3}{2}^+$	3.1	4.0
^{35}Cl	^{35}Ar	+0.82	+0.63	$\frac{3}{2}^+$	6.2	5.6

a) Taken from the compilation [Shirley and Lederer (1975)].
b) From the approximate relation (12.43).
c) Taken from the compilations [Ajzenberg-Selove (1971), (1972); Endt and Van der Leun (1973)].

For a beta transition between corresponding states in mirror nuclei one has $J_i = J_f = J$ and $T_i = T_f = \frac{1}{2}$. Combining eqs. (12.41) and (12.42), substituting $g_p^s - g_n^s = 9.41$ and $\langle M_F \rangle^2 = 1$, one obtains the approximate relation

$$ft \approx \frac{6163 \text{ sec}}{1 + 0.063 \dfrac{J+1}{J} (\mu_A - \mu_B)^2}, \tag{12.43}$$

with μ expressed in nuclear magnetons.

Some examples illustrating this relation are given in table 12.4. It is seen that reasonable agreement is obtained, in particular so if one keeps in mind that the orbital contribution to μ_1 has been ignored completely.

CHAPTER 13

THE SECOND-QUANTIZATION FORMALISM

The formalism of creation and annihilation operators is discussed in this chapter as an introduction to chapter 14. This formalism is especially useful in cases where one deals with many active particles distributed over several orbits. The angular-momentum coupled states as well as the operators acting on them are represented by spherical tensors. The important consequence of this approach is that one can couple and recouple wave functions and operators, as well as combinations of these.

We start in sect. 13.1 with the construction of states of uncoupled angular momenta. In sect. 13.2 the one- and two-body operators in second quantization are discussed. Angular-momentum coupled states are treated in sect. 13.3. Some relations between particles and holes are investigated in sect. 13.4. In sect. 13.5 operators are defined that create states with many particles or holes in a single orbit. General multishell state operators are discussed in sect. 13.6. The final step, being the calculation of the various matrix elements to be evaluated in nuclear spectroscopy, is discussed in chapters 14 and 15.

13.1. Creation and annihilation operators

For the description of a many-nucleon system one can take advantage of the properties of the fermion creation and annihilation operators to generate a complete set of many-body wave functions. In this formalism there is a direct relation between the algebra of the anticommuting creation and annihilation operators and the required antisymmetry of the many-nucleon wave functions. An important aspect is also that all operators occurring in the theory of nuclear spectroscopy can be expressed in terms of the creation and annihilation operators. It will be shown that this feature leads to a considerable simplification in the evaluation of the expressions that describe processes involving only a few particles at a time, e.g. excitations of the nucleus, electromagnetic transitions, beta decay, stripping or pick-up reactions.

The formalism of creation and annihilation operators is often referred to as the *formalism of second quantization.* A more appropriate, but less common name is the *occupation number formalism,* as it exploits the fact that for completely antisymmetric wave functions only the occupation numbers of the various single-particle states are relevant. This means that one does not have to introduce any particle numbering, as e.g. in eq. (5.4).

If the functions $\phi_\alpha(\boldsymbol{r})$ form a complete, orthonormal set of single-particle functions, then a normalized and antisymmetric wave function for A independent fermions can be written as a Slater determinant (see also chapter 1)

$$\Phi_{\alpha_1\alpha_2\ldots\alpha_A}(1,2,\ldots,A) = \frac{1}{\sqrt{A!}} \begin{vmatrix} \phi_{\alpha_1}(\boldsymbol{r}(1))\ \phi_{\alpha_1}(\boldsymbol{r}(2)) \ldots \phi_{\alpha_1}(\boldsymbol{r}(A)) \\ \phi_{\alpha_2}(\boldsymbol{r}(1))\ \phi_{\alpha_2}(\boldsymbol{r}(2)) \ldots \phi_{\alpha_2}(\boldsymbol{r}(A)) \\ \vdots \qquad\qquad\qquad\qquad \vdots \\ \phi_{\alpha_A}(\boldsymbol{r}(1))\ \phi_{\alpha_A}(\boldsymbol{r}(2)) \ldots \phi_{\alpha_A}(\boldsymbol{r}(A)) \end{vmatrix} . \tag{13.1}$$

Here $\phi_{\alpha_i}(\boldsymbol{r}(k))$ denotes a single-particle wave function for particle k in the state α_i.

Instead of the Slater determinant one can, equivalently, also give the labels $\alpha_1\alpha_2 \ldots \alpha_A$ of the occupied single-particle states with, for example, the labels α_i representing the quantum numbers $n_il_ij_im_i$. The particular order of the labels $\alpha_1\alpha_2 \ldots \alpha_A$ fixes the overall sign of the wave function. This approach is the essence of the occupation number formalism.

For a further discussion it is most convenient to make use of the Dirac bra-ket notation. Let us define a vacuum state as the state where no particles are present and let us denote this state by the symbol $|\rangle$. Applying the *creation operator* $a^\dagger_{\alpha_i}$ to the vacuum state, one obtains the single-particle state

$$|\alpha_i\rangle = a^\dagger_{\alpha_i}|\rangle . \tag{13.2}$$

In first quantization this state is represented by $\phi_{\alpha_i}(\boldsymbol{r})$. To the vacuum state one attributes the following normalization property

$$\langle|\rangle = 1 . \tag{13.3}$$

The creation process (13.2) can be continued and in general one can generate the A-particle state from the $(A-1)$ particle state employing the relation

$$a^\dagger_{\alpha_A}|\alpha_1\alpha_2 \ldots \alpha_{A-2}\alpha_{A-1}\rangle = |\alpha_1\alpha_2 \ldots \alpha_{A-2}\alpha_{A-1}\alpha_A\rangle , \tag{13.4}$$

where the newly created particle state is written at the end. Thus one can write, starting from the vacuum state,

$$a^\dagger_{\alpha_A}a^\dagger_{\alpha_{A-1}} \ldots a^\dagger_{\alpha_2}a^\dagger_{\alpha_1}|\rangle = |\alpha_1\alpha_2 \ldots \alpha_{A-1}\alpha_A\rangle . \tag{13.5}$$

Note the opposite order of the labelling on the left- and right-hand sides of eq. (13.5). This convention is commonly used. The antisymmetry of the state (13.5) is guaranteed by the requirement that the creation operators anticommute

$$\{a^\dagger_{\alpha_i}, a^\dagger_{\alpha_j}\} \equiv a^\dagger_{\alpha_i}a^\dagger_{\alpha_j} + a^\dagger_{\alpha_j}a^\dagger_{\alpha_i} = 0 , \tag{13.6}$$

i.e. the interchange of the state labels α_i and α_j introduces a minus sign. This relation also implies directly that states $|\alpha_1\alpha_2 \ldots \alpha_i \ldots \alpha_j \ldots \alpha_A\rangle$ with repeated labels $\alpha_i = \alpha_j$ must vanish as they should, of course, to satisfy the Pauli exclusion principle.

Taking the adjoint of eq. (13.2) one obtains

$$\langle\alpha_i| = \langle|a_{\alpha_i}\,, \tag{13.7}$$

where a_{α_i} represents the hermitian conjugate of $a^\dagger_{\alpha_i}$. The adjoint many-particle state, i.e. the bra corresponding to the ket $|\alpha_1\alpha_2 \ldots \alpha_{A-1}\alpha_A\rangle$ is denoted by $\langle\alpha_1\alpha_2 \ldots \alpha_{A-1}\alpha_A|$. Note here that for bra and ket the same order of labels is maintained.

We shall now derive some further commutation relations for the operators $a^\dagger$ and a, which are essential for the application of the second-quantization formalism. Since under hermitian conjugation of a product of operators their order is reversed, one obtains from eq. (13.5) the equation

$$\langle\alpha_1 \ldots \alpha_A| = \langle|(a^\dagger_{\alpha_A} \ldots a^\dagger_{\alpha_1})^\dagger = \langle|a_{\alpha_1} \ldots a_{\alpha_A}\,. \tag{13.8}$$

Thus the operators a_{α_i}, when acting to left, create particles. Note that now the state labels appear in the same order in the left- and right-hand side of the last equation. The adjoint operators a_{α_i} obey similarly the anticommutation relation

$$\{a_{\alpha_i}, a_{\alpha_j}\} = 0\,, \tag{13.9}$$

which follows directly from eq. (13.6) by hermitian conjugation.

The operators a_{α_i}, when acting to the right, annihilate a particle as will be shown below. Therefore they are called *annihilation operators.* In order to determine the action of a_λ on a particular ket vector $|\alpha\beta\gamma \ldots\rangle$ one calculates the matrix elements $\langle\alpha'\beta'\gamma' \ldots|a_\lambda|\alpha\beta\gamma \ldots\rangle$ for all values of $\alpha'\beta'\gamma' \ldots$. From the way the operators a_λ were introduced as the hermitian adjoints of $a^\dagger_\lambda$, it is clear that one has the relation

$$\langle\alpha'\beta'\gamma' \ldots |a_\lambda|\alpha\beta\gamma \ldots\rangle = \langle\alpha'\beta'\gamma' \ldots \lambda|\alpha\beta\gamma \ldots\rangle = \begin{cases} 0 & \text{for } \{\alpha'\beta'\gamma' \ldots \lambda\} \neq \{\alpha\beta\gamma \ldots\} \\ \pm 1 & \text{for } \{\alpha'\beta'\gamma' \ldots \lambda\} = \{\alpha\beta\gamma \ldots\}\,, \end{cases} \tag{13.10}$$

where the upper (lower) sign must be used if the set $\{\alpha'\beta'\gamma' \ldots \lambda\}$ is an even (odd) permutation of $\{\alpha\beta\gamma \ldots\}$.

The matrix element (13.10) vanishes when the set $\{\alpha'\beta'\gamma' \ldots \lambda\}$ is no permutation (including the identity) of the set $\{\alpha\beta\gamma \ldots\}$. This includes the case $\lambda \in \{\alpha'\beta'\gamma' \ldots\}$. The values of the matrix elements (13.10) can be regarded as the projections of the state $a_\lambda|\alpha\beta\gamma \ldots\rangle$ onto the complete set of states $|\alpha'\beta'\gamma' \ldots\rangle$.

Let us consider a state λ that does not belong to the set $\{\alpha\beta\gamma \ldots \omega\}$. It then follows from eq. (13.10) that all matrix elements $\langle\alpha'\beta'\gamma' \ldots \psi'|a_\lambda|\alpha\beta\gamma \ldots \omega\rangle$ vanish for the complete set of states $\{\alpha'\beta'\gamma' \ldots \psi'\}$. Since all components of the state $a_\lambda|\alpha\beta\gamma \ldots \omega\rangle$ vanish, one has

$$a_\lambda|\alpha\beta\gamma \ldots \omega\rangle = 0 \quad \text{for } \lambda \notin \{\alpha\beta\gamma \ldots \omega\}. \tag{13.11a}$$

On the other hand one has $\langle\alpha\beta\gamma \ldots \omega|a_\lambda|\alpha\beta\gamma \ldots \omega\lambda\rangle = +1$ and thus one obtains the relation

$$a_\lambda|\alpha\beta\gamma\,...\,\omega\lambda\rangle = |\alpha\beta\gamma\,...\,\omega\rangle \qquad \text{for } \lambda \notin \{\alpha\beta\gamma\,...\,\omega\}\,. \tag{13.11b}$$

In particular one finds

$$a_\lambda|\rangle = 0\,, \qquad a_\lambda|\lambda\rangle = |\rangle \qquad \text{for all } \lambda\,. \tag{13.12}$$

The equations given above clearly show that the operator a_λ acts as an annihilation or destruction operator for a particle in the state $|\lambda\rangle$. From the anticommutation relation (13.9), which is equivalent to the antisymmetry of the many-particle wave function, one determines the sign that accompanies the annihilation of a particle in any of the other orbits. Some simple examples showing the action of $a_\beta^\dagger$ and a_β are given by the relations

$$a_\beta^\dagger|\beta\rangle = 0\,, \qquad \langle\beta|a_\beta = 0\,,$$

$$a_\beta^\dagger|\alpha\rangle = |\alpha\beta\rangle\,, \qquad \langle\alpha|a_\beta = \langle\alpha\beta|\,,$$

$$a_\beta|\alpha\beta\rangle = |\alpha\rangle\,, \qquad \langle\alpha\beta|a_\beta^\dagger = \langle\alpha|\,. \tag{13.13}$$

We shall now derive the anticommutator of the operators $a_{\alpha_i}^\dagger$ and a_{α_j}. If $a_{\alpha_A}^\dagger a_{\alpha_{A-1}}$ and $a_{\alpha_{A-1}} a_{\alpha_A}^\dagger$ are applied to a state where the orbit α_{A-1} is occupied and the orbit α_A is not, it follows that

$$a_{\alpha_A}^\dagger a_{\alpha_{A-1}}|\alpha_1\alpha_2\,...\,\alpha_{A-2}\alpha_{A-1}\rangle = a_{\alpha_A}^\dagger|\alpha_1\alpha_2\,...\,\alpha_{A-2}\rangle = |\alpha_1\alpha_2\,...\,\alpha_{A-2}\alpha_A\rangle\,, \tag{13.14a}$$

$$\begin{aligned} a_{\alpha_{A-1}} a_{\alpha_A}^\dagger|\alpha_1\alpha_2\,...\,\alpha_{A-2}\alpha_{A-1}\rangle &= a_{\alpha_{A-1}}|\alpha_1\alpha_2\,...\,\alpha_{A-2}\alpha_{A-1}\alpha_A\rangle \\ &= -a_{\alpha_{A-1}}|\alpha_1\alpha_2\,...\,\alpha_{A-2}\alpha_A\alpha_{A-1}\rangle \\ &= -|\alpha_1\alpha_2\,...\,\alpha_{A-2}\alpha_A\rangle\,. \end{aligned} \tag{13.14b}$$

Thus one has the relation

$$(a_{\alpha_A}^\dagger a_{\alpha_{A-1}} + a_{\alpha_{A-1}} a_{\alpha_A}^\dagger)|\alpha_1\alpha_2\,...\,\alpha_{A-2}\alpha_{A-1}\rangle = 0\,. \tag{13.15}$$

The derivation also holds of course for any state where the orbit α_A is occupied or the orbit α_{A-1} is not. Taking into account the antisymmetry of the state $|\alpha_1\alpha_2\,...\,\alpha_{A-2}\alpha_{A-1}\rangle$ one finds from eq. (13.15) that the relation $a_{\alpha_i}^\dagger a_{\alpha_j} + a_{\alpha_j} a_{\alpha_i}^\dagger = 0$ holds in general for $\alpha_i \neq \alpha_j$.

For the case $\alpha_i = \alpha_j$ one obtains from a derivation as given above that either (i) $a_{\alpha_i}^\dagger a_{\alpha_i} \to 1$ and $a_{\alpha_i} a_{\alpha_i}^\dagger \to 0$ or (ii) $a_{\alpha_i}^\dagger a_{\alpha_i} \to 0$ and $a_{\alpha_i} a_{\alpha_i}^\dagger \to 1$, depending on the orbit α_i being occupied or not, respectively. Thus one can summarize the rules given above by saying that the anticommutator of creation and annihilation operators satisfies the condition

$$\{a_{\alpha_i}^\dagger, a_{\alpha_j}\} = \delta_{\alpha_i\alpha_j} \tag{13.16}$$

which introduces an extra term 1 when $a^\dagger_{\alpha_i}$ and a_{α_j} are interchanged for $\alpha_i = \alpha_j$.

The anticommutation relations (13.6), (13.9) and (13.16) completely determine the algebra of second quantization. The notation of the state vectors $|\alpha_1\alpha_2 \ldots \alpha_A\rangle$ is such, that only the labels of the occupied orbits are given. It should be remarked that in the derivations discussed above the creation operator $a^\dagger_\alpha$ was introduced first and that subsequently the annihilation operator a_α was introduced as its hermitian conjugate. From the notation, which has grown historically, one would expect differently. This will be considered in more detail later when instead of a_α the adjoint operator $\tilde{a}_\alpha$ is introduced.

As an application of the commutation relations discussed above we derive some values of matrix elements that will be used later. Consider the matrix element $\langle|a_\alpha a^\dagger_\beta|\rangle$. From the anticommutator (13.16) it follows immediately that one has

$$\langle|a_\alpha a^\dagger_\beta|\rangle = \langle|\rangle\, \delta_{\alpha\beta} - \langle|a^\dagger_\beta a_\alpha|\rangle = \delta_{\alpha\beta}\ , \tag{13.17a}$$

where eqs. (13.3) and (13.12) were used for the last step. Of course, this result can be obtained also from the orthonormality of the states $|\alpha\rangle$ and $|\beta\rangle$

$$\langle|a_\alpha a^\dagger_\beta|\rangle = \langle\alpha|\beta\rangle = \delta_{\alpha\beta}\ . \tag{13.17b}$$

Let us treat next the matrix element $\langle|a_\alpha a_\beta a^\dagger_\gamma a^\dagger_\delta|\rangle$. Since we create and then annihilate two particles, the value of this matrix element is 0 or ± 1 depending upon the values of α, β, γ and δ. For an evaluation of the matrix element we make repeated use of the anticommutator (13.16)

$$\begin{aligned} a_\alpha a_\beta a^\dagger_\gamma a^\dagger_\delta &= a_\alpha \delta_{\beta\gamma} a^\dagger_\delta - a_\alpha a^\dagger_\gamma a_\beta a^\dagger_\delta \\ &= a_\alpha a^\dagger_\delta\, \delta_{\beta\gamma} - a_\alpha a^\dagger_\gamma \delta_{\beta\delta} + a_\alpha a^\dagger_\gamma a^\dagger_\delta a_\beta\ . \end{aligned} \tag{13.18}$$

The vacuum expectation value of the last term in eq. (13.18) vanishes because the annihilation operator a_β acting to the right on the vacuum yields zero. The vacuum expectation values of the other two terms follow immediately from eqs. (13.17) and one finds

$$\langle|a_\alpha a_\beta a^\dagger_\gamma a^\dagger_\delta|\rangle = \delta_{\alpha\delta}\, \delta_{\beta\gamma} - \delta_{\alpha\gamma}\delta_{\beta\delta}\ . \tag{13.19}$$

A more systematic and general way to evaluate vacuum expectation values of arbitrary products of creation and annihilation operators is offered by Wick's theorem, which is discussed in sect. 17.1.

Let us consider now the operator

$$N_\alpha \equiv a^\dagger_\alpha a_\alpha\ . \tag{13.20}$$

In the discussion preceding eq. (13.16) it was seen already that this operator yields zero when acting on a state with orbit α unoccupied, and unity when orbit α is occupied. Thus since N_α measures the occupancy of the single-particle orbit α, we can introduce the operator

$$\mathcal{N} \equiv \sum_{\alpha} N_{\alpha} = \sum_{\alpha} a_{\alpha}^{\dagger} a_{\alpha} , \tag{13.21}$$

which measures the total number of particles present in a many-particle state.

13.2. Operators in second-quantized form

It was seen in the preceding section that the second-quantization formalism could be introduced for the description of many-fermion states, since these particles are indistinguishable and only the occupation numbers of each state are relevant. Similarly operators referring to indistinguishable particles can be represented in the same formalism. Such operators are *symmetric operators,* i.e. they act the same way on all particles in a given wave function, since otherwise they would produce many-particle wave functions that are no longer fully antisymmetric.

One-body operators. A symmetric one-body operator acting on a system of A identical particles is given by

$$O^{(1)} = \sum_{k=1}^{A} O(\boldsymbol{r}(k)) , \tag{13.22}$$

where $\boldsymbol{r}(k)$ represents position and spin coordinate of particle k. This means that each term operates on all coordinates of one of the particles. The matrix elements in first quantization for the single-particle states $\phi_{\alpha}(\boldsymbol{r})$ and $\phi_{\beta}(\boldsymbol{r})$ are defined by

$$\langle \alpha | O | \beta \rangle = \int \phi_{\alpha}^{*}(\boldsymbol{r})\, O(\boldsymbol{r})\, \phi_{\beta}(\boldsymbol{r})\, \mathrm{d}\boldsymbol{r} , \tag{13.23}$$

where the integration over $\boldsymbol{r}$ includes a possible summation over the discrete spin variables of the particle.

It will be shown that a symmetric single-particle operator in second quantization can be defined as

$$\hat{O} = \sum_{\alpha\beta} \langle \alpha | O | \beta \rangle\, a_{\alpha}^{\dagger} a_{\beta} , \tag{13.24}$$

where the summation runs over all single-particle states considered and $\langle \alpha | O | \beta \rangle$ is defined in eq. (13.23). The circumflex will be used here to indicate operators in second quantization, in order to prevent confusion with operators in first quantization. It should be noted that in eq. (13.24) no longer explicit reference is made to the number of particles on which the operator acts. The only nonvanishing matrix elements of a number conserving one-body operator are those between A-particle states that differ in at most one particle state label.

For the *diagonal matrix elements* one obtains with the definition of the operator given in eq. (13.24) and the relations (13.5) and (13.8)

$$\langle\alpha_1\alpha_2 \ldots \alpha_A|\hat{O}|\alpha_1\alpha_2 \ldots \alpha_A\rangle = \sum_{\alpha\beta} \langle\alpha|O|\beta\rangle\langle|a_{\alpha_1}a_{\alpha_2} \ldots a_{\alpha_A}a^\dagger_\alpha a_\beta a^\dagger_{\alpha_A} \ldots a^\dagger_{\alpha_2}a^\dagger_{\alpha_1}|\rangle . \tag{13.25}$$

For the evaluation of the matrix element given above one should realize that all labels $\alpha_1\alpha_2 \ldots \alpha_A$ are different. The annihilation operator a_β acting to the right yields zero unless β equals $\alpha_1, \alpha_2, \ldots$ or α_A, in which case it yields plus or minus unity. Similarly the operator $a^\dagger_\alpha$ acting to the left yields zero unless α equals $\alpha_1, \alpha_2, \ldots$ or α_A. Suppose $\beta = \alpha_i$, then one should have also $\alpha = \alpha_i$ in order that none of the annihilation operators $a_{\alpha_1}a_{\alpha_2} \ldots a_{\alpha_A}$ when acting to the right, leads to a vanishing result. For each case $\alpha = \beta = \alpha_i$ $(i = 1, 2, \ldots, A)$ the expectation value of the annihilation and creation operators in eq. (13.25) will be equal to unity. Thus one obtains

$$\langle\alpha_1\alpha_2 \ldots \alpha_A|\hat{O}|\alpha_1\alpha_2 \ldots \alpha_A\rangle = \sum_{i=1}^{A} \langle\alpha_i|O|\alpha_i\rangle . \tag{13.26}$$

A more systematic way of arriving at this result is given by Wick's theorem (see sect. 17.1).

Due to the antisymmetry of the many-nucleon states, all nonvanishing *off-diagonal matrix elements* can be represented by a single one, since a reordering of the state labels only affects the sign. One thus obtains from a similar discussion as given above

$$\langle\alpha_1\alpha_2 \ldots \alpha_A|\hat{O}|\gamma_1\alpha_2 \ldots \alpha_A\rangle$$

$$= \sum_{\alpha\beta} \langle\alpha|O|\beta\rangle\langle|a_{\alpha_1}a_{\alpha_2} \ldots a_{\alpha_A}a^\dagger_\alpha a_\beta a^\dagger_{\alpha_A} \ldots a^\dagger_{\alpha_2}a^\dagger_{\gamma_1}|\rangle$$

$$= \langle\alpha_1|O|\gamma_1\rangle \qquad \text{for} \quad \alpha_1 \neq \gamma_1 . \tag{13.27}$$

Eqs. (13.25) and (13.27) show that definition (13.24) leads to matrix elements of a symmetric one-body operator in second quantization that are the same as those in first quantization. In particular it follows from eqs. (13.26) and (13.27) that one has

$$\langle\alpha|\hat{O}|\gamma\rangle = \langle\alpha|O|\gamma\rangle . \tag{13.28}$$

Hence the circumflex may be omitted from the one-body matrix elements.

Two-body operators. A symmetric two-body operator acting on a system of A identical particles is given by

$$O^{(2)} = \sum_{1=j<k}^{A} O(\boldsymbol{r}(j), \boldsymbol{r}(k)) \tag{13.29}$$

with $O(\boldsymbol{r}(j), \boldsymbol{r}(k)) = O(\boldsymbol{r}(k), \boldsymbol{r}(j))$.

In first quantization the matrix elements between normalized, antisymmetrized states are defined by

$$\langle\alpha\beta|O|\gamma\delta\rangle = \int \phi_\alpha^*(\boldsymbol{r}(1))\, \phi_\beta^*(\boldsymbol{r}(2))\, O(\boldsymbol{r}(1), \boldsymbol{r}(2))(1-P_{12})\, \phi_\gamma(\boldsymbol{r}(1))\, \phi_\delta(\boldsymbol{r}(2))\, \mathrm{d}\boldsymbol{r}(1)\, \mathrm{d}\boldsymbol{r}(2)\,, \tag{13.30}$$

where the operator P_{12} permutes all coordinates of particles 1 and 2. In chapter 5 two-body matrix elements were introduced for antisymmetric states of well-defined total angular momentum and isospin. The combination of antisymmetry and angular-momentum coupling then leads to a normalization factor in eq. (5.17) that depends on whether the two-particle states are constructed from one and the same orbit or not. In eq. (13.30), however, the two-particle states occur in uncoupled form and no such normalization factor is present. The two-body operator (13.29) is represented in second quantization by

$$\hat{O} = \tfrac{1}{4} \sum_{\alpha\beta\gamma\delta} \langle\alpha\beta|O|\gamma\delta\rangle\, a_\alpha^\dagger a_\beta^\dagger a_\delta a_\gamma\,, \tag{13.31}$$

where the order of the creation and annihilation operators should be noted. Of course, one could also write $a_\alpha^\dagger a_\beta^\dagger a_\gamma a_\delta$ provided one adds an overall minus sign.

We will verify again that with definition (13.31) the same matrix elements between antisymmetrized states are obtained in first and in second quantization. It should be realized that in second quantization the exchange term is always included. From definition (13.31) it follows that the *diagonal matrix elements* of a two-body operator can be written as

$$\langle\alpha_1\alpha_2 \ldots \alpha_A|\hat{O}|\alpha_1\alpha_2 \ldots \alpha_A\rangle$$

$$= \tfrac{1}{4} \sum_{\alpha\beta\gamma\delta} \langle\alpha\beta|O|\gamma\delta\rangle \langle|a_{\alpha_1} a_{\alpha_2} \ldots a_{\alpha_A} a_\alpha^\dagger a_\beta^\dagger a_\delta a_\gamma a_{\alpha_A}^\dagger \ldots a_{\alpha_2}^\dagger a_{\alpha_1}^\dagger|\rangle\,. \tag{13.32}$$

In order that the annihilation operators $a_\delta a_\gamma$ acting to the right do not vanish, one should have that the labels $\delta \neq \gamma$ each are equal to one of the labels $\alpha_1, \alpha_2, \ldots$ or α_A, say $\gamma = \alpha_i$ and $\delta = \alpha_j$. Then also one must have either $\alpha = \alpha_i$ and $\beta = \alpha_j$ or $\alpha = \alpha_j$ and $\beta = \alpha_i$ so that the expectation value in eq. (13.32) does not vanish. These two possibilities for α and β lead to the terms $\frac{1}{4}\langle\alpha_i\alpha_j|O|\alpha_i\alpha_j\rangle$ and $-\frac{1}{4}\langle\alpha_j\alpha_i|O|\alpha_i\alpha_j\rangle = \frac{1}{4}\langle\alpha_i\alpha_j|O|\alpha_i\alpha_j\rangle$, respectively, where the phases can be verified by counting the number of transpositions required to write annihilation and creation operators as adjacent pairs $a_{\alpha_k} a_{\alpha_k}^\dagger$ (cf. eqs. (13.6), (13.9) and (13.16)). Similarly the case $\gamma = \alpha_j$ and $\delta = \alpha_i$ leads also to a contribution $2 \times \frac{1}{4}\langle\alpha_i\alpha_j|O|\alpha_i\alpha_j\rangle$. Thus one finds, adding the various contributions,

$$\langle\alpha_1\alpha_2 \ldots \alpha_A|\hat{O}|\alpha_1\alpha_2 \ldots \alpha_A\rangle = \sum_{1=i<j}^{A} \langle\alpha_i\alpha_j|O|\alpha_i\alpha_j\rangle\,, \tag{13.33}$$

where the restriction $i<j$ prevents double counting.

Along the same lines as for the one-body operators one can derive for the two possibilities of *off-diagonal matrix elements*:

$$\langle\alpha_1\alpha_2\,...\,\alpha_A|\hat{O}|\gamma_1\alpha_2\,...\,\alpha_A\rangle = \sum_{j=2}^{A}\langle\alpha_1\alpha_j|O|\gamma_1\alpha_j\rangle \qquad \text{for} \quad \alpha_1 \neq \gamma_1\,, \tag{13.34}$$

$$\langle\alpha_1\alpha_2\,...\,\alpha_A|\hat{O}|\gamma_1\gamma_2\,...\,\alpha_A\rangle = \langle\alpha_1\alpha_2|O|\gamma_1\gamma_2\rangle \qquad \text{for} \quad \alpha_1, \alpha_2 \neq \gamma_1, \gamma_2\,. \tag{13.35}$$

Again the use of Wick's theorem offers a more systematic way of deriving eqs. (13.33), (13.34) and (13.35).

Summarizing one sees that with definitions (13.24) and (13.31) the two formalisms of first and second quantization lead to the same matrix elements between antisymmetrized states. In particular one finds from eqs. (13.33)–(13.35) the relation

$$\langle\alpha\beta|\hat{O}|\gamma\delta\rangle = \langle\alpha\beta|O|\gamma\delta\rangle\,, \tag{13.36}$$

which renders the circumflex superfluous in these two-body matrix elements. The formalism of second quantization can be used also to represent three- or more-body operators. As these will not be employed here we shall not elaborate on this straightforward extension.

13.3. Angular-momentum coupled states

In the preceding sections we have restricted ourselves to a discussion of many-particle states of which the total angular momentum was not specified. For a description of finite nuclei, however, we avail ourselves of the rotational symmetry to construct states of well-defined angular momentum. This requires an extensive use of Racah algebra, in particular for the evaluation of the matrix elements of one- and two-body operators between many-body states.

The construction of a creation operator for an angular-momentum coupled two-body state is quite analogous to the procedure in first quantization (cf. eq. (4.2))

$$|j_a j_b; JM\rangle = N_{ab}\sum_{m_a m_b}\langle j_a m_a j_b m_b|JM\rangle\, a^\dagger_{j_b m_b} a^\dagger_{j_a m_a}|\rangle\,. \tag{13.37}$$

Here $N_{ab} = (1 + \delta_{ab})^{-1/2}$ is a normalization factor with $\delta_{ab} = 1$ when the two particles possess the same set of radial and angular-momentum quantum numbers, and with $\delta_{ab} = 0$ otherwise. This normalization factor is determined by the requirement that the norm of the two-particle state defined in eq. (13.37) be equal to one, i.e.

$$1 = \langle j_a j_b; JM|j_a j_b; JM\rangle$$

$$= (N_{ab})^2 \sum_{\substack{m'_a m'_b \\ m_a m_b}} \langle| a_{j_a m'_a} a_{j_b m'_b} a^\dagger_{j_b m_b} a^\dagger_{j_a m_a} |\rangle \langle j_a m'_a j_b m'_b | JM\rangle \langle j_a m_a j_b m_b | JM\rangle$$

$$= (N_{ab})^2 \sum_{\substack{m'_a m'_b \\ m_a m_b}} \{\delta_{m_a m'_a} \delta_{m_b m'_b} - \delta_{ab} \delta_{m_a m'_b} \delta_{m_b m'_a}\}$$

$$\times \langle j_a m'_a j_b m'_b | JM\rangle \langle j_a m_a j_b m_b | JM\rangle \,, \tag{13.38}$$

where for the last step relation (13.19) is used. Now the summation over the projection quantum numbers in the Clebsch-Gordan coefficients can be performed and one finds finally

$$(N_{ab})^2 = \frac{1}{1 - \delta_{ab}(-1)^{J - j_a - j_b}} = \frac{1}{1 + \delta_{ab}} \,, \tag{13.39}$$

where use is made of eqs. (2.79), (A.1.a4) and the fact that for antisymmetric two-particle wave functions with $j_a = j_b$ only even values of J are allowed (cf. eq. (2.81)).

Inserting the normalization factor (13.39), one can write eq. (13.37) as

$$|j_a j_b; JM\rangle = -\frac{1}{\sqrt{1+\delta_{ab}}} \sum_{m_a m_b} \langle j_a m_a j_b m_b | JM\rangle \, a^\dagger_{j_a m_a} a^\dagger_{j_b m_b} |\rangle$$

$$\equiv -\frac{1}{\sqrt{1+\delta_{ab}}} [a^\dagger_{j_a} \times a^\dagger_{j_b}]^J_M |\rangle \,, \tag{13.40}$$

where the minus sign derives from the anticommutation property of the creation operators and the square brackets are used to denote the angular-momentum coupling $\boldsymbol{j}_a + \boldsymbol{j}_b = \boldsymbol{J}$. Alternatively one also could have interchanged $j_a m_a$ and $j_b m_b$ in the Clebsch-Gordan coefficient to obtain

$$|j_a j_b; JM\rangle = \frac{(-1)^{J - j_a - j_b}}{\sqrt{1+\delta_{ab}}} [a^\dagger_{j_b} \times a^\dagger_{j_a}]^J_M |\rangle \,. \tag{13.41}$$

In eq. (13.37) no isospin labels were used and thus the results apply to the case of identical particles, i.e. either protons or neutrons. For the general case, the creation and annihilation operators should be provided with isospin labels ($t = \frac{1}{2}$, t_z) as well. Instead of eq. (13.41) one then obtains for a two-particle state of total spin J and isospin T, the relation

$$|j_a j_b; JM, TT_z\rangle = \frac{1}{\sqrt{1+\delta_{ab}}} \sum_{\substack{m_a m_b \\ t_{az} t_{bz}}} \langle j_a m_a j_b m_b | JM\rangle$$

$$\times \langle \tfrac{1}{2} t_{az} \tfrac{1}{2} t_{bz} | TT_z\rangle \, a^\dagger_{j_b m_b \frac{1}{2} t_{bz}} a^\dagger_{j_a m_a \frac{1}{2} t_{az}} |\rangle$$

$$= -\frac{1}{\sqrt{1+\delta_{ab}}} \sum_{\substack{m_a m_b \\ t_{az} t_{bz}}} \langle j_a m_a j_b m_b | JM \rangle$$

$$\times \langle \tfrac{1}{2} t_{az} \tfrac{1}{2} t_{bz} | TT_z \rangle \, a^{\dagger}_{j_a m_a \frac{1}{2} t_{az}} a^{\dagger}_{j_b m_b \frac{1}{2} t_{bz}} |\rangle$$

$$\equiv -\frac{1}{\sqrt{1+\delta_{ab}}} [a^{\dagger}_{j_a \frac{1}{2}} \times a^{\dagger}_{j_b \frac{1}{2}}]^{JT}_{MT_z} |\rangle \,. \tag{13.42}$$

Using eq. (13.42) one can define a *state operator*

$$Z^{JT}_{MT_z}(a, b) \equiv -\frac{1}{\sqrt{1+\delta_{ab}}} [a^{\dagger}_{j_a \frac{1}{2}} \times a^{\dagger}_{j_b \frac{1}{2}}]^{JT}_{MT_z} \,, \tag{13.43}$$

that creates the two-particle state given by

$$| j_a j_b ; JM, TT_z \rangle = Z^{JT}_{MT_z}(a, b) |\rangle \,. \tag{13.44}$$

For the construction of a state with more than two particles, one must add one particle at a time with the aid of Clebsch-Gordan coefficients and normalize the wave function afterwards.

It may seem now that in second quantization one could do without c.f.p. (see sect. 4.2) and that Clebsch-Gordan coefficients were sufficient for the construction of all many-particle states. It can be shown, however, that a many-particle single-orbit state thus constructed requires a normalization factor that is given essentially by c.f.p. In fact such explicit constructions soon get very complicated. This concerns the orthogonality and normalization of states that contain particles within the same orbit. A first indication of these problems is the normalization factor that had to be introduced into eq. (13.37) for two particles in one orbit, i.e. $N_{ab} = \sqrt{\frac{1}{2}}$ for $a = b$. In chapter 4 we have discussed in detail, however, the procedures how to construct in first quantization single-shell, many-particle states with the help of c.f.p. Therefore general single-shell state operators can be defined by the implicit relation ★

$$Z^{JT}_{\alpha MT_z}(j^n) |\rangle = \Psi^{j^n JT}_{\alpha MT_z}(r(1), \ldots, r(n)) \,, \tag{13.45}$$

where the right-hand side represents the normalized single-shell n-particle state and $Z(j^n)$ is constructed exclusively from creation operators $a^{\dagger}_{jm\frac{1}{2}t_z}$. Here the symbol α denotes any set of additional quantum numbers that may be necessary for a complete description of the state j^n. It should be remarked here that the advantages of

★ Strictly speaking this equation is not quite well formulated. The ket on the left-hand side is set equal to a wave function in the Schrödinger representation on the right-hand side. It would have been more appropriate to write the left-hand side as $\langle \boldsymbol{r}(1), \ldots, \boldsymbol{r}(n) | Z^{JT}_{\alpha MT_z}(j^n) |\rangle$, but since in this book we make use of the coordinate representation only, we adopt the common usage of equating kets and wave functions (and similarly bras and complex conjugate wave functions as seen in eq. (13.64)).

the second-quantization formalism become very apparent as soon as more than two orbits are involved.

Before we can continue, it is necessary to discuss the adjoint operators, i.e. the annihilation operators $a_{jm\frac{1}{2}t_z}$ and the state operators that can be constructed from them.

13.4. Particle-hole conjugation

In the shell model the closure of orbits plays an important role. The closed-shell states possess an isotropic density distribution and are characterized by a total angular momentum $J = 0$. For the light and medium-weight nuclei it is possible that the protons and the neutrons fill the same orbits. A doubly closed-shell state is characterized by also a total isospin $T = 0$.

As closed orbits or shells form a rather well bound system of nucleons, they can be assumed to constitute an inert core in nuclei. The spectroscopic properties are then ascribed to the active nucleons outside the core. In many cases, however, a more accurate description requires a break-up of the closed shell, i.e. excitation of core particles into higher lying shells. The states that result from removing one or more particles from a closed shell can be described either as particle states or alternatively as *hole states.* The latter description can be quite convenient, since there is a one-to-one correspondence between the matrix elements of N-particle states on the one side and N-hole states on the other side. Establishment of the phase relations between the particle and hole description is usually the most difficult part of the correspondence. We shall not elaborate on this problem. Let us now investigate, though, how a single-hole state should be defined properly.

Consider shell-model states $|nljm\rangle$. Removal of a particle in a state with the angular-momentum quantum numbers l, j, m from the closed-shell state $|0\rangle \equiv |j^{2j+1}; J = 0, M = 0\rangle$ leads to a $2j$-particle state, i.e. the hole state $a_{jm}|0\rangle = |0; (jm)^{-1}\rangle$ with the quantum numbers $l, j, -m$. Thus in fact this hole state represents the state $|j^{2j}; j - m\rangle$, i.e. an antisymmetric state of $2j$ identical nucleons (isospin is not yet considered here) in the orbits $n\, l\, j$, coupled to total spin $J = j$ and projection $M = -m$. Although it is obvious that a hole state is defined with respect to some closed-shell state, the presence of the latter is indicated explicitly by the symbol 0 in $|0; (jm)^{-1}\rangle$. This enables us to distinguish between the single-particle state $|\alpha\rangle$ and the core-plus-one-particle state $a_\alpha^\dagger|0\rangle = |0; \alpha\rangle$. This is necessary when matrix elements are considered of operators for which the core yields a contribution, as is the case for example with the binding energy.

Let us consider now two different ways of constructing a closed-shell state. The transformation properties of a hole state are determined by the relation

$$N_j \mathcal{A} |jm\rangle|0; (jm)^{-1}\rangle = |\text{closed shell } J = 0, M = 0\rangle\,, \tag{13.46}$$

where $\mathcal{A}$ denotes the antisymmetrization operator for the $2j + 1$ nucleons and N_j is a normalization factor. In this equation the particle that was removed from the orbit jm, is replaced subsequently. The antisymmetrized result is the closed-shell state by construction. As eq. (13.46) holds for any value of m between $-j$ and $+j$, one may also sum over all values m to obtain

$$\frac{N_j}{2j+1}\,\mathcal{A}\sum_m |jm\rangle|0;(jm)^{-1}\rangle = |\text{closed shell } J=0, M=0\rangle\,. \tag{13.47}$$

Another way of constructing the closed-shell state is given in the diagrammatic notation, discussed in sect. 4.1, as

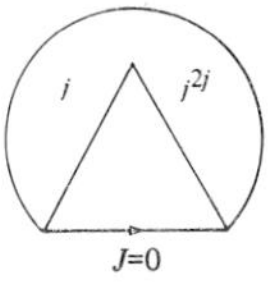

$$= |\text{closed shell } J=0, M=0\rangle \tag{13.48}$$

or, written more explicitly,

$$\mathcal{A}\sum_{mm'} \langle jmjm'|00\rangle|jm\rangle|j^{2j};jm'\rangle$$

$$= \mathcal{A}\sum_m \frac{(-1)^{j-m}}{\sqrt{2j+1}}\,|jm\rangle|j^{2j};j-m\rangle = |\text{closed shell } J=0, M=0\rangle\,, \tag{13.49}$$

where the value of the Clebsch-Gordan coefficient is inserted. Comparison of eqs. (13.47) and (13.49) shows that the hole state $|0;(jm)^{-1}\rangle$ transforms as does the particle state $(-1)^{j-m}|j^{2j};j-m\rangle$.

It should be remarked that the normalization factor N_j can be ignored here, since it is not relevant for the transformation properties considered. We shall adopt the phase convention *

$$|0;(jm)^{-1}\rangle = (-1)^{j-m}|j^{2j};j-m\rangle\,. \tag{13.50}$$

Multiplying eq. (13.50) by $(-1)^{j-m}$ and then replacing each m by $-m$, one obtains

$$(-1)^{j+m}|0;(j-m)^{-1}\rangle = |j^{2j};jm\rangle \equiv |0;j^{-1}m\rangle\,. \tag{13.51}$$

Now the transformation character of the one-hole state $|0;j^{-1}m\rangle$ is well defined, since it is exactly the same as that of the $2j$-particle state with total angular momentum $J=j$ and $M=m$. In other words, the hole state $|0;j^{-1}m\rangle$ is obtained by the removal of a particle in the state $(-1)^{j+m}|j-m\rangle$.

Let us now translate the results into terms of creation and annihilation operators. When $a^\dagger_{jm}$ creates a particle state

$$a^\dagger_{jm}|\rangle = |jm\rangle\,, \tag{13.52}$$

* It is noted here that for the phase factor $(-1)^{j-m}$ only the m-dependence is essential. The combination $j-m$ is chosen to prevent the appearance of imaginary factors for the half-integer values of m. We could also have taken $(-1)^{j+m}$ instead of $(-1)^{j-m}$, since this only implies an overall sign change in the definition of the closed-shell state.

then the hole state with the same transformation character is obtained according to eq. (13.51) as

$$(-1)^{j+m} a_{j-m}|0\rangle \equiv \tilde{a}_{jm}|0\rangle = |0; j^{-1}m\rangle , \qquad (13.53)$$

where the symbol $|0\rangle$ denotes the closed-shell state.

The operator $\tilde{a}_{jm}$ is defined such that it annihilates a particle in the state $(-1)^{j+m}|j - m\rangle$, i.e. not only a reversal of the sign of m is involved, but also an m-dependent phase factor.

The resulting operator $\tilde{a}_{jm}$ is a tensor operator, just like $a^\dagger_{jm}$. This means for instance that the Wigner-Eckart theorem (see appendix A.3) can be applied to the operator $\tilde{a}_{jm}$ but not to the operator a_{jm}. The proper transformation character of the operator $\tilde{a}_{jm}$ is also important when angular-momentum coupled particle-hole or hole-hole states must be constructed. In other words, there is no problem about the labels that should be used in the Clebsch-Gordan coefficients when the operators $a^\dagger_{jm}$ and $\tilde{a}_{jm}$ are involved. For example the state

$$|0; j_a j_b^{-1}; JM\rangle = \sum_{m_a m_b} \langle j_a m_a j_b m_b|JM\rangle\, \tilde{a}_{j_b m_b} a^\dagger_{j_a m_a}|0\rangle \equiv -[a^\dagger_{j_a} \times \tilde{a}_{j_b}]^J_M|0\rangle \qquad (13.54)$$

represents the configuration where a particle in orbit j_a and a hole in orbit j_b are coupled to total spin J and projection M.

Similarly a two-hole state is described by

$$|0; j_a^{-1} j_b^{-1}; JM\rangle = \frac{1}{\sqrt{1+\delta_{ab}}} \sum_{m_a m_b} \langle j_a m_a j_b m_b|JM\rangle\, \tilde{a}_{j_b m_b} \tilde{a}_{j_a m_a}|0\rangle$$

$$\equiv -\frac{1}{\sqrt{1+\delta_{ab}}} [\tilde{a}_{j_a} \times \tilde{a}_{j_b}]^J_M|0\rangle . \qquad (13.55)$$

When acting to the left, the operator $\tilde{a}_{jm}$ creates a particle state

$$\langle|\tilde{a}_{jm} = \langle|a_{j-m}(-1)^{j+m} = \langle j - m|(-1)^{j+m} . \qquad (13.56)$$

The wave function $\phi^*_{jm}(\boldsymbol{r})$ represents the bra $\langle jm|$, just as the wave function $\phi_{jm}(\boldsymbol{r})$ represents the ket $|jm\rangle$. The right-hand side of eq. (13.56), corresponding to $(-1)^{j+m}\phi^*_{j-m}(\boldsymbol{r})$, transforms like a spherical tensor (cf. eq. (A.2.6)). This also follows from the left-hand side where the scalar vacuum is combined with the spherical tensor $\tilde{a}_{jm}$.

What has been remarked above concerning the angular-momentum labels of creation and annihilation operators for identical particles applies just as well to the isospin labels when the isospin formalism is used. For instance, when a proton ($t = \frac{1}{2}$, $t_z = -\frac{1}{2}$) is removed from a doubly closed-shell state, a state $T = \frac{1}{2}$, $T_z = +\frac{1}{2}$ is left, i.e. the proton hole is described by $t = \frac{1}{2}$, $t_z = +\frac{1}{2}$. Analogously to eq. (13.53) we then define the operator

$$\tilde{a}_{jm\frac{1}{2}t_z} \equiv (-1)^{j+m+1/2+t_z} a_{j-m\frac{1}{2}-t_z} = (-1)^{j+m+1/2+t_z} (a^\dagger_{j-m\frac{1}{2}-t_z})^\dagger \,. \tag{13.57}$$

This operator, when acting on the closed-shell state $|0\rangle$, produces the hole state

$$\tilde{a}_{jm\frac{1}{2}t_z}|0\rangle = |0; j^{-1}m\,\tfrac{1}{2}^{-1}\,t_z\rangle \,. \tag{13.58}$$

13.5. Many-particle state operators

In analogy with the state operator given in eq. (13.43), we can now introduce the adjoint state operator, which is defined by

$$\tilde{Z}^{JT}_{MT_z}(a,b) \equiv +\frac{1}{\sqrt{1+\delta_{ab}}}\,[\tilde{a}_{j_a\frac{1}{2}} \times \tilde{a}_{j_b\frac{1}{2}}]^{JT}_{MT_z} \,. \tag{13.59}$$

This definition is chosen such that the relation between Z and $\tilde{Z}$ will turn out to be identical to the one between $a^\dagger$ and $\tilde{a}$ given in eq. (13.57). For a derivation of this relation we shall consider identical particles first, in order that for simplicity the isospin labels may be suppressed.

One obtains from the definitions (13.42) and (13.43)

$$\begin{aligned} Z^J_{-M}(a,b) &= -\frac{1}{\sqrt{1+\delta_{ab}}}\,[a^\dagger_{j_a} \times a^\dagger_{j_b}]^J_{-M} \\ &= -\frac{1}{\sqrt{1+\delta_{ab}}}\sum_{m_a m_b} \langle j_a m_a j_b m_b | J - M\rangle\, a^\dagger_{j_a m_a} a^\dagger_{j_b m_b} \,. \end{aligned} \tag{13.60}$$

Taking the hermitian conjugate one finds

$$\begin{aligned} \{Z^J_{-M}(a,b)\}^\dagger &= -\frac{1}{\sqrt{1+\delta_{ab}}}\sum_{m_a m_b} \langle j_a m_a j_b m_b | J - M\rangle\, a_{j_b m_b} a_{j_a m_a} \\ &= -\frac{1}{\sqrt{1+\delta_{ab}}}\sum_{m_a m_b} (-1)^{j_a-m_a+j_b-m_b} \langle j_a m_a j_b m_b | J - M\rangle\, \tilde{a}_{j_b -m_b} \tilde{a}_{j_a -m_a} \\ &= \frac{1}{\sqrt{1+\delta_{ab}}}(-1)^{j_a+j_b+M}\sum_{m_a m_b} \langle j_a m_a j_b m_b | J - M\rangle\, \tilde{a}_{j_a -m_a} \tilde{a}_{j_b -m_b} \,, \end{aligned} \tag{13.61}$$

where for the last two steps eq. (13.53) and the commutation relation (13.9) have been used. Replacing finally the projection quantum numbers in the Clebsch-Gordan coefficient by their opposite values one obtains

$$\begin{aligned} \{Z^J_{-M}(a,b)\}^\dagger &= \frac{1}{\sqrt{1+\delta_{ab}}}(-1)^{J+M}\sum_{m_a m_b} \langle j_a - m_a j_b - m_b | JM\rangle\, \tilde{a}_{j_a -m_a} \tilde{a}_{j_b -m_b} \\ &= (-1)^{J+M}\, \tilde{Z}^J_M(a,b) \,. \end{aligned} \tag{13.62}$$

Including the isospin labels one derives similarly the relation

$$\widetilde{Z}^{JT}_{MT_z}(a, b) = (-1)^{J+M}(-1)^{T+T_z}\{Z^{JT}_{-M-T_z}(a, b)\}^\dagger \,. \tag{13.63}$$

In eq. (13.45) an implicit definition of the state operator Z for a single-shell, many-particle state has been given. Now also an implicit definition of the adjoint state operator $\widetilde{Z}$ can be given by

$$\langle|\widetilde{Z}^{JT}_{\alpha MT_z}(j^n) = (-1)^{J+M+T+T_z}\{\Psi^{j^n\,JT}_{\alpha-M-T_z}(r(1), \ldots, r(n))\}^* \,, \tag{13.64}$$

where $\widetilde{Z}$ is constructed exclusively from operators $\widetilde{a}_{jm\frac{1}{2}t_z}$. In eq. (13.64) the operator $\widetilde{Z}$ is seen to act to the left. The combination of the scalar vacuum and the operator $\widetilde{Z}$ should yield a state that transforms like a proper spherical tensor. From eq. (A.2.6) it is clear that the right-hand side of eq. (13.64) transforms like a proper spherical tensor indeed.

Simplifying the notation by employing, as was done before, a Greek letter for a set of quantum numbers we write a single-shell, n-particle state operator from now on as

$$Z^\Gamma(n) \equiv Z^{JT}_{MT_z}(j^n) \,. \tag{13.65}$$

Some (anti) commutation properties for the operators $Z^\Gamma(n)$ can be derived from the anticommutators (13.6), (13.9) and (13.16). One should realize that the state operators Z and $\widetilde{Z}$ are constructed exclusively from the operators $a^\dagger$ and $\widetilde{a}$, respectively. An interchange of the order of e.g. $Z^\Gamma(n)$ and $Z^\Gamma(n')$ will thus lead to nn' transpositions of creation operators, each involving a minus sign. One thus finds

$$[Z^\Gamma(n), Z^{\Gamma'}(n')] = [\widetilde{Z}^\Gamma(n), \widetilde{Z}^{\Gamma'}(n')] = 0 \quad \text{for } nn' \text{ even} \,, \tag{13.66a}$$

$$\{Z^\Gamma(n), Z^{\Gamma'}(n')\} = \{\widetilde{Z}^\Gamma(n), \widetilde{Z}^{\Gamma'}(n')\} = 0 \quad \text{for } nn' \text{ odd} \,, \tag{13.66b}$$

where the brackets [] and {} denote commutation and anticommutation, respectively. One also finds the relations

$$[Z^\Gamma(n), \widetilde{Z}^{\Gamma'}(n')] = 0 \qquad \text{for } nn' \text{ even} \,, \tag{13.67a}$$

$$\{Z^\Gamma(n), \widetilde{Z}^{\Gamma'}(n')\} = 0 \qquad \text{for } nn' \text{ odd} \,, \tag{13.67b}$$

provided the operators Z and $\widetilde{Z}$ do not have any orbit in common with each other, as follows from eq. (13.16).

As soon as the state operator $Z^\Gamma(n)$ involves more than two particles in one and the same orbit, the explicit construction is far more difficult than in other cases. The implicit definitions (13.45) and (13.64) suffice, however, since the construction of the single-shell, many-particle states in first quantization has been discussed in chapter 4.

13.6. Multishell operators

In order to calculate nuclear properties one has to evaluate matrix elements of the type $\langle\Phi|O|\Phi'\rangle$. In this section we introduce a standard form for the operators [French, Halbert, McGrory and Wong (1969)] used to construct the multishell states Φ and Φ'. We also define a standard form for the operators O that correspond to physical processes, for example transitions.

We shall discuss first the construction of multishell state operators from single-shell state operators. Suppose we wish to set up a shell-model calculation with the active nucleons occupying the orbits $\rho_1\rho_2 \ldots \rho_k$. Let us, for each orbit ρ_i, take together all single-particle creation operators to form one normalized state operator $Z^{\gamma_i}(n_i)$. For the multishell state operator a particular coupling scheme and phase will be defined in the standard form by

$$Z^{\Gamma_k}(\boldsymbol{n},\boldsymbol{x},\boldsymbol{\gamma},\boldsymbol{\Gamma}) \equiv (-1)^{\sum_{i=2}^{k} N_{i-1} n_i}$$ (13.68)

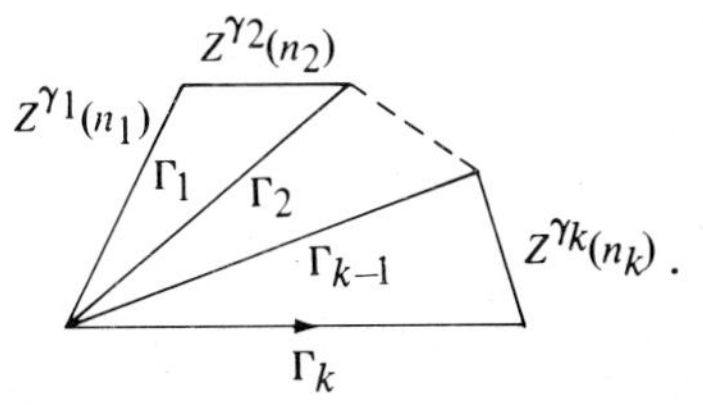

The set of quantum numbers specified by $\boldsymbol{n} = \{n_1, n_2, \ldots, n_k\}$ denotes the number of particles in each orbit. The set $\gamma = \{\gamma_1, \gamma_2, \ldots, \gamma_k\}$ represents the spin and isospin of each single-shell component. The diagram in eq. (13.68) indicates how the γ_i are coupled to intermediate spins and isospins denoted by the set $\boldsymbol{\Gamma} = \{\Gamma_1, \Gamma_2, \ldots, \Gamma_k\}$ with $\Gamma_1 = \gamma_1$. The set $\boldsymbol{x} = \{x_1, x_2, \ldots, x_k\}$, representing all further labels (e.g. radial quantum numbers, seniority etc.), may be necessary to specify the multishell, many-particle state operator uniquely. The number $N_{i-1} = \sum_{r=1}^{i-1} n_r$, entering the phase factor, denotes a partial sum of the number of particles. Its presence will become clear from the definition of the adjoint state operator that is discussed below. It is understood that the state operators act to the right in the order $Z^{\gamma_k}, Z^{\gamma_{k-1}}, \ldots, Z^{\gamma_1}$. More details will be given in the following chapter.

Correspondingly the adjoint state operator $\tilde{Z}$ is then given by the coupling scheme

$$\tilde{Z}^{\Gamma_k}(\boldsymbol{n},\boldsymbol{x},\boldsymbol{\gamma},\boldsymbol{\Gamma}) =$$ (13.69)

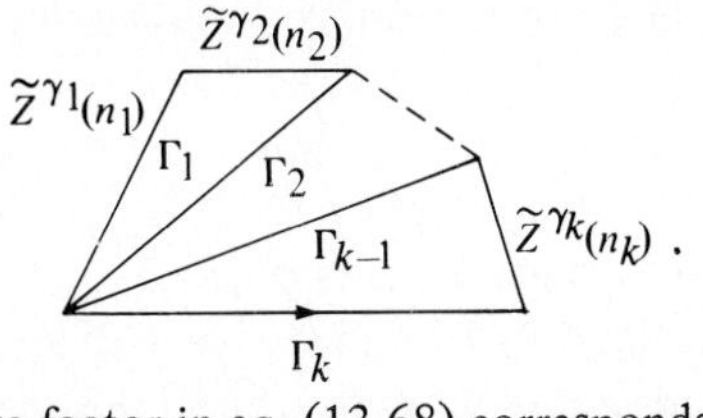

The particular phase factor in eq. (13.68) corresponds with the absence of such a factor in the adjoint equation (13.69). If this phase were omitted from eq. (13.68) then it should be present in eq. (13.69), since hermitian conjugation inverses the order of the operators. Thus one can maintain the same coupling order in both Z and $\tilde{Z}$.

We now turn to the operators describing physical processes. It was seen in sect. 13.2 that all such operators could be expressed in terms of creation and annihilation operators that are summed over all single-particle labels. Thus the matrix elements of these operators, taken between many-particle states described by the state operators Z^{Γ} and $\widetilde{Z}^{\Gamma'}$, can be reduced to summations over vacuum expectation values of products of creation and annihilation operators. For a systematic reduction it is useful first to agree upon a standard-form expansion of operators in second quantization. This standard-form expansion is given by

$$O^{\Omega_k} = \sum_{\boldsymbol{q},\boldsymbol{y},\boldsymbol{\omega},\boldsymbol{\Omega}} K(\boldsymbol{q},\boldsymbol{y},\boldsymbol{\omega},\boldsymbol{\Omega})\, F^{\Omega_k}(\boldsymbol{q},\boldsymbol{y},\boldsymbol{\omega},\boldsymbol{\Omega}) \tag{13.70}$$

with the definition

$F^{\Omega_k}(\boldsymbol{q},\boldsymbol{y},\boldsymbol{\omega},\boldsymbol{\Omega}) \equiv$ 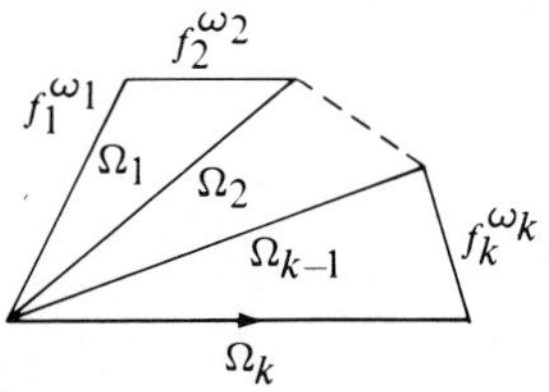 . (13.71)

The operator F^{Ω_k} consists of coupled products of creation and annihilation operators and nothing else. It thus depends only on the number of particles that are to be created and/or annihilated in each orbit and on the way the spins and isospins of these particles are coupled. The physical aspects of the operator O^{Ω_k} are combined in the expansion coefficients K. As an illustration we refer to a two-body operator that is given in second quantization by eq. (13.31) as $\frac{1}{4}\Sigma_{\alpha\beta\gamma\delta}\langle\alpha\beta|O|\gamma\delta\rangle \times a_\alpha^\dagger a_\beta^\dagger a_\delta a_\gamma$. The two-body matrix elements $\langle\alpha\beta|O|\gamma\delta\rangle$ now determine the coefficients K, while the operators $a_\alpha^\dagger$, $a_\beta^\dagger$, a_γ and a_δ are used to construct the operators F^{Ω_k}. The operator F^{Ω_k}, defined in the space spanned by the orbits $\rho_1\rho_2 \ldots \rho_k$, is decomposed into coupled products of single-shell operators $f_i^{\omega_i} \equiv f_{y_i}^{\omega_i}(q_i)$. Each $f_{y_i}^{\omega_i}(q_i)$ consists of operators $a_{\rho_i}^\dagger$ and $\widetilde{a}_{\rho_i}$ for one and the same orbit ρ_i only. The rank ω_i denotes the spin and isospin of the coupled product of the operators $a_{\rho_i}^\dagger$ and $\widetilde{a}_{\rho_i}$. The ω_i are coupled subsequently to intermediate values Ω_j. The symbols q_i and y_i represent additional labels that may be necessary to specify the coupled products of the operators $a_{\rho_i}^\dagger$ and $\widetilde{a}_{\rho_i}$ (see eq. (14.12)). The bold-face arguments in the expansion coefficients $K(\boldsymbol{q},\boldsymbol{y},\boldsymbol{\omega},\boldsymbol{\Omega})$ denote sets of labels, i.e. $\boldsymbol{q} = \{q_1, q_2, \ldots, q_k\}$, $\boldsymbol{y} = \{y_1, y_2, \ldots, y_k\}$, $\boldsymbol{\omega} = \{\omega_1, \omega_2, \ldots, \omega_k\}$, $\boldsymbol{\Omega} = \{\Omega_1, \Omega_2, \ldots, \Omega_k\}$ with $\Omega_1 = \omega_1$.

For a derivation of the expansion coefficients $K(\boldsymbol{q},\boldsymbol{y},\boldsymbol{\omega},\boldsymbol{\Omega})$ one starts from eqs. (13.24) or (13.31). The coefficient K is determined for each set $\boldsymbol{q} = \{q_1, q_2, \ldots, q_k\}$ by particular matrix elements $\langle\alpha|O|\gamma\rangle$ or $\langle\alpha\beta|O|\gamma\delta\rangle$. Since the creation and annihilation operators are coupled to angular momenta and spins $\boldsymbol{\omega}, \boldsymbol{\Omega}$ in eq. (13.71), however, one also has to apply corresponding couplings to the matrix elements $\langle\alpha|O|\gamma\rangle$ or $\langle\alpha\beta|O|\gamma\delta\rangle$ before the coefficients $K(\boldsymbol{q},\boldsymbol{y},\boldsymbol{\omega},\boldsymbol{\Omega})$ are obtained. The evaluation will be discussed in detail in the next chapter.

Whereas the multishell state operators Z^{Γ} and $\widetilde{Z}^{\Gamma}$ are constructed from normalized single-shell state operators with a particular phase convention and normalization, no such conditions are imposed on the single-shell operators $f_{y_i}^{\omega_i}(q_i)$. Moreover, the operators $f_{y_i}^{\omega_i}(q_i)$ may contain operators $a^{\dagger}$ as well as $\tilde{a}$ at the same time. The only requirement for the standard-form operator O^{Ω_k} in eq. (13.70) is that the different single-shell operators $f_{y_i}^{\omega_i}(q_i)$ are coupled in the order given. In other words, for the standard state operators Z and $\widetilde{Z}$, as well as for the standard-form operator F defined in eq. (13.71), a definite order of allowed orbits $\rho_1\rho_2\rho_3 \ldots \rho_k$ is specified.

With the standard form expansions (13.68)–(13.71) it is possible to reduce the many-particle, multishell matrix elements in terms of single-shell matrix elements. This is achieved by means of successive decouplings of all operators referring to one particular orbit.

CHAPTER 14

MATRIX ELEMENTS IN SECOND QUANTIZATION

In the previous chapter it has been demonstrated that wave functions as well as operators can be represented in the formalism of second quantization. In this chapter we investigate how in this formalism matrix elements between many-particle, multishell states can be evaluated in a very systematic way. The present treatment leans heavily on the approach [French, Halbert, McGrory and Wong (1969)] used for the construction of a general shell-model code.

In sect. 14.1 the crucial reduction formula is derived that expresses matrix elements for particles in more than one shell in terms of products of matrix elements for particles in a single shell. The evaluation of the single-shell matrix elements can be performed conveniently once the relation between c.f.p. in first and second quantization is established, as is done in sect. 14.2. In sect. 14.3 the calculation of the single-shell matrix elements is discussed in detail. The second-quantization formalism is applied first to the Hamiltonian, the operators of which are treated in sect. 14.4. The detailed discussion of the one- and two-body operators of the Hamiltonian is given in sects. 14.5 and 14.6, respectively. This involves the expansion coefficients in the reduction of the many-particle, multishell matrix elements in terms of single-shell matrix elements.

14.1. General reduction formula

It was seen in chapter 13 that a many-particle, multishell state can be generated with the state operators defined in eqs. (13.68) and (13.69) and that operators can be written in the standard-form expansion (13.70).

Let us consider a general k-shell matrix element represented by

$$\langle (-1)^{\Sigma_{i=2}^{k} N_{i-1} n_i} Z^{\Gamma_k}(\boldsymbol{n}, \boldsymbol{x}, \boldsymbol{\gamma}, \boldsymbol{\Gamma}) | O^{\Omega_k} | (-1)^{\Sigma_{i=2}^{k} N'_{i-1} n'_i} Z^{\Gamma'_k}(\boldsymbol{n}', \boldsymbol{x}', \boldsymbol{\gamma}', \boldsymbol{\Gamma}') \rangle , \qquad (14.1)$$

where the states are represented by their state operators only and the symbol for the vacuum state $|\rangle$ is suppressed. In line with the Dirac notation the left-hand wave function in eq. (14.1) must be understood as an adjoint. The geometrical dependence of the matrix elements on the projection quantum numbers can be factored out with the aid of the Wigner-Eckart theorem (see appendix A.3.a). Let us denote a matrix element reduced in space and isospace by

$$\langle Z^{\Gamma_k}|||O^{\Omega_k}|||Z^{\Gamma'_k}\rangle = \sum_{q,y,\omega,\Omega} K(q,y,\omega,\Omega)\,\langle Z^{\Gamma_k}|||F^{\Omega_k}(q,y,\omega,\Omega)|||Z^{\Gamma'_k}\rangle\,, \tag{14.2}$$

where eq. (13.70) is used to obtain the right-hand side and where for brevity many of the labels are suppressed.

The approach for the further evaluation of the reduced matrix element (14.2) is that successively the dependence on each subshell ρ_j is peeled off. Of course, this requires that the operators $a^\dagger_{\rho_j}$ and $\widetilde{a}_{\rho_j}$, present in each of the three parts of the reduced matrix elements, are separated off and for each subshell are taken together. In the first place this necessitates the recoupling of angular momenta and isospins, which can be done with the use of Racah algebra. In the second place the necessary reshuffling of the operators $a^\dagger_{\rho_j}$ and $\widetilde{a}_{\rho_j}$ can be performed when their anticommutation relations are taken into account. It is in particular the systematic way in which one can reorder creation and annihilation operators that makes the second-quantization formalism such a preeminent tool for the reduction of multishell matrix elements.

From eq. (13.68) one obtains for the state operator

$$Z^{\Gamma_k} = (-1)^{N_{k-1}n_k}[Z^{\Gamma_{k-1}} \times Z^{\gamma_k}]^{\Gamma_k}\,. \tag{14.3}$$

Similarly one finds from eq. (13.71) for the standard-form operators

$$F^{\Omega_k} = [F^{\Omega_{k-1}} \times f^{\omega_k}]^{\Omega_k}\,. \tag{14.4}$$

Thus the reduced matrix elements of F^{Ω_k} can be expressed as

$$\langle Z^{\Gamma_k}|||F^{\Omega_k}|||Z^{\Gamma'_k}\rangle$$

$$= \langle (-1)^{N_{k-1}n_k}[Z^{\Gamma_{k-1}} \times Z^{\gamma_k}]^{\Gamma_k}|||[F^{\Omega_{k-1}} \times f^{\omega_k}]^{\Omega_k}|||(-1)^{N'_{k-1}n'_k}[Z^{\Gamma'_{k-1}} \times Z^{\gamma'_k}]^{\Gamma'_k}\rangle\,. \tag{14.5}$$

Before evaluating the general case, let us first consider the simpler two-shell case $k = 2$,

$$\langle Z^{\Gamma_2}|||F^{\Omega_2}|||Z^{\Gamma'_2}\rangle$$

$$= \langle (-1)^{n_1n_2}[Z^{\gamma_1} \times Z^{\gamma_2}]^{\Gamma_2}|||[f^{\omega_1} \times f^{\omega_2}]^{\Omega_2}|||(-1)^{n'_1n'_2}[Z^{\gamma'_1} \times Z^{\gamma'_2}]^{\Gamma'_2}\rangle\,. \tag{14.6}$$

The next step is to write the two-shell matrix element (14.6) as a product of two matrix elements that each refer to one particular orbit. The latter two matrix elements are called *single-shell matrix elements* (s.s.m.e.). In order to express the two-shell matrix element (14.6) in terms of single-shell matrix elements $\langle Z^{\gamma_1}|||f^{\omega_1}|||Z^{\gamma_1}\rangle$ for orbit 1 and $\langle Z^{\gamma_2}|||f^{\omega_2}|||Z^{\gamma_2}\rangle$ for orbit 2, the angular-momentum coupling scheme must be changed. Not only a recoupling of the angular momenta is involved, however, but also a reordering of creation and annihilation operators. This leads to an additional phase factor. For a determination of this phase factor one must count the number of transpositions of anticommuting annihilation and creation operators. The necessary reordering can be illustrated by the arrows (I) and (II) as

(I)

$$\tilde{Z}^{\gamma_1} \; \tilde{Z}^{\gamma_2} \; f^{\omega_1} \; f^{\omega_2} \; Z^{\gamma_1'} \; Z^{\gamma_2'} .$$

(II)

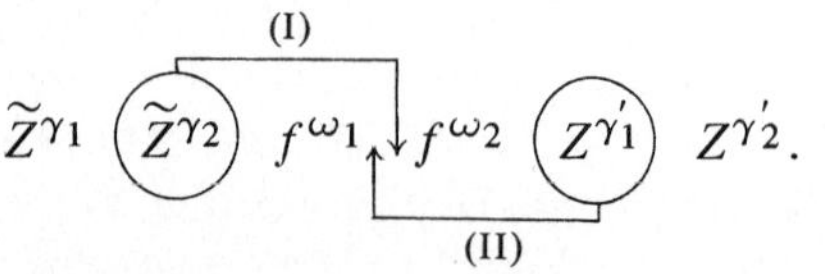

The state operators $\tilde{Z}^{\gamma_i}$ $(Z^{\gamma_i'})$ contain n_i (n_i') operators $\tilde{a}_i$ $(a_i^\dagger)$. The operators f^{ω_i} contain n_{ω_i} operators consisting of a mixture of both $a_i^\dagger$ and $\tilde{a}_i$. The reordering (I) implies that the n_2 operators $\tilde{a}_2$ in $\tilde{Z}^{\gamma_2}$ must be interchanged with n_{ω_1} operators $a_1^\dagger$ and $\tilde{a}_1$ in f^{ω_1}. This leads, according to eqs. (13.6) (13.9) and (13.16), to a phase factor $(-1)^{n_2 n_{\omega_1}}$. It should be remarked that no Kronecker deltas are involved, since the operators $a^\dagger$ or $\tilde{a}$ in $\tilde{Z}^{\gamma_2}$ and f^{ω_1} refer to different orbits. In the present formalism matrix elements like $\langle Z^{\gamma_1} ||| f^{\omega_1} ||| Z^{\gamma_1'} \rangle$ are evaluated by taking the vacuum expectation value of the product of all creation and annihilation operators contained in $Z^{\gamma_1}, f^{\omega_1}$ and $Z^{\gamma_1'}$. Hence, for a nonvanishing matrix element, the total number of operators $a^\dagger$ must be equal to that of $\tilde{a}$. One thus has the requirement that $n_1 + n_{\omega_1} + n_1'$ must be even, i.e. $(-1)^{n_{\omega_1}} = (-1)^{n_1 + n_1'}$. Therefore the phase factor corresponding to the reordering (I) can be written as $(-1)^{n_2(n_1+n_1')}$. Similarly it follows that a phase factor $(-1)^{n_1' n_2'}$ corresponds with the subsequent reordering (II). Taking all phases together one obtains the relation

$$\tilde{Z}^{\gamma_1} \tilde{Z}^{\gamma_2} f^{\omega_1} f^{\omega_2} (-1)^{n_1' n_2'} Z^{\gamma_1'} Z^{\gamma_2'} = (-1)^{(n_1+n_1')n_2} \tilde{Z}^{\gamma_1} f^{\omega_1} Z^{\gamma_1'} \tilde{Z}^{\gamma_2} f^{\omega_2} Z^{\gamma_2'} . \qquad (14.7)$$

After having determined the phase factor involved in the reshuffling of the various operators, we are now left with the corresponding change in angular-momentum coupling. Here one should realize that in addition to the vector couplings $\boldsymbol{\gamma}_1 + \boldsymbol{\gamma}_2 = \boldsymbol{\Gamma}_2$, $\boldsymbol{\omega}_1 + \boldsymbol{\omega}_2 = \boldsymbol{\Omega}_2$ and $\boldsymbol{\gamma}_1' + \boldsymbol{\gamma}_2' = \boldsymbol{\Gamma}_2'$, the reduced matrix element (14.6) contains also the vector coupling $\boldsymbol{\Gamma}_2' + \boldsymbol{\Omega}_2 = \boldsymbol{\Gamma}_2$, as is clear from eq. (A.3.a16).

The relation between the two coupling schemes considered can be illustrated most conveniently in terms of diagrams as (cf. eq. (A.1.c1))

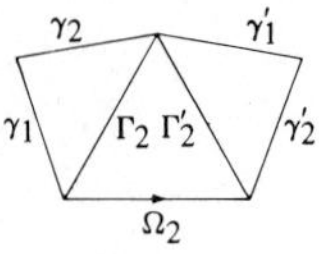

$$= \sum_{\omega_1 \omega_2} \sqrt{(2\Gamma_2+1)(2\Gamma_2'+1)(2\omega_1+1)(2\omega_2+1)}$$

$$\times \begin{Bmatrix} \gamma_1 & \gamma_2 & \Gamma_2 \\ \gamma_1' & \gamma_2' & \Gamma_2' \\ \omega_1 & \omega_2 & \Omega_2 \end{Bmatrix}$$

. (14.8)

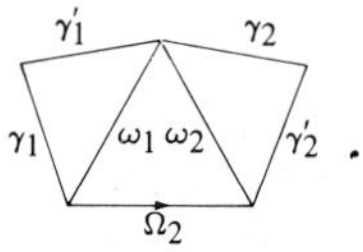

Applying eqs. (14.7) and (14.8) to eq. (14.6) one arrives at the final relation

$$\langle Z^{\Gamma_2}|||F^{\Omega_2}|||Z^{\Gamma'_2}\rangle = (-1)^{(n_1+n'_1)n_2}\sqrt{(2\Gamma_2+1)(2\Gamma'_2+1)(2\Omega_2+1)}\begin{Bmatrix}\gamma_1 & \gamma_2 & \Gamma_2\\ \gamma'_1 & \gamma'_2 & \Gamma'_2\\ \omega_1 & \omega_2 & \Omega_2\end{Bmatrix}$$

$$\times \langle Z^{\gamma_1}|||f^{\omega_1}|||Z^{\gamma'_1}\rangle\langle Z^{\gamma_2}|||f^{\omega_2}|||Z^{\gamma'_2}\rangle\,. \qquad (14.9)$$

For a further evaluation we must calculate the single-shell matrix elements $\langle Z^{\gamma_i}|||f^{\omega_i}|||Z^{\gamma'_i}\rangle$, where all particle and operator labels refer to one and the same orbit. It should be pointed out that the second-quantization formalism does no longer offer an advantage over the first-quantization procedures when single-shell matrix elements must be calculated. In neither formalism the explicit use of coefficients of fractional parentage can be avoided as soon as equivalent particles are involved.

The derivation of the two-shell formula (14.9) can be generalized in a straightforward manner to the case of an arbitrary number of orbits. Again we start from eq. (14.5), where $\widetilde{Z}^{\gamma_k}$, f^{ω_k} and $Z^{\gamma'_k}$ contain all operators acting in the orbit k, i.e. the operators $\widetilde{Z}^{\Gamma_{k-1}}$, $F^{\Omega_{k-1}}$ and $Z^{\Gamma'_{k-1}}$ contain none of the latter. Exactly as orbit 2 was decoupled to obtain eq. (14.9), we can now decouple orbit k to obtain an expression in $\langle Z^{\Gamma_{k-1}}|||F^{\Omega_{k-1}}|||Z^{\Gamma'_{k-1}}\rangle$ and $\langle Z^{\gamma_k}|||f^{\omega_k}|||Z^{\gamma'_k}\rangle$. The next step now is, of course, to decouple orbit $k-1$ from the first of the latter two reduced matrix elements. Repeated decouplings then yield the final result for the operator O^{Ω_k} given by the general expansion

$$\langle Z^{\Gamma_k}(\boldsymbol{n},\boldsymbol{x},\boldsymbol{\gamma},\boldsymbol{\Gamma})|||O^{\Omega_k}|||Z^{\Gamma'_k}(\boldsymbol{n}',\boldsymbol{x}',\boldsymbol{\gamma}',\boldsymbol{\Gamma}')\rangle$$

$$= (-1)^{\sum_{i=1}^{k} n_i(N_{i-1}-N'_{i-1})}\sum_{\boldsymbol{q},\boldsymbol{y},\boldsymbol{\omega},\boldsymbol{\Omega}} K(\boldsymbol{q},\boldsymbol{y},\boldsymbol{\omega},\boldsymbol{\Omega})\langle n_1x_1\gamma_1|||f^{\omega_1}_{y_1}(q_1)|||n'_1x'_1\gamma'_1\rangle$$

$$\times\prod_{i=2}^{k}\sqrt{(2\Gamma_i+1)(2\Omega_i+1)(2\Gamma'_i+1)}\begin{Bmatrix}\Gamma_{i-1} & \gamma_i & \Gamma_i\\ \Gamma'_{i-1} & \gamma'_i & \Gamma'_i\\ \Omega_{i-1} & \omega_i & \Omega_i\end{Bmatrix}\langle n_ix_i\gamma_i|||f^{\omega_i}_{y_i}(q_i)|||n'_ix'_i\gamma'_i\rangle\,. \qquad (14.10)$$

For convenience the meaning of all symbols appearing in eq. (14.10) is given once more.

The many-particle, multishell state operators are defined according to eq. (13.68) by

$$Z^{\Gamma_k}(\boldsymbol{n},\boldsymbol{x},\boldsymbol{\gamma},\boldsymbol{\Gamma}) \equiv (-1)^{\sum_{i=2}^{k}N_{i-1}n_i}$$

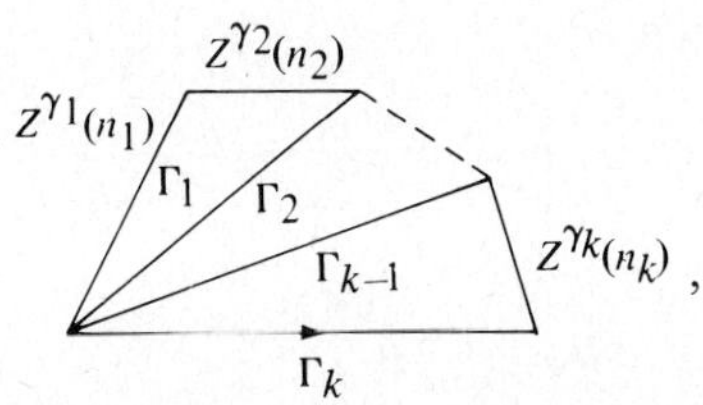

, (14.11)

where the single-shell state operators $Z^{\gamma_i}(n_i)$ are defined in eqs. (13.45) and (13.65). The symbol k denotes the number of orbits ρ_i ($i = 1, ..., k$) taken into account. The following sets of labels are used:

$\boldsymbol{n} = (n_1, ..., n_k)$: the number of particles in each orbit ρ_i,
$\boldsymbol{\gamma} = (\gamma_1, ..., \gamma_k)$: spin and isospin of each state $\rho_i^{n_i}$,
$\boldsymbol{x} = (x_1, ..., x_k)$: further quantum numbers for each state $\rho_i^{n_i}$ (e.g. seniority),
$\boldsymbol{\Gamma} = (\Gamma_1, ..., \Gamma_k)$: the intermediate spins and isospins as indicated in the diagram given above, and
$N_i = \Sigma_{r=1}^{i} n_r$: the total number of particles in the orbits $\rho_1, \rho_2, ..., \rho_i$.

The operator O^{Ω_k} can be expanded in terms of coefficients $K(\boldsymbol{q}, \boldsymbol{y}, \boldsymbol{\omega}, \boldsymbol{\Omega})$ and standard-form operators $F^{\Omega_k}(\boldsymbol{q}, \boldsymbol{y}, \boldsymbol{\omega}, \boldsymbol{\Omega})$ according to eq. (13.70). The coefficients K contain the one- or two-body matrix elements. Their evaluation for specific operators is discussed later in this and the following chapter. The operators F are defined according to eq. (13.71) as

$F^{\Omega_k}(\boldsymbol{q}, \boldsymbol{y}, \boldsymbol{\omega}, \boldsymbol{\Omega}) \equiv$ 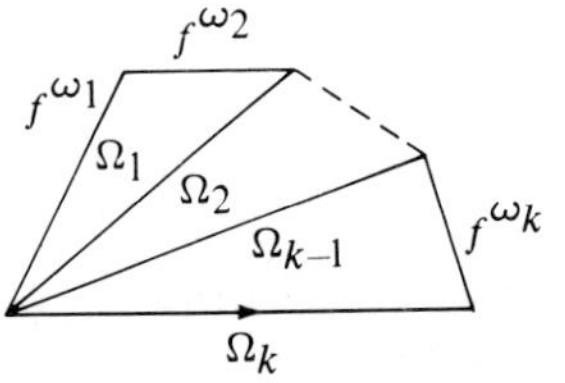

, (14.12)

where the single-shell operators $f^{\omega_i} \equiv f_{y_i}^{\omega_i}(q_i)$ are coupled products of creation and annihilation operators referring to one orbit ρ_i. The following sets of labels are used:

$\boldsymbol{q} = (q_1, ..., q_k)$: specifies the coupled products of $a_{\rho_i}^\dagger$ and $\tilde{a}_{\rho_i}$ for each orbit ρ_i; for one- and two-body operators the nine possibilities are given in eq. (14.24),
$\boldsymbol{y} = (y_1, ..., y_k)$: further quantum numbers to specify f^{ω_i},
$\boldsymbol{\omega} = (\omega_1, ..., \omega_k)$: the rank of each single-shell operator f^{ω_i},
$\boldsymbol{\Omega} = (\Omega_1, ..., \Omega_k)$: the intermediate ranks as indicated in the diagram given above.

The expression (14.10) is the starting point for a large computer program [French, Halbert, McGrory and Wong (1969)]. This reduction turns out to be far more convenient than that in first quantization as soon as three or more orbits are involved. It is seen that the many-particle, multishell matrix element of the operator O^{Ω_k} is reduced to a summation over products of coefficients K, determined by the particular operator O^{Ω_k}, and what one calls the single-shell matrix elements $\langle nx\gamma|||f^{\omega}|||n'x'\gamma'\rangle$. The latter concern one orbit only and are discussed in sect. 14.3. For the calculation of the matrix element of O^{Ω_k} between actual wave functions of mixed-configuration, the result of eq. (14.10) still must be multiplied with the amplitudes of the components $Z^{\Gamma_k}(\boldsymbol{n}, \boldsymbol{x}, \boldsymbol{\gamma}, \boldsymbol{\Gamma})|\rangle$ and $Z^{\Gamma'_k}(\boldsymbol{n}', \boldsymbol{x}', \boldsymbol{\gamma}', \boldsymbol{\Gamma}')|\rangle$ and a summation over these contributions must be performed. The expansion coefficients $K(\boldsymbol{q}, \boldsymbol{y}, \boldsymbol{\omega}, \boldsymbol{\Omega})$ will be discussed later in this chapter.

14.2. Relation between c.f.p. in first and second quantization

Before the calculation of the single-shell matrix elements is discussed, we derive first a relation between c.f.p. in first and second quantization. Consider the operator of rank Δ defined by

$$U^{\Delta}_{\rho\sigma} = \frac{[a^{\dagger}_{\rho} \times \tilde{a}_{\sigma}]^{\Delta}}{\sqrt{2\Delta + 1}} \,. \tag{14.13}$$

The matrix elements between the single-particle states α and β for this product operator can be written according to eq. (A.3.d13) as

$$\langle\alpha ||| U^{\Delta}_{\rho\sigma} ||| \beta\rangle = \frac{1}{\sqrt{2\Delta+1}} \langle\alpha ||| [a^{\dagger}_{\rho} \times \tilde{a}_{\sigma}]^{\Delta} ||| \beta\rangle$$
$$= (-1)^{\alpha+\Delta+\beta} \sum_{\Lambda} \begin{Bmatrix} \beta & \alpha & \Delta \\ \rho & \sigma & \Lambda \end{Bmatrix} \langle\alpha ||| a^{\dagger}_{\rho} ||| \Lambda\rangle \langle\Lambda ||| \tilde{a}_{\sigma} ||| \beta\rangle \,. \tag{14.14}$$

The only intermediate state contributing to this summation is the vacuum state with $\Lambda = 0$ and hence one finds, inserting the explicit value of the 6-*j* symbol,

$$\langle\alpha ||| U^{\Delta}_{\rho\sigma} ||| \beta\rangle = \frac{\langle\rho ||| a^{\dagger}_{\rho} |||\rangle \langle ||| \tilde{a}_{\sigma} ||| \sigma\rangle}{\sqrt{(2\rho+1)(2\sigma+1)}} \delta_{\alpha\rho}\delta_{\beta\sigma} = \delta_{\alpha\rho}\delta_{\beta\sigma} \,. \tag{14.15}$$

Within a single orbit the operator $U^{\Delta}_{\rho\sigma}$, introduced in eq. (14.13), reduces to Racah's unit tensor, $\langle\alpha ||| U^{\Delta}_{\rho\rho} ||| \beta\rangle = \delta_{\alpha\beta}\delta_{\alpha\rho}$. In fact eq. (14.13) gives this unit tensor in second-quantization formalism.

We shall evaluate the matrix element of $U^{\Delta}_{\rho\rho}$ between the states $|\rho^n\Gamma\rangle$ in first-quantization formalism to start with. In an n-particle system the operator $U^{\Delta}_{\rho\rho}$ acts symmetrically on all n particles and therefore can be written in first quantization as $U^{\Delta}_{\rho\rho} = \Sigma_{i=1}^{n} u^{\Delta}_{\rho\rho}(i)$. Now the methods of sect. 10.5 can be used for the evaluation of the reduced matrix element

$\langle\rho^n\Gamma ||| U^{\Delta}_{\rho\rho} ||| \rho^n\Gamma'\rangle = \langle$ 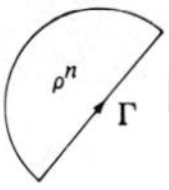 $||| U^{\Delta}_{\rho\rho} |||$ 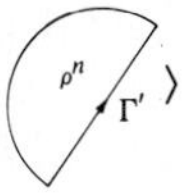 $\rangle = n\langle$ 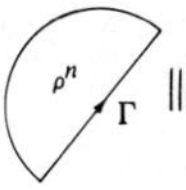 $||| u^{\Delta}_{\rho\rho}(n) |||$ 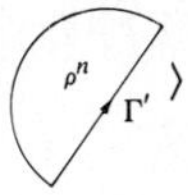 $\rangle$, (14.16)

where $u^{\Delta}_{\rho\rho}(n)$ denotes the operator that acts in first quantization on the coordinates of particle n only. With the standard c.f.p. expansion we then obtain

$\langle\rho^n\Gamma ||| U^{\Delta}_{\rho\rho} ||| \rho^n\Gamma'\rangle$

$= n \sum_{\Gamma_1\Gamma_1'} \langle\rho^n\Gamma | \} \rho^{n-1}\Gamma_1\rangle \langle\rho^n\Gamma' | \} \rho^{n-1}\Gamma_1'\rangle \langle$ 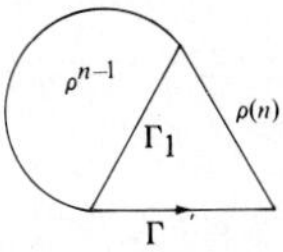 $||| u^{\Delta}_{\rho\rho}(n) |||$ 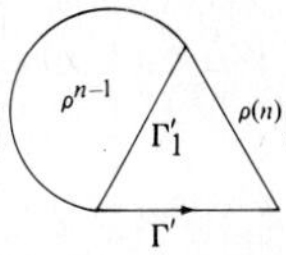 $\rangle$.

(14.17)

Since we are dealing with reduced matrix elements and the operator $u^{\Delta}_{\rho\rho}(n)$ acts on the particle n only, relation (A.3.d8) can be used to obtain

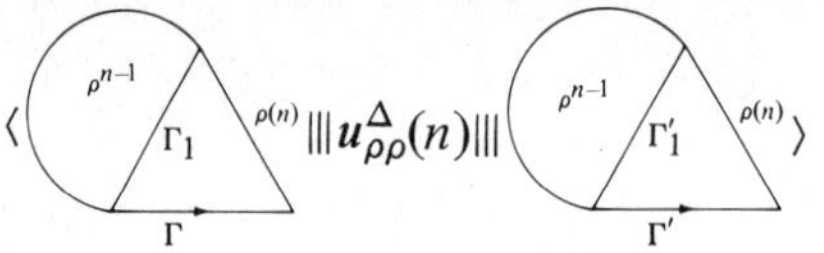

$$= (-1)^{\Gamma_1+\rho+\Gamma+\Delta}\sqrt{(2\Gamma+1)(2\Gamma'+1)}\begin{Bmatrix}\rho & \rho & \Delta\\ \Gamma' & \Gamma & \Gamma_1\end{Bmatrix}\langle\rho(n)|||u^{\Delta}_{\rho\rho}(n)|||\rho(n)\rangle\,\delta_{\Gamma_1\Gamma'_1}\,. \tag{14.18}$$

Since according to eq. (14.15) the value of the reduced matrix element in eq. (14.18) is equal to unity, one obtains, combining eqs. (14.17) and (14.18),

$$\langle\rho^n\Gamma|||U^{\Delta}_{\rho\rho}|||\rho^n\Gamma'\rangle = n\sum_{\Gamma_1}\langle\rho^n\Gamma|\}\rho^{n-1}\Gamma_1\rangle\langle\rho^n\Gamma'|\}\rho^{n-1}\Gamma_1\rangle$$

$$\times(-1)^{\Gamma_1+\rho+\Gamma+\Delta}\sqrt{(2\Gamma+1)(2\Gamma'+1)}\begin{Bmatrix}\rho & \rho & \Delta\\ \Gamma' & \Gamma & \Gamma_1\end{Bmatrix}. \tag{14.19}$$

For an evaluation of the reduced matrix element $\langle\rho^n\Gamma|||U^{\Delta}_{\rho\rho}|||\rho^n\Gamma'\rangle$, with the operator $U^{\Delta}_{\rho\rho}$ represented in second quantization according to eq. (14.13), a complete set of intermediate states is inserted between the operators $a^{\dagger}_{\rho}$ and $\widetilde{a}_{\rho}$. As a result we obtain, employing eq. (A.3.d13),

$$\langle\rho^n\Gamma|||U^{\Delta}_{\rho\rho}|||\rho^n\Gamma'\rangle$$

$$= (-1)^{\Gamma+\Delta+\Gamma'}\sum_{\Gamma_1}\begin{Bmatrix}\rho & \rho & \Delta\\ \Gamma' & \Gamma & \Gamma_1\end{Bmatrix}\langle\rho^n\Gamma|||a^{\dagger}_{\rho}|||\rho^{n-1}\Gamma_1\rangle\langle\rho^{n-1}\Gamma_1|||\widetilde{a}_{\rho}|||\rho^n\Gamma'\rangle\,. \tag{14.20}$$

From the relation (see (A.3.b8))

$$\langle\rho^{n-1}\Gamma_1|||\widetilde{a}_{\rho}|||\rho^n\Gamma'\rangle = (-1)^{\Gamma_1+\rho-\Gamma'}\langle\rho^n\Gamma'|||a^{\dagger}_{\rho}|||\rho^{n-1}\Gamma_1\rangle \tag{14.21}$$

we obtain

$$\langle\rho^n\Gamma|||U^{\Delta}_{\rho\rho}|||\rho^n\Gamma'\rangle$$

$$= \sum_{\Gamma_1}(-1)^{\Gamma_1+\rho+\Gamma+\Delta}\begin{Bmatrix}\rho & \rho & \Delta\\ \Gamma' & \Gamma & \Gamma_1\end{Bmatrix}\langle\rho^n\Gamma|||a^{\dagger}_{\rho}|||\rho^{n-1}\Gamma_1\rangle\langle\rho^n\Gamma'|||a^{\dagger}_{\rho}|||\rho^{n-1}\Gamma_1\rangle\,. \tag{14.22}$$

Comparing eqs. (14.19) and (14.22) we see that we may put

$$\langle\rho^n\Gamma|\}\rho^{n-1}\Gamma_1\rangle = \frac{\langle\rho^n\Gamma|||a^{\dagger}_{\rho}|||\rho^{n-1}\Gamma_1\rangle}{\sqrt{n(2\Gamma+1)}}, \tag{14.23}$$

where the left-hand side denotes a c.f.p. in first quantization and the numerator at the right-hand side a single-shell matrix element. This correspondence involves a fixing of phases between wave functions in first- and second-quantization representation. The c.f.p. are defined to decouple the *last* particle of a group of equivalent particles. The phase choice made in eq. (14.23) is consistent with the convention of eq. (13.5) that the numbering of the operators $a_\rho^\dagger$ runs opposite to the way the wave function in first quantization is labelled. The first (i.e. the very left) operator of a product of creation operators $a_\rho^\dagger$ acts last! Thus, if another convention is chosen an extra phase factor in eq. (14.23) is appropriate. For instance, when one takes $a_{\rho_1}^\dagger a_{\rho_2}^\dagger \ldots a_{\rho_n}^\dagger|0\rangle = |\rho_1\rho_2 \ldots \rho_n\rangle$, a factor $(-1)^{n-1}$ must be added to eq. (14.23) in order to account for the $n-1$ transpositions that are necessary to bring the particle created by $a_{\rho_n}^\dagger$ to the last position.

14.3. The evaluation of single-shell matrix elements

Let us consider one- and two-body operators only. Hence we are dealing with products of either one creation and one annihilation operator or two creation and two annihilation operators (cf. eqs. (13.24) and (13.31)) acting in one or more orbits. Any possible *single*-shell one- or two-body operator $f_y^\omega(q)$, constructed from operators $a^\dagger$ and $\tilde{a}$ given above, must belong to one of the following nine categories (cf. chapter 15) labelled by q as follows:

$q = 1 : 1 \qquad q = 2 : a_\rho^\dagger \qquad q = 3 : \tilde{a}_\rho$

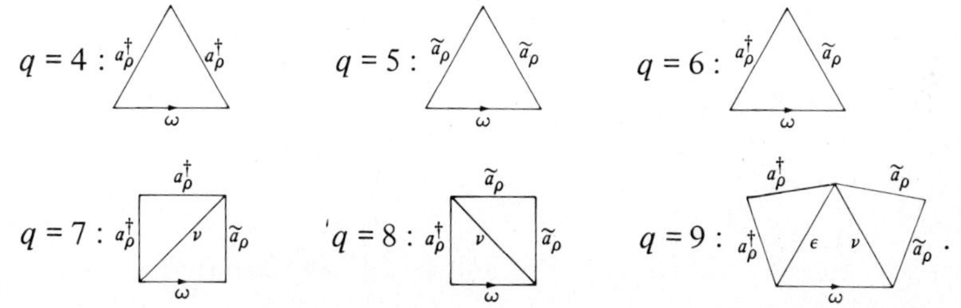

(14.24)

The label y denotes the further quantum numbers ϵ and ν, where necessary. A complete set of single-shell matrix elements (s.s.m.e.) is obtained as soon as the matrix elements of the operators (14.24) are calculated for all possible single-shell states $|\rho^n\Gamma\rangle$. It turns out that all s.s.m.e. can be expressed in terms of c.f.p. and Racah coefficients. For the evaluation of the s.s.m.e. of products of two or more creation and/or annihilation operators use is made of the intermediate-state expansion (A.3.d14). The relation for c.f.p. in the second-quantization formalism is given in eq. (14.23). The s.s.m.e. $\langle\rho^n\Gamma|||f^\omega|||\rho^{n'}\Gamma'\rangle$ for each of the nine categories of f^ω, given in eq. (14.24), are derived below.

$\underline{q = 1}$: The evaluation of the s.s.m.e. of the unit tensor operator follows immediately from the Wigner-Eckart theorem, which leads to (cf. eq. (A.3.c2))

$$\langle \rho^n \Gamma ||| \mathbf{1} ||| \rho^{n'} \Gamma' \rangle = \sqrt{2\Gamma + 1}\, \delta_{\Gamma\Gamma'} \delta_{nn'} \,. \tag{14.25}$$

$\underline{q = 2}$: The s.s.m.e. of one creation operator is essentially a c.f.p. and follows from eq. (14.23) as

$$\langle \rho^n \Gamma ||| a_\rho^\dagger ||| \rho^{n'} \Gamma \rangle = \sqrt{n(2\Gamma + 1)}\, \langle \rho^n \Gamma |\} \rho^{n-1} \Gamma' \rangle \delta_{n',n-1} \,. \tag{14.26}$$

$\underline{q = 3}$: Similarly one obtains for one annihilation operator with relation (14.21)

$$\langle \rho^n \Gamma ||| \tilde{a}_\rho ||| \rho^{n'} \Gamma' \rangle = (-1)^{\Gamma + \rho - n - 1} \sqrt{n'(2\Gamma' + 1)}\, \langle \rho^{n'} \Gamma' |\} \rho^n \Gamma \rangle \, \delta_{n',n+1} \,. \tag{14.27}$$

$\underline{q = 4}$: Inserting a complete set of intermediate states $|\rho^m \Delta\rangle$ between the two creation operators one finds with eq. (A.3.d14)

$$\langle \rho^n \Gamma ||| [a_\rho^\dagger \times a_\rho^\dagger]^\omega ||| \rho^{n'} \Gamma' \rangle$$

$$= (-1)^{\omega - 2\rho} \sum_{m\Delta} \frac{1}{\sqrt{2\Delta + 1}} U(\Gamma' \rho \Gamma \rho; \Delta\omega) \langle \rho^n \Gamma ||| a_\rho^\dagger ||| \rho^m \Delta \rangle \langle \rho^m \Delta ||| a_\rho^\dagger ||| \rho^{n'} \Gamma' \rangle \,. \tag{14.28}$$

Evaluating the s.s.m.e. with eq. (14.26), one obtains

$$\langle \rho^n \Gamma ||| [a_\rho^\dagger \times a_\rho^\dagger]^\omega ||| \rho^{n'} \Gamma' \rangle$$

$$= -\sqrt{n(n-1)(2\Gamma + 1)} \sum_{\Delta} U(\Gamma' \rho \Gamma \rho; \Delta\omega) \langle \rho^n \Gamma |\} \rho^{n-1} \Delta \rangle \langle \rho^{n-1} \Delta |\} \rho^{n-2} \Gamma' \rangle \delta_{n',n-2}$$

$$= -\sqrt{n(n-1)(2\Gamma + 1)} \langle \rho^n \Gamma |\} \rho^{n-2} \Gamma' (\rho^2 \omega) \rangle \delta_{n',n-2} \,, \tag{14.29}$$

where for the expression in terms of a two-particle c.f.p. eq. (4.45) has been used. The minus sign in eq. (14.29) results from the fact that $\omega - 2\rho$ is always odd, since $2\rho = 2(j_\rho + t_\rho) = 2j_\rho + 1$ is even and $\omega = J_\omega + T_\omega$ is odd for two particles in the same orbit.

$\underline{q = 5}$: Similarly one finds for the s.s.m.e. of two annihilation operators

$$\langle \rho^n \Gamma ||| [\tilde{a}_\rho \times \tilde{a}_\rho]^\omega ||| \rho^{n'} \Gamma' \rangle$$

$$= (-1)^{\omega - 2\rho} \sum_{m\Delta} \frac{1}{\sqrt{2\Delta + 1}} U(\Gamma' \rho \Gamma \rho; \Delta\omega) \langle \rho^n \Gamma ||| \tilde{a}_\rho ||| \rho^m \Delta \rangle \langle \rho^m \Delta ||| \tilde{a}_\rho ||| \rho^{n'} \Gamma' \rangle \,. \tag{14.30}$$

Substitution of the s.s.m.e. given in eq. (14.27) then leads to

$$\langle \rho^n \Gamma ||| [\tilde{a}_\rho \times \tilde{a}_\rho]^\omega ||| \rho^{n'} \Gamma' \rangle$$

$$= (-1)^{\omega + \Gamma - \Gamma'} \sqrt{(n+1)(n+2)(2\Gamma' + 1)} \sum_{\Delta} U(\Gamma' \rho \Gamma \rho; \Delta\omega)$$

$$\times \langle \rho^{n+2}\Gamma' | \} \rho^{n+1}\Delta\rangle \langle \rho^{n+1}\Delta | \} \rho^n \Gamma\rangle \delta_{n',n+2}$$

$$= (-1)^{\omega+\Gamma-\Gamma'} \sqrt{(n+1)(n+2)(2\Gamma'+1)} \langle \rho^{n+2}\Gamma' | \} \rho^n \Gamma(\rho^2\omega)\rangle \delta_{n',n+2} . \quad (14.31)$$

$q = 6$: The s.s.m.e. of the coupled product of one creation and one annihilation operator can be treated analogously. One thus finds

$$\langle \rho^n \Gamma ||| [a_\rho^\dagger \times \tilde{a}_\rho]^\omega ||| \rho^{n'}\Gamma'\rangle = (-1)^{\omega-2\rho} \sum_{m\Delta} \frac{1}{\sqrt{2\Delta+1}} U(\Gamma'\rho\Gamma\rho;\Delta\omega) \langle \rho^n\Gamma ||| a_\rho^\dagger ||| \rho^m \Delta\rangle$$

$$\times \langle \rho^m \Delta ||| \tilde{a}_\rho ||| \rho^{n'}\Gamma'\rangle$$

$$= -\sum_\Delta (-1)^{\Delta+\rho-\Gamma'} n \sqrt{\frac{(2\Gamma+1)(2\Gamma'+1)}{2\Delta+1}} U(\Gamma\rho\Gamma'\rho;\Delta\omega) \langle \rho^n\Gamma | \} \rho^{n-1}\Delta\rangle$$

$$\times \langle \rho^n \Gamma' | \} \rho^{n-1}\Delta\rangle \delta_{nn'} . \quad (14.32)$$

Application of the intermediate state expansion (A.3.d14) reduces the more complicated cases $q = 7, 8$ and 9 to the cases $q = 2, 3, 4$ or 5. Thus one finds

$q = 7$: $\langle \rho^n \Gamma ||| [[a_\rho^\dagger \times a_\rho^\dagger]^\nu \times \tilde{a}_\rho]^\omega ||| \rho^{n'}\Gamma'\rangle$

$$= (-1)^{\omega-\rho-\nu} \sum_{m\Delta} \frac{1}{\sqrt{2\Delta+1}} U(\Gamma'\rho\Gamma\nu;\Delta\omega) \langle \rho^n\Gamma ||| [a_\rho^\dagger \times a_\rho^\dagger]^\nu ||| \rho^m\Delta\rangle$$

$$\times \langle \rho^m \Delta ||| \tilde{a}_\rho ||| \rho^{n'}\Gamma'\rangle$$

$$= \sum_\Delta (-1)^{\omega+\Delta-\Gamma'} \sqrt{\frac{(n+1)n(n-1)(2\Gamma+1)(2\Gamma'+1)}{2\Delta+1}} U(\Gamma'\rho\Gamma\nu;\Delta\omega)$$

$$\times \langle \rho^n \Gamma | \} \rho^{n-2}\Delta(\rho^2\nu)\rangle \langle \rho^{n-1}\Gamma' | \} \rho^{n-2}\Delta\rangle \delta_{n',n-1} . \quad (14.33)$$

Similarly one finds

$q = 8$: $\langle \rho^n \Gamma ||| [a_\rho^\dagger \times [\tilde{a}_\rho \times \tilde{a}_\rho]^\nu]^\omega ||| \rho^{n'}\Gamma'\rangle$

$$= (-1)^{\omega-\rho-\nu} \sum_{m\Delta} \frac{1}{\sqrt{2\Delta+1}} U(\Gamma'\nu\Gamma\rho;\Delta\omega) \langle \rho^n\Gamma ||| a_\rho^\dagger ||| \rho^m\Delta\rangle \langle \rho^m\Delta ||| [\tilde{a}_\rho \times \tilde{a}_\rho]^\nu ||| \rho^{n'}\Gamma'\rangle$$

$$= \sum_\Delta (-1)^{\omega+\Delta-\rho-\Gamma'} n \sqrt{\frac{(n+1)(2\Gamma+1)(2\Gamma'+1)}{2\Delta+1}} U(\Gamma'\nu\Gamma\rho;\Delta\omega)$$

$$\times \langle \rho^n \Gamma | \} \rho^{n-1}\Delta\rangle \langle \rho^{n+1}\Gamma' | \} \rho^{n-1}\Delta(\rho^2\nu)\rangle \delta_{n',n+1} . \quad (14.34)$$

Finally one obtains

$q = 9$: $\langle \rho^n \Gamma ||| [[a_\rho^\dagger \times a_\rho^\dagger]^\epsilon \times [\tilde{a}_\rho \times \tilde{a}_\rho]^\nu]^\omega ||| \rho^{n'}\Gamma'\rangle$

$$= (-1)^{\omega-\epsilon-\nu} \sum_{m\Delta} \frac{1}{\sqrt{2\Delta+1}} \; U(\Gamma'\nu\Gamma\epsilon;\,\Delta\omega) \langle \rho^n \Gamma ||| [a_\rho^\dagger \times a_\rho^\dagger]^\epsilon ||| \rho^m \Delta \rangle$$

$$\times \langle \rho^m \Delta ||| [\tilde{a}_\rho \times \tilde{a}_\rho]^\nu ||| \rho^{n'} \Gamma' \rangle$$

$$= \sum_{\Delta} (-1)^{\omega+\Delta-\Gamma'} \frac{1}{\sqrt{2\Delta+1}} \; U(\Gamma'\nu\Gamma\epsilon;\,\Delta\omega)\, n(n-1)\sqrt{(2\Gamma+1)(2\Gamma'+1)}$$

$$\times \langle \rho^n \Gamma | \} \rho^{n-2} \Delta(\rho^2 \epsilon) \rangle \langle \rho^n \Gamma' | \} \rho^{n-2} \Delta(\rho^2 \nu) \rangle \delta_{n,n'} \,. \tag{14.35}$$

The calculation of the single-shell matrix elements is rather lengthy. Therefore it makes sense, especially when eq. (14.10) is programmed for a computer, to pre-calculate the s.s.m.e. and save these. Tables of calculated s.s.m.e. are useful each time many-body, multishell matrix elements must be computed from eq. (14.10). Since

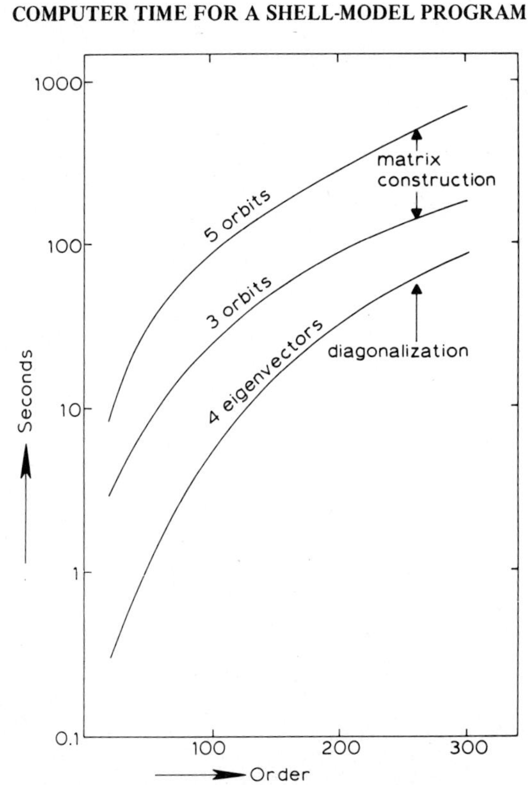

Fig. 14.1. The computer time taken for the construction and diagonalization with the Oak-Ridge–Rochester shell-model code [French, Halbert, McGrory and Wong (1969)] is given as a function of the order of the matrices. The plotted values refer to calculations performed on a CDC CYBER 74-16 computer.

neither the radial quantum number n nor the orbital angular momentum l are relevant for the numerical value of the s.s.m.e., these tables apply to all orbits of the same j-value (the dependence on the radial coordinate r is concealed in the coefficients K).

An impression of the computer time needed for the construction and diagonalization of the Hamiltonian matrix based on eq. (14.10) is given in fig. 14.1. The curves shown are obtained with the Oak-Ridge–Rochester computer code. The diagonalization time involved in obtaining the eigenvalues and eigenvectors for the lowest four states of a given matrix is indicated also.

14.4. Operators of the nuclear Hamiltonian

Let us now consider the construction of the coefficients $K(\boldsymbol{q}, \boldsymbol{y}, \boldsymbol{\omega}, \boldsymbol{\Omega})$ given in eq. (14.2). In order to illustrate their evaluation, we apply the general expression (14.10) to the matrix elements of the nuclear Hamiltonian. In first quantization we start from a sum of kinetic-energy terms and two-body interactions (cf. eq. (3.2))

$$H = \sum_{k=1}^{A} T(k) + \sum_{k<l}^{A} W(k,l) . \tag{14.36}$$

According to eqs. (13.24) and (13.31) this Hamiltonian can be represented in second quantization as (cf. eqs. (13.28) and (13.36))

$$H = \sum_{\alpha\gamma} \langle\alpha|T|\gamma\rangle a_\alpha^\dagger a_\gamma + \tfrac{1}{4} \sum_{\alpha\beta\gamma\delta} \langle\alpha\beta|W|\gamma\delta\rangle a_\alpha^\dagger a_\beta^\dagger a_\delta a_\gamma , \tag{14.37}$$

where the summations cover all single-particle states. For a shell-model calculation, however, a shell-model potential $\Sigma_k U(k)$ is introduced and the Hamiltonian (14.36) is rewritten as

$$H = \sum_{k=1}^{A} \{T(k) + U(k)\} + \{\sum_{k<l}^{A} W(k,l) - \sum_{k=1}^{A} U(k)\} = H^{(0)} + V . \tag{14.38}$$

The basis wave functions are eigenfunctions of the unperturbed Hamiltonian $H^{(0)} = \Sigma_{k=1}^{A} \{T(k) + U(k)\}$ and the residual interaction $V = \Sigma_{k<l}^{A} W(k,l) - \Sigma_{k=1}^{A} U(k)$ is diagonalized subsequently. In the second-quantization formalism one then obtains for the Hamiltonian (cf. sect. 17.2)

$$H = \sum_{\alpha} e_\alpha a_\alpha^\dagger a_\alpha + \tfrac{1}{4} \sum_{\alpha\beta\gamma\delta} \langle\alpha\beta|V|\gamma\delta\rangle a_\alpha^\dagger a_\beta^\dagger a_\delta a_\gamma = H^{(0)} + V , \tag{14.39}$$

where the Greek indices refer to the particular shell-model basis states that diagonalize the unperturbed Hamiltonian.

In most shell-model calculations the presence of an inert core is assumed. Thus the Hamiltonian takes the form

$$H = E_0 + \sum_{\alpha} e_\alpha a_\alpha^\dagger a_\alpha + \tfrac{1}{4} \sum_{\alpha\beta\gamma\delta} \langle\alpha\beta|V|\gamma\delta\rangle a_\alpha^\dagger a_\beta^\dagger a_\delta a_\gamma \,, \tag{14.40}$$

where the constant $E_0 = \langle 0|H|0\rangle$ represents the binding energy of the core $|0\rangle$ and the summations exclude all core states. The term $\Sigma_\alpha e_\alpha a_\alpha^\dagger a_\alpha$ denotes the total energy of the independent single-particle excitations with e_α representing the single-particle energies and $a_\alpha^\dagger a_\alpha$ counting the number of particles in the state α. The term $\frac{1}{4}\Sigma_{\alpha\ldots\delta}\langle\alpha\beta|V|\gamma\delta\rangle a_\alpha^\dagger a_\beta^\dagger a_\delta a_\gamma$ describes the two-body residual interaction between the active particles. Our first task now is to write the Hamiltonian (14.40) in the form of eq. (13.70). It is remarked that both the one-body operator and the two-body operator that are considered here are scalar operators, i.e. they do not depend on orientation in the coordinate space. Hence eq. (14.10) is to be applied for the case $\Omega_k = 0$. In chapter 15 we will discuss the reduction for nonscalar, one-body operators; such a discussion applies to the electromagnetic transitions.

14.5. The single-particle energy contribution

Let us consider the single-particle contributions to the Hamiltonian for a two-orbit configuration with n_i particles in orbit ρ_i coupled to spin and isospin γ_i $(i = 1,2)$, and total spin and isospin Γ_2. These contributions were discussed in first quantization in eq. (3.34) as

$$M_{\text{s.p.}} = \langle \rho_1^{n_1}\gamma_1, \rho_2^{n_2}\gamma_2|H^{(0)}|\rho_1^{n_1}\gamma_1, \rho_2^{n_2}\gamma_2\rangle_{\Gamma_2} = n_1 e_{\rho_1} + n_2 e_{\rho_2} \,, \tag{14.41}$$

where e_{ρ_1} and e_{ρ_2} denote the single-particle energies.

It is very instructive to calculate the single-particle contributions also with the general reduction formula (14.10), although the result can be given immediately as seen above. Since eq. (14.10) applies to reduced matrix elements, one obtains after application of the Wigner-Eckart theorem to the matrix element $M_{\text{s.p.}}$ given in eq. (14.41) the relation

$$M_{\text{s.p.}} = \frac{M_{\text{s.p.}}^{\text{red}}}{\sqrt{2\Gamma_2 + 1}} \,. \tag{14.42}$$

The single-particle states are the eigenvectors of the unperturbed shell-model Hamiltonian $H^{(0)}$ in eq. (14.39) and hence the single-particle term is diagonal in the shell-model basis. Thus we have to combine only products $a_\rho^\dagger a_\rho$ in the coupled form f^ω (cf. eq. (13.71)). Omitting isospin labels for simplicity, one can write the single-particle term, employing eq. (13.53) to introduce the adjoint $\tilde{a}$, as

$$H^{(0)} = \sum_{jm} e_j a_{jm}^\dagger a_{jm} = \sum_{jm} e_j \sqrt{2j+1}\, a_{jm}^\dagger \frac{(-1)^{j-m}}{\sqrt{2j+1}} \tilde{a}_{j-m} \,. \tag{14.43}$$

Inserting the Clebsch-Gordan coefficient $\langle jmj-m|00\rangle = (-1)^{j-m}/\sqrt{2j+1}$, one arrives at the desired expression

$$H^{(0)} = \sum_j e_j \sqrt{2j+1} \sum_m \langle jmj-m|00\rangle a^\dagger_{jm}\tilde{a}_{j-m} \equiv \sum_j e_j\sqrt{2j+1}\,[a^\dagger_j \times \tilde{a}_j]^0_0 . \quad (14.44)$$

With the isospin labels taken into account the single-particle energy operator becomes

$$H^{(0)} = \sum_{i=1}^{2} e_{\rho_i}\sqrt{2\rho_i+1}\,[\boldsymbol{a}^\dagger_{\rho_i} \times \tilde{\boldsymbol{a}}_{\rho_i}]^0_0 , \quad (14.45)$$

where ρ_i denotes spin labels as well as isospin labels.

The single-particle operator is now in the standard form of eq. (13.70). It is seen that eq. (14.45) contains a sum over the orbits ρ_i with $i = 1, 2$. One thus finds

$$K(\boldsymbol{q}, \boldsymbol{y}, \boldsymbol{\omega}, \boldsymbol{\Omega}) = e_{\rho_i}\sqrt{2\rho_i+1} , \quad (14.46a)$$

$F^{\Omega_2}(\boldsymbol{q}, \boldsymbol{y}, \boldsymbol{\omega}, \boldsymbol{\Omega}) =$ 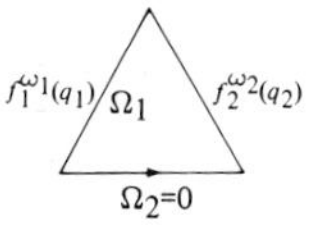

(14.46b)

with

$$f_i^{\omega_i}(q_i = 6) = [\boldsymbol{a}^\dagger_{\rho_i} \times \tilde{\boldsymbol{a}}_{\rho_i}]^0_0 , \qquad f_j^{\omega_j}(q_j = 1) = 1 . \quad (14.46c)$$

The only arguments of the coefficients K and the operator F given above are seen to be either $\boldsymbol{q} = \{q_1, q_2\} = \{6, 1\}$ or $\boldsymbol{q} = \{q_1, q_2\} = \{1, 6\}$ (cf. eq. (14.24)). The other labels are $\boldsymbol{\omega} = \{\omega_1, \omega_2\} = \{0, 0\}$ and $\boldsymbol{\Omega} = \{\Omega_1, \Omega_2\} = \{0, 0\}$. The set of labels $\boldsymbol{y}$ can be omitted in this case. It should be realized that the sum over i in eq. (14.45) is contained in the general expansion (13.70) as a sum over the various sets $\boldsymbol{q}$.

The single-particle contribution to the Hamiltonian can be obtained from the evaluation of the reduced diagonal matrix element

$$M^{\text{red}}_{\text{s.p.}} = \langle Z^{\Gamma_2} ||| H^{(0)} ||| Z^{\Gamma_2}\rangle = \langle \rho_1^{n_1}\gamma_1, \rho_2^{n_2}\gamma_2 ||| \sum_{i=1}^{2} e_{\rho_i}\boldsymbol{a}^\dagger_{\rho_i}\boldsymbol{a}_{\rho_i} ||| \rho_1^{n_1}\gamma_1, \rho_2^{n_2}\gamma_2\rangle_{\Gamma_2}$$

$$= \langle \rho_1^{n_1}\gamma_1, \rho_2^{n_2}\gamma_2 ||| \sum_{i=1}^{2} e_{\rho_i}\sqrt{2\rho_i+1}\,[\boldsymbol{a}^\dagger_{\rho_i} \times \tilde{\boldsymbol{a}}_{\rho_i}]^0_0 ||| \rho_1^{n_1}\gamma_1, \rho_2^{n_2}\gamma_2\rangle_{\Gamma_2} . \quad (14.47)$$

With eq. (14.10) one can write, since one has $k = 2$,

$$M^{\text{red}}_{\text{s.p.}} = (-1)^{n_2(n_1-n_1)} \sum_{\boldsymbol{q}, \boldsymbol{y}, \boldsymbol{\omega}, \boldsymbol{\Omega}} K(\boldsymbol{q}, \boldsymbol{y}, \boldsymbol{\omega}, \boldsymbol{\Omega}) \langle \rho_1^{n_1}\gamma_1 ||| f_1^{\omega_1}(q_1) ||| \rho_1^{n_1}\gamma_1\rangle$$

$$\times \sqrt{(2\Gamma_2+1)(2\Omega_2+1)(2\Gamma_2+1)} \begin{Bmatrix} \gamma_1 & \gamma_2 & \Gamma_2 \\ \gamma_1 & \gamma_2 & \Gamma_2 \\ 0 & 0 & 0 \end{Bmatrix} \langle \rho_2^{n_2}\gamma_2 ||| f_2^{\omega_2}(q_2) ||| \rho_2^{n_2}\gamma_2\rangle .$$

(14.48)

The sum over the sets $\boldsymbol{q}, \boldsymbol{y}$, $\boldsymbol{\omega}$ and $\boldsymbol{\Omega}$ reduces in this example to a sum over two terms, i.e.

$$\text{(i)}\ f_1^{\omega_1} = f_1^{\omega_1=0}(q_1 = 6) = [a_{\rho_1}^\dagger \times \tilde{a}_{\rho_1}]_0^0\,, \qquad f_2^{\omega_2} = f_2^{\omega_2=0}(q_2 = 1) = 1\,;$$

$$\text{(ii)}\ f_1^{\omega_1} = f_1^{\omega_1=0}(q_1' = 1) = 1\,, \qquad f_2^{\omega_2} = f_2^{\omega_2=0}(q_2' = 6) = [a_{\rho_2}^\dagger \times \tilde{a}_{\rho_2}]_0^0\,, \tag{14.49}$$

where the labels $\boldsymbol{q}$ follow from eq. (14.24). Inserting the expression for K given in eq. (14.46a), one obtains

$$M_{\text{s.p.}}^{\text{red}} = \sum_{q} e_{\rho_i} \sqrt{\frac{(2\rho_i+1)(2\Gamma_2+1)}{(2\gamma_1+1)(2\gamma_2+1)}} \langle \rho_1^{n_1}\gamma_1 |||f_1^{\omega_1}(q_1)||| \rho_1^{n_1}\gamma_1\rangle \langle \rho_2^{n_2}\gamma_2 |||f_2^{\omega_2}(q_2)||| \rho_2^{n_2}\gamma_2\rangle \tag{14.50}$$

where the explicit value of the 9-j symbol (see eq. (A.1.c5)) has been substituted. The value to be used for the index i of ρ_i corresponds with the matrix element for which one has $q_i = 6$.

The values of the single-shell matrix elements have been calculated before. Thus one obtains from eq. (14.32) with $\omega = 0$

$$\langle \rho^n\gamma ||| [a_\rho^\dagger \times \tilde{a}_\rho]^0 ||| \rho^n\gamma\rangle = n\sqrt{\frac{2\gamma+1}{2\rho+1}}\,, \tag{14.51}$$

where the explicit value of the U-coefficient is inserted and the normalization condition of the c.f.p. (see eq. (4.12)) is used.

From eq. (14.25) one obtains immediately

$$\langle \rho^n\gamma ||| \mathbf{1} ||| \rho^n\gamma\rangle = \sqrt{2\gamma+1}\,. \tag{14.52}$$

Substitution of eqs. (14.51) and (14.52) into eq. (14.50) according to eq. (14.49) then leads to the expression

$$M_{\text{s.p.}}^{\text{red}} = (n_1 e_{\rho_1} + n_2 e_{\rho_2})\sqrt{2\Gamma_2+1}\,. \tag{14.53}$$

Inserting eq. (14.53) into eq. (14.42), we have shown that the general reduction (14.10) leads to the same result for the single-particle contributions as the one given by eq. (14.41). It is clear that expansion (14.10) is impractical for this particular case. Its merits will become apparent, however, in applications that will be discussed later.

14.6. The residual two-body interaction

In order to obtain the standard-form expansion (13.70) for the two-body term in the Hamiltonian (14.39), we must couple the products of creation and annihilation operators. Using the orthogonality relation for Clebsch-Gordan coefficients

$$\sum_{JM} \langle j_a m_a j_b m_b | JM\rangle \langle j_a m_a' j_b m_b' | JM\rangle = \delta_{m_a m_a'} \delta_{m_b m_b'}\,, \tag{14.54}$$

one can rewrite the two-body term of the Hamiltonian (14.39) as

$$V = \frac{1}{4} \sum_{j_a m_a \dots j_d m_d} \langle j_a m_a j_b m_b | V | j_c m_c j_d m_d \rangle a^\dagger_{j_a m_a} a^\dagger_{j_b m_b} a_{j_d m_d} a_{j_c m_c}$$

$$= \frac{1}{4} \sum_{j_a m_a \dots j_d m_d} \langle j_a m_a j_b m_b | V | j_c m_c j_d m_d \rangle \sum_{m'_a \dots m'_d} a^\dagger_{j_a m'_a} a^\dagger_{j_b m'_b} a_{j_d m'_d} a_{j_c m'_c}$$

$$\times \delta_{m_a m'_a} \delta_{m_b m'_b} \delta_{m_c m'_c} \delta_{m_d m'_d}$$

$$= \frac{1}{4} \sum_{j_a \dots j_d} \sum_{\substack{JM \\ \bar{J}\bar{M}}} \sum_{\substack{m_a \dots m_d \\ m'_a \dots m'_d}} \langle j_a m_a j_b m_b | JM \rangle \langle j_a m'_a j_b m'_b | JM \rangle \langle j_c m_c j_d m_d | \bar{J}\bar{M} \rangle$$

$$\times \langle j_c m'_c j_d m'_d | \bar{J}\bar{M} \rangle \langle j_a m_a j_b m_b | V | j_c m_c j_d m_d \rangle a^\dagger_{j_a m'_a} a^\dagger_{j_b m'_b} a_{j_d m'_d} a_{j_c m'_c} \,. \tag{14.55}$$

Replacing the two annihilation operators in eq. (14.55) by the adjoint operators (cf. eq. (13.53))

$$a_{j_d m'_d} a_{j_c m'_c} = \tilde{a}_{j_d - m'_d} \tilde{a}_{j_c - m'_c} (-1)^{j_d - m'_d + j_c - m'_c} \,, \tag{14.56a}$$

and substituting the notations (cf. eqs. (13.40) and (13.55))

$$\sum_{m'_a m'_b} \langle j_a m'_a j_b m'_b | JM \rangle a^\dagger_{j_a m'_a} a^\dagger_{j_b m'_b} = [a^\dagger_{j_a} \times a^\dagger_{j_b}]^J_M \,, \tag{14.56b}$$

$$\sum_{m'_c m'_d} \langle j_c m'_c j_d m'_d | \bar{J}\bar{M} \rangle a_{j_d m'_d} a_{j_c m'_c} = (-1)^{\bar{J} - \bar{M} + 1} [\tilde{a}_{j_c} \times \tilde{a}_{j_d}]^{\bar{J}}_{-\bar{M}} \,, \tag{14.56c}$$

one obtains

$$V^{\text{res}} = \frac{1}{4} \sum_{j_a \dots j_d} \sum_{\substack{JM \\ \bar{J}\bar{M}}} \sum_{m_a \dots m_d} \langle j_a m_a j_b m_b | JM \rangle \langle j_c m_c j_d m_d | \bar{J}\bar{M} \rangle$$

$$\times (-1)^{\bar{J} - \bar{M} + 1} \langle j_a m_a j_b m_b | V | j_c m_c j_d m_d \rangle [a^\dagger_{j_a} \times a^\dagger_{j_b}]^J_M [\tilde{a}_{j_c} \times \tilde{a}_{j_d}]^{\bar{J}}_{-\bar{M}} \,. \tag{14.57}$$

The summation over $m_a \dots m_d$ now leads to

$$V^{\text{res}} = \frac{1}{4} \sum_{j_a \dots j_d} \sum_{\substack{JM \\ \bar{J}\bar{M}}} \langle j_a j_b ; JM | V | j_c j_d ; \bar{J}\bar{M} \rangle \sqrt{(1 + \delta_{ab})(1 + \delta_{cd})}$$

$$\times [a^\dagger_{j_a} \times a^\dagger_{j_b}]^J_M [\tilde{a}_{j_c} \times \tilde{a}_{j_d}]^{\bar{J}}_{-\bar{M}} (-1)^{\bar{J} - \bar{M} + 1} \,. \tag{14.58}$$

Here the factor $\sqrt{(1 + \delta_{ab})(1 + \delta_{cd})}$ is necessary since the two-body matrix element is, by definition, evaluated for *normalized*, coupled two-body states (see also eq. (5.17)). Since the residual interaction is a scalar, its coupled matrix elements vanish unless we have $J = \bar{J}$ and $M = \bar{M}$. With the explicit value of the Clebsch-Gordan coefficient $\langle JMJ - M|00\rangle = (2J+1)^{-1/2}(-1)^{J-M}$, the two-body term of the Hamiltonian can then be rewritten after summation over M as

$$V = -\tfrac{1}{4} \sum_{\substack{j_a \cdots j_d \\ J}} \langle j_a j_b | V | j_c j_d \rangle_{JM} \rangle \sqrt{(2J+1)(1+\delta_{ab})(1+\delta_{cd})}$$

$$\times \, [[a^\dagger_{j_a} \times a^\dagger_{j_b}]^J \times [\tilde{a}_{j_c} \times \tilde{a}_{j_d}]^J]^0_0 \,. \tag{14.59}$$

The extension of eq. (14.59) to the case where the isospin numbers are taken into account, is straightforward. After application of the Wigner-Eckart theorem to the coupled two-body matrix elements, one can write the operator as

$$V = -\tfrac{1}{4} \sum_{\substack{\rho_1 \cdots \rho_4 \\ \Gamma}} \langle \rho_1 \rho_2 ||| V ||| \rho_3 \rho_4 \rangle_\Gamma \sqrt{(1+\delta_{\rho_1\rho_2})(1+\delta_{\rho_3\rho_4})} \, [\, [a^\dagger_{\rho_1} \times a^\dagger_{\rho_2}]^\Gamma \times [\tilde{a}_{\rho_3} \times \tilde{a}_{\rho_4}$$

$$= - \sum_{\substack{\rho_1 \leqslant \rho_2 \\ \rho_3 \leqslant \rho_4 \\ \Gamma}} \langle \rho_1 \rho_2 ||| V ||| \rho_3 \rho_4 \rangle_\Gamma \, [\, [a^\dagger_{\rho_1} \times a^\dagger_{\rho_2}]^\Gamma \times [\tilde{a}_{\rho_3} \times \tilde{a}_{\rho_4}]^\Gamma]^0_0$$

$$= - \sum_{\substack{\rho_1 \leqslant \rho_2 \\ \rho_3 \leqslant \rho_4 \\ \Gamma}} \langle \rho_1 \rho_2 ||| V ||| \rho_3 \rho_4 \rangle_\Gamma \tag{14.60}$$

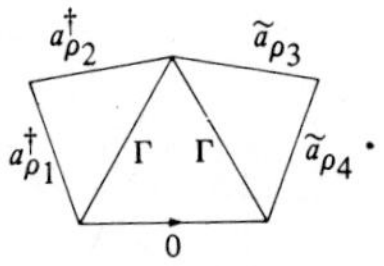

The Greek letters ρ_i refer to all single-particle quantum numbers (i.e. coordinate space and isospace) with the exception of the projection quantum numbers; the summation over Γ concerns J and T only, i.e. no summation over projection quantum numbers is involved. The restrictions $\rho_1 \leqslant \rho_2$ and $\rho_3 \leqslant \rho_4$ refer to some ordering of the single-particle states. Their introduction exploits the hermitian symmetry of the energy matrix and reduces the number of terms appreciably. Note that the factor $\sqrt{(1+\delta_{\rho_1\rho_2})(1+\delta_{\rho_3\rho_4})}$ is absent when the restricted summations apply.

The creation and annihilation operators now occur in coupled form. Expansion (14.60) does not yet give the correct coefficient K, however, since for the desired standard form expansion (13.70) a recoupling and/or reordering may be necessary to combine all operators $a^\dagger_{\rho_i}$ and $\tilde{a}_{\rho_i}$ that refer to one and the same orbit ρ_i. For the possibly necessary reordering the anticommutators of the operators have to be taken into account. The recoupling is achieved with the aid of Racah techniques.

Let us illustrate this with an example, where one has three active orbits ρ_1, ρ_2 and ρ_3. Assume that the orbits are ordered in the sequence $\rho_1 < \rho_2 < \rho_3$. Thus one of the contributions to the two-body part (14.60) is given by

$$V = -\sum_\Gamma \langle \rho_1 \rho_2 ||| V ||| \rho_1 \rho_3 \rangle_\Gamma \tag{14.61}$$

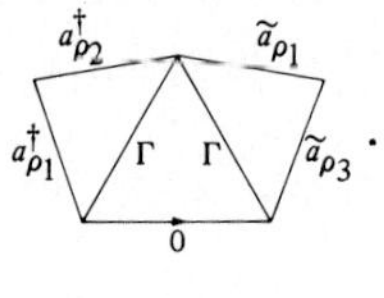

It should be pointed out that the summation in eq. (14.60) does not include the matrix element given by e.g. $\langle \rho_1\rho_2 ||| V ||| \rho_3\rho_1\rangle_\Gamma$, because of the ordering $\rho_3 > \rho_1$. The coupled tensors $a^\dagger$ and $\tilde{a}$ must still be brought into the standard form, i.e. coupled together for each orbit separately. The required recouplings are achieved with the aid of 9-*j* and 6-*j* coefficients as (see eq. (A.1.c1))

$$V^{\text{res}} = -\sum_{\Gamma\Delta} \langle \rho_1\rho_2 ||| V ||| \rho_1\rho_3\rangle_\Gamma (2\Gamma+1)(2\Delta+1)$$

$$\times \begin{Bmatrix} \rho_1 & \rho_2 & \Gamma \\ \rho_1 & \rho_3 & \Gamma \\ \Delta & \Delta & 0 \end{Bmatrix} \qquad (14.62)$$

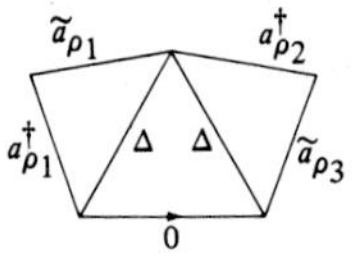

One more recoupling then leads to (see eq. (A.1.b5))

$$V = \sum_{\Gamma\Delta} \langle \rho_1\rho_2 ||| V ||| \rho_1\rho_3\rangle_\Gamma (2\Gamma+1)(2\Delta+1) \begin{Bmatrix} \rho_1 & \rho_2 & \Gamma \\ \rho_1 & \rho_3 & \Gamma \\ \Delta & \Delta & 0 \end{Bmatrix} U(\Delta\rho_2 0\rho_3;\rho_3\Delta)$$

$$\times \qquad (14.63)$$

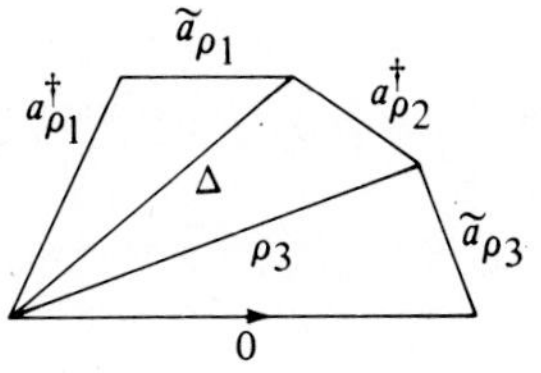

Since the 9-*j* coefficient reduces to a 6-*j* coefficient and the *U*-coefficient equals unity (see appendix A.1) one finds for the expansion coefficient *K* given in eq. (13.70) the expression

$$K(\boldsymbol{q},\boldsymbol{y},\boldsymbol{\omega},\boldsymbol{\Omega}) = \langle \rho_1\rho_2 ||| V ||| \rho_1\rho_3\rangle_\Gamma (-1)^{\rho_1+\rho_3-\Gamma-\Delta}\, U(\rho_2\rho_1\rho_3\rho_1;\Gamma\Delta) \qquad (14.64)$$

with the sets $\boldsymbol{q} = \{6, 2, 3\}$, $\boldsymbol{\omega} = \{\Delta, \rho_2, \rho_3\}$ and $\boldsymbol{\Omega} = \{\Delta, \rho_3, 0\}$. The special case considered in eq. (14.64), corresponds to

$$f_1^{\omega_1} = [a^\dagger_{\rho_1} \times \tilde{a}_{\rho_1}]^\Delta \qquad \text{with } \omega_1 = \Omega_1 = \Delta\,,$$

$$f_2^{\omega_2} = a^\dagger_{\rho_2} \qquad \text{with } \omega_2 = \rho_2\,,$$

$$f_3^{\omega_3} = \tilde{a}_{\rho_3} \qquad \text{with } \Omega_2 = \omega_3 = \rho_3\,, \qquad \Omega_3 = 0\,. \qquad (14.65)$$

A detailed discussion of all possible terms appearing in eq. (14.60) is given in the following chapter.

CHAPTER 15

FURTHER APPLICATIONS OF SECOND QUANTIZATION

In the preceding chapter it has been shown that many-particle, multishell matrix elements can be expressed in terms of single-shell matrix elements. This general reduction, given in eq. (14.10), can be performed in a very systematic way.

In this chapter some further examples are given that illustrate the procedure for various one- and two-particle operators. In sect. 15.1 the matrix elements of the two-body Hamiltonian are evaluated in the second-quantization formalism and the result is compared with that obtained previously with the first-quantization procedure. In sect. 15.2 the formalism is applied to the single-particle electromagnetic operators. The single-particle spectroscopic factors are discussed in sect. 15.3, and two-particle transfer is treated in sect. 15.4.

15.1. Comparison between first and second quantization

In order to see how the reduction of matrix elements for a two-body interaction proceeds in second quantization, we work out a simple case in detail. Consider the matrix elements of the two-body interaction V for states described by several particles in two orbits. Let the matrix elements be given by

$$M = \langle \rho_\alpha^n \, \lambda_\beta^m \, |||V||| \, \rho_\gamma^{n'} \, \lambda_\delta^{m'} \rangle_\Gamma \, , \qquad (15.1)$$

where ρ and λ denote the two orbits and Γ specifies the total angular momentum and isospin. For a systematic treatment of the cases to be summed over in eq. (14.60), all possible orderings of the four single-particle orbits involved must be considered, subject only to the two conditions $\rho_1 \leqslant \rho_2$ and $\rho_3 \leqslant \rho_4$. Due to the equality $\langle \rho_1 \rho_2 | V | \rho_3 \rho_4 \rangle_\Gamma = \langle \rho_3 \rho_4 | V | \rho_1 \rho_2 \rangle_\Gamma$, which expresses the hermiticity of the real two-body matrix elements, it is no restriction to impose the condition $\rho_1 \leqslant \rho_3$. This leaves still fourteen possibilities, which are listed in table 15.1. Due to the restriction on the two orbits ρ and λ in eq. (15.1), it follows that only six categories of two-body operators out of the fourteen listed in table 15.1, are to be summed over in eq. (14.60). These six categories are given by

(I) $\rho_1 = \rho_2 = \rho < \rho_3 = \rho_4 = \lambda$,

(II) $\rho_1 = \rho_2 = \rho_3 = \rho < \rho_4 = \lambda$,

(III) $\rho_1 = \rho < \rho_2 = \rho_3 = \rho_4 = \lambda$,

Table 15.1
All possible orderings of orbits satisfying the conditions $\rho_1 \leqslant \rho_2$ and $\rho_3 \leqslant \rho_4$ for the operator

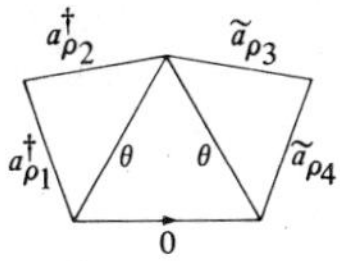

are given by the fourteen possibilities

(1) $\rho_1 < \rho_2 < \rho_3 < \rho_4$,	(8) $\rho_1 = \rho_2 = \rho_3 = \rho_4$,
(2) $\rho_1 = \rho_2 < \rho_3 < \rho_4$,	(9) $\rho_1 < \rho_3 < \rho_2 < \rho_4$,
(3) $\rho_1 < \rho_2 = \rho_3 < \rho_4$,	(10) $\rho_1 = \rho_3 < \rho_2 < \rho_4$,
(4) $\rho_1 < \rho_2 < \rho_3 = \rho_4$,	(11) $\rho_1 < \rho_3 < \rho_2 = \rho_4$,
(5) $\rho_1 = \rho_2 = \rho_3 < \rho_4$,	(12) $\rho_1 = \rho_3 < \rho_2 = \rho_4$,
(6) $\rho_1 = \rho_2 < \rho_3 = \rho_4$,	(13) $\rho_1 < \rho_3 < \rho_4 < \rho_2$,
(7) $\rho_1 < \rho_2 = \rho_3 = \rho_4$,	(14) $\rho_1 < \rho_3 = \rho_4 < \rho_2$.

$$\text{(IV)}\ \rho_1 = \rho_2 = \rho_3 = \rho_4 = \rho\,,$$

$$\text{(V)}\ \rho_1 = \rho_2 = \rho_3 = \rho_4 = \lambda\,,$$

$$\text{(VI)}\ \rho_1 = \rho_3 = \rho < \rho_2 = \rho_4 = \lambda\,. \tag{15.2}$$

Let us derive the standard-form expansion (13.70) for each of these two-body operators (cf. eq. (14.60)).

The first category is given by

$$V_{\text{I}} = -\langle \rho^2 \,|||V|||\, \lambda^2 \rangle_\theta$$
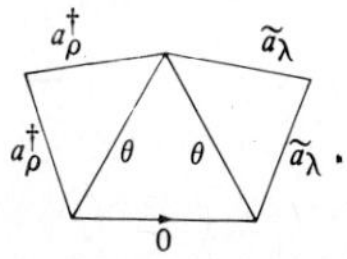

. (15.3a)

Since the operators $a^\dagger$ and $\tilde{a}$ are already coupled together for each orbit separately, no further recoupling is necessary. Thus one has from comparison with eqs. (13.70) and (13.71)

$$K = -\langle \rho^2 \,|||V|||\, \lambda^2 \rangle_\theta \delta_{q_1 4} \delta_{q_2 5}\,,$$

$$f_1^{\omega_1}(q_1 = 4) = [a^\dagger_\rho \times a^\dagger_\rho]^\theta \qquad \text{with } \omega_1 = \Omega_1 = \theta\,,$$

$$f_2^{\omega_2}(q_2 = 5) = [\tilde{a}_\lambda \times \tilde{a}_\lambda]^\theta \qquad \text{with } \omega_2 = \theta, \Omega_2 = 0\,, \tag{15.3b}$$

where the categories labelled by q are given in eq. (14.24). The evaluation of the single-shell matrix elements for the operators $f_1^{\omega_1}(q_1)$ and $f_2^{\omega_2}(q_2)$ will be illustrated in more detail later in this section. Note that in this particular example, with a scalar interaction and only two orbits, one always has $\Omega_2 = 0$.

The second category is given by

$$V_{\mathrm{II}} = -\langle \rho^2 |||V||| \rho\lambda\rangle_\theta$$ 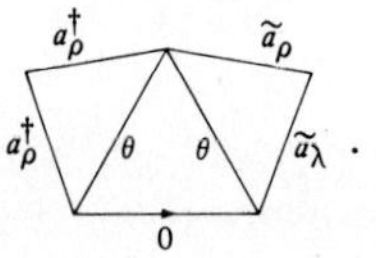 (15.4)

In this case the creation and annihilation operators acting on orbit ρ must first be coupled together. Utilizing the recoupling given in eq. (A.1.b5), one obtains

$$V_{\mathrm{II}} = -\langle \rho^2 |||V||| \rho\lambda\rangle_\theta \; U(\theta\rho 0\lambda; \lambda\theta)$$ 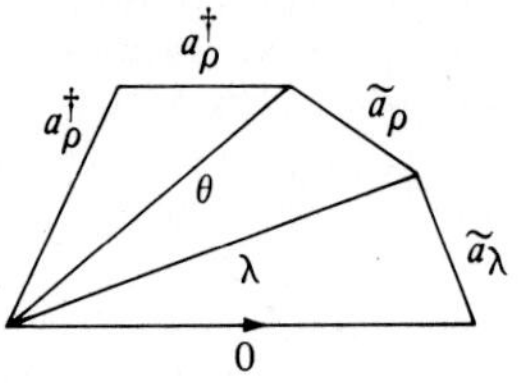 (15.5a)

Since the U-coefficient given above is equal to unity, one finds

$$K = -\langle \rho^2 |||V||| \rho\lambda\rangle_\theta \, \delta_{q_1 7}\delta_{q_2 3} \,,$$

$$f_1^{\omega_1}(q_1 = 7) = [[a_\rho^\dagger \times a_\rho^\dagger]^\theta \times \tilde{a}_\rho]^\lambda \qquad \text{with } \omega_1 = \Omega_1 = \lambda \,,$$

$$f_2^{\omega_2}(q_2 = 3) = \tilde{a}_\lambda \qquad \text{with } \omega_2 = \lambda, \Omega_2 = 0 \,. \tag{15.5b}$$

The third category is given by

$$V_{\mathrm{III}} = -\langle \rho\lambda |||V||| \lambda^2\rangle_\theta$$ 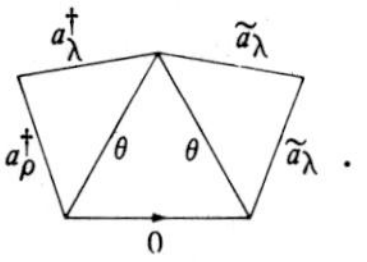 (15.6)

Coupling the operators $a_\lambda^\dagger$ and $\tilde{a}_\lambda$ leads to

$$V_{\mathrm{III}} = -\langle \rho\lambda |||V||| \lambda^2\rangle_\theta \; U(\rho\lambda 0\theta; \theta\rho)$$ 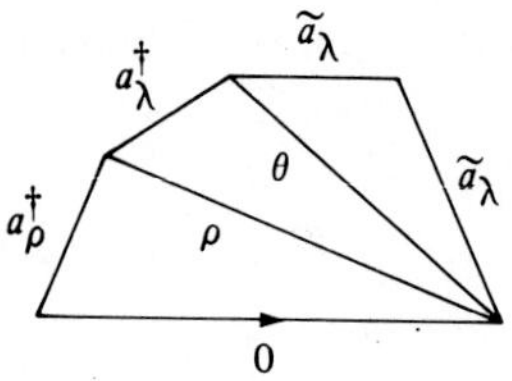 (15.7a)

Since the U-coefficient is equal to unity one obtains

$$K = -\langle \rho\lambda |||V||| \lambda^2\rangle_\theta \, \delta_{q_1 2}\, \delta_{q_2 8} \,,$$

$$f_1^{\omega_1}(q_1 = 2) = a_\rho^\dagger \qquad \text{with } \omega_1 = \Omega_1 = \rho \,,$$

$$f_2^{\omega_2}(q_2 = 8) = [a_\lambda^\dagger \times [\tilde{a}_\lambda \times \tilde{a}_\lambda]^\theta]^\rho \qquad \text{with } \omega_2 = \rho \,, \Omega_2 = 0 \,. \tag{15.7b}$$

The fourth category is represented by

$$V_{IV} = -\langle\rho^2|||V|||\rho^2\rangle_\theta$$ 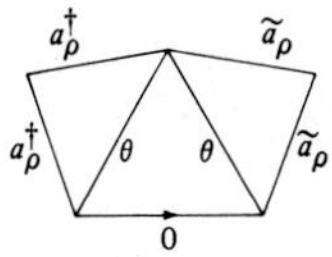 . (15.8a)

Since all creation and annihilation operators refer to one orbit only, no recoupling is necessary. One thus has

$$K = -\langle\rho^2|||V|||\rho^2\rangle_\theta\, \delta_{q_19}\, \delta_{q_21}\ ,$$

$$f_1^{\omega_1}(q_1 = 9) = [[a_\rho^\dagger \times a_\rho^\dagger]^\theta \times [\tilde{a}_\rho \times \tilde{a}_\rho]^\theta]^0 \qquad \text{with } \omega_1 = \Omega_1 = 0\ ,$$

$$f_2^{\omega_2}(q_2 = 1) = 1 \qquad \text{with } \omega_2 = \Omega_2 = 0\ . \tag{15.8b}$$

The fifth category is similar to the fourth and is given by

$$V_{V} = -\langle\lambda^2|||V|||\lambda^2\rangle_\theta$$ 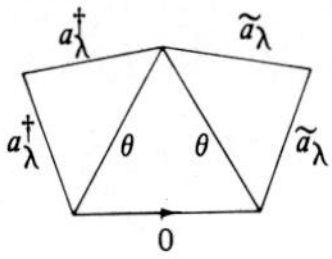 . (15.9a)

Thus follows the relation

$$K = -\langle\lambda^2|||V|||\lambda^2\rangle_\theta\, \delta_{q_11}\, \delta_{q_29}\ ,$$

$$f_1^{\omega_1}(q_1 = 1) = 1 \qquad \text{with } \omega_1 = \Omega_1 = 0\ ,$$

$$f_2^{\omega_2}(q_2 = 9) = [[a_\lambda^\dagger \times a_\lambda^\dagger]^\theta \times [\tilde{a}_\lambda \times \tilde{a}_\lambda]^\theta]^0 \qquad \text{with } \omega_2 = \Omega_2 = 0\ . \tag{15.9b}$$

The last category is given by

$$V_{VI} = -\langle\rho\lambda|||V|||\rho\lambda\rangle_\theta$$ 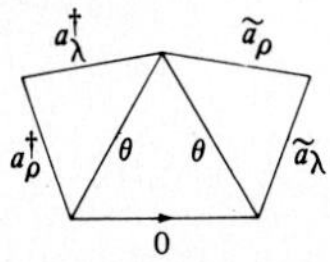 . (15.10)

Here again a recoupling is necessary such that the operators $a^\dagger$ and $\tilde{a}$ referring to a given orbit are first coupled together. This can be done with a 9-*j* expansion (cf. eq. (A.1.c1)), which leads to

$$V_{VI} = +\sum_\omega \langle\rho\lambda|||V|||\rho\lambda\rangle_\theta\, (2\theta + 1)\, (2\omega + 1) \begin{Bmatrix} \rho & \lambda & \theta \\ \rho & \lambda & \theta \\ \omega & \omega & 0 \end{Bmatrix}$$ 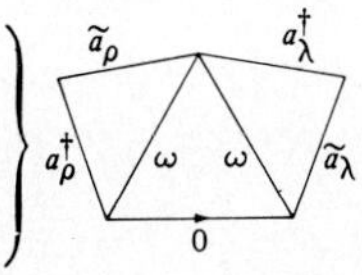 . (15.11a)

The sign change of the operator follows from the anticommutation property of $a_\lambda^\dagger$ and $\tilde{a}_\rho$. Since a 9-j symbol with a zero reduces to a 6-j symbol one obtains

$$K = \sum_{\omega} \langle \rho\lambda ||| V ||| \rho\lambda \rangle_\theta \, (-1)^{\theta+\omega-\rho-\lambda} \, U(\rho\lambda\rho\lambda; \theta\omega) \, \delta_{q_1 6} \, \delta_{q_2 6} \, ,$$

$$f_1^{\omega_1}(q_1 = 6) = [a_\rho^\dagger \times \tilde{a}_\rho]^\omega \qquad \text{with } \omega_1 = \Omega_1 = 0 \, ,$$

$$f_2^{\omega_2}(q_2 = 6) = [a_\lambda^\dagger \times \tilde{a}_\lambda]^\omega \qquad \text{with } \omega_2 = \omega, \Omega_2 = 0 \, . \tag{15.11b}$$

Let us now derive the complete expression for the matrix element (15.1). The single-shell matrix elements have been evaluated in sect. 14.3. One obtains, writing down the general reduction (14.10) for a two-orbit case,

$M =$ 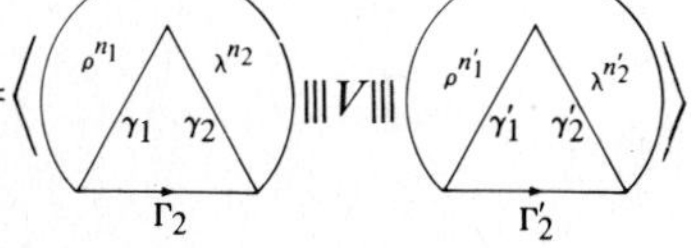

$$= (-1)^{n_2(n_1 - n_1')} \sum_{q,\, y,\, \omega\, \Omega} K(q, y, \omega, \Omega) \langle n_1 x_1 \gamma_1 ||| f_{y_1}^{\omega_1} ||| n_1' x_1' \gamma_1' \rangle$$

$$\times \sqrt{(2\Gamma_2 + 1)(2\Omega_2 + 1)(2\Gamma_2' + 1)} \begin{Bmatrix} \gamma_1 & \gamma_2 & \Gamma_2 \\ \gamma_1' & \gamma_2' & \Gamma_2' \\ \omega_1 & \omega_2 & \Omega_2 \end{Bmatrix} \langle n_2 x_2 \gamma_2 ||| f_{y_2}^{\omega_2} ||| n_2' x_2' \gamma_2' \rangle \, . \tag{15.12}$$

For simplicity we discuss the case with $n_1 = n_1' = n$ and $n_2 = n_2' = m$, such that only the single-shell matrix elements with an equal number of creation and annihilation operators for each orbit (i.e. the categories IV, V and VI) are required. Substitution of the quantum numbers for this particular case leads to

$M =$ 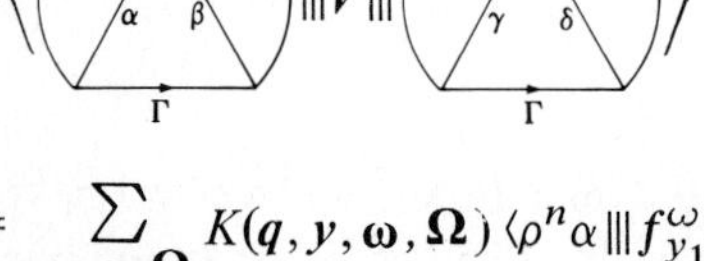

$$= \sum_{q,\, y,\, \omega,\, \Omega} K(q, y, \omega, \Omega) \langle \rho^n \alpha ||| f_{y_1}^{\omega_1} ||| \rho^n \gamma \rangle (2\Gamma + 1) \begin{Bmatrix} \alpha & \gamma & \Gamma \\ \gamma & \delta & \Gamma \\ \omega_1 & \omega_2 & 0 \end{Bmatrix} \langle \lambda^m \beta ||| f_{y_2}^{\omega_2} ||| \lambda^m \delta \rangle \, . \tag{15.13}$$

Now we can use the expressions for the single-shell operators $f_{y_i}^{\omega_i}$ and coefficients K that have been derived before. Inserting eqs. (15.8), (15.9) and (15.11) into eq. (15.13), one obtains

$$M = (2\Gamma+1)\{-\sum_\theta \langle\rho^2 |||V||| \rho^2\rangle_\theta \langle\rho^n\alpha||| [[a_\rho^\dagger \times a_\rho^\dagger]^\theta \times [\tilde{a}_\rho \times \tilde{a}_\rho]^\theta]^0 ||| \rho^n\gamma\rangle$$

$$\times \begin{Bmatrix} \alpha & \beta & \Gamma \\ \gamma & \delta & \Gamma \\ 0 & 0 & 0 \end{Bmatrix} \langle\lambda^m\beta||| \mathbf{1} ||| \lambda^m\delta\rangle$$

$$-\sum_\theta \langle\lambda^2 |||V||| \lambda^2\rangle_\theta \langle\rho^n\alpha||| \mathbf{1} ||| \rho^n\gamma\rangle \begin{Bmatrix} \alpha & \beta & \Gamma \\ \gamma & \delta & \Gamma \\ 0 & 0 & 0 \end{Bmatrix} \langle\lambda^m\beta||| [[a_\lambda^\dagger \times a_\lambda^\dagger]^\theta \times [\tilde{a}_\lambda \times \tilde{a}_\lambda]^\theta]^0 |||\lambda^m\delta\rangle$$

$$+\sum_\theta \sum_\omega \langle\rho\lambda |||V||| \rho\lambda\rangle_\theta (-1)^{\theta+\omega-\rho-\lambda} U(\rho\lambda\rho\lambda;\theta\omega) \langle\rho^n\alpha||| [a_\rho^\dagger \times \tilde{a}_\rho]^\omega ||| \rho^n\gamma\rangle$$

$$\times \begin{Bmatrix} \alpha & \beta & \Gamma \\ \gamma & \delta & \Gamma \\ \omega & \omega & 0 \end{Bmatrix} \langle\lambda^m\beta||| [a_\lambda^\dagger \times \tilde{a}_\lambda]^\omega ||| \lambda^m\delta\rangle\}. \qquad (15.14)$$

Expressions for the s.s.m.e. have been given in sect. 14.3. Substituting these expressions into eq. (15.14) and reducing the 9-j symbols (see appendix A.1.c), one finds

$$\langle\rho^n\alpha\lambda^m\beta |||V||| \rho^n\gamma\lambda^m\delta\rangle_\Gamma$$

$$= \sum_\theta \sqrt{\frac{2\Gamma+1}{2\theta+1}} \langle\rho^2 |||V||| \rho^2\rangle_\theta \sum_\Delta n(n-1) \langle\rho^n\alpha|\} \rho^{n-2}\Delta(\rho^2\theta)\rangle^2 \delta_{\alpha\gamma}\delta_{\beta\delta}$$

$$+ \sum_\theta \sqrt{\frac{2\Gamma+1}{2\theta+1}} \langle\lambda^2 |||V||| \lambda^2\rangle_\theta \sum_\Delta m(m-1) \langle\lambda^m\beta|\} \lambda^{m-2}\Delta(\lambda^2\theta)\rangle \delta_{\alpha\gamma}\delta_{\beta\delta}$$

$$+ \sum_{\theta\omega\epsilon\eta} \sqrt{(2\Gamma+1)(2\alpha+1)(2\beta+1)(2\gamma+1)(2\delta+1)(2\theta+1)}\,(2\omega+1)\,nm$$

$$\times \begin{Bmatrix} \alpha & \beta & \Gamma \\ \delta & \gamma & \omega \end{Bmatrix} \begin{Bmatrix} \alpha & \rho & \epsilon \\ \rho & \gamma & \omega \end{Bmatrix} \begin{Bmatrix} \beta & \lambda & \eta \\ \lambda & \delta & \omega \end{Bmatrix} \begin{Bmatrix} \rho & \lambda & \theta \\ \lambda & \rho & \omega \end{Bmatrix}$$

$$\times \langle\rho^n\alpha|\} \rho^{n-1}\epsilon\rangle \langle\rho^n\gamma|\} \rho^{n-1}\epsilon\rangle \langle\lambda^m\beta|\} \lambda^{m-1}\eta\rangle \langle\lambda^m\delta|\} \lambda^{m-1}\eta\rangle$$

$$\times (-1)^{\alpha+\gamma+\epsilon+\Gamma-\theta-\eta-2\lambda} \langle\rho\lambda |||V||| \rho\lambda\rangle_\theta\,. \qquad (15.15)$$

The result is seen to consist of three parts that are each a summation. They correspond to expressions (5.33), (5.34) and (5.40) that were derived in first quantization. It is obvious that the first two parts of eq. (15.15) correspond to the expansions of eqs. (5.33) and (5.34) with two-body c.f.p. Note that here in second quantization the reduced matrix elements are evaluated. Since the angular-momentum (de)coupling scheme in second-quantization formalism is different from the one used for $\langle V_{\rho\lambda}\rangle$ in first quantization, the equivalence of the third term of eq. (15.15) and eq. (5.40) appears only after some further algebra is applied. Using the Biedenharn-Elliott sum rule [Edmonds (1957)] twice, one finds

$$\sum_{\pi}(2\pi+1)\begin{Bmatrix}\epsilon & \rho & \alpha\\ \beta & \Gamma & \pi\end{Bmatrix}\begin{Bmatrix}\epsilon & \rho & \gamma\\ \delta & \Gamma & \pi\end{Bmatrix}\begin{Bmatrix}\eta & \delta & \lambda\\ \rho & \theta & \pi\end{Bmatrix}\begin{Bmatrix}\eta & \beta & \lambda\\ \rho & \theta & \pi\end{Bmatrix}$$

$$=\sum_{\pi}(2\pi+1)\sum_{\omega}(2\omega+1)(-1)^{\epsilon+\rho+\gamma+\delta+\Gamma+\pi+\alpha+\beta+\rho+\omega}\begin{Bmatrix}\delta & \rho & \pi\\ \rho & \beta & \omega\end{Bmatrix}\begin{Bmatrix}\rho & \gamma & \epsilon\\ \alpha & \rho & \omega\end{Bmatrix}\begin{Bmatrix}\delta & \gamma & \Gamma\\ \alpha & \beta & \omega\end{Bmatrix}$$

$$\times\sum_{\zeta}(2\zeta+1)(-1)^{\eta+\lambda+\delta+\rho+\pi+\theta+\beta+\rho+\lambda+\zeta}\begin{Bmatrix}\rho & \lambda & \theta\\ \lambda & \rho & \zeta\end{Bmatrix}\begin{Bmatrix}\lambda & \delta & \eta\\ \beta & \lambda & \zeta\end{Bmatrix}\begin{Bmatrix}\rho & \delta & \pi\\ \beta & \rho & \zeta\end{Bmatrix}$$

$$=\sum_{\omega}(2\omega+1)\begin{Bmatrix}\rho & \gamma & \epsilon\\ \alpha & \rho & \omega\end{Bmatrix}\begin{Bmatrix}\delta & \gamma & \Gamma\\ \alpha & \beta & \omega\end{Bmatrix}\begin{Bmatrix}\rho & \lambda & \theta\\ \lambda & \rho & \omega\end{Bmatrix}\begin{Bmatrix}\lambda & \delta & \eta\\ \beta & \lambda & \omega\end{Bmatrix}(-1)^{\alpha+\gamma+\epsilon+\Gamma-\theta-\eta-2\lambda}. \tag{15.16}$$

Here for the last equality the orthogonality relation for 6-j symbols (see eq. (A.1.b8)) has been used to reduce the summation over π to $(2\omega+1)^{-1}\,\delta_{\zeta\omega}$. After substitution of eq. (15.16) into eq. (5.40), one obtains exactly the same result as in eq. (15.15). Thus it is verified that the methods of first and second quantization do in fact yield the same results.

15.2. Single-particle operators

Up till here the discussion of eq. (14.10) has been specialized to the case of number-conserving scalar operators. Such a restriction is not necessary, of course. For instance, another important application is the evaluation of the matrix elements of electromagnetic transition operators. The latter are given for a 2^L pole transition by a sum of an isoscalar and an isovector term (see chapter 9). Let now, as usual, Λ represent the transformation character in both spaces, then each of the two parts of the electromagnetic transition operator is represented in the second-quantization formalism by (cf. eq. (13.24))

$$O^{\Lambda} = \sum_{i,j=1}^{k} \langle \rho_i | O^{\Lambda} | \rho_j \rangle \, a_{\rho_i}^{\dagger} a_{\rho_j} \,, \tag{15.17}$$

where the summation runs over all single-particle states ρ_i. Applying the Wigner-Eckart theorem, eq. (A3.a14), to the matrix element in eq. (15.17) and using the appearing Clebsch-Gordan coefficient to couple the creation and annihilation operators, one obtains from eq. (15.17) the equivalent expression

$$O^{\Lambda} = \sum_{i,j=1}^{k} \frac{\langle \rho_i ||| \boldsymbol{O}^{\Lambda} ||| \rho_j \rangle}{\sqrt{2\Lambda + 1}} \, [a_{\rho_i}^{\dagger} \times \tilde{a}_{\rho_j}]^{\Lambda} \,. \tag{15.18}$$

The operator (15.18) must be brought into the standard form of eq. (13.70). Let us assume that the single-particle states are ordered in the sequence $\rho_1, \rho_2, \ldots, \rho_k$. This order must be maintained also for the coupled creation and annihilation operators. The summation in eq. (15.18) can be split up as follows

$$\sum_{i,j=1}^{k} = \sum_{i=j}^{k} + \sum_{i<j}^{k} + \sum_{j<i}^{k} \,. \tag{15.19}$$

Interchanging the summation indices i and j one can rewrite the last term as

$$\sum_{j<i}^{k} \langle \rho_i ||| \boldsymbol{O}^{\Lambda} ||| \rho_j \rangle \, [a_{\rho_i}^{\dagger} \times \tilde{a}_{\rho_j}]^{\Lambda} = \sum_{i<j}^{k} \langle \rho_j ||| \boldsymbol{O}^{\Lambda} ||| \rho_i \rangle \, [a_{\rho_j}^{\dagger} \times \tilde{a}_{\rho_i}]^{\Lambda}$$

$$= \sum_{i<j}^{k} (-1)^{\rho_i - \rho_j} \langle \rho_i ||| \boldsymbol{O}^{\Lambda} ||| \rho_j \rangle \, [a_{\rho_j}^{\dagger} \times \tilde{a}_{\rho_i}]^{\Lambda} \,, \tag{15.20}$$

where for the last step eq. (A.3.b5) has been used. The operators $a_{\rho_j}^{\dagger}$ and $\tilde{a}_{\rho_i}$ can be interchanged with the relation

$$[a_{\rho_j}^{\dagger} \times \tilde{a}_{\rho_i}]^{\Lambda} = (-1)^{\rho_i + \rho_j - \Lambda + 1} \, [\tilde{a}_{\rho_i} \times a_{\rho_j}^{\dagger}]^{\Lambda} \qquad \text{for } \Lambda \neq 0 \,. \tag{15.21}$$

The assumption $\Lambda \neq 0$ is no restriction for a transition operator, since monopole radiation does not exist. For $\Lambda = 0$ the anticommutator of $a_{\rho}^{\dagger}$ and $\tilde{a}_{\rho}$ would lead to extra terms in eq. (15.21).

With eqs. (15.20) and (15.21) the operator (15.18) can be written as

$$O = \sum_{i=1}^{k} \frac{\langle \rho_i ||| \boldsymbol{O}^{\Lambda} ||| \rho_i \rangle}{\sqrt{2\Lambda + 1}} \, [a_{\rho_i}^{\dagger} \times \tilde{a}_{\rho_i}]^{\Lambda}$$

$$+ \sum_{i<j}^{k} \frac{\langle \rho_i ||| \boldsymbol{O}^{\Lambda} ||| \rho_j \rangle}{\sqrt{2\Lambda + 1}} \, \{[a_{\rho_i}^{\dagger} \times \tilde{a}_{\rho_j}]^{\Lambda} + (-1)^{2\rho_i - \Lambda + 1} \, [\tilde{a}_{\rho_i} \times a_{\rho_j}^{\dagger}]^{\Lambda}\} \qquad \text{for } \Lambda \neq 0 \,. \tag{15.22}$$

Thus one has for the first contribution to the transition operator (15.22), written in the standard-form expansion (13.70) and for given orbits ρ_i and ρ_j, the relations

$$K = \frac{\langle \rho_i \| O^\Lambda \| \rho_i \rangle}{\sqrt{2\Lambda + 1}} \delta_{q_i 6} \delta_{q_r 1} \qquad \text{for } r \neq i \,,$$

$$f_i^{\omega_i}(q_i = 6) = [a^\dagger_{\rho_i} \times \tilde{a}_{\rho_i}]^\Lambda \qquad \text{with } \omega_i = \Omega_i = \Lambda \,,$$

$$f_r^{\omega_r}(q_r = 1) = 1 \qquad \text{with } \omega_r = 0 \text{ for } r \neq i; \quad \Omega_r = \begin{cases} 0 \text{ for } r < i \\ \Lambda \text{ for } r \geqslant i \,. \end{cases} \tag{15.23a}$$

Similarly one finds for the second term in eq. (15.22)

$$K = \frac{\langle \rho_i \| O^\Lambda \| \rho_j \rangle}{\sqrt{2\Lambda + 1}} \delta_{q_i 2} \delta_{q_j 3} \delta_{q_r 1} \qquad \text{for } r \neq i, j \,,$$

$$f_i^{\omega_i}(q_i = 2) = a^\dagger_{\rho_i} \quad \text{with } \omega_i = \rho_i = \Omega_i \,,$$

$$f_j^{\omega_j}(q_j = 3) = \tilde{a}_{\rho_j} \qquad \text{with } \omega_j = \rho_j, \qquad \Omega_j = \Lambda \,,$$

$$f_r^{\omega_r}(q_r = 1) = 1 \qquad \text{with } \omega_r = 0 \text{ for } r \neq i, j; \quad \Omega_r = \begin{cases} 0 \text{ for } r < i \\ \omega_i \text{ for } i \leqslant r < j \\ \Lambda \text{ for } r \geqslant j \,. \end{cases} \tag{15.23b}$$

Finally the third term in eq. (15.22) can be calculated with

$$K = (-1)^{2\rho_i - \Lambda + 1} \frac{\langle \rho_i \| O^\Lambda \| \rho_j \rangle}{\sqrt{2\Lambda + 1}} \delta_{q_i 3} \delta_{q_j 2} \delta_{q_r 1} \qquad \text{for } r \neq i, j \,,$$

$$f_i^{\omega_i}(q_i = 3) = \tilde{a}_{\rho_i} \qquad \text{with } \omega_i = \rho_i = \Omega_i \,,$$

$$f_j^{\omega_j}(q_j = 2) = a^\dagger_{\rho_j} \qquad \text{with } \omega_j = \rho_j \,, \qquad \Omega_j = \Lambda \,,$$

$$f_r^{\omega_r}(q_r = 1) = 1 \qquad \text{with } \omega_r = 0 \text{ for } r \neq i, j; \quad \Omega_r = \begin{cases} 0 \text{ for } r < i \\ \omega_i \text{ for } i \leqslant r < j \\ \Lambda \text{ for } r \geqslant j \,. \end{cases} \tag{15.23c}$$

A discussion of the single-particle reduced matrix elements $\langle \rho_i \| O^\Lambda \| \rho_j \rangle$ appearing in the coefficients K, has been given in chapter 10. The many-particle, multishell matrix elements for the operator (15.17) can now be evaluated with the general expression (14.10). The single-shell matrix elements for the operators f^{ω_i} given in eqs. (15.23) have been discussed in sect. 14.3. The summation over ρ_i and ρ_j in eqs. (15.22) is contained in the sum over $\boldsymbol{q}, \boldsymbol{y}, \boldsymbol{\omega}, \boldsymbol{\Omega}$.

15.3. Spectroscopic factors

The expression (14.10) can also be used for the calculation of spectroscopic factors for multishell configurations. This is an application to the case of a one-body operator that is not number conserving. For single-shell configurations the relation between a spectroscopic factor and the corresponding c.f.p. was given in eq. (8.13). Combining this relation with eq. (14.23) one obtains

$$S(\lambda) = \frac{\langle \lambda^n \gamma ||| a_\lambda^\dagger ||| \lambda^{n-1} \gamma' \rangle^2}{2\gamma + 1} = \frac{\langle \lambda^{n-1} \gamma' ||| \tilde{a}_\lambda ||| \lambda^n \gamma \rangle^2}{2\gamma + 1}, \tag{15.24}$$

where the spectroscopic factor is expressed in terms of the second-quantization formalism. A very similar expression applies to the case with active particles in different orbits. In order to show this, we first turn to the results of chapter 8. The derivation of eq. (8.25) applies not only when the whole group of unaffected particles belongs to one particular orbit, but also when instead configurations consisting of many different orbits are substituted. The resulting spectroscopic factor depends only on the total angular momentum and isospin of the unaffected configuration. Thus we have for the spectroscopic factor

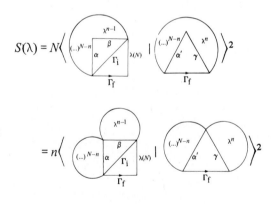

$S(\lambda) = N$ 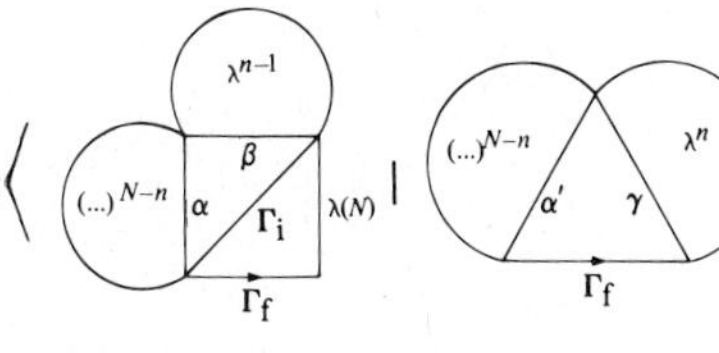

$= n$ 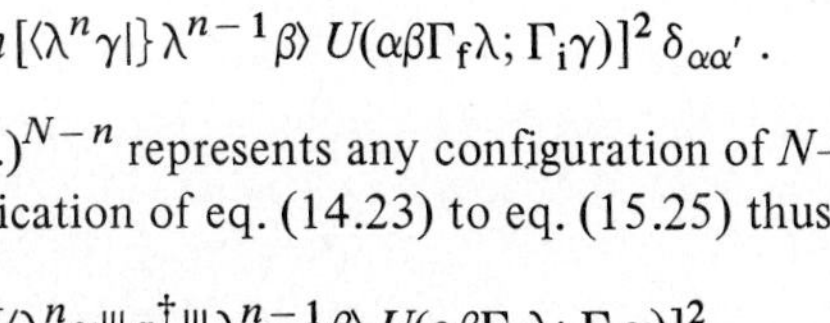

$$= n\,[\langle \lambda^n \gamma | \} \lambda^{n-1} \beta \rangle\, U(\alpha\beta\Gamma_f\lambda; \Gamma_i\gamma)]^2\, \delta_{\alpha\alpha'}\,. \tag{15.25}$$

Here $(\ldots)^{N-n}$ represents any configuration of N–n particles not occupying the orbit λ. Application of eq. (14.23) to eq. (15.25) thus leads to

$$S(\lambda) = \frac{[\langle \lambda^n \gamma ||| a_\lambda^\dagger ||| \lambda^{n-1} \beta \rangle\, U(\alpha\beta\Gamma_f\lambda; \Gamma_i\gamma)]^2}{2\gamma + 1}\, \delta_{\alpha\alpha'}\,. \tag{15.26}$$

An expression quite analogous to eq. (15.24) and appropriate for the general reduction scheme of eq. (14.10) is given by

$$S(\lambda) = \frac{\langle (...)^{N-n}\lambda^n; \Gamma |||a_\lambda^\dagger||| (...)^{N-n}\lambda^{n-1}; \Gamma' \rangle^2}{2\Gamma + 1} . \tag{15.27}$$

Let the configuration $(...)^{N-n}$ be represented by

$$|(...)_\alpha^{N-n}\rangle = Z^\alpha(N-n)|\rangle , \tag{15.28}$$

where, as usual, α denotes the total angular momentum and isospin. We then obtain with the definition of the standard state operators and single-shell operator given by eqs. (13.68) and (13.71)

$S(\lambda) = \dfrac{1}{2\Gamma + 1}$

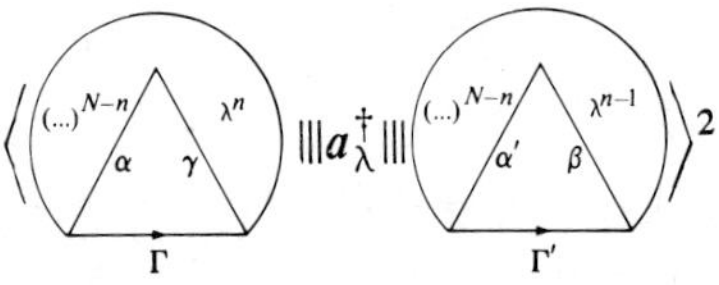

$$= \frac{1}{2\Gamma + 1} \langle (-1)^{(N-n)n} [Z^\alpha(N-n) \times Z^\gamma(\lambda^n)]^\Gamma ||| [1 \times a_\lambda^\dagger]^\lambda ||| (-1)^{(N-n)(n-1)}$$

$$\times [Z^{\alpha'}(N-n) \times Z^\beta(\lambda^{n-1})]^{\Gamma'} \rangle^2 . \tag{15.29}$$

Application of the general reduction (14.10) then leads to

$$S(\lambda) = (2\Gamma' + 1)(2\lambda + 1) \left[\begin{Bmatrix} \alpha & \gamma & \Gamma \\ \alpha' & \beta & \Gamma' \\ 0 & \lambda & \lambda \end{Bmatrix} \langle Z^\alpha(N-n) |||1||| Z^{\alpha'}(N-n) \rangle \right.$$

$$\left. \times \langle Z^\gamma(\lambda^n) |||a_\lambda^\dagger||| Z^\beta(\lambda^{n-1}) \rangle \right]^2$$

$$= \frac{1}{2\gamma + 1} [\langle \lambda^n \gamma |||a_\lambda^\dagger||| \lambda^{n-1} \beta \rangle \, U(\alpha \beta \Gamma \lambda; \Gamma' \gamma)]^2 \, \delta_{\alpha\alpha'} , \tag{15.30}$$

where in the last step the explicit value of the 9-j symbol has been inserted. Comparison of eqs. (15.26) and (15.30) shows that indeed the definition (15.27) is equivalent with the familiar definition (15.25) given in first quantization. With the spectroscopic factor expressed as the single-shell matrix element of a creation operator, one can apply a computer program based on the general expansion (14.10) for its numerical evaluation.

Let the orbits involved be numbered $j = 1, 2, 3, ...$ and let the orbit λ of the stripped (or picked up) particle be labeled $j = i$, then one has the coefficients and operators in the standard expression (13.70) given by $K(\boldsymbol{q}, \boldsymbol{y}, \boldsymbol{\omega}, \boldsymbol{\Omega}) = 1$:

$$\text{(i) } f_j^{\omega_j}(q_j = 1) = 1 \qquad \text{with } \omega_j = \Omega_j = 0 \qquad \text{for } j < i\,,$$

$$\text{(ii) } f_j^{\omega_j}(q_j = 2) = a_\lambda^\dagger \qquad \text{with } \omega_j = \Omega_j = \lambda \qquad \text{for } j = i\,,$$

$$\text{(iii) } f_j^{\omega_j}(q_j = 1) = 1 \qquad \text{with } \omega_j = 0,\ \Omega_j = \lambda \quad \text{for } j > i\,. \tag{15.31}$$

The use of the second-quantization formalism allows a direct derivation of the sum rules for the spectroscopic factors given in eqs. (8.64) and (8.69). Consider the state $|(...)_{\alpha'}^{N-n}\lambda_\gamma^n; \Gamma\rangle$ that appears in eq. (15.27). The expectation value of the number operator, defined in eq. (13.20), yields immediately the number of particles in a particular shell-model orbit λ, i.e.

$$n = \langle(...)_{\alpha'}^{N-n}\lambda_\gamma^n; \Gamma\,\Gamma_z|\sum_{\lambda_z} a_{\lambda\lambda_z}^\dagger a_{\lambda\lambda_z}|(...)_{\alpha'}^{N-n}\lambda_\gamma^n; \Gamma\,\Gamma_z\rangle\,. \tag{15.32}$$

After insertion of a complete set of intermediate states,

$$\sum_{\alpha''\gamma' k\Gamma'\Gamma_z'} |(...)_{\alpha''}^{N-k-1}\lambda_{\gamma'}^k; \Gamma'\,\Gamma_z'\rangle\langle(...)_{\alpha''}^{N-k-1}\lambda_{\gamma'}^k; \Gamma'\,\Gamma_z'| = 1\,, \tag{15.33}$$

one finds

$$n = \sum_{\alpha''\gamma'\Gamma'}\ \sum_{\Gamma_z'\lambda_z} \langle(...)_{\alpha'}^{N-n}\lambda_\gamma^n; \Gamma\,\Gamma_z|a_{\lambda\lambda_z}^\dagger|(...)_{\alpha''}^{N-n}\lambda_{\gamma'}^{n-1}; \Gamma'\,\Gamma_z'\rangle^2\,, \tag{15.34}$$

where the summation over k has been reduced to one term, $k = n - 1$, and use has been made of the fact that the (real) matrix elements of $a^\dagger$ and a are hermitian conjugates. Application of the Wigner-Eckart theorem, eq. (A.3.a17), and the normalization property of the Clebsch-Gordan coefficients, eq. (A.1.a4), now yield

$$n = \sum_{\alpha\beta\Gamma'} \frac{\langle(...)_{\alpha'}^{N-n}\lambda_\gamma^n; \Gamma|||a_\lambda^\dagger|||(...)_\alpha^{N-n}\lambda_\beta^{n-1}; \Gamma'\rangle^2}{2\Gamma + 1}\,. \tag{15.35}$$

Substitution of eq. (15.27) leads to the result (cf. eq. (8.64))

$$n = \sum_{\alpha\beta\Gamma_\mathrm{f}} S^{\mathrm{p.u.}}(\lambda) \tag{15.36}$$

with n representing the number of particles λ in the initial state. The summation extends over the final-state quantum numbers. Similarly one finds the number of holes as the expectation value of the operator

$$\sum_{\lambda_z} \{1 - a_{\lambda\lambda_z}^\dagger a_{\lambda\lambda_z}\} = \sum_{\lambda_z} a_{\lambda\lambda_z} a_{\lambda\lambda_z}^\dagger\,. \tag{15.37}$$

When $N_\lambda = 2(2j_\lambda + 1)$ denotes the maximum number of nucleons in the orbit λ, one finds

$$N_\lambda - n + 1 = \langle(\ldots)_{\alpha'}^{N-n}\lambda_\beta^{n-1}; \Gamma\,\Gamma_z | \sum_{\lambda_z} a_{\lambda\lambda_z} a_{\lambda\lambda_z}^\dagger |(\ldots)_{\alpha'}^{N-n}\lambda_\beta^{n-1}; \Gamma\,\Gamma_z\rangle$$

$$= \sum_{\alpha\gamma\Gamma'} \sum_{\Gamma_z'\lambda_z} \langle(\ldots)_\alpha^{N-n}\lambda_\gamma^n; \Gamma'\,\Gamma_z' | a_{\lambda\lambda_z}^\dagger |(\ldots)_{\alpha'}^{N-n}\lambda_\beta^{n-1}; \Gamma\,\Gamma_z\rangle^2$$

$$= \sum_{\alpha\gamma\Gamma'} \frac{2\Gamma' + 1}{2\Gamma + 1} \frac{\langle(\ldots)_\alpha^{N-n}\lambda_\gamma^n; \Gamma' ||| a_\lambda^\dagger ||| (\ldots)_{\alpha'}^{N-n}\lambda_\beta^{n-1}; \Gamma\rangle^2}{2\Gamma' + 1} \tag{15.38}$$

or (cf. eq. (8.69))

$$N_\lambda - n + 1 = \sum_{\alpha\gamma\Gamma_\mathrm{f}} \frac{2\Gamma_\mathrm{f} + 1}{2\Gamma_\mathrm{i} + 1} S^{\mathrm{str}}(\lambda)\,. \tag{15.39}$$

Here n represents the number of particles λ in the final state, i.e. $N_\lambda - n + 1$ equals the number of holes in the initial state.

Eq. (15.24) is also very useful to elucidate the role of the isospin Clebsch-Gordan coefficient in the quantity $\langle C\rangle^2 S$ (cf. eqs. (8.7) and (8.45)). Performing the reduction in isospace only we find for the spectroscopic factor for proton or neutron transfer the relation

$$S(j, t_z) = \frac{\langle j^n J; T\,T_z \| a_{j;\frac{1}{2}t_z}^\dagger \| j^{n-1} J'; T'\,T_z'\rangle^2}{2J + 1}$$

$$= \langle T\,T_z | T'\,T_z'\,\tfrac{1}{2}\,t_z\rangle^2 \frac{\langle j^n J\,T ||| a_{j\frac{1}{2}}^\dagger ||| j^{n-1} J'\,T'\rangle^2}{(2J+1)(2T+1)} = \langle C\rangle^2 S(j)\,. \tag{15.40}$$

Here $S(j, t_z)$ denotes the spectroscopic factor for the transfer of either a proton ($t_z = -\frac{1}{2}$) or a neutron ($t_z = +\frac{1}{2}$), expressed in terms of the spectroscopic factor $S(j)$ for the transfer of a nucleon.

15.4. Double-parentage coefficients and spectroscopic amplitudes

The double-parentage coefficients (d.p.c.) and the spectroscopic amplitudes for two-particle transfer reactions, that were discussed in chapters 4 and 8, can be represented very concisely in the second-quantization formalism. It will be shown that instead of eq. (8.82) one can write for the spectroscopic amplitude

$$S^{1/2}(\lambda_\mathrm{a}\lambda_\mathrm{b}; \Gamma) = \frac{\langle\Gamma_\mathrm{A} ||| Z^\Gamma(\lambda_\mathrm{a}\lambda_\mathrm{b}) ||| \Gamma_\mathrm{B}\rangle}{\sqrt{2\Gamma_\mathrm{A} + 1}}\,, \tag{15.41}$$

where the state operator Z^Γ is defined in eq. (13.43). Here the two states connected by the two-particle transfer reaction are labelled by Γ_A and Γ_B; this definition is not restricted to one- or two-shell states. For a consistent phase of the spectroscopic amplitude, however, both states Γ_A and Γ_B must be given in standard form (see eqs. (13.68) and (13.69)). No restrictions are imposed on the labels λ_a and λ_b, i.e. they may be identical or not.

The equality (15.41) will be verified for the one- and two-shell cases by comparison with eqs. (8.93) and (8.107), respectively. Let us first consider the case where λ_a and λ_b refer to the same orbit, i.e. $\lambda_a = \lambda_b \equiv \lambda$ and let the two states involved be given by

$$|\Gamma_A\rangle = (-1)^{nm}\,|[Z^{\alpha}(n) \times Z^{\gamma}(\lambda^m)]^{\Gamma_A}\rangle\,, \tag{15.42}$$

$$|\Gamma_B\rangle = (-1)^{n(m-2)}|\,[Z^{\alpha'}(n) \times Z^{\beta}(\lambda^{m-2})]^{\Gamma_B}\rangle\,. \tag{15.43}$$

Here no single-particle labels have been specified in the state operator $Z(n)$, since any number of single-particle orbits may be involved for the n particles, except the orbit λ. From eqs. (13.43) and (14.29) one finds immediately the relation

$$\langle\!\langle Z^{\gamma}(\lambda^m)|||Z^{\Gamma}(\lambda^2)|||Z^{\beta}(\lambda^{m-2})\rangle\!\rangle = \sqrt{\tfrac{1}{2}m(m-1)(2\gamma+1)}\,\langle\!\langle\lambda^m\gamma|\}\,\lambda^{m-2}\beta(\lambda^2\Gamma)\rangle\!\rangle\,. \tag{15.44}$$

Now eq. (15.41) can be reduced with the aid of eqs. (A.3.d8) and (15.44) as

$$S^{1/2}\,(\lambda^2;\Gamma) = \frac{\langle[Z^{\alpha}(n)\times Z^{\gamma}(\lambda^m)]^{\Gamma_A}|||Z^{\Gamma}(\lambda^2)|||\,[Z^{\alpha'}(n)\times Z(\lambda^{m-2})]^{\Gamma_B}\rangle}{\sqrt{2\Gamma_A+1}}$$

$$= (-1)^{\alpha+\beta+\Gamma_A+\Gamma}\sqrt{2\Gamma_B+1}\begin{Bmatrix}\gamma & \beta & \Gamma\\ \Gamma_B & \Gamma_A & \alpha\end{Bmatrix}\langle\!\langle Z^{\gamma}(\lambda^m)|||Z^{\Gamma}(\lambda^2)|||Z^{\beta}(\lambda^{m-2})\rangle\!\rangle\,\delta_{\alpha\alpha'}$$

$$= (-1)^{\alpha+\beta+\Gamma_A+\Gamma}\sqrt{\tfrac{1}{2}m(m-1)(2\Gamma_B+1)(2\gamma+1)}\begin{Bmatrix}\gamma & \beta & \Gamma\\ \Gamma_B & \Gamma_A & \alpha\end{Bmatrix}\langle\!\langle\lambda^m\gamma|\}\,\lambda^{m-2}\beta(\lambda^2\Gamma)\rangle\!\rangle\,\delta_{\alpha\alpha'}\,. \tag{15.45}$$

It is seen that in the case of single-orbit states, i.e. $n = 0$ and hence $\alpha = \alpha' = 0$, eq. (15.45) reduces exactly to eq. (8.93).

Let us consider now the cases where in eq. (15.41) the labels λ_a and λ_b refer to different orbits, i.e. $\lambda_a \neq \lambda_b$, with the two nuclear states given by

$$|\Gamma_A\rangle = (-1)^{nm}|\,[Z^{\alpha}(\lambda_a^n)\times Z^{\beta}(\lambda_b^m)]^{\Gamma_A}\rangle\,, \tag{15.46}$$

$$|\Gamma_B\rangle = (-1)^{(n-1)(m-1)}|\,[Z^{\alpha'}(\lambda_a^{n-1})\times Z^{\beta'}(\lambda_b^{m-1})]^{\Gamma_B}\rangle\,. \tag{15.47}$$

Application of eq. (A.3.d4) to the right-hand side of eq. (15.41) yields

$$S^{1/2}(\lambda_a\lambda_b;\Gamma)=(-1)^{m+1}\sqrt{(2\Gamma+1)(2\Gamma_B+1)(2\Gamma_A+1)}\begin{Bmatrix}\alpha & \beta & \Gamma_A\\ \alpha' & \beta' & \Gamma_B\\ \lambda_a & \lambda_b & \Gamma\end{Bmatrix}$$

$$\times\langle Z^{\alpha}(\lambda_a^n)\,|||a^{\dagger}_{\lambda_a}|||\,Z^{\alpha'}(\lambda_a^{n-1})\rangle\langle Z^{\beta}(\lambda_b^m)\,|||a^{\dagger}_{\lambda_b}|||\,Z^{\beta'}(\lambda_b^{m-1})\rangle\,. \tag{15.48}$$

Substitution of eq. (14.23), which relates the reduced matrix elements in eq. (15.48) and c.f.p., now yields

$$S^{1/2}(\lambda_a\lambda_b;\Gamma)=(-1)^{m+1}\sqrt{nm(2\alpha+1)(2\beta+1)(2\Gamma+1)(2\Gamma_B+1)}\begin{Bmatrix}\alpha & \beta & \Gamma_A\\ \alpha' & \beta' & \Gamma_B\\ \lambda_a & \lambda_b & \Gamma\end{Bmatrix}$$

$$\times\langle\lambda_a^n\alpha|\}\,\lambda_a^{n-1}\alpha'\rangle\langle\lambda_b^m\beta|\}\,\lambda_b^{m-1}\beta'\rangle\,. \tag{15.49}$$

Comparison of eqs. (15.49) and (8.107) shows that also for $\lambda_a\neq\lambda_b$ the definition (15.41) agrees with the spectroscopic amplitudes introduced in chapter 8. The definition (15.41) of spectroscopic amplitudes for two-particle transfer reactions is more general, however, since no restriction to one- or two-orbit configurations is made. For the evaluation of eq. (15.41) in the case $\lambda_a\neq\lambda_b$ more general states $|\Gamma_A\rangle$ and $|\Gamma_B\rangle$ could have been chosen, of course. If in both $|\Gamma_A\rangle$ and $|\Gamma_B\rangle$ a group of particles $\rho^k\gamma$ (with $\rho\neq\lambda_a$ and $\rho\neq\lambda_b$) would have been present, the essential change in the final equation (15.49) would have been an extra 6-*j* symbol only.

CHAPTER 16

REALISTIC AND EFFECTIVE OPERATORS

Before a shell-model calculation can be set up, one has to make a choice of the model space to be used. First of all the size of the model space should be considered. The number of possible configurations, and thus the dimension of the matrices involved, grows very fast with the number of active nucleons and the number of single-particle orbits. In order to keep the calculations feasible, a truncation of the space cannot be avoided and as a consequence effective operators have to be used.

In chapters 6 and 7 effective interactions were introduced in a phenomenological, empirical approach. In this chapter perturbation theory is used to derive an effective interaction and effective transition operators. The starting point then is a realistic interaction, i.e. a potential that reproduces the nucleon-nucleon scattering phase shifts in the energy region 0–300 MeV. In sect. 16.1 these two approaches are summarily compared. The general principles that underlie a perturbation calculation of an effective interaction from a realistic interaction are given in sect. 16.2. In sect. 16.3 it is explained how the various terms of the perturbation expansions can be rendered in diagrams. The importance of the choice of the single-particle basis is discussed in sect. 16.4. The repulsive hard core of the realistic interaction leads to large, or even infinite, matrix elements that are calculated in the customary basis of unperturbed wave functions. It is shown in sect. 16.5 how this problem can be dealt with by partial summations in the Brueckner approximation. In sect. 16.6 effective operators are introduced for the description of electromagnetic transitions; for the case of electric quadrupole transitions these can be expressed in terms of effective charges, as is done in sect. 16.7. The magnetic dipole transitions are treated in sect. 16.8, where also a numerical example is discussed. Some remarks on higher-order terms and many-particle systems are made in sects. 16.9 and 16.10.

16.1. Effective interaction operators

In order to reduce the dimensions of the configuration space, one can restrict the configurations to one major oscillator shell, or even to one or more subshells, considering the (sub)shells of lower energy as forming an inert core of occupied states. It is not to be expected that in such a restricted model space the nucleon-nucleon interaction is given by the free-space interaction. One introduces an *effective* internucleon interaction, assuming that such an interaction appropriately will account for the configurations that were omitted from the model space. There are two different approaches to the problem of determining the effective interaction for a particular shell-model calculation.

In the first approach the existence of an effective interaction is assumed. A complete description of this interaction requires the knowledge of all its matrix elements between the many-particle states in the configuration space involved. On the assumption that the interaction can be represented as a sum of two-body interactions and by virtue of the symmetry conditions imposed on the interaction (hermiticity and charge independence, invariance under space rotations and reflection), one can describe the interaction with a relatively small number of parameters, i.e. the two-particle matrix elements. The latter can be determined in a least-squares fitting procedure applied to known experimental spectroscopic data, e.g. excitation energies.

One may also assume that the effective interaction can be represented by some particular, few-parameter operator which describes its dependence on spatial coordinates, spin and isospin. (In principle one could introduce also a momentum dependence.) This alternative approach reduces the number of adjustable parameters. These phenomenological methods have been treated in detail in chapters 6 and 7.

In the second approach to be discussed here one starts from a realistic interaction, i.e. the interaction between free nucleons, as determined from scattering experiments, and then tries to construct from it an effective interaction. This procedure requires the application of many-body perturbation theory, of which we shall give the general outline only.

16.2. General principles

In order to understand the difference between the free nucleon-nucleon interaction $\mathcal{V}$ and an effective interaction V, let us consider a system described by the Hamiltonian

$$\mathcal{H} = H^{(0)} + \mathcal{V} . \tag{16.1}$$

Here $H^{(0)}$ denotes the unperturbed Hamiltonian defining the set of unperturbed wave functions Φ_i that satisfy the Schrödinger equation

$$H^{(0)}\Phi_i = E_i\Phi_i \qquad (i = 1, 2, ...) . \tag{16.2}$$

For a particular state the true wave function Ψ obeys the Schrödinger equation with the perturbing residual interaction $\mathcal{V}$ taken into account

$$\mathcal{H}\Psi = (H^{(0)} + \mathcal{V})\,\Psi = \mathcal{E}\,\Psi , \tag{16.3}$$

where $\mathcal{E}$ represents the true energy of the system.

The standard perturbational procedure is to expand the true wave function in terms of the unperturbed basis wave functions as

$$\Psi = \sum_{i=1}^{\infty} a_i\Phi_i , \tag{16.4}$$

where the summation runs over a complete set of eigenfunctions Φ_i. For a truncated configuration space, however, only a limited number of basis states Φ_i that span the model space M, are selected. One obtains the model wave function Ψ' from the expansion

$$\Psi' = \sum_{i \in M} a_i \Phi_i \,, \tag{16.5}$$

i.e. the model wave function is given by the part of the true wave function that lies within the model space. We now require the effective Hamiltonian, H^{eff}, to reproduce the true eigenvalue $\mathcal{E}$ for the model wave function Ψ', i.e. $\langle\Psi'|H^{\text{eff}}|\Psi'\rangle = \mathcal{E}$. It is clear from eqs. (16.4) and (16.5) that the wave functions Ψ and Ψ' cannot both be normalized. It will be assumed in the following that the model wave function Ψ' is normalized.

The division of the full Hilbert space into a model space M and a discarded part, can be accomplished by the use of the projection operators

$$P = \sum_{i \in M} |\Phi_i\rangle\langle\Phi_i| \,, \tag{16.6}$$

which projects onto the model space, and

$$Q = \sum_{i \notin M} |\Phi_i\rangle\langle\Phi_i| \,, \tag{16.7}$$

which projects off the model space. These operators clearly obey the relations

$$P + Q = 1, \qquad P^2 = P\,, \qquad Q^2 = Q\,, \qquad PQ = QP = 0\,. \tag{16.8}$$

Since P and Q are defined in terms of the eigenfunctions of the unperturbed Hamiltonian $H^{(0)}$, they satisfy the commutation relations

$$[P, H^{(0)}] = 0\,, \qquad [Q, H^{(0)}] = 0\,. \tag{16.9}$$

Writing for the true wave function

$$\Psi = (P + Q)\,\Psi = \Psi' + Q\Psi\,, \tag{16.10}$$

where

$$\Psi' = P\Psi \tag{16.11}$$

represents the model wave function, one can bring the Schrödinger equation (16.3) to the form of two coupled equations by applying Q and P. With the use of eqs. (16.3), (16.8) and (16.9) one then obtains

$$Q(\mathcal{H} - \mathcal{E})\,\Psi = 0 \quad \text{or} \quad (H^{(0)} - \mathcal{E} + Q\mathcal{V}Q)\,Q\Psi = -Q\mathcal{V}(P\Psi)\,, \tag{16.12}$$

and

$$P(\mathcal{H} - \mathcal{E})\,\Psi = 0 \quad \text{or} \quad (H^{(0)} - \mathcal{E} + P\mathcal{V}P)\,P\Psi = -P\mathcal{V}(Q\Psi)\,. \tag{16.13}$$

Eq. (16.12) can be solved for $Q\Psi$ to give

$$Q\Psi = -Q(H^{(0)} - \mathcal{E} + Q\mathcal{V}Q)^{-1}Q\mathcal{V}P(P\Psi)\,. \tag{16.14}$$

Substitution into eq. (16.13) then yields

$$\{H^{(0)} - \mathcal{E} + P\mathcal{V}P - P\mathcal{V}Q(H^{(0)} - \mathcal{E} + Q\mathcal{V}Q)^{-1}Q\mathcal{V}P\}P\Psi = 0 \tag{16.15}$$

or

$$P\{H^{(0)} - \mathcal{E} + \mathcal{V} - \mathcal{V}Q(H^{(0)} - \mathcal{E} + Q\mathcal{V}Q)^{-1}Q\mathcal{V}\}P\Psi = 0\,. \tag{16.16}$$

This can be rewritten with the use of eq. (16.11) as

$$P(H^{(0)} - \mathcal{E} + V)\,\Psi' = 0\,, \tag{16.17}$$

where V represents the *effective interaction* defined by

$$V = \mathcal{V} + \mathcal{V}Q(\mathcal{E} - H^{(0)} - Q\mathcal{V}Q)^{-1}Q\mathcal{V}. \tag{16.18}$$

One observes that eq. (16.17) defines an eigenvalue problem in the model space M for the true eigenvalues $\mathcal{E}$, but the effective interaction V turns out to be dependent on the very energy $\mathcal{E}$ one wishes to calculate.

In order to bring eq. (16.18) to a more useful form we make use of the operator identity

$$1 = \frac{1}{A}(A - B) + \frac{1}{A}B \tag{16.19}$$

or

$$\frac{1}{A-B} = \frac{1}{A} + \frac{1}{A}B\frac{1}{A-B}\,, \tag{16.20}$$

which holds for any two operators A and B. We find

$$\begin{aligned} V &= \mathcal{V} + \mathcal{V}Q\left\{\frac{1}{\mathcal{E} - H^{(0)}} + \frac{1}{\mathcal{E} - H^{(0)}}\,Q\mathcal{V}Q\,\frac{1}{\mathcal{E} - H^{(0)} - Q\mathcal{V}Q}\right\}Q\mathcal{V} \\ &= \mathcal{V} + \mathcal{V}Q\,\frac{1}{\mathcal{E} - H^{(0)}}\,Q\left\{\mathcal{V} + \mathcal{V}Q\,\frac{1}{\mathcal{E} - H^{(0)} - Q\mathcal{V}Q}\,Q\mathcal{V}\right\} \\ &= \mathcal{V} + \mathcal{V}Q\,\frac{1}{\mathcal{E} - H^{(0)}}\,QV = \mathcal{V} + \mathcal{V}\,\frac{Q}{\mathcal{E} - H^{(0)}}\,V\,. \end{aligned} \tag{16.21}$$

For the last step use has been made of the fact that Q and $H^{(0)}$ are commuting operators (cf. eq. (16.9)). Thus no ambiguities should arise from the notation

$$\frac{Q}{\mathcal{E} - H^{(0)}} \quad \text{or from} \quad \frac{Q}{\mathcal{E} - H^{(0)} - Q\mathcal{V}Q}\,.$$

The evaluation of the inverse operators in these expressions should be clear when they act on eigenstates. If they act on an arbitrary function, however, then the latter must be expanded in eigenstates before a well-defined result can be obtained. Eq. (16.21) can be iterated to yield

$$V = \mathcal{V} + \mathcal{V} \frac{Q}{\mathcal{E} - H^{(0)}} \mathcal{V} + \mathcal{V} \frac{Q}{\mathcal{E} - H^{(0)}} \mathcal{V} \frac{Q}{\mathcal{E} - H^{(0)}} \mathcal{V} + \dots . \qquad (16.22)$$

Similarly from eqs. (16.10), (16.11), (16.14) and (16.20) one can derive an expression for the true wave function Ψ in terms of the model wave function Ψ'

$$\Psi = \Psi' + \frac{Q}{\mathcal{E} - H^{(0)} - Q\mathcal{V}Q} \mathcal{V}\Psi'$$

$$= \Psi' + Q \left\{ \frac{1}{\mathcal{E} - H^{(0)}} + \frac{1}{\mathcal{E} - H^{(0)}} Q\mathcal{V}Q \frac{1}{\mathcal{E} - H^{(0)} - Q\mathcal{V}Q} \right\} \mathcal{V}\Psi'$$

$$= \Psi' + \frac{Q}{\mathcal{E} - H^{(0)}} \left\{ \mathcal{V}\Psi' + Q\mathcal{V}Q \frac{1}{\mathcal{E} - H^{(0)} - Q\mathcal{V}Q} \mathcal{V}\Psi' \right\}$$

$$= \Psi' + \frac{Q}{\mathcal{E} - H^{(0)}} \mathcal{V}\Psi . \qquad (16.23)$$

Thus an operator is constructed that restores the part of the wave function that was projected off the model space. This surprising fact can be understood if one realizes that for the actual evaluation of eq. (16.23) one needs to know the matrix elements of the residual interaction between *all* basis states Φ_i, i.e. with the inclusion of the states outside the model space.

Eq. (16.23) can also be iterated to give

$$\Psi = \Psi' + \frac{Q}{\mathcal{E} - H^{(0)}} \mathcal{V}\Psi' + \frac{Q}{\mathcal{E} - H^{(0)}} \mathcal{V} \frac{Q}{\mathcal{E} - H^{(0)}} \mathcal{V}\Psi' + \dots . \qquad (16.24)$$

Since the operator Q projects off the model space, i.e. $Q|\Psi'\rangle = 0$, one observes immediately from the previous equations that the true wave functions Ψ are normalized according to the relation

$$\langle\Psi|\Psi'\rangle = \langle\Psi'|\Psi'\rangle = 1 . \qquad (16.25)$$

When the norm of Ψ is evaluated with the use of eq. (16.24) it is seen that the deviation from unity is given in terms of second and higher order in $\mathcal{V}$. The construction of the true wave function Ψ can be drawn schematically as in fig. 16.1. The projection operator Q in eq. (16.23) leads to a component that is orthogonal to the model wave function Ψ'. This drawing may serve to visualize the normalization condition, given in eq. (16.25).

Using eqs. (16.22) and (16.24) one now easily verifies the relation

$$V\Psi' = \mathcal{V}\Psi , \qquad (16.26)$$

RELATION BETWEEN TRUE AND MODEL WAVE FUNCTION

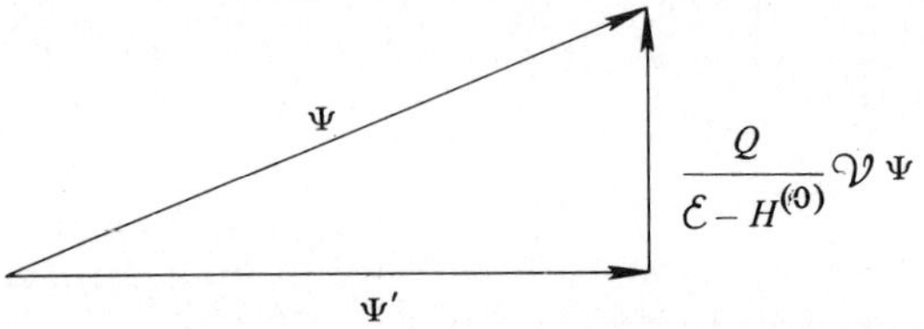

Fig. 16.1. Schematic picture of the construction of the true wave function $|\Psi\rangle$ from the model wave function $|\Psi'\rangle$ according to eq. (16.23). Thus the normalization condition (16.25) is clearly illustrated.

which shows that the action of the effective interaction on the model wave function yields the same result as the action of the realistic interaction on the true wave function.

The perturbation expansion given in eq. (16.22) is of the Brillouin-Wigner type, with the unknown energy $\mathcal{E}$ occurring in the energy denominators. Further manipulation is required before a closer resemblance to the usual shell-model equations is obtained. In the first place the effective interaction V can be reformulated such that it is independent of the energy of the core, and the resulting equations refer to the valence particles only. In the second place these equations can be presented in such a way that the true energies for the valence particles are not required but only the unperturbed energies.

It is beyond the scope of this book to elaborate on the removal of the energy of the core from the formalism and we give the results only.

Let us put

$$\mathcal{E} = E_c + \Delta E_c + E_v + \Delta E_{cv} , \tag{16.27}$$

with $E_c + \Delta E_c$ the true core energy, E_c the unperturbed core energy (i.e. the energy of the system of the core nucleons if described by the unperturbed Hamiltonian $H^{(0)}$), E_v the unperturbed energy of the valence nucleons (i.e. the energy of the system of the valence nucleons if described by the unperturbed Hamiltonian $H^{(0)}$), and ΔE_{cv} the remainder. One can show [Brandow (1967)] that eq. (16.17) can be rewritten in the model space as

$$P(H_v^{(0)} + V)\,\Psi' = (E_v + \Delta E_{cv})\,\Psi' \tag{16.28}$$

with

$$H_v^{(0)} = H^{(0)} - E_c . \tag{16.29}$$

Eq. (16.28) now has the form of the Schrödinger equation with eigenvalue $E_v + \Delta E_{cv}$ and with the projector P indicating that it is defined for the model space only. Similarly one can rewrite eq. (16.22) for the effective interaction as

$$V = \mathcal{V} + \mathcal{V} \frac{Q}{E_v - H_v^{(0)}} V$$

$$= \mathcal{V} + \mathcal{V} \frac{Q}{E_v - H_v^{(0)}} \mathcal{V} + \mathcal{V} \frac{Q}{E_v - H_v^{(0)}} \mathcal{V} \frac{Q}{E_v - H_v^{(0)}} \mathcal{V} + \dots . \qquad (16.30)$$

The same symbol V was used in chapter 3 to represent the same quantity in a different approach.

The Brillouin-Wigner series expansion for the effective interaction, given in eq. (16.22), has been transformed into the Rayleigh-Schrödinger perturbation series given in eq. (16.30). The latter expansion contains only the *un*perturbed energy E_v in the denominators. The removal of ΔE_c and ΔE_{cv} (cf. eq. (16.27)) from the denominators has to be compensated for by a particular restriction on the expansion (16.30). This restriction can best be described in terms of diagrams, which are discussed in sect. 16.3. The diagrammatic expansion should contain only *linked diagrams* and *folded diagrams.* Linked diagrams are those diagrams that cannot be divided into two or more parts without cutting at least one particle or interaction line. The complications that are caused by the presence of the folded diagrams arise beyond the second-order terms in the expansion. For details of the resulting *linked, folded-diagram valence expansion* one is referred to [Brandow (1967); Sprung (1972); Barrett and Kirson (1973); Kuo (1974)].

It is noted here that, although eqs. (16.28) and (16.30) lead in principle to the exact eigenvalues, the wave functions Ψ' are projections of the true, orthogonal eigenfunctions onto the model space and therefore in general are not mutually orthogonal. The effective interaction V is not necessarily a hermitian operator. The present line of approach has not been followed in chapters 6 and 7, where from the beginning the existence of a hermitian, effective interaction was postulated.

Another consequence of the model wave functions Ψ' being projections is that one cannot expect them to reproduce e.g. electromagnetic transition rates correctly. Just as an effective residual interaction was introduced to make up for the truncation of the configuration space, one has to introduce effective electromagnetic operators (see sect. 16.6).

16.3. Diagrammatic representation

For an evaluation of the matrix elements of the effective interaction given in eq. (16.30), one inserts complete sets of intermediate states between each two adjacent operators. The presence of the projector Q prevents summation over intermediate states in the model space.

For the discussion of the various terms that must be summed over to obtain the effective valence interaction in eq. (16.30) and for similar expansions of effective operators describing electromagnetic transitions, use will be made of a diagrammatic representation. Such diagrams are known as *Feynman diagrams.* For each fermion a vertical line is drawn, labeled by its quantum numbers. Interaction between two fermions is represented by a horizontal dashed line, which may be regarded as the exchange of mesons. The Feynman diagrams are actually meant to be a picture of the development of the system under consideration. Thus time is thought as running upwards along the vertical time axis. In many cases, as in this book, one does not use the time-dependent picture, however, but one employs a Fourier transformed description. The time-variable is integrated over and the picture must be reinterpreted in terms of energy [Baranger (1969)]. Hence, although one still may think of time as running upwards, no time labels should be written along the vertical axis.

The antisymmetrized two-body matrix element is represented diagrammatically by

$\langle ab|\mathcal{V}|cd\rangle =$ 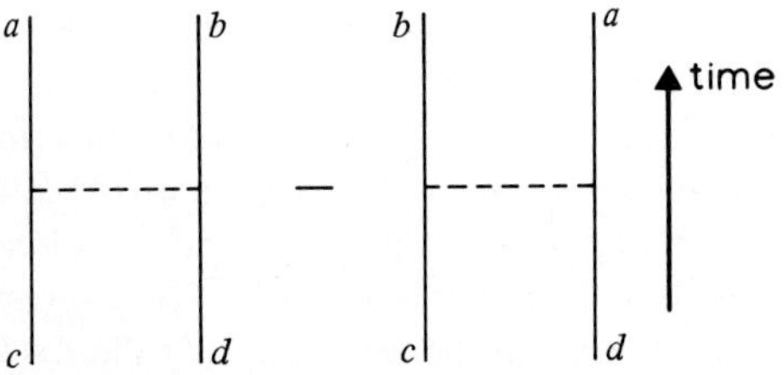

(16.31)

Since the Pauli exclusion principle requires the fermion states to be antisymmetric, two diagrams are drawn in eq. (16.31), where the first one represents the direct term $\langle a(1)\, b(2)|\mathcal{V}|c(1)\, d(2)\rangle$ and the second the exchange term $\langle a(2)\, b(1)|\mathcal{V}|c(1) d(2)\rangle$. For brevity, however, usually the exchange terms are tacitly understood, and only one diagram is drawn. Alternatively, one sometimes omits the dashed line that represents the meson exchange and represents the two-body matrix element by a single vertex:

$\langle ab|\mathcal{V}|cd\rangle =$ 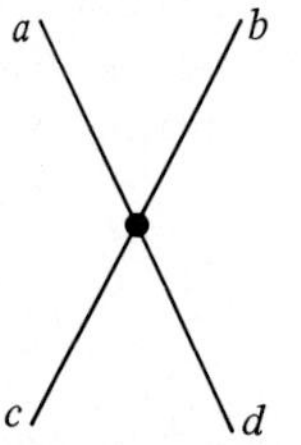

(16.32)

This vertex is assumed to represent both diagrams of eq. (16.31).

Let us consider next the possible contributions from the second-order term of eq. (16.30) to the two-body matrix element of the effective interaction, $\langle ab|V|cd\rangle$, where the two-body states $|ab\rangle$ and $|cd\rangle$ belong to the model space, of course. The first possibility that comes to mind is the case of a two-particle intermediate state

$|p_1p_2\rangle$, which can be represented as (cf. eq. (16.30))

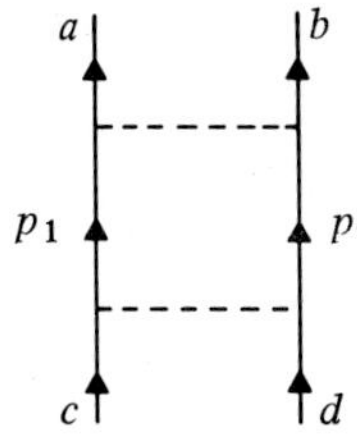

$$= \sum_{p_1p_2} \langle ab|\mathcal{V}|p_1p_2\rangle \frac{1}{e_c + e_d - e_{p_1} - e_{p_2}} \langle p_1p_2|\mathcal{V}|cd\rangle\,. \quad (16.33)$$

The energy denominator, being diagonal in the single-particle basis, is simply the difference $E_v - H_v^{(0)}$, i.e. the unperturbed energy of the initial (or final) two-particle state minus the unperturbed energy of the intermediate state. The summation must be performed over all sets of two-particle states p_1 and p_2 *not both* belonging to the model space.

It would be inconvenient to have to draw all fermion lines representing the occupied single-particle states that form the inert core. Therefore the core is considered as a reference state, represented by no lines at all. Lines should be drawn only for the active nucleons outside the core. However, the assumption of a completely inert core cannot be maintained in all cases; in particular for the evaluation of effective operators one needs to take into account (intermediate) excited-core states. In such states one or more particles are excited, due to the residual interaction, from the core into higher states, leaving holes in the core. These holes are represented also by vertical lines, but in order to distinguish particles from holes, the former are given an arrow pointing upwards and the latter an arrow pointing downwards. We shall use the convention that intermediate lines in diagrams are always taken to be summed over, even if they are labelled.

Other contributions derive from diagrams with e.g. three-particle, one-hole intermediate states. In sect. 17.3 it is discussed how after insertion of many-particle, many-hole intermediate states the reduction to two-particle matrix elements can be achieved in the second-quantization formalism. Thus one finds as another contribution the expression

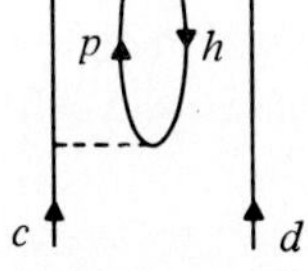

$$= \sum_{ph} \langle bh|\mathcal{V}|dp\rangle \frac{1}{e_c - e_a - e_p + e_h} \langle ap|\mathcal{V}|ch\rangle\,. \quad (16.34)$$

The energy denominator is obtained again as the eigenvalue of the operator $E_v - H_v^{(0)}$ acting upon the intermediate state, i.e. $(e_c + e_d) - (e_a + e_p - e_h + e_d)$ (cf. eq.

(17.36)). There is no restriction on the summation over the particle states p, since owing to the presence of the hole h any combination ph is outside the model space.

For the evaluation of complicated diagrams in terms of two-body matrix elements and energy denominators it is not necessary each time to go through a complete derivation *ab initio*. A concise set of rules can be given for immediate evaluation of the diagrams [Brandow (1967)]. The principal rules read as follows.

Every diagram represents an expression that contains for each vertex $\mathcal{V}$ an antisymmetric two-body matrix element of $\mathcal{V}$ with the labels of the two incoming lines written at the right (ket vector) and those of the two outgoing lines written at the left (bra vector). It is understood that one pair of the throughgoing lines is represented by the first label in bra and ket state, whereas the other throughgoing pair is denoted by the second label in bra and ket state. For instance, the lower vertex in eq. (16.34) has the incoming lines c and h and the outgoing lines a and p, which thus leads to a factor $\langle ap|\mathcal{V}|ch\rangle$. Similarly the matrix element that corresponds to the upper vertex can be read off immediately from the diagram.

The particle and hole lines between each two successive vertices correspond to an energy denominator $E_{\text{v}} + \Sigma_{\text{holes}}\, e_h - \Sigma_{\text{particles}}\, e_p$, where the summations cover all downgoing (h) and upgoing (p) lines. These energy denominators can thus be found by drawing horizontal lines between the vertices and taking into account all particle and hole lines that are crossed.

A factor $\frac{1}{2}$ must be included for each equivalent pair of lines. Two lines form an equivalent pair if they (i) both begin at the same interaction, (ii) both end at the same interaction and (iii) both go in the same direction, e.g. the pair of hole lines l and m in diagram (16.50). This factor $\frac{1}{2}$ prevents double counting of diagrams with equivalent pairs of lines.

The reduction with the use of the second-quantization formalism also yields a particular sign for each contribution. This sign is given by $(-1)^{l+h}$, where l represents the number of closed loops in the diagram (see loop in diagram (16.34)) and h represents the number of hole lines in the diagram.

The use of antisymmetrix matrix elements of $\mathcal{V}$ implies that exchange diagrams, usually not drawn but tacitly understood to be taken into account, are also included in the evaluation. It is noted here that even then one often still has to antisymmetrize explicitly the incoming and outgoing two-body states. For instance, the contribution that is represented by eq. (16.34), must still be antisymmetrized in the states a and b and in the states c and d.

For the preceding considerations it was assumed that the residual interaction $\mathcal{V}$ leads only to two-body matrix elements in the expansions. As the residual interaction involves the single-particle potential, some attention should be paid to the definition of the single-particle basis in which the calculation is performed.

16.4. Single-particle basis

Till here it was assumed implicitly that an appropriate single-particle basis and a residual interaction can be defined. The Hamiltonian of the many-nucleon system

$$H = \sum_k T(k) + \sum_{k<l} W(k, l) \tag{16.35}$$

can be rewritten as (cf. eqs. (1.10) and (3.3))

$$H = \sum_k \{T(k) + U(k)\} + \{\sum_{k<l} W(k,l) - \sum_k U(k)\}\,, \tag{16.36}$$

where, in principle, one may use any single-particle potential $U(k)$. But when

$$H^{(0)} = \sum_k \{T(k) + U(k)\} \tag{16.37}$$

is going to define the unperturbed basis for the calculation and

$$V = \sum_{k<l} W(k,l) - \sum_k U(k) \tag{16.38}$$

represents the perturbation, i.e. the residual interaction, it is desirable and advantageous to choose the potential $U(k)$ such that the perturbation expansions converge well.

In a self-consistent Hartree-Fock basis (see below) the potential $U(k)$ is determined such that the expectation value of the unperturbed Hamiltonian $H^{(0)}$ is minimized for the set of determinantal wave functions used. And thus one should expect that the contributions of the residual interaction to the total energy are as small as possible for this class of wave functions. This requirement imposes simultaneous conditions on the single-particle potential and the single-particle wave functions. The relevant equations are given by (cf. eq. (17.19))

$$\sum_h \langle \alpha h | W | \beta h \rangle = \langle \alpha | U | \beta \rangle\,, \tag{16.39}$$

where the summation covers all occupied states. Here we meet a kind of two-body matrix elements that we have not yet tried to render in diagrams. They represent the scattering of a particle at a core particle, while the latter does not change orbit, i.e. the process

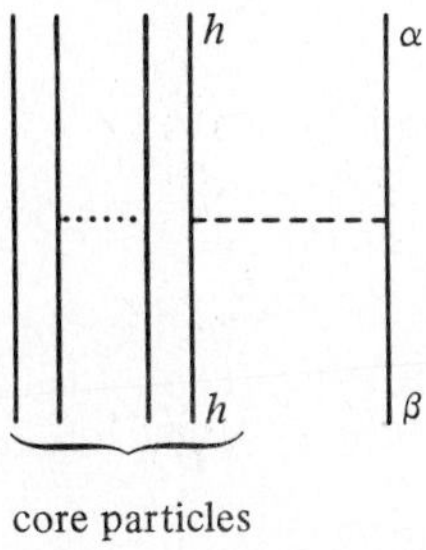

(16.40)

In this diagram *all* particles of the nuclear system appear explicitly, i.e. no reference state represented by no lines at all, is assumed (as in eq. (16.31)). Arrows are not drawn since hole lines do not occur. The core particles are said to be in states below the Fermi surface, the other particles above the Fermi surface. If we wish to represent this process in terms of a diagram with the core particles forming the reference state, it is not clear how we can draw the interaction with the state h since the latter is occupied before and after the interaction.

By convention the process represented in diagram (16.40) is drawn as

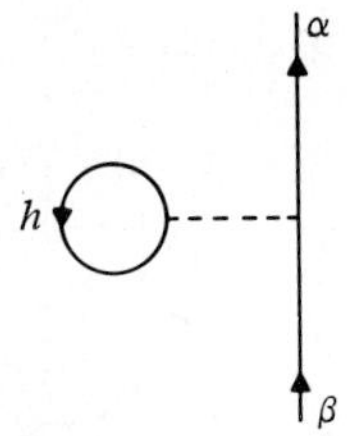

(16.41)

The exchange process, which is also implied by the antisymmetric matrix elements $\langle \alpha h|W|\beta h\rangle$, is denoted by

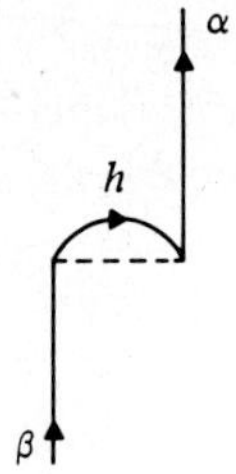

(16.42)

Diagram (16.41) is usually referred to as the Hartree-Fock bubble diagram. Here it was assumed that the states α and β were both above the Fermi surface. If α and/or β denote states below the Fermi surface, hole lines appear. The latter indicate that before and/or after the scattering process particular orbits are unoccupied in the reference state. Eq. (16.39), defining the self-consistent single-particle potential for our basis states, can now be given for the four possible particle-hole combinations of α and β by the diagrams

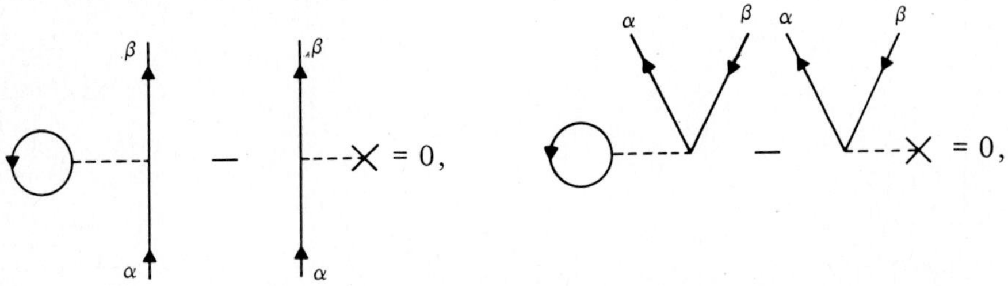

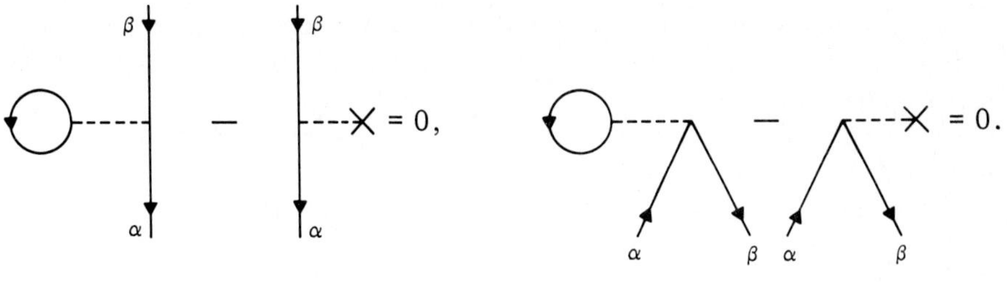

(16.43)

Here the dashed line ending in a cross, denotes the single-particle potential U. Omission of the label for the bubble with downward arrow implies summation over all hole states, i.e. the occupied states making up the core.

The self-consistency means that on the one hand the single-particle potential U defines the single-particle wave functions $|\alpha\rangle$ as the eigenfunctions of $T(k) + U(k)$ (cf. eq. (16.37)) and that on the other hand the single-particle wave functions $|\alpha\rangle$ determine the single-particle potential U as given in eq. (16.39).

Although the definition of the residual interaction V, given in eq. (16.38), certainly leads to diagrams containing U, these are all cancelled by corresponding diagrams of W according to the self-consistency conditions (16.43), i.e. neither of these diagrams appear.

It is important to remark that one employs for most shell-model calculations a harmonic-oscillator single-particle basis and hence the self-consistency conditions are not exactly met. Experience has indicated, however, that the self-consistent, Hartree-Fock basis is very similar to the harmonic-oscillator basis, at least for the lighter nuclei and provided the appropriate value is taken for the size parameter. Thus most shell-model calculations have been done in a harmonic-oscillator basis, but on the assumption that at the same time eqs. (16.43) are satisfied. In such a nonselfconsistent basis, however, one should actually insert any number of single-particle potentials and Hartree-Fock bubbles and subsequently sum over all resulting diagrams. Matters are complicated further when the nucleon-nucleon interaction is replaced by the G matrix (see next section). We shall assume in the following, however, that the diagrams of the single-particle potential and those of the appropriate bubble diagrams in the perturbational expansion cancel each other. Nevertheless, it is remarked here that some calculations have indicated that the self-consistency corrections, which are due to incomplete cancellation of diagrams may be significant [Ellis and Mavromatis (1971); Starkand and Kirson (1976)].

16.5. The *G* matrix

We have seen that the calculation of matrix elements of the effective interaction V leads to terms containing two-body matrix elements of the realistic (residual) nucleon-nucleon interaction $\mathcal{V}$. This calculation is performed by the use of the perturbational expansion (16.30) after insertion of intermediate states. The independent-particle wave functions possess a nonvanishing value near the origin. Hence the repulsive hard core of the nucleon-nucleon interaction causes the matrix elements of $\mathcal{V}$ to be infinite or anyway very large. This feature prevents the application of perturbation theory.

In the Brueckner theory one considers a pair of nucleons and treats the scattering of the two nucleons moving in nuclear matter exactly. The exact treatment of the two-body correlations removes the occurrence of the infinities that occur when two-body matrix elements of the realistic interaction $\mathcal{V}$ are calculated with the usual single-particle wave functions. The correlated two-body wave function vanishes in the region where $\mathcal{V}$ is strongly repulsive. The *reaction matrix* or *G matrix* then emerges as the result of a partial summation over a certain class of diagrams, the ladder diagrams (see below).

In fig. 16.2 a relative two-particle wave function (i.e. the c.m. motion has been removed) is drawn for a hard-core potential and compared with the uncorrelated wave function. The former vanishes inside the hard core, while the latter still possesses a non-zero value. The difference between the two functions, i.e. the defect wave function, vanishes exponentially for large distances. This is the *healing property* of nuclear matter. It is in contrast with the scattering process in free space, where at large distances one still finds a phase shift.

Similarly to eq. (16.26) one finds for the two-particle part of the interaction, the relation

$$G\Psi' = \mathcal{V}\Psi \,, \tag{16.44}$$

which shows that the G matrix is well-behaved, even at small distances where $\mathcal{V}$ may become infinite but Ψ vanishes.

DEFECT WAVE FUNCTION

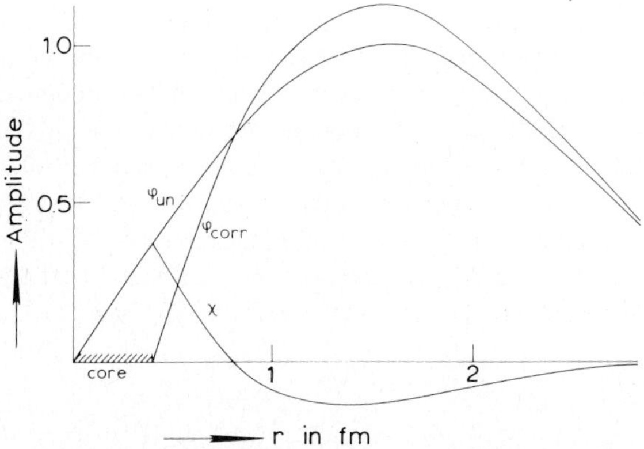

Fig. 16.2. Example of the defect wave function, $\chi = \phi_{\mathrm{un}} - \phi_{\mathrm{corr}}$, representing the difference between the uncorrelated (or unperturbed) relative two-particle wave function and the correlated wave function. It vanishes exponentially at large values of r.

The nucleon pair in the Brueckner theory is allowed to interact any number of times. All possible cases are summed over with the two interacting nucleons always above the Fermi surface.

The G matrix is a solution of the Bethe-Goldstone equation

$$G(\omega) = \mathcal{V} + \mathcal{V}\,\frac{Q^{\mathrm{Br}}}{\omega - H_0}\,G(\omega)\,. \tag{16.45}$$

Here the operator Q^{Br} vanishes unless it acts on a two-particle state with both particles above the Fermi surface of the occupied states. In the latter case it yields unity. It is often referred to as the Pauli operator since it enforces the Pauli exclusion principle for the two-particle states with respect to the occupied states. The variable ω represents an energy, the starting energy that will be defined below. The matrix elements of G are given by

$$\begin{aligned}\langle ab|G(\omega)|cd\rangle &= \langle ab|\mathcal{V}|cd\rangle \\ &+ \sum_{p_1p_2}{}' \langle ab|\mathcal{V}|p_1p_2\rangle \frac{1}{\omega - e_{p_1} - e_{p_2}} \langle p_1p_2|\mathcal{V}|cd\rangle \\ &+ \sum_{p_1p_2p_3p_4}{}' \langle ab|\mathcal{V}|p_1p_2\rangle \frac{1}{\omega - e_{p_1} - e_{p_2}} \langle p_1p_2|\mathcal{V}|p_3p_4\rangle \\ &\times \frac{1}{\omega - e_{p_3} - e_{p_4}} \langle p_3p_4|\mathcal{V}|cd\rangle + \dots\,,\end{aligned} \tag{16.46}$$

where the prime restricts the summations to two-particle states above the Fermi surface. It is obvious that the series expansion (16.46) is meaningless if the interaction $\mathcal{V}$ possesses an infinitely hard core, since then all matrix elements in eq. (16.46) are infinite. For such cases different methods must be used to solve eq. (16.45).

For realistic interactions $\mathcal{V}$ that are sufficiently smooth, however, the perturbational expansion (16.46) can be used to calculated the G matrix. In diagrams eq. (16.46) becomes

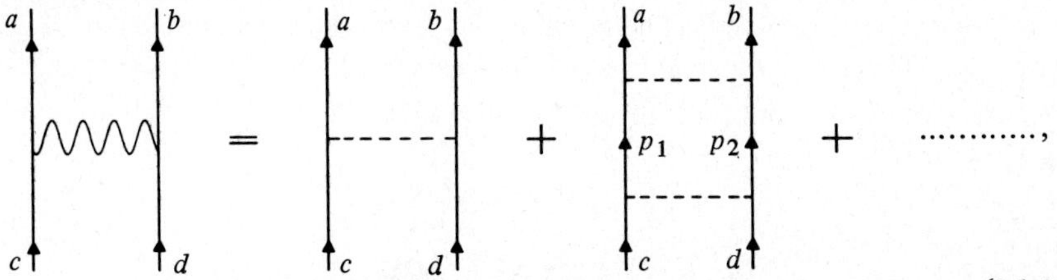

(16.47)

where the wavy line denotes the G matrix. The particular diagrams that are summed over in eq. (16.47) are referred to as *ladder diagrams* for obvious reasons. From eq.

(16.45) it is seen that the G matrix depends on the energy variable ω. This energy dependence reflects the fact that the successive interactions of the nucleons take a finite time.

A consequence of the finite lifetime of the intermediate states is that energy is not conserved at the scattering processes according to the uncertainty relation $\Delta E \Delta t \gtrsim \hbar$. If one employs a quasidegenerate model space, i.e. a space spanned by single-particle states of practically the same energy, it may be necessary to evaluate the G matrix between the model states $|ab\rangle$ and $|cd\rangle$, as depicted in eq. (16.47). The starting energy ω then is given by [Day (1967)]

$$\omega = e_c + e_d \approx e_a + e_b \,. \tag{16.48}$$

For such cases the G matrix is said to be evaluated completely *on the energy shell,* i.e. when the starting energy is equal to the energy of the initial and final two-particle state. When, however, one has either

$$\omega = e_a + e_b \qquad \text{or} \qquad \omega = e_c + e_d \,, \tag{16.49}$$

the G matrix is said to be *half on the energy shell.* Often, though, the two-particle states forming the ladder diagrams are part of a larger system of active nucleons. Then the G matrix may be needed *off the energy shell.*

For example, in the diagram

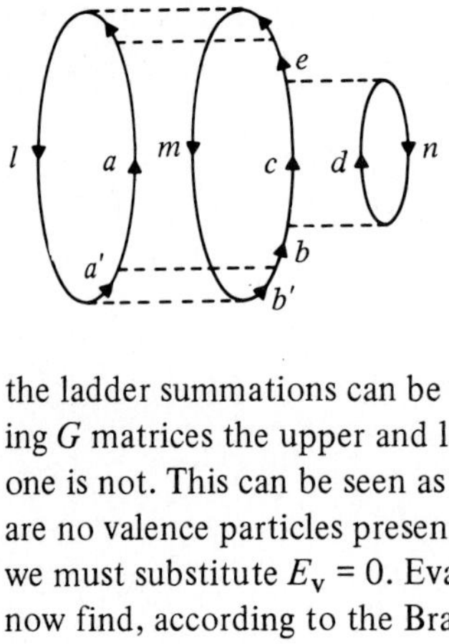

(16.50)

the ladder summations can be performed at three different positions. Of the resulting G matrices the upper and lower one are (half) on the energy shell, but the middle one is not. This can be seen as follows. In the initial state of diagram (16.50) there are no valence particles present and hence in the perturbation expansion, eq. (16.30), we must substitute $E_v = 0$. Evaluating the second-order term of the lower ladder we now find, according to the Brandow rules that were given in sect. 16.3, the result

$$\sum_{a'b'} \langle ab|\mathcal{V}|a'b'\rangle \frac{1}{e_l + e_m - e_{a'} - e_{b'}} \langle a'b'|\mathcal{V}|lm\rangle \,. \tag{16.51}$$

Comparison with eq. (16.46) shows that the starting energy is given by

$$\omega = e_l + e_m \,, \tag{16.52}$$

which means that the G matrix is taken half on the energy shell. The same result follows easily for the upper ladder. The second-order term of the middle ladder, however, is found to be (again according to the rules given earlier)

$$\sum_{cd}{}' \langle en|\mathcal{V}|cd\rangle \frac{1}{e_l + e_m + e_n - e_a - e_c - e_d} \langle cd|\mathcal{V}|bn\rangle . \tag{16.53}$$

Hence the starting energy is given by the relation

$$\omega = e_l + e_m + e_n - e_a , \tag{16.54}$$

and the G matrix is off the energy shell. This is due to the fact that the intermediate states that result from the interactions of the lower ladder, last only a finite time and thus energy is not conserved for the system.

For the evaluation of the G matrix the scattering process of two nucleons only is considered. These two nucleons, however, are part of a larger system. The way in which the system evolves between two such scattering events is determined by the energy of the total system and not only by the energy of the two nucleons under consideration. Thus the starting energy accounts for the dependence on the energy of the total system.

It should be noted that the ladder summations (16.51) and (16.53) cover *particle* states only. The reader is referred to the literature [Day (1967); Barrett and Kirson (1973); Sprung (1972); Kuo (1974)] for a discussion of the various methods that are in use for the actual calculation of the reaction matrix G. With the G matrix, however, one has not yet obtained an effective interaction since only a partial summation has been performed to convert the residual interaction $\mathcal{V}$ with a possible strong short-range repulsion into the well-behaved G matrix. The partial summation is to be considered as the first step of a two-step procedure for the calculation of the effective interaction (16.30). For instance, one still has to consider intermediate states that account for the possibility of break-up of the core. The reader should not be confused by the presence of the hole states in diagram (16.50). The three G matrices were calculated by ladder summation only, i.e. for the evaluation of the matrices themselves no intermediate hole states for the scattering process were considered.

After the calculation of the G matrix from the realistic interaction $\mathcal{V}$ the second step is to write the effective interaction V in terms of the G matrix according to the equation

$$V = G + G \frac{Q}{E_\text{v} - H_\text{v}^{(0)}} V \tag{16.55a}$$

or

$$V = G + G \frac{Q}{E_\text{v} - H_\text{v}^{(0)}} G + G \frac{Q}{E_\text{v} - H_\text{v}^{(0)}} G \frac{Q}{E_\text{v} - H_\text{v}^{(0)}} G + \dots , \tag{16.55b}$$

where the symbols have the same meaning as in eqs. (16.30). Insertion of intermediate states then leads to the diagrammatic expansion

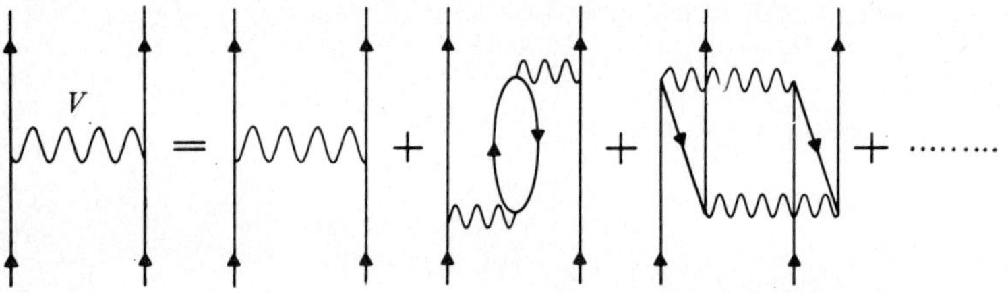

(16.56)

In order to prevent double counting of some diagrams, however, one must exclude ladders of G matrices from the summation over diagrams. This is because for the calculation of the G matrix all ladder diagrams of $\mathcal{V}$ have already been summed over and hence the (part of a) diagram

$V_{2p} =$ 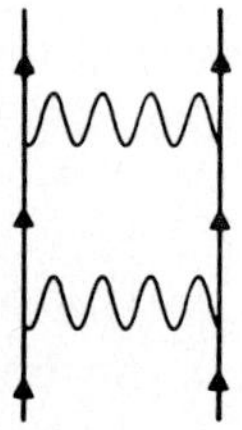

(16.57)

contains these summations twice.

The third diagram of the right-hand side of eq. (16.56) is certainly *not* excluded, since here the two G matrices are connected by two *hole* lines. In fact this diagram is the result of summing over the ladder diagrams

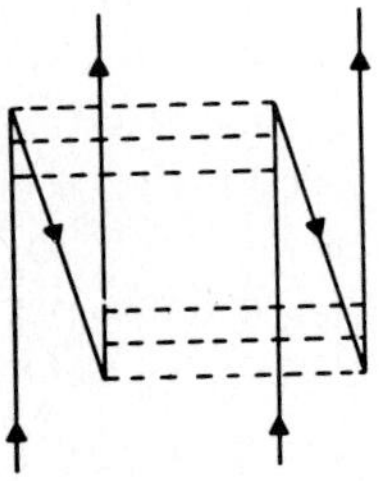

(16.58)

Effective interactions, i.e. sets of matrix elements $\langle ab|V|cd\rangle_{JT}$ which were calculated along the lines indicated above and have been widely used, are those of Kuo-Brown and Kuo [Kuo and Brown (1966); Kuo (1967)]. The realistic interaction they started from was the Hamada-Johnston nucleon-nucleon potential, which is obtained from a fit to phase shifts of free nucleon-nucleon scattering. It had been pointed out earlier [Bertsch (1965)] that the process of core polarization, represented by the second diagram of the right-hand side of eq. (16.56), yielded an important contribution, to be denoted by $V_{3p\,1h}$, to the effective interaction. It was demonstrated by Bertsch that the core polarization had the useful property of lowering energy levels of low values of J and raising those of high values of J. Such an effect was needed since the early calculations with the bare G matrix reproduced the low-lying states too high in energy.

The approximations Kuo and Brown had to make for the treatment of the intermediate states in their G matrix calculation, have caused many problems as to whether certain higher-order terms should be included in the perturbation expansiọn for V or not. In particular there is the problem of double counting of particular diagrams.

Initially Kuo and Brown did their calculations for $A = 18$ nuclei (^{16}O core) and later calculated the effective interaction V in the fp shell for $A = 42$ and $A = 50$ nuclei (^{40}Ca and ^{48}Ca cores) [Kuo and Brown (1968)]. For some of these calculations the effective interaction was evaluated as the sum of the bare G matrix and the core-polarization contribution, i.e. $V = G + V_{3\text{p}\,1\text{h}}$, for others also the 4-particle-2-hole contributions $V_{4\text{p}2\text{h}}$ (the third diagram of the right-hand side of eq. (16.56)) and the 2-particle contributions $V_{2\text{p}}$ were taken into account, i.e. $V = G + V_{3\text{p}1\text{h}} + V_{4\text{p}2\text{h}} + V_{2\text{p}}$. The latter term, given in eq. (16.57), is a second-order ladder diagram restricted to intermediate states of excitation energy $2\hbar\omega$, i.e. twice the separation of major shells. Since this term should have been accounted for already in the calculation of the bare G matrix, it was omitted from the initial calculations. However,

THE ^{18}O SPECTRUM FOR DIFFERENT APPROXIMATIONS

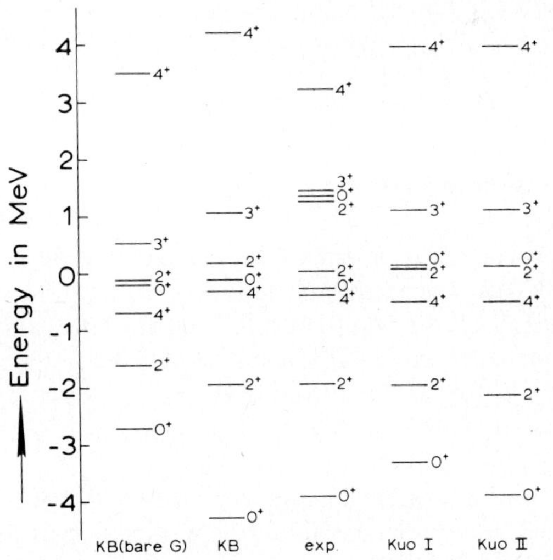

Fig. 16.3. Spectrum of ^{18}O calculated for two protons in the 2s-1d model space. The first two spectra represent the results of [Kuo and Brown (1966)]. The first spectrum is calculated with the bare G matrix, whereas for the second spectrum the core polarization is also taken into account, i.e. $G + V_{3\text{p}1\text{h}}$. The last two spectra represent the results of [Kuo (1967)]. The last but one spectrum is calculated for $G + V_{3\text{p}1\text{h}}$ and the last spectrum for $G + V_{3\text{p}1\text{h}} + V_{4\text{p}2\text{h}} + V_{2\text{p}}$.

when Kuo recalculated the G matrix with a different treatment of the short-range repulsion of the realistic interaction [Kuo (1967)], he observed that the inclusion of V_{4p2h} and V_{2p} improved the agreement with the experimental spectra of ^{18}O and ^{18}F. The apparent double counting caused by the inclusion of V_{2p} could be justified by the observation that the approximate treatment of the intermediate states for the evaluation of the bare G matrix, i.e. by the use of plane waves and an angle-averaged Pauli operator Q^{Br}, underestimated the contribution of the low-lying, e.g. $2\hbar\omega$, intermediate states. Of course, it is an unsatisfactory feature of these calculations that no unambiguous prescription exists as to which diagrams should be included and which should be omitted.

After it was observed that the terms of second order in G made a significant contribution to the effective interaction, the evaluation of the third-order terms raised some further doubts concerning the convergence of the perturbation expansion for V. Investigation of the algebraic structure of the equations that underlie the perturbation expansion [Schucan and Weidenmüller (1973); Weidenmüller (1975)] indicated that poor convergence, or even no convergence at all, for the order-by-order summations is to be expected owing to the presence of intruder states. The latter are states outside the model space that, however, possess an energy within the range of the spectrum of the states calculated in the model space. Unfortunately this is the prevailing situation for shell-model calculations at present.

In spite of the problems of convergence, the shell-model calculations with the effective interactions of up to second order in G have produced reasonably good agreement with the spectra and transition rates of the low-lying states.

As an example the spectrum calculated for the nucleus ^{18}O is presented in fig. 16.3.

16.6. Effective transition operators

For the calculation of electromagnetic transition rates from model wave functions one cannot expect in general to obtain correct results when one uses the bare transition operators that were derived in chapter 9. The latter lead to the proper results only if the complete, true wave functions are used. In the model space one has available only projections of the true wave functions, however. Hence, parts that yield important contributions to the transition matrix elements may have been lost in the truncation procedure.

Just as for the two-body residual interaction, one can derive effective operators for the single-particle transition operators. A definition of the effective operator O_{eff} can be written down immediately as

$$\langle \Psi'_a | O_{eff} | \Psi'_b \rangle = \frac{\langle \Psi_a | O | \Psi_b \rangle}{\sqrt{\langle \Psi_a | \Psi_a \rangle \langle \Psi_b | \Psi_b \rangle}} , \tag{16.59}$$

where the denominator in the right-hand member accounts for the fact that Ψ is not normalized to unity (see eq. (16.25)). Substitution of eq. (16.24) into eq. (16.59) leads to a series expansion for $\langle\Psi'_a|O_{\text{eff}}|\Psi'_b\rangle$ that can be evaluated term by term. Again we can perform partial summations over all ladder diagrams and hence replace the residual interaction $\mathcal{V}$ by the G matrix in all terms.

It can be shown [Brandow (1967)] that, as in the case of the expansion for the effective interaction, the energy denominators $\mathcal{E} - H^{(0)}$ may be replaced by the unperturbed valence energy denominators $E_{\text{v}} - H_{\text{v}}^{(0)}$ in a linked folded-diagram valence expansion for the effective operator O_{eff}. As a result one must sum over all linked diagrams in which the operator O appears just once. The proper normalization of the resulting expansion is guaranteed by the inclusion of the folded diagrams.

After partial summation over ladder diagrams the interaction $\mathcal{V}$ is replaced by the G matrix in the expansion. Since the G matrix contains all ladder diagrams in $\mathcal{V}$ the diagrams with ladders of G matrices must be excluded in order to prevent double counting. Some examples of the diagrams that must be taken into account are given by

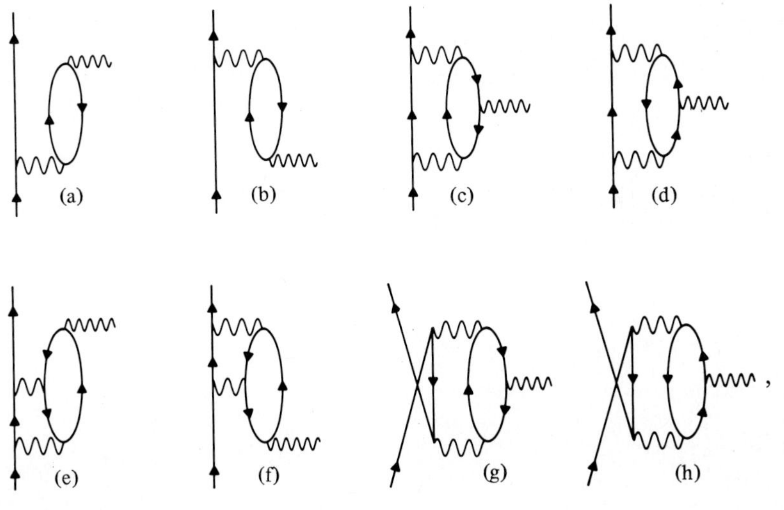

(16.60)

where the open wavy line denotes the single-particle transition operator.

After evaluation of the individual diagrams one can, adding their contributions, calculate the transition amplitude for given initial and final states. This can be done e.g. up to a certain order in G. It is noted here that in these diagrams the G matrix, defined in eqs. (16.44), (16.45) and (16.46), should be used and not the effective interaction V, defined in eqs. (16.55) and (16.56). Use of the latter interaction would imply double counting of some diagrams.

Up till here no angular-momentum coupling was used in the two-body matrix elements of the interaction. It is a straightforward application of Racah algebra to derive the expressions for the various diagrams with angular-momentum coupled two-particle states. In the next section we shall give an example how to apply the Racah techniques.

16.7. Effective charges

In the foregoing discussion we have seen how the true values of the matrix elements of the single-particle transition operators can be approximated in terms of a perturbational expansion. For example, let us consider a particle outside a closed core making an $\mathcal{E}L$ transition. If the particle is a proton the zeroth-order matrix element can be represented as

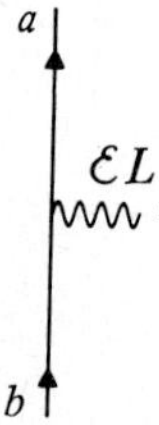

$$= \langle a|O(\mathcal{E}L)|b\rangle \,. \qquad (16.61)$$

After substitution of eq. (16.24) into eq. (16.59) one obtains for the first-order contributions in $\mathcal{V}$

$$\langle \Psi_a'|O_{\text{eff}}|\Psi_b'\rangle = \frac{\langle \Psi_a|O|\Psi_b\rangle}{\sqrt{\langle \Psi_a|\Psi_a\rangle\langle \Psi_b|\Psi_b\rangle}}$$

$$= \langle \Psi_a'|O + O\,\frac{Q}{\mathcal{E}-H^{(0)}}\,\mathcal{V} + \mathcal{V}\,\frac{Q}{\mathcal{E}-H^{(0)}}\,O + \dots|\Psi_b'\rangle \,. \qquad (16.62)$$

It should be noted here that terms like

$$\langle \Psi'|\mathcal{V}\frac{Q}{\mathcal{E}-H^{(0)}}|\Psi'\rangle$$

vanish, since Ψ' is defined within the model space and Q projects off the model space.

After replacement of the residual interaction $\mathcal{V}$ by the G matrix, one obtains for the terms of first order in G the expression

$$\langle a|O\,\frac{Q}{E_{\text{v}}-H_{\text{v}}^{(0)}}\,G|b\rangle + \langle a|G\,\frac{Q}{E_{\text{v}}-H_{\text{v}}^{(0)}}\,O|b\rangle \,. \qquad (16.63)$$

This equation contains the unperturbed valence energy denominators, i.e. $\mathcal{E}$ is replaced by E_{v} and hence only linked folded diagrams are meant, as mentioned in sect. 16.5. According to the rules given in sect. 16.5 these terms are simply evaluated as

$$\langle a|O \frac{Q}{E_{\mathrm{v}} - H_{\mathrm{v}}^{(0)}} G|b\rangle =$$

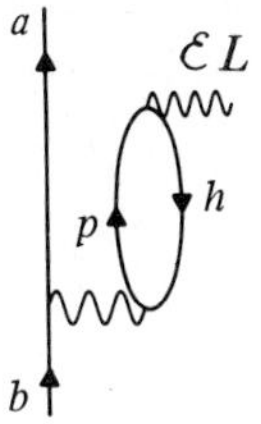

$$= \sum_{ph} \langle h|O(\mathcal{E}L)|p\rangle \frac{1}{e_b - e_a - e_p + e_h} \langle ap|G(e_b + e_h)|bh\rangle \,, \tag{16.64}$$

$$\langle a|G \frac{Q}{E_{\mathrm{v}} - H_{\mathrm{v}}^{(0)}} O|b\rangle =$$

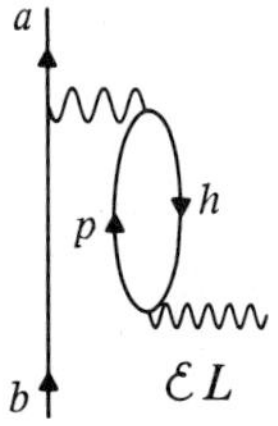

$$= \sum_{ph} \langle ah|G(e_b + e_h)|bp\rangle \frac{1}{e_a - e_b - e_p + e_h} \langle p|O(\mathcal{E}L)|h\rangle \,, \tag{16.65}$$

where the summation covers all possible particle-hole states. The starting energy $\omega = e_b + e_h$ for the G matrix in eqs. (16.64) and (16.65) can be found along the same lines as in eq. (16.51).

The energy denominators in eqs. (16.64) and (16.65) must represent the excitation energy of the intermediate state with respect to the unperturbed valence states $|a\rangle$ and $|b\rangle$. Strictly speaking, however, the latter are not degenerate since their energies differ by the amount E_γ of the emitted or absorbed $\mathcal{E}L$ radiation. For applications to $\mathcal{E}2$ radiation in cases of closed-shell nuclei such as ^{16}O and ^{40}Ca, one can circumvent the ensuing ambiguities as follows. Owing to parity conservation, the particle-hole bubbles in eqs. (16.64) and (16.65) represent excitation energies of at least $2\hbar\omega$, i.e. twice the energy separation of major shells. Since in all applications the inequality $E_\gamma \ll 2\hbar\omega$ is well satisfied, the energy denominators may be approximated by the value of the particle-hole excitation energy $-2\hbar\omega \approx -20$ MeV. In principle, of course, $4\hbar\omega$ excitations also exist, but in view of the approximations involved they are not considered here, nor are second-order contributions taken into account. In diagram (16.64) the valence particle in state b interacts, due to the residual interaction, with a core particle. As a result the former particle is scattered into the state a outside the core, while the core particle is promoted to the state p outside the core, thus leaving a hole h in the core. The particle and the hole afterwards recombine under the emission or absorption of a gamma quantum. Because of the antisymmetry of the two-body matrix elements, diagram (16.64) also represents the diagram that is obtained by the interchange of either the incoming lines b

and h or the outgoing lines a and p

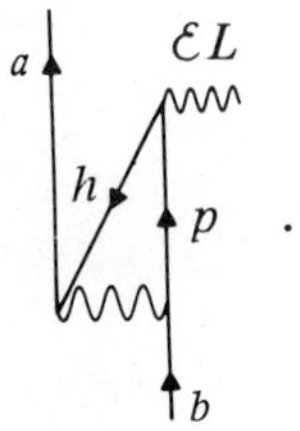

(16.66)

Diagram (16.65) denotes the process where first, due to the interaction with the radiation field, a gamma quantum is emitted (or absorbed) and a core particle is excited into an unoccupied orbit. The resulting particle-hole state then later recombines in a scattering process with the initial single particle outside the core. The first-order contributions that are depicted in diagrams (16.64) and (16.65) must be added to the zeroth-order contribution (16.61). Thus for a given electric 2^L pole transition of a nucleon from state Ψ_i into state Ψ_f, one can introduce an *effective charge* as the ratio of first- and zeroth-order reduced matrix elements (the latter always taken for a proton)

$$\Delta e(j_\mathrm{i}, j_\mathrm{f}, t_z) = \frac{\Delta^{(1)}\langle j_\mathrm{f}, t_z \| O(\mathcal{E}L) \| j_\mathrm{i}, t_z\rangle}{\langle j_\mathrm{f}, t_z = -\frac{1}{2} \| O(\mathcal{E}L) \| j_\mathrm{i}, t_z = -\frac{1}{2}\rangle}\, e \tag{16.67}$$

with

$$\Delta^{(1)}\langle j_\mathrm{f}, t_z \| O(\mathcal{E}L) \| j_\mathrm{i}, t_z\rangle$$

$$\equiv \langle j_\mathrm{f}, t_z \| (O(\mathcal{E}L) \frac{Q}{E_\mathrm{v} - H_\mathrm{v}^{(0)}} G + G \frac{Q}{E_\mathrm{v} - H_\mathrm{v}^{(0)}} O(\mathcal{E}L)) \| j_\mathrm{i}, t_z\rangle\,. \tag{16.68}$$

For a neutron, bearing no electric charge, the zeroth-order matrix elements vanish, of course. One does find nonvanishing first-order contributions, however, since the neutron can excite a proton particle-hole pair that recombines in an electric 2^L pole transition. Similarly a proton particle-hole pair formed after emission (or absorption) of a gamma quantum can be deexcited in a collision process with a neutron. Again, as in the case of the proton, one can ascribe these first-order contributions to the zeroth-order process by assigning an effective charge to the neutron.

The matrix elements in eq. (16.67) are reduced in coordinate space only. They can be expressed in terms of triple-bar matrix elements (see e.g. eq. (9.106)) as

$$\langle j_\mathrm{f}; \tfrac{1}{2}, t_z \| O(\bar{\omega} L) \| j_\mathrm{i}; \tfrac{1}{2}, t_z\rangle = \sqrt{\tfrac{1}{2}}\, \langle j_\mathrm{f}, \tfrac{1}{2} \||| O(\bar{\omega}L) \||| j_\mathrm{i}, \tfrac{1}{2}\rangle_{I_\Lambda = 0}$$

$$+ \frac{(-1)^{t_z + 1/2}}{\sqrt{6}} \langle j_\mathrm{f}, \tfrac{1}{2} \||| O(\bar{\omega}L) \||| j_\mathrm{i}, \tfrac{1}{2}\rangle_{I_\Lambda = 1}\,. \tag{16.69}$$

A similar relation holds, of course, for the first-order correction $\Delta^{(1)}\langle j_\mathrm{f}, t_z \| O(\bar{\omega}L) \| j_\mathrm{i}, t_z\rangle$.

The triple-bar matrix elements of the isoscalar and isovector parts of eq. (16.69) can be obtained from eqs. (16.64) and (16.65) by application of the Wigner-Eckart theorem, eq. (A.3.a14).

Let us consider the evaluation of eq. (16.64) in some detail. For brevity of notation we shall omit all isospin labels; the discussion may be considered as to apply to a system of protons only. The inclusion of isospin is straightforward, however. Using the Wigner-Eckart theorem to reduce the single-particle matrix element and taking care of the proper normalization of the angular-momentum coupled two-particle states, one obtains for eq. (16.64) the expression

$$\langle j_a m_a | O(\bar{\omega} LM) \frac{Q}{E_\mathrm{v} - H_\mathrm{v}^{(0)}} G | j_b m_b \rangle$$

$$= \sum_{\substack{j_p m_p \\ j_h m_h \\ JM}} \langle j_p m_p LM | j_h m_h \rangle \frac{\langle j_h \| O(\bar{\omega} L) \| j_p \rangle}{\sqrt{2j_h + 1}} \frac{1}{e_b - e_a - e_p + e_h}$$

$$\times \langle j_a m_a j_p m_p | JM \rangle \langle j_b m_b j_h m_h | JM \rangle \langle j_a j_p | G | j_b j_h \rangle_J \sqrt{(1 + \delta_{ap})(1 + \delta_{bh})} \,. \qquad (16.70)$$

According to eq. (A.1.b11) the summation over the three Clebsch-Gordan coefficients can be performed to yield a 3-j symbol and a 6-j symbol. One finds

$$\langle j_a m_a | O(\bar{\omega} LM) \frac{Q}{E_\mathrm{v} - H_\mathrm{v}^{(0)}} G | j_b m_b \rangle$$

$$= (-1)^{j_a - m_a} \begin{pmatrix} j_a & L & j_b \\ -m_a & M & m_b \end{pmatrix} \sum_{j_p j_h J} \langle j_h \| O(\bar{\omega} L) \| j_p \rangle \frac{1}{e_b - e_a - e_p + e_h}$$

$$\times (2J + 1) \begin{Bmatrix} j_a & j_b & L \\ j_h & j_p & J \end{Bmatrix} (-1)^{j_p + j_h + J} \sqrt{(1 + \delta_{ap})(1 + \delta_{bh})} \langle j_a j_p | G | j_b j_h \rangle_J \,. \qquad (16.71)$$

Using now the concise notation of Greek symbols to denote quantum numbers in coordinate space and isospace, we obtain from eq. (16.71) the result

$$\langle \alpha ||| O(\bar{\omega} \Lambda) \frac{Q}{E_\mathrm{v} - H_\mathrm{v}^{(0)}} G ||| \beta \rangle = \sum_{\alpha_1 \alpha_2 \Gamma} \frac{(-1)^{\beta + \alpha_2 + \Gamma}}{e_\beta - e_\alpha - e_{\alpha_1} + e_{\alpha_2}} (2\Gamma + 1)$$

$$\times \begin{Bmatrix} \alpha & \beta & \Lambda \\ \alpha_2 & \alpha_1 & \Gamma \end{Bmatrix} \sqrt{(1 + \delta_{\alpha_1 \alpha})(1 + \delta_{\alpha_2 \beta})} \langle \alpha \alpha_1 | G | \beta \alpha_2 \rangle_\Gamma \langle \alpha_2 ||| O(\bar{\omega} \Lambda) ||| \alpha_1 \rangle \,, \qquad (16.72)$$

where the index α_1 runs over particle states and α_2 over hole states. As was mentioned earlier, the energy denominators are usually approximated by the excitation energy of the particle-hole bubble. The other contribution to eq. (16.63), which is represented by eq. (16.65), can be evaluated similarly. For

$$\langle\alpha|||G \frac{Q}{E_v - H_v^{(0)}} O(\overline{\omega}\Lambda)|||\beta\rangle$$

one finds the same expression as in eq. (16.72) except for (i) the index α_1 running over hole states and α_2 over particle states and (ii) an overall minus sign to restore the proper energy denominator.

With the equations given above one now can evaluate the first-order (in G) corrections to single-particle transitions. A numerical example illustrating the application of eq. (16.72) is given in the next section. It is remarked here that for *hole* states α and β one finds expressions that are very similar to eq. (16.72). The evaluation is left to the reader as an exercise. It should be clear now that effective charges are a means to account for the processes that do contribute to electric multipole transition rates or moments but that are disregarded in the truncated space used for a shell-model calculation.

It is seen from the discussion above that effective charges are dependent on the multipolarity of the transition, on the initial and final states concerned and on the configuration space. Moreover, the effective charges for proton and neutron are expected to be different, as for a proton in diagrams (16.64) and (16.65) only $T = 1$ two-body matrix elements occur, but for a neutron $T = 1$ as well as $T = 0$ matrix elements are to be summed over. In general the latter are of larger magnitude than the former, and indeed one often finds larger effective charges for neutrons than for protons.

The occurrence of effective charges for $\mathcal{E}2$ transitions can be understood clearly from a classical picture, when the core is considered as a homogeneously charged sphere that is surrounded by the active valence nucleons. Due to the interaction between an extra nucleon and the core nucleons the core will be deformed, polarized [Bohr and Mottelson (1969) p. 334]. And thus, when the extra nucleon makes a transition from one state to another, also the polarization of the core changes. As a result the charged core will contribute to the electromagnetic transition. Since the nuclear interaction is attractive, a nucleon moving in an orbit "along the equator", i.e. with negative quadrupole moment, will induce a disk-shaped deformation of the positively charged core that thus assumes also a negative quadrupole moment. This way it is made plausible that effective charges for $\mathcal{E}2$ moments are positive, i.e. the polarization effects constructively interfere with the zeroth-order process. The calculation of effective charges does not have to be restricted to the first-order (in G) terms, in particular if all first-order terms vanish.

16.8. Magnetic dipole transitions

Let us consider magnetic multipole transitions and moments. The same equations and diagrams as for the electric case apply with the operator O representing a magnetic 2^L pole operator. Here the magnetic dipole operator constitutes a special case, since if the core consists of shells closed in *j-j* coupling as well as in *L-S* coupling, all first-order terms vanish, i.e.

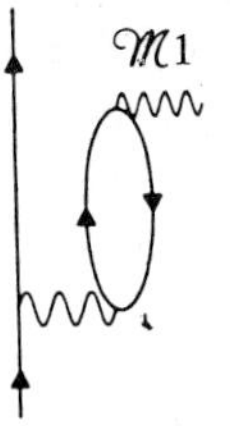

$= 0\,,$

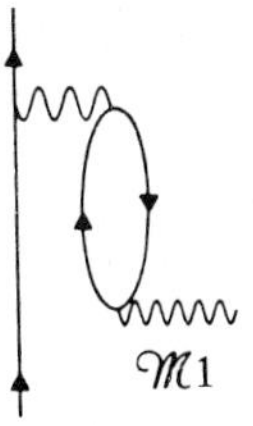

$= 0\,.$ (16.73)

This is because each term of eq. (16.73) contains a factor $\langle p \| O(\mathcal{M}1) \| h \rangle$ for which the selection rules $\Delta l = 0$ and $\Delta n = 0$ apply. These selection rules can be satisfied, however, if the core is closed in *j-j* coupling only; e.g. for a ${}^{28}_{14}\mathrm{Si}_{14}$ core one has for ${}^{29}_{14}\mathrm{Si}_{15}$ or ${}^{29}_{15}\mathrm{P}_{14}$ the processes

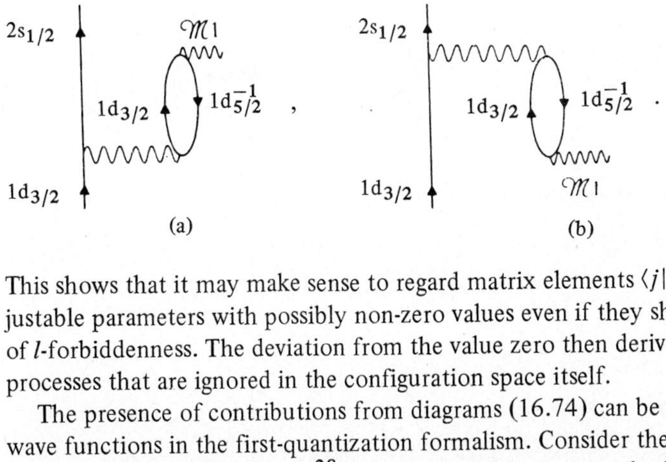

(16.74)

This shows that it may make sense to regard matrix elements $\langle j \| O(\mathcal{M}1) \| j' \rangle$ as adjustable parameters with possibly non-zero values even if they should vanish because of *l*-forbiddenness. The deviation from the value zero then derives completely from processes that are ignored in the configuration space itself.

The presence of contributions from diagrams (16.74) can be illustrated also with wave functions in the first-quantization formalism. Consider the nucleus ${}^{29}\mathrm{Si}$ and allow at most one hole in the ${}^{28}\mathrm{Si}$ core. Let the active particles be distributed over the $2s_{1/2}\,1d_{3/2}$ orbits. The ground state, $J^\pi = \frac{1}{2}^+$, consists mainly of a $2s_{1/2}$ neutron outside the closed core ${}^{28}\mathrm{Si}$, and the first excited state, $J^\pi = \frac{3}{2}^+$, mainly of a $1d_{3/2}$ neutron outside the closed core ${}^{28}\mathrm{Si}$. For an $\mathcal{M}1$ transition from the first excited state to the ground state one has the following wave functions

$$|J^\pi = \tfrac{1}{2}^+\rangle = a_1|2s_{1/2}\rangle_{1/2} + a_2|1d_{5/2}^{-1}\,2s_{1/2}\,1d_{3/2}\rangle_{1/2} + a_3|1d_{5/2}^{-1}\,1d_{3/2}^2\rangle_{1/2}\,, \tag{16.75}$$

$$|J^\pi = \tfrac{3}{2}^+\rangle = b_1|1d_{3/2}\rangle_{3/2} + b_2|1d_{5/2}^{-1}\,2s_{1/2}^2\rangle_{3/2}$$
$$+ b_3|1d_{5/2}^{-1}\,2s_{1/2}\,1d_{3/2}\rangle_{3/2} + b_4|1d_{5/2}^{-1}\,1d_{3/2}^2\rangle_{3/2} \tag{16.76}$$

with the amplitudes $a_1 \gg a_2, a_3$ and $b_1 \gg b_2, b_3, b_4$. The zeroth-order contribution, proportional to $a_1 b_1$, vanishes due to *l*-forbiddenness. The first-order contributions are proportional to a_1b_2, a_1b_3, a_1b_4, b_1a_2 or b_1a_3. Because of l-forbiddenness only the terms a_1b_3 and a_3b_1 survive, which can be represented by the diagrams (16.74) with the through-going particle line describing the transition $1d_{3/2} \to 2s_{1/2}$.

Although this discussion of the first-order correction to $\mathcal{M}1$ transitions is very illuminating, the quantitative evaluation for e.g. $A = 29$ nuclei presents some problems. In the perturbational approach it is assumed that the unperturbed states span a quasidegenerate space. This would imply for the diagram (16.74) that the inequality $e_{2s_{1/2}} - e_{1d_{3/2}} \ll e_{1d_{3/2}} - e_{1d_{5/2}}$ should hold and the energy denominators in eq. (16.72) can be approximated by $-e_{1d_{3/2}} + e_{1d_{5/2}} \approx -6$ MeV. If the latter approximations were not made, the numerical value of the energy denominator in eq. (16.72) would be ambiguous since the initial and final states would differ in energy. It should perhaps be pointed out here that for first-order corrections to magnetic moments this ambiguity does not arise, since then the states α and β in eq. (16.72) are identical.

Let us now calculate as an example the first-order correction to the $\mathcal{M}1$ reduced matrix element for the transition $1d_{3/2} \to 2s_{1/2}$ in the nuclei ${}^{29}_{14}Si_{15}$ and ${}^{29}_{15}P_{14}$. Denoting the contribution from diagram (16.74a) by Δ_a and substituting $\alpha_1 = 1d_{3/2}$ and $\alpha_2 = 1d_{5/2}$ into eq. (16.72), one obtains

$$\Delta_a = -\sum_{JT} (-1)^{J+T} \frac{(2J+1)(2T+1)}{\Delta E} \begin{Bmatrix} \frac{1}{2} & \frac{3}{2} & 1 \\ \frac{5}{2} & \frac{3}{2} & J \end{Bmatrix} \begin{Bmatrix} \frac{1}{2} & \frac{1}{2} & I_\Lambda \\ \frac{1}{2} & \frac{1}{2} & T \end{Bmatrix}$$

$$\times \langle 2s_{1/2} 1d_{3/2} | G | 1d_{3/2} 1d_{5/2} \rangle_{JT} \langle 1d_{5/2} ||| O(\mathcal{M}1) ||| 1d_{3/2} \rangle_{I_\Lambda}, \tag{16.77}$$

with

$$\Delta E \approx e_{1d_{5/2}} - e_{1d_{3/2}} \approx -6 \text{ MeV} \tag{16.78}$$

and $I_\Lambda = 0$ or 1 denoting the isoscalar or isovector contribution. Similarly one finds for diagram (16.74b) after substitution of $\alpha_1 = 1d_{5/2}$ and $\alpha_2 = 1d_{3/2}$, the expression

$$\Delta_b = \sum_{JT} (-1)^{J+T} \frac{(2J+1)(2T+1)}{\Delta E} \begin{Bmatrix} \frac{1}{2} & \frac{3}{2} & 1 \\ \frac{3}{2} & \frac{5}{2} & J \end{Bmatrix} \begin{Bmatrix} \frac{1}{2} & \frac{1}{2} & I_\Lambda \\ \frac{1}{2} & \frac{1}{2} & T \end{Bmatrix}$$

$$\times \sqrt{2} \langle 2s_{1/2} 1d_{5/2} | G | 1d^2_{3/2} \rangle_{JT} \langle 1d_{3/2} ||| O(\mathcal{M}1) ||| 1d_{5/2} \rangle_{I_\Lambda}. \tag{16.79}$$

Let us take the off-diagonal two-body matrix elements in these expressions from the G matrix calculated by Kuo from the Hamada-Johnston interaction [Kuo (1967)]. For convenience the required matrix elements are listed in table 16.1. Note that eq. (5.14) has to be applied to obtain the correct sign of the matrix elements. The reduced single-particle matrix elements can be obtained from appendix B.6 and are given by $\langle 1d_{5/2} ||| O(\mathcal{M}1) ||| 1d_{3/2} \rangle = -\langle 1d_{3/2} ||| O(\mathcal{M}1) ||| 1d_{5/2} \rangle = -0.406\ \mu_N$ (isoscalar and $-7.798\ \mu_N$ (isovector). Summing the isoscalar contributions ($I_\Lambda = 0$) for dia-

Table 16.1
Matrix elements of the bare G matrix (in MeV)

J	T	$\langle 2s_{1/2}1d_{3/2}\|G\|1d_{3/2}1d_{5/2}\rangle_{JT}$	J	T	$\langle 2s_{1/2}1d_{5/2}\|G\|d_{3/2}^2\rangle_{JT}$
1	0	+1.4233	2	1	−0.7504
1	1	−0.1678	3	0	+0.1152
2	0	−1.5937			
2	1	+0.6568			

grams (16.74) one finds

$$\Delta_{a+b}^{\text{isoscalar}} = -0.0757\ \mu_N\ , \tag{16.80}$$

and similarly for the isovector contribution ($I_\Lambda = 1$)

$$\Delta_{a+b}^{\text{isovector}} = -0.9395\ \mu_N\ . \tag{16.81}$$

The strength of the $\mathcal{M}1$ transition expressed in Weisskopf units can now be calculated with the use of eqs. (9.106), (9.107) and (10.9a). One thus finds

$$M_W^2(\mathcal{M}1) = \frac{0.559}{(2J_i+1)(2T_f+1)}\left[\Delta_{a+b}^{\text{isoscalar}} - \frac{T_z}{\sqrt{T(T+1)}}\Delta_{a+b}^{\text{isovector}}\right]^2$$

$$= 0.070[\Delta_{a+b}^{\text{isoscalar}} \mp 0.577\ \Delta_{a+b}^{\text{isovector}}]^2 \qquad \text{for } T_z = \pm\tfrac{1}{2}\ . \tag{16.82}$$

Substitution of eqs. (16.80) and (16.81) into eq. (16.82) leads to the result $M_W^2(\mathcal{M}1\text{: }^{29}\text{Si}) = 0.015$ W.u. and $M_W^2(\mathcal{M}1\text{: }^{29}\text{P}) = 0.027$ W.u.. These numbers should be compared with the experimental values given by 0.037 ± 0.003 W.u. and 0.056 ± 0.006 W.u., respectively [Endt and Van der Leun (1974a)].

For an evaluation of second-order corrections to $\mathcal{M}1$ transitions the reader is referred to [Dieperink and Brussaard (1969)].

16.9. Terms of higher order in *G*

When one goes to terms of second or higher order in G the number of diagrams representing the various contributions to the perturbation expansion of transition matrix elements increases fast and the diagrams become much more complicated. A few of the diagrams of second order in G were listed among the diagrams (16.60). The rules for their evaluation have been summarized in sect. 16.3.

A complication for the second- and higher-order terms arises from the occurrence of the normalization diagrams in the denominator of eq. (16.59). The normalization leads to the appearance of folded diagrams, which are not discussed here. It was seen that effective charges could be introduced that are dependent on the multipolarity, the initial and final states and on whether it concerns a neutron or a proton (instead of distinguishing neutron and proton, one can equivalently distinguish between the isoscalar and isovector part of the transition).

Similarly for magnetic transitions one can introduce effective matrix elements for the orbital part and the spin part that are dependent on the multipolarity, initial and final states, distinguishing neutrons from protons (or isoscalar from isovector parts). Rather than use the foregoing to calculate effective charges or matrix elements one can use it to justify the introduction of such effective parameters that are to be fitted to the experimental data. A strict application of the theoretical considerations would lead to a far too large number of effective charges or matrix elements. Calculations show, however, that the effective charges for protons or for neutrons are of the same order of magnitude, and that even those for protons and neutrons could be considered equal in some approximation.

16.10. Many-particle systems

The preceding considerations apply to the case of one particle (or hole) with a core. If there are several particles and/or holes then not only the diagrams that were discussed contribute, but in addition other diagrams occur, even of first order in G. For instance, for the description of a nucleus like ^{40}K as a ^{40}Ca core plus one particle and one hole, contributing processes are

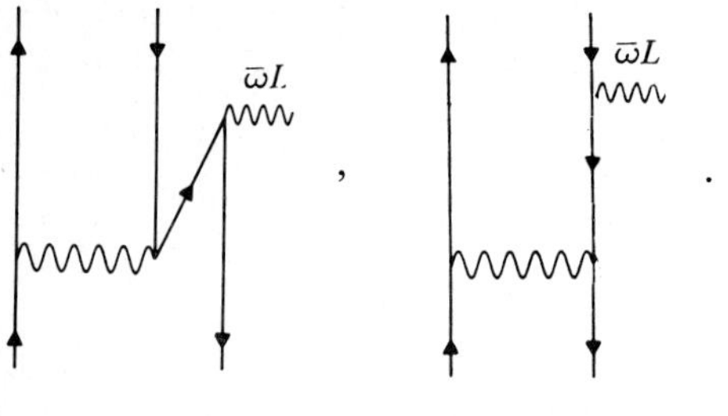

(16.83)

For these nuclei the numerical contributions of these diagrams are relatively small since there exist only few intermediate states. It is seen, however, that these contributions do not fit into a description with effective charges as they depend on the initial and final labels not only of the particle under consideration but of two particles (or holes).

The results that have been reached and the many problems that are still waiting for a solution in this field of nuclear physics, have been reviewed at the Tucson conference in 1975. The reader is referred to the proceedings for further study and references [Barrett (1975)].

CHAPTER 17

APPLICATIONS OF WICK'S THEOREM

For the application of the second-quantization formalism it is often required to determine the vacuum expectation value of a product of annihilation and creation operators. The purpose of Wick's theorem is to perform this evaluation in a systematic way.

Wick's theorem is introduced in sect. 17.1. In sect. 17.2 this theorem is used to write the many-body Hamiltonian in a selfconsistent basis. The terms of a perturbation expansion can be evaluated with the use of the second-quantization formalism, as is shown in sect. 17.3. The correspondence with Feynman diagrams is demonstrated. For some nuclei a description in terms of particle-hole configurations is quite convenient. The simplest case, i.e. one-particle, one-hole states, is treated in sect. 17.4.

17.1. Wick's theorem

The vacuum can be either the state of zero particles denoted by $|\rangle$ or a closed-shell state, i.e. the generalized vacuum $|0\rangle$. In the latter case particles as well as holes may occur. These can be treated on the same footing if some modifications are introduced.

Let us use the labels $h_1, h_2, ...$ for the single-particle states that constitute the closed-shell state $|0\rangle$ and denote all states that lie above these occupied states by the labels $p_1, p_2, ...$. Now introduce creation and annihilation operators according to the definition

$$\xi_p^\dagger = a_p^\dagger, \qquad \xi_p = a_p, \qquad \xi_h^\dagger = a_h, \qquad \xi_h = a_h^\dagger . \tag{17.1}$$

The operator $\xi_\alpha^\dagger$ creates a particle for $\alpha = p$ and a hole for $\alpha = h$. Similarly the operator ξ_α annihilates a particle for $\alpha = p$ and a hole for $\alpha = h$. The name generalized vacuum for the closed-shell state is now justified by the relation

$$\xi_\alpha |0\rangle = 0 \qquad \text{for all } \alpha , \tag{17.2a}$$

which implies of course

$$\langle 0|\xi_\alpha^\dagger = 0 \qquad \text{for all } \alpha . \tag{17.2b}$$

The new set of operators obey again the fermion anticommutation relations

$$\{\xi_\alpha^\dagger, \xi_\beta\} \equiv \xi_\alpha^\dagger \xi_\beta + \xi_\beta \xi_\alpha^\dagger = \delta_{\alpha\beta} , \qquad \{\xi_\alpha^\dagger, \xi_\beta^\dagger\} = 0 , \qquad \{\xi_\alpha, \xi_\beta\} = 0 . \tag{17.3}$$

The operators $\xi_\alpha^\dagger$ are said to create quasiparticles and ξ_β to annihilate these, respectively. Here the quasiparticles are either genuine particles or holes. A more general definition of quasiparticles is used in the theory of superfluidity in terms of linear combinations of particle and hole states.

Now we can define the notion of a *normal product*. Let us consider a product of creation and annihilation operators $\xi^\dagger_\alpha$ and ξ_α. This product is defined to be in normal order if all creation operators $\xi^\dagger_\alpha$ are positioned to the left of all annihilation operators ξ_α. This means that in order to write a given product of annihilation and creation operators in normal order, a rearrangement may be required. This rearrangement will add a factor +1 or −1 to the product depending on whether it involves an even or odd permutation of the operators. It is emphasized that the normal product is calculated as if all fermion operators anticommute, i.e. the Kronecker deltas that usually appear in the anticommutator of an annihilation and a creation operator must be ignored here. For instance, denoting by $N(...)$ the normal product, one has with eq. (17.1)

$$N(a^\dagger_{h_1} a^\dagger_{p_1} a_{p_2} a_{h_2}) = N(\xi_{h_1} \xi^\dagger_{p_1} \xi_{p_2} \xi^\dagger_{h_2}) = -\xi^\dagger_{p_1} \xi^\dagger_{h_2} \xi_{h_1} \xi_{p_2}$$

$$= -a^\dagger_{p_1} a_{h_2} a^\dagger_{h_1} a_{p_2} . \tag{17.4}$$

The definitions of the operators $\xi^\dagger_\alpha$ and ξ_α depend on the vacuum chosen and hence a normal product is defined with respect to that particular vacuum.

From eqs. (17.2) one deduces the important property that the vacuum expectation value of a normal product vanishes, i.e. one has

$$\langle 0|N(...)|0\rangle = 0 \tag{17.5}$$

(except when all operators are contracted, see below).

Before we can formulate Wick's theorem we must introduce the notion of the *contraction* of two operators. Contraction yields a number, which is defined as the expectation value of the product of the two operators in the generalized vacuum. Contractions are indicated by a horizontal bar connecting the two operators. Thus one has for example

$$\overline{\alpha^\dagger_\alpha \alpha_\beta} = \langle 0|a^\dagger_\alpha a_\beta|0\rangle \tag{17.6}$$

or, when two operators out of a larger product are contracted,

$$\overline{\alpha^\dagger_\alpha a^\dagger_\beta \alpha_\gamma}\,\alpha_\delta = -\langle 0|a^\dagger_\alpha a_\gamma|0\rangle\, a^\dagger_\beta a_\delta \ , \tag{17.7}$$

where the minus sign follows from the odd permutation that brings the contracted operators in adjacent positions.

Similarly one can also apply contractions to operators in a normal product, e.g.

$$N(\overline{a^\dagger_\alpha a^\dagger_\beta a_\gamma}\, a_\delta) = -\langle 0|a^\dagger_\alpha a_\gamma|0\rangle\, N(a^\dagger_\beta a_\delta) \ . \tag{17.8}$$

The same rule as before defines the sign and the noncontracted operators remain in the same normal order after the contracted operators have been taken out of the normal product. One can make several contractions in one product, e.g.

$$N(\overline{a_\alpha^\dagger a_\beta^\dagger a_\gamma^\dagger a_\delta} a_\epsilon a_\zeta) = -\langle 0|a_\alpha^\dagger a_\delta|0\rangle \langle 0|a_\beta^\dagger a_\epsilon|0\rangle N(a_\gamma^\dagger a_\zeta) \; . \tag{17.9}$$

Each time an odd permutation is required to bring successively two contracted operators in adjacent positions, a minus sign results.

Wick's theorem states that any product of annihilation and creation operators is equal to the sum of all its contracted normal products. This sum includes all partly and, if possible, fully contracted normal products and also the term with no contraction at all. Denoting the operators $a_\alpha^\dagger$ and a_α by A_α one can formulate Wick's theorem as

$$A_1 A_2 A_3 \ldots A_\omega = N(A_1 A_2 A_3 \ldots A_\omega) + \sum_{\alpha<\beta} N(A_1 A_2 \ldots \overline{A_\alpha \ldots A_\beta} \ldots A_\omega)$$

$$+ \sum_{\substack{\alpha<\beta \\ \gamma<\delta}} N(A_1 A_2 \ldots \overline{A_\alpha \ldots A_\gamma \ldots A_\beta \ldots A_\delta} \ldots A_\omega) + \ldots + \text{fully contracted terms} \; . \tag{17.10}$$

It is remarked that the fully contracted terms can occur only for ω = even.

Wick's theorem can be proven simply when only two operators are involved. In this case one has the relation

$$A_\alpha A_\beta = N(A_\alpha A_\beta) + N(\overline{A_\alpha A_\beta}) = N(A_\alpha A_\beta) + \overline{A_\alpha A_\beta} \; . \tag{17.11}$$

If the operators $A_\alpha A_\beta$ are in normal order their contraction vanishes and eq. (17.11) is obviously true. If they are not in normal order, i.e. $A_\alpha = \xi_\alpha$ and $A_\beta = \xi_\beta^\dagger$, eq. (17.11) is equivalent to

$$A_\alpha A_\beta + A_\beta A_\alpha = \overline{A_\alpha A_\beta} \; . \tag{17.12}$$

The anticommutator at the left-hand side is equal to the Kronecker delta $\delta_{\alpha\beta}$, as is the expectation value $\langle 0|\xi_\alpha \xi_\beta^\dagger|0\rangle$ on the right-hand side.

Wick's theorem for the general case can be proven by the method of induction. The reader is referred to the literature for such a proof [March, Young and Sampanthar (1967)].

It is seen that the contraction $\overline{A_\alpha A_\beta}$ accounts for the possible Kronecker delta that is ignored when for the rearrangement into a normal product a permutation is required. It is the power of Wick's theorem that for more complicated products these contributions to the vacuum expectation value are treated in a systematic and concise way.

The total number of contractions one has to perform is reduced appreciably if one takes into account that the contraction of two creation operators or two annihilation operators vanishes

$$\overline{a_\alpha^\dagger a_\beta^\dagger} \equiv \langle 0|a_\alpha^\dagger a_\beta^\dagger|0\rangle = 0\,, \qquad \overline{a_\alpha a_\beta} \equiv \langle 0|\alpha_\alpha a_\beta|0\rangle = 0\,. \tag{17.13}$$

This is immediately obvious if one realizes that the (generalized) vacuum state $|0\rangle$ has a definite particle number (which is zero for the bare vacuum $|\rangle$).

17.2. Hartree-Fock equations

Let us apply Wick's theorem to rewrite the Hamiltonian for a many-particle system in such a way that it applies to the case of a core plus active particles.

The Hamiltonian, consisting of the kinetic energy T and a two-body interaction W, assumes the following form in the second-quantization formalism

$$H = T + W = \sum_{\alpha\gamma} \langle\alpha|T|\gamma\rangle\, a_\alpha^\dagger a_\gamma + \tfrac{1}{4} \sum_{\alpha\beta\gamma\delta} \langle\alpha\beta|W|\gamma\delta\rangle\, a_\alpha^\dagger a_\beta^\dagger a_\delta a_\gamma\,. \tag{17.14}$$

According to Wick's theorem every product of annihilation and creation operators can be written as the sum of all its possible normal products with contractions. Thus one obtains

$$\begin{aligned} H = \sum_{\alpha\gamma} \langle\alpha|T|\gamma\rangle \{N(a_\alpha^\dagger a_\gamma) + \overline{a_\alpha^\dagger a_\gamma}\} + \tfrac{1}{4} \sum_{\alpha\beta\gamma\delta} \langle\alpha\beta|W|\gamma\delta\rangle \{N(a_\alpha^\dagger a_\beta^\dagger a_\delta a_\gamma) \\ + N(a_\alpha^\dagger a_\gamma)\, \overline{a_\beta^\dagger a_\delta} + N(a_\beta^\dagger a_\delta)\, \overline{a_\alpha^\dagger a_\gamma} - N(a_\alpha^\dagger a_\delta)\, \overline{a_\beta^\dagger a_\gamma} - N(a_\beta^\dagger a_\gamma)\, \overline{a_\alpha^\dagger a_\delta} \\ + \overline{a_\alpha^\dagger a_\gamma}\, \overline{a_\beta^\dagger a_\delta} - \overline{a_\alpha^\dagger a_\delta}\, \overline{a_\beta^\dagger a_\gamma}\}\,. \end{aligned} \tag{17.15}$$

A contraction $\overline{a_\alpha^\dagger a_\gamma}$ vanishes unless $\alpha = \gamma$ refers to an occupied state. Taking into account the antisymmetrization of the matrix element $\langle\alpha\beta|W|\gamma\delta\rangle$ and labelling occupied states h and h', we find

$$\begin{aligned} H = \sum_h \langle h|T|h\rangle + \tfrac{1}{2} \sum_{hh'} \langle hh'|W|hh'\rangle + \sum_{\alpha\gamma} \{\langle\alpha|T|\gamma\rangle + \sum_h \langle\alpha h|W|\gamma h\rangle\}\, N(a_\alpha^\dagger a_\gamma) \\ + \tfrac{1}{4} \sum_{\alpha\beta\gamma\delta} \langle\alpha\beta|W|\gamma\delta\rangle\, N(a_\alpha^\dagger a_\beta^\dagger a_\delta a_\gamma)\,. \end{aligned} \tag{17.16}$$

In this expression the constant term

$$\sum_h \langle h|T|h\rangle + \tfrac{1}{2} \sum_{hh'} \langle hh'|W|hh'\rangle = \langle 0|H|0\rangle \tag{17.17}$$

represents the total energy of the reference state, i.e. the core. The next term, a one-body operator, is the Hartree-Fock Hamiltonian, which describes independent single-particle excitations.

Up till here the choice of the single-particle basis $|\alpha\rangle$ has been arbitrary. Let us now use this freedom to simplify the equations and diagonalize the matrix of the Hartree-Fock Hamiltonian. This leads to the Hartree-Fock equations

$$\langle\alpha|T+U|\gamma\rangle \equiv \langle\alpha|T|\gamma\rangle + \sum_h \langle\alpha h|W|\gamma h\rangle = e_\alpha \delta_{\alpha\gamma} \,. \tag{17.18}$$

The single-particle energies e_α are the Hartree-Fock energies for the self-consistent set of eigenfunctions $|\alpha\rangle$, which are seen to be defined by the Hartree-Fock single-particle potential

$$\langle\alpha|U|\gamma\rangle = \sum_h \langle\alpha h|W|\gamma h\rangle \,, \tag{17.19}$$

that in turn they define themselves (cf. eq. (16.39)).

Here we have not proven that eqs. (17.18) indeed represent the Hartree-Fock equations, i.e. that they result from the requirement of minimum energy for determinantal wave functions. The variational approach to this problem can be made quite conveniently with the aid of the second-quantization formalism. Then one can show in a concise and straightforward manner that the solutions of eqs. (17.18) meet the desired requirements [DeShalit and Feshbach (1974) eq. (7.2.21)].

The two-body operator

$$\tfrac{1}{4} \sum_{\alpha\beta\gamma\delta} \langle\alpha\beta|W|\gamma\delta\rangle \, N(a_\alpha^\dagger a_\beta^\dagger a_\delta a_\gamma)$$

is the residual interaction for the system under consideration. The residual character of the interaction is borne out by the normal product, since the vacuum expectation value of any two operators taken out of the normal product vanishes. These expectation values are accounted for in the constant term $\langle 0|H|0\rangle$ and the single-particle energies $\langle\alpha|T+U|\gamma\rangle$. The correspondence with the expressions (3.3) and (3.27) in first quantization is easily seen after eq. (17.16) is rewritten with the use of eqs. (17.17) and (17.18) as

$$H = \langle 0|H|0\rangle + \sum_\alpha e_\alpha N(a_\alpha^\dagger a_\alpha) + \tfrac{1}{4} \sum_{\alpha\beta\gamma\delta} \langle\alpha\beta|W|\gamma\delta\rangle \, N(a_\alpha^\dagger a_\beta^\dagger a_\delta a_\gamma) \,. \tag{17.20}$$

From eqs. (17.17) and (17.18) it is seen that the total energy of the core is not given by the sum of the single-particle energies, but one has

$$\langle 0|H|0\rangle = \sum_h \{\langle h|T|h\rangle + \tfrac{1}{2} \sum_{h'} \langle hh'|W|hh'\rangle\}$$

$$= \sum_h e_h - \tfrac{1}{2} \sum_{hh'} \langle hh'|W|hh'\rangle \,. \tag{17.21}$$

For the selfconsistent definition of the single-particle energies the two-body interaction with *all* other nucleons is taken into account. Hence, the summation over the single-particle energies involves a double-counting of the two-body interaction, which is corrected for in the last member of eq. (17.21) by subtraction of $\Sigma_{h<h'} \langle hh'|W|hh'\rangle$.

17.3. Evaluation of Feynman diagrams

For the calculation of the matrix elements of the effective residual interaction V, given as a perturbational expansion in eq. (16.30), one has to insert complete sets of intermediate states between the operators of each term. The reduction of the resulting expressions can be most easily performed in the second-quantization formalism.

As an example we shall discuss the second-order term

$$\left\langle ab|\mathcal{V}\frac{Q}{E_{\mathrm{V}}-H_{\mathrm{V}}^{(0)}}\mathcal{V}|cd\right\rangle .$$

The intermediate states here can be 2p-0h, 3p-1h or 4p-2h states, since no more than two hole lines can connect the two vertices $\mathcal{V}$. These three possibilities must be considered separately. Since each time the techniques are the same in principle, we shall treat the 3p-1h case only.

Let the three particle states be labelled p_1, p_2 and p_3 and the hole state h_1, then we have

$$\langle\mathcal{V}\mathcal{V}\rangle \equiv \left\langle ab|\mathcal{V}\frac{Q}{E_{\mathrm{V}}-H_{\mathrm{V}}^{(0)}}\mathcal{V}|cd\right\rangle$$

$$= \sum_{p_1p_2p_3h_1} \langle ab|\mathcal{V}|p_1p_2p_3h_1^{-1}\rangle \frac{1}{E_{\mathrm{V}}-(e_{p_1}+e_{p_2}+e_{p_3}-e_{h_1})}$$

$$\times \langle p_1p_2p_3h_1^{-1}|\mathcal{V}|cd\rangle . \tag{17.22}$$

Since intermediate states like $|p_1p_2p_3h_1^{-1}\rangle$ are all outside the model space, the projector Q is properly accounted for in eq. (17.22). In the second-quantization formalism we obtain, applying eq. (13.31) to the interaction $\mathcal{V}$,

$$\langle\mathcal{V}\mathcal{V}\rangle = (\tfrac{1}{4})^2 \sum_{p_1p_2p_3h_1}\ \sum_{\rho\sigma\tau\nu}\ \sum_{\rho'\sigma'\tau'\nu'} \frac{\langle\rho\sigma|\mathcal{V}|\tau\nu\rangle\langle\rho'\sigma'|\mathcal{V}|\tau'\nu'\rangle}{E_{\mathrm{V}}-(e_{p_1}+e_{p_2}+e_{p_3}-e_{h_1})}$$

$$\times \langle 0|a_a a_b N(a_\rho^\dagger a_\sigma^\dagger a_\nu a_\tau)a_{h_1}a_{p_3}^\dagger a_{p_2}^\dagger a_{p_1}^\dagger|0\rangle$$

$$\times \langle 0|a_{p_1}a_{p_2}a_{p_3}a_{h_1}^\dagger N(a_{\rho'}^\dagger a_{\sigma'}^\dagger a_{\nu'}a_{\tau'})a_d^\dagger a_c^\dagger|0\rangle . \tag{17.23}$$

The problem now is to evaluate the expectation values of the products of creation and annihilation operators given above. According to Wick's theorem the expectation value is given by the sum of all possible contractions. The normal products in this equation reflect the fact that $\mathcal{V}$ represents the *residual* interaction with respect to the reference state $|0\rangle$ (cf. eq. (17.20)). Thus no contractions are to be made among the states ρ, σ, τ and ν (and similarly ρ', σ', τ' and ν'). Two complete contractions (one for each vacuum expectation value in eq. (17.23)) are given by, for example,

$$a_a a_b a^\dagger_\rho a^\dagger_\sigma a_\nu a_\tau a_{h_1} a^\dagger_{p_3} a^\dagger_{p_2} a^\dagger_{p_1} = \delta_{\rho h_1}\delta_{\sigma b}\delta_{\tau p_1}\delta_{\nu p_2}\delta_{a p_3}\,, \tag{17.24}$$

$$a_{p_1} a_{p_2} a_{p_3} a^\dagger_{h_1} a^\dagger_{\rho'} a^\dagger_{\sigma'} a_{\nu'} a_{\tau'} a^\dagger_d a^\dagger_c = \delta_{\rho' p_3}\delta_{\sigma' p_1}\delta_{\tau' c}\delta_{\nu' h_1}\delta_{d p_2}\,. \tag{17.25}$$

Substitution leads to a contribution to $\langle \mathcal{V}\mathcal{V}\rangle$ given by

$$(\tfrac{1}{4})^2 \frac{\langle h_1 b|\mathcal{V}|p_1 p_2\rangle\langle p_3 p_1|\mathcal{V}|c h_1\rangle}{E_\mathrm{v} - (e_{p_1} + e_{p_2} + e_{p_3} - e_{h_1})}\,\delta_{a p_3}\delta_{d p_2}\,, \tag{17.26}$$

which can be represented schematically as

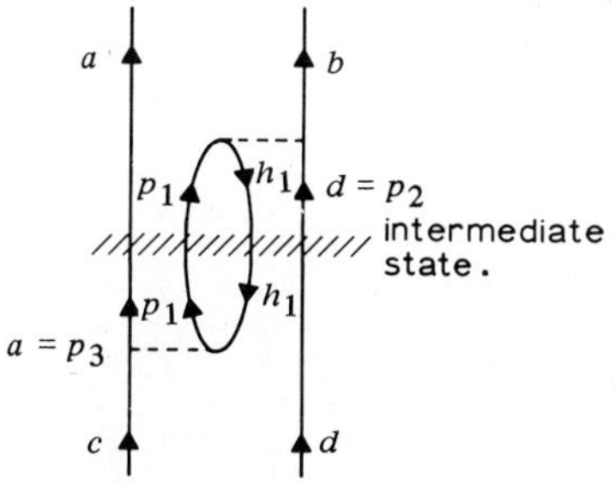

(17.27)

Here the two vertices correspond to the two matrix elements according to the rule that the two incoming lines appear in the ket state and the two outgoing lines in the bra state. With the given intermediate state one then easily constructs the diagram from the formula.

In the derivation of the expression (17.26) we have made an arbitrary choice out of several for the contractions. Other choices also lead to a product of Kronecker deltas, possibly with a different sign. Each possible choice of contractions leads to a term that contributes to the summation in eq. (17.22). Because of the antisymmetry of the two-body matrix elements many of these terms are of the same numerical value (and of the same sign). However, not all terms are the same, i.e. we also obtain terms that reflect the antisymmetry of the initial and final two-particle states $|ab\rangle$ and $|cd\rangle$. This leads to the explicit appearance of operators $P(ab)$ and $P(cd)$ that exchange the single-particle labels a and b or c and d, respectively. Properly counting and taking the terms of the same value together, one finds

$$\langle \mathcal{V}\mathcal{V}\rangle = \tfrac{1}{2}\{1 - P(ab)\}\{1 - P(cd)\}$$

$$\times \left\{ \sum_{p_1 h_1} \langle bh_1|\mathcal{V}|dp_1\rangle \frac{1}{e_c - e_a - e_{p_1} + e_{h_1}} \langle ap_1|\mathcal{V}|ch_1\rangle \right.$$

$$\left. + \sum_{p_1 h_1} \langle ah_1|\mathcal{V}|cp_1\rangle \frac{1}{e_d - e_b - e_{p_1} + e_{h_1}} \langle bp_1|\mathcal{V}|dh_1\rangle \right\}. \qquad (17.28)$$

These two sums can be represented by the diagrams, again according to the rule mentioned above, which are represented by

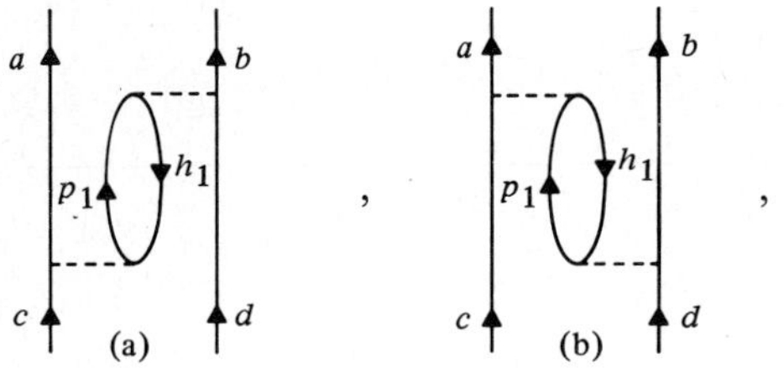

(17.29)

respectively.

In case the same single-particle state occurs in the initial and final two-particle states, another set of diagrams results in addition to those of eq. (17.29), i.e.

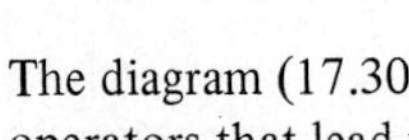

(17.30)

The diagram (17.30) corresponds to contractions of the annihilation and creation operators that lead to products of Kronecker deltas containing δ_{ap_3} for one vertex and δ_{cp_3} for the other. These unlinked diagrams, however, are excluded from the summations as mentioned before.

Along the same lines one finds the terms that contribute for other choices of intermediate states. If in eq. (16.30) 4p-2h intermediate states are chosen one finds the diagrams

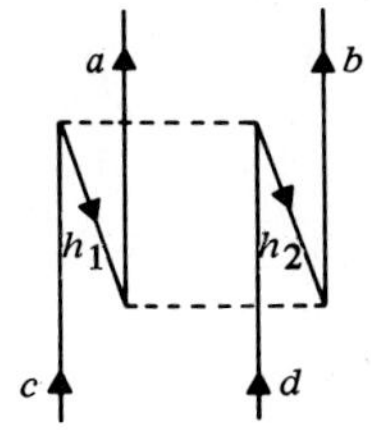

, (17.31)

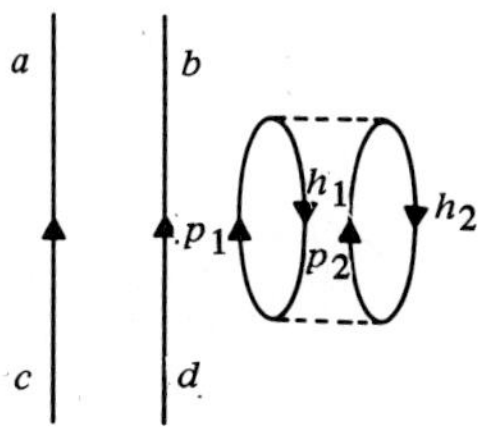

. (17.32)

The unlinked diagram (17.32) is excluded again from the expansion, of course.

In the present chapter we have treated as an example the evaluation of the second-order term of the perturbation expansion for the effective interaction, eq. (17.22), for a particular choice of intermediate states (3p-1h). From the resulting expressions we could construct the diagrams that contribute, omitting those that are not linked. This approach, that shows how the diagrammatic expansion is obtained from the perturbational formalism, should give us some understanding of the meaning and merits of the diagrammatic techniques.

Instead of starting from the perturbational formulas one can, alternatively, write down from the beginning a systematic expansion in terms of diagrams. That is, for the various orders in $\mathcal{V}$ (or G) all possible, linked diagrams must be drawn. Subsequently the corresponding formulas for each diagram are constructed either according to the Brandow rules (sect. 16.3) or again with the use of the second-quantization formalism. Since for this treatment particular intermediate states are taken from the beginning, the evaluation in the second-quantization formalism is somewhat less complicated than when one starts from the perturbational formulas.

Let us, as an example, reconsider diagram (17.29a) with the intermediate state $|ap_1h_1^{-1}d\rangle$. The corresponding expression then is

$$\sum_{p_1h_1} \langle ab|\mathcal{V}|ap_1h_1^{-1}d\rangle \frac{1}{E_{\mathrm{v}} - H_{\mathrm{v}}^{(0)}} \langle ap_1h_1^{-1}d|\mathcal{V}|cd\rangle$$

$$= (\tfrac{1}{4})^2 \sum_{p_1h_1} \sum_{\rho\sigma\tau\nu} \sum_{\rho'\sigma'\tau'\nu'} \frac{\langle\rho\sigma|\mathcal{V}|\tau\nu\rangle\langle\rho'\sigma'|\mathcal{V}|\tau'\nu'\rangle}{e_c - e_a - e_{p_1} + e_{h_1}}$$

$$\times \langle 0|a_a a_b N(a_\rho^\dagger a_\sigma^\dagger a_\nu a_\tau)\, a_d^\dagger a_{h_1} a_{p_1}^\dagger a_a^\dagger |0\rangle \langle 0|a_a a_{p_1} a_{h_1}^\dagger a_d\, N(a_{\rho'}^\dagger a_{\sigma'}^\dagger a_{\nu'} a_{\tau'})\, a_d^\dagger a_c^\dagger |0\rangle\,. \tag{17.33}$$

The two expectation values are reduced with the now familiar method. Of course, again there are no contractions to be made among the states, ρ, σ, τ, ν and ρ', σ', τ', ν'. After contraction of the operators a_a and $a_a^\dagger$ (see diagram (17.29a)) in the first expectation value, one of the possible complete contractions is given by $-\delta_{\rho h_1}\delta_{\sigma b}\delta_{\tau p_1}\delta_{\nu d}$; similarly for the second expectation value (now the operators a_d and $a_d^\dagger$ must be taken together, of course) $-\delta_{\rho' a}\delta_{\sigma' p_1}\delta_{\tau' c}\delta_{\nu' h_1}$. As there are four complete contractions possible for the expectation values that each lead to the same result in combination with the antisymmetric two-body matrix elements, one finds for the expression (17.33) the result

$$\sum_{p_1 h_1} \frac{\langle bh_1|\mathcal{V}|dp_1\rangle \langle ap_1|\mathcal{V}|ch_1\rangle}{e_c - e_a - e_{p_1} + e_{h_1}}\,. \tag{17.34}$$

As for this evaluation the intermediate state was taken *a priori* to contain the states a and d rather than b and c, the antisymmetry of the initial and final states is not a direct result. Application of the operator $\frac{1}{4}\{1 - P(ab)\}\{1 - P(cd)\}$ will restore this antisymmetry afterwards. After one has understood how the various diagrams are obtained and can be evaluated *ab initio*, it is much faster in practice to make use of the rules given by Brandow (cf. sect. 16.3)

17.4. Particle-hole configurations

The simplest configuration for a nucleus such as ^{16}O or ^{40}Ca is a doubly closed shell. It is not a very interesting configuration, as it leads to one state $J^\pi = 0^+$, $T = 0$ only. It also turns out not to be a good description of the ground state of such nuclei, although it may constitute one of the larger components of a more realistic ground-state wave function. The next simple configurations consist of one-particle, one-hole excitations of the closed core, which are represented by

$$|0; ph^{-1}\rangle = a_h a_p^\dagger |0\rangle\,. \tag{17.35}$$

Here we follow again the convention to denote particle states by the labels p_1, p_2 ... and hole states by the labels $h_1, h_2, \ldots$.

The particle-hole state is an eigenstate of the single-particle part of the shell-model Hamiltonian as one easily verifies with the use of eqs. (17.16) and (17.18), i.e.

$$H_{\text{s.p.}}|0; ph^{-1}\rangle = \sum_\alpha e_\alpha N(a_\alpha^\dagger a_\alpha)\, a_h a_p^\dagger |0\rangle$$

$$= (e_p - e_h)\, a_h a_p^\dagger |0\rangle = (e_p - e_h)|0; ph^{-1}\rangle\,. \tag{17.36}$$

Thus one can construct a basis of one-particle, one-hole states with unperturbed energies as given in eq. (17.36). For a description of excited states in nuclei one still has to perform the angular-momentum coupling and, once a sufficiently large set of basis functions is obtained, the eigenvalues and eigenvectors of the Hamiltonian can be determined. Before that can be done the particle-hole matrix elements of the residual interaction must be expressed in terms of the known particle-particle matrix elements.

The coupled particle-hole states are given by (cf. eqs. (13.54) and (13.53))

$$|0; ph^{-1}; JM\rangle = \sum_{m_p m_h} \langle j_p m_p j_h m_h | JM\rangle \, \tilde{a}_{j_h m_h} a^{\dagger}_{j_p m_p} |0\rangle$$

$$= \sum_{m_p m_h} (-1)^{j_h + m_h} \langle j_p m_p j_h m_h | JM\rangle \, a_{j_h - m_h} a^{\dagger}_{j_p m_p} |0\rangle \, . \qquad (17.37)$$

Thus one obtains for the matrix elements of the residual interaction (suppressing the symbol 0 for the closed-shell state)

$$\langle j_{p_1} j_{h_1}^{-1}; JM | V | j_{p_2} j_{h_2}^{-1}; JM\rangle = \tfrac{1}{4} \sum_{\alpha\beta\gamma\delta} \langle \alpha\beta | V | \gamma\delta\rangle$$

$$\times \sum_{m_{p_1} m_{h_1} m_{p_2} m_{h_2}} (-1)^{j_{h_1} - m_{h_1}} \langle j_{p_1} m_{p_1} j_{h_1} - m_{h_1} | JM\rangle \, (-1)^{j_{h_2} - m_{h_2}}$$

$$\times \langle j_{p_2} m_{p_2} j_{h_2} - m_{h_2} | JM\rangle \, \langle 0 | a_{j_{p_1} m_{p_1}} a^{\dagger}_{j_{h_1} m_{h_1}} N(a^{\dagger}_{\alpha} a^{\dagger}_{\beta} a_{\delta} a_{\gamma}) \, a_{j_{h_2} m_{h_2}} a^{\dagger}_{j_{p_2} m_{p_2}} |0\rangle \, .$$

$$(17.38)$$

In order that the expectation value of the eight annihilation and creation operators does not vanish, the normal product must contain one particle creation, one particle annihilation, one hole creation and one hole annihilation operator, all to be contracted with the other four operators (the normal ordering prevents any contraction among $a^{\dagger}_{\alpha} a^{\dagger}_{\beta} a_{\delta} a_{\gamma}$ from contributing). Thus one gets

$$\langle 0 | \ldots | 0\rangle = \delta_{\alpha h_2} \delta_{\beta p_1} \delta_{\gamma p_2} \delta_{\delta h_1} - \delta_{\alpha p_1} \delta_{\beta h_2} \delta_{\gamma p_2} \delta_{\delta h_1}$$

$$+ \delta_{\alpha p_1} \delta_{\beta h_2} \delta_{\gamma h_1} \delta_{\delta p_2} - \delta_{\alpha h_2} \delta_{\beta p_1} \delta_{\gamma h_1} \delta_{\delta p_2} \, . \qquad (17.39)$$

Substituting eq. (17.39) into eq. (17.38) and employing the antisymmetry of the two-body matrix elements: $\langle \alpha\beta | V | \gamma\delta\rangle = -\langle \beta\alpha | V | \gamma\delta\rangle = \langle \beta\alpha | V | \delta\gamma\rangle = -\langle \beta\alpha | V | \gamma\delta\rangle$ to reduce the four terms to one term, one obtains

$$\langle j_{p_1} j_{h_1}^{-1}; JM|V|j_{p_2} j_{h_2}^{-1}; JM\rangle = -\sum_{m_{p_1} m_{h_1} m_{p_2} m_{h_2}} \langle j_{p_1} j_{h_2}|V|j_{p_2} j_{h_1}\rangle$$

$$\times \langle j_{p_2} m_{p_2} j_{h_2} - m_{h_2}|JM\rangle \langle j_{p_1} m_{p_1} j_{h_1} - m_{h_1}|JM\rangle (-1)^{j_{h_2} - m_{h_2}} (-1)^{j_{h_1} - m_{h_1}}$$

$$= -\sum_{J'} (2J'+1) \begin{Bmatrix} j_{p_1} & j_{h_2} & J' \\ j_{p_2} & j_{h_1} & J \end{Bmatrix} \langle j_{p_1} j_{h_2}|V|j_{p_2} j_{h_1}\rangle_{J'} . \tag{17.40}$$

For the second equality use has been made of eq. (A.1.b13) to effect the required change in angular-momentum coupling. Eq. (17.40) is known as the *Pandya relation*. It should be remarked that the two-body matrix elements appearing in this relation are independent of the projection quantum numbers. With the use of the orthogonality relation for 6-*j* symbols, eq. (A.1.b8), one immediately finds the inverse relation

$$\langle j_{p_1} j_{h_2}|V|j_{p_2} j_{h_1}\rangle_{J'} = -\sum_{J} (2J+1) \begin{Bmatrix} j_{p_1} & j_{h_2} & J' \\ j_{p_2} & j_{h_1} & J \end{Bmatrix} \langle j_{p_1} j_{h_1}^{-1}; JM|V|j_{p_2} j_{h_2}^{-1}; JM\rangle . \tag{17.41}$$

Up to here the discussion of hole states concerned identical particles, i.e. the isospin label has not been considered. The inclusion of isospin involves a straightforward extension of the formalism treated thus far. One can generalize eq. (17.40) and include isospin to obtain

$$\langle j_{p_1} j_{h_1}^{-1}; JM, TT_z|V|j_{p_2} j_{h_2}^{-1}; JM, TT_z\rangle$$

$$= -\sum_{J'T'} (2J'+1)(2T'+1) \begin{Bmatrix} j_{p_1} & j_{h_2} & J' \\ j_{p_2} & j_{h_1} & J \end{Bmatrix} \begin{Bmatrix} \frac{1}{2} & \frac{1}{2} & T' \\ \frac{1}{2} & \frac{1}{2} & T \end{Bmatrix} \langle j_{p_1} j_{h_2}|V|j_{p_2} j_{h_1}\rangle_{J'T'} . \tag{17.42}$$

It is seen that the matrix elements for particle-hole states coupled to J, T are given by a sum of particle-particle matrix elements coupled to different values J', T' and *vice versa.* Expression (17.42) is quite useful if one wishes to calculate the spectrum and wave functions in a one-particle, one-hole configuration space, e.g. for the nucleus ^{40}Ca. These states can be expected to yield the most important components for the low-lying negative-parity levels. Another application is the calculation of particle-particle matrix elements from empirical particle-hole matrix elements [Schiffer (1971)].

In order to perform a calculation of the spectrum of one-particle, one-hole states one still needs a set of single-particle energies of the particle and hole states that are considered in the basis wave functions. The unperturbed energies of the one-particle, one-hole configurations with respect to the ground state of the doubly closed-shell nucleus considered, such as ^{40}Ca, are usually derived from ground-state binding energies of neighbouring nuclei, like e.g. ^{39}Ca, ^{39}K and ^{41}Ca. These are interpreted as pure single-particle or single-hole shell-model states. For instance, the difference between $1f_{7/2}$ particle and $1d_{3/2}$ hole single-neutron energies is determined from the relation

$$E_{\text{s.p}}(1f_{7/2}\,1d_{3/2}^{-1}) = e_{1f_{7/2}} - e_{1d_{3/2}}$$

$$= E^{\text{b}}(^{41}\text{Ca}) - E^{\text{b}}(^{40}\text{Ca}) + E^{\text{b}}(^{39}\text{Ca}) - E^{\text{b}}(^{40}\text{Ca}) = 7.3 \text{ MeV} . \tag{17.43}$$

If, however, the neighbouring ground states are not regarded as pure shell-model states, eq. (17.40) no longer applies, but has to be replaced by a much more complicated relation that may lead to appreciably different values for the energy splittings of the unperturbed single-particle states.

The wave functions in a one-particle, one-hole configuration space are represented by (cf. eq. (17.35))

$$|\Gamma\rangle = -\sum_{ph} x_{ph}^{(\Gamma)} [a_p^\dagger \times \tilde{a}_h]^\Gamma |0\rangle = \sum_{ph} x_{ph}^{(\Gamma)} |0; ph^{-1}, \Gamma\rangle , \tag{17.44}$$

where the amplitudes $x_{ph}^{(\Gamma)}$ must be determined from a diagonalization of the residual interaction, quite analogously to the procedures for particle configurations. Thus the ground state is taken to be a closed-subshell configuration and the excited states are mixed one-particle, one-hole configurations. This approach is usually referred to as the *Tamm-Dancoff approximation* (TDA). In case the residual interaction is given by the MSDI, defined in eq. (6.47), the matrix of the Hamiltonian can be derived with the aid of eqs. (6.44), (6.49) and (17.42). The result is

$$\langle p_1 h_1^{-1} |H| p_2 h_2^{-1}\rangle_\Gamma = (e_{p_1} - e_{h_1})\, \delta_{p_1 p_2} \delta_{h_1 h_2} + \langle p_1 h_1^{-1} |V| p_2 h_2^{-1}\rangle_\Gamma \tag{17.45}$$

with

$$\begin{aligned}
\langle p_1 h_1^{-1} |V| p_2 h_2^{-1}\rangle_{JT} &= \tfrac{1}{4}\sqrt{(2j_{p_1}+1)(2j_{p_2}+1)(2j_{h_1}+1)(2j_{h_2}+1)} \\
&\times (-1)^{j_{h_1}+j_{h_2}+l_{p_1}+l_{h_1}+J+T} \Big[[A_0 \{1 + 2(-1)^{l_{h_2}+l_{p_2}+J}\} + A_1 \{1 + 2(-1)^T\}] \\
&\times \begin{pmatrix} j_{p_2} & j_{h_1} & J \\ \frac{1}{2} & -\frac{1}{2} & 0 \end{pmatrix} \begin{pmatrix} j_{h_2} & j_{p_2} & J \\ \frac{1}{2} & -\frac{1}{2} & 0 \end{pmatrix} + (-1)^{l_{h_1}+l_{p_2}+j_{h_1}+j_{p_2}} \\
&\times [A_0 - A_1 \{1 + 2(-1)^T\}] \begin{pmatrix} j_{p_1} & j_{h_1} & J \\ \frac{1}{2} & \frac{1}{2} & -1 \end{pmatrix} \begin{pmatrix} j_{h_2} & j_{p_2} & J \\ \frac{1}{2} & \frac{1}{2} & -1 \end{pmatrix} \Big] \delta^{\text{even}}_{l_{p_1}+l_{p_2}+l_{h_1}+l_{h_2}} \\
&- [C + B\{1 + 2(-1)^T\}]\, \delta_{p_1 p_2} \delta_{h_1 h_2}
\end{aligned} \tag{17.46}$$

with the secular equation

$$\sum_{p_2 h_2} \langle p_1 h_1^{-1} | H | p_2 h_2^{-1} \rangle_\Gamma \, x^{(\Gamma)}_{p_2 h_2} = E_\Gamma \, x^{(\Gamma)}_{p_1 h_1} \,. \tag{17.47}$$

It is clear that in the TDA there is an asymmetry in the way the ground state is treated on the one hand and the excited states on the other. That is, the ground state is described in terms of one configuration only that in fact corresponds to independent-particle motion. The ground-state wave function is the angular-momentum coupled, antisymmetrized product of single-particle wave functions. The omission of correlations in the ground-state wave function may in some cases substantially reduce the calculated electromagnetic transition rates to the ground state.

A method by which the ground state is treated on the same footing as the excited states, is the *random-phase approximation* (RPA). It entails a doubling of the dimension of the wave functions in order to describe the correlations of the nucleons in the ground state. The theory of the RPA is fundamental to the theory of collective motion in nuclei. We shall not discuss it here but the reader is referred to the literature, e.g. [Rowe (1970)].

CHAPTER 18

MISCELLANEOUS SUBJECTS

18.1. The Lanczos method

We have seen in chapter 3 that the eigenvalues and eigenfunctions of the Schrödinger equation

$$H\Psi = E\Psi \,, \tag{18.1}$$

with

$$H = H^{(0)} + V \,, \tag{18.2}$$

$$H^{(0)}\Phi_i = E_i^{(0)}\Phi_i \,, \tag{18.3}$$

can be approximated in perturbation theory by diagonalization of the Hamiltonian H in the, usually large, basis of unperturbed wave functions Φ_i. In most practical cases, however, we are interested in low-lying states only, i.e. the lower eigenvalues and corresponding eigenvectors. Therefore, since the dimensions of the configuration spaces may be very large, it would be quite economic not to have to diagonalize the complete and large matrices if only the lower eigenvalues are desired. Most procedures that are in use, e.g. the Householder method [Householder (1964)], do require such a complete diagonalization of the full matrix. An exception is the Lanczos iterative method of tri-diagonalization, which permits one to obtain some eigenvalues and eigenvectors quite accurately from only part of the full matrix. The principles of the method are given in [Wilkinson (1965) p. 388], and we shall sketch here the outline of the procedure only.

The first step is to operate with the Hamiltonian H on some normalized initial vector v_1, that is arbitrarily chosen in the configuration space considered. For example $v_1 = \Sigma_i c_i \Phi_i$ with Φ_i denoting a basis state. It is remarked here that the initial vector v_1 does not necessarily have to possess good spin and isospin (see the m-scheme discussed below). The resulting vector Hv_1 can be decomposed uniquely into two orthogonal components $\alpha_1 v_1$ and $\beta_1 v_2$. In a similar way a third unit vector v_3 orthogonal to v_1 and v_2 is generated by acting with H on v_2. When H acts on v_3 one finds no component along v_1, since this component is determined by the overlap $\langle v_1|H|v_3\rangle$. The latter matrix element vanishes, however, since one has (H is hermitian)

$$\langle v_1|H|v_3\rangle = \langle v_3|H|v_1\rangle = \alpha_1\langle v_3|v_1\rangle + \beta_1\langle v_3|v_2\rangle = 0 \,, \tag{18.4}$$

as follows from the definition of v_3, i.e. $\langle v_3|v_1\rangle = 0$ and $\langle v_3|v_2\rangle = 0$. Thus one may write

$$
\begin{aligned}
H|v_1\rangle &= |v_1\rangle\langle v_1|H|v_1\rangle + |v_2\rangle\langle v_2|H|v_1\rangle\,,\\
H|v_2\rangle &= |v_1\rangle\langle v_1|H|v_2\rangle + |v_2\rangle\langle v_2|H|v_2\rangle + |v_3\rangle\langle v_3|H|v_2\rangle\,,\\
H|v_3\rangle &= \qquad\qquad\qquad\quad |v_2\rangle\langle v_2|H|v_3\rangle + |v_3\rangle\langle v_3|H|v_3\rangle + |v_4\rangle\langle v_4|H|v_3\rangle\,.
\end{aligned}
\tag{18.5}
$$

This iteration procedure can be continued until a complete set of orthonormal vectors v_i is obtained from the initial vector v_1. For a configuration space of dimension N one thus finds

$$
\begin{aligned}
Hv_1 &= \alpha_1 v_1 + \beta_1 v_2\,,\\
Hv_2 &= \beta_1 v_1 + \alpha_2 v_2 + \beta_2 v_3\,,\\
Hv_3 &= \qquad \beta_2 v_2 + \alpha_3 v_3 + \beta_3 v_4\,,\\
&\vdots\\
Hv_n &= \qquad\qquad \beta_{n-1} v_{n-1} + \alpha_n v_n + \beta_n v_{n+1}\,,\\
&\vdots\\
Hv_N &= \qquad\qquad\qquad \beta_{N-1} v_{N-1} + \alpha_N v_N\,.
\end{aligned}
\tag{18.6}
$$

Here the coefficients α_i and β_i are matrix elements of the Hamiltonian in the basis $v_1, v_2, \ldots, v_N$ with

$$\alpha_i = \langle v_i|H|v_i\rangle\,, \tag{18.7}$$

$$\beta_i = \langle v_{i+1}|H|v_i\rangle = \langle v_i|H|v_{i+1}\rangle\,, \tag{18.8}$$

whereas all other matrix elements of H vanish, i.e.

$$\langle v_j|H|v_i\rangle = \langle v_i|H|v_j\rangle = 0 \qquad \text{for } |i-j| \geqslant 2\,. \tag{18.9}$$

Eqs. (18.6) show that the Hamiltonian in the basis $v_1, v_2, \ldots, v_N$ assumes the tridiagonal form

$$
H \Rightarrow \begin{pmatrix}
\alpha_1 & \beta_1 & 0 & \cdots & & & 0\\
\beta_1 & \alpha_2 & \beta_2 & \ddots & & & \vdots\\
0 & \beta_2 & \alpha_3 & \beta_3 & \ddots & & \vdots\\
\vdots & \ddots & \ddots & \ddots & \ddots & & \vdots\\
 & & \beta_{n-1} & \alpha_n & \beta_{n+1} & \ddots & 0\\
 & & & \ddots & \ddots & \ddots & \beta_{N-1}\\
0 & \cdots & & 0 & & \beta_{N-1} & \alpha_N
\end{pmatrix}.
\tag{18.10}
$$

In general the iterations terminate as soon as the generated set of functions v_i exhausts the chosen configuration space, i.e. one finds $\beta_N = 0$. If the initial vector v_1 happens to be orthogonal to any eigenvector of H, say Ψ_i, then the iterative procedure terminates earlier (e.g. in the case of degeneracy). Then one has to continue with a new starting vector orthogonal to those already obtained. It turns out, however, that one does not have to worry about this complication in the practice of nuclear shell-model calculations.

In order to obtain the eigenvalues and eigenvectors of H we must diagonalize the matrix (18.10). The procedure is as follows. One first generates n basis states $v_1, ..., v_n$ $(n \leqslant N)$ with the procedure (18.6). The Lanczos tri-diagonal matrix possesses the property that the eigenvalues that are obtained after diagonalization of the upper left $n \times n$ corner of the matrix (18.10), all converge to the eigenvalues of the full $N \times N$ matrix. The main feature is that convergence for the lower eigenvalues generally is obtained long before the dimension of the full configuration space has been reached, i.e. for $n \ll N$. This can be made plausible as is shown below.

Let us denote the eigenfunctions of the complete Hamiltonian (18.10) by Ψ_i with $i = 1, ..., N$. These Ψ_i obey the equations

$$H\Psi_i = E_i\Psi_i \,. \tag{18.11}$$

The arbitrarily chosen initial vector v_1 can always be expanded in terms of the complete set Ψ_i as

$$v_1 = \sum_{i=1}^{N} a_i\Psi_i \,. \tag{18.12}$$

The basis states $v_1, v_2, ..., v_n$, defined according to the procedure of eqs. (18.6), are generated essentially by repeated operation of H on v_1, as can be easily seen from a slight rearrangement of eqs. (18.6). The first two of these equations yield

$$v_2 = \frac{1}{\beta_1}(H - \alpha_1)v_1 \,, \tag{18.13}$$

$$v_3 = \frac{1}{\beta_2}\{-\beta_1 v_1 + (H - \alpha_2)v_2\} = \frac{1}{\beta_2}\{-\beta_1 v_1 + \frac{1}{\beta_1}(H - \alpha_2)(H - \alpha_1)v_1\} \,. \tag{18.14}$$

Similarly one can express v_n as a linear combination of $H^p v_1$ with $p = 0,1,2, ..., n-1$. From eqs. (18.11) and (18.12) one finds, applying H on v_1 say p times,

$$H^p v_1 = \sum_{i=1}^{N} a_i H^p \Psi_i = \sum_{i=1}^{N} E_i^p a_i \Psi_i \,. \tag{18.15}$$

When the Hamiltonian H describes a bound system (with negative eigenvalues) it is seen that for increasing values of p the lower-lying states Ψ_i, i.e. with large values $|E_i|$, will eventually predominate in the expansion (18.15). It is this "purifying" action of the operator H^p that generates a set of basis functions appropriate for low-lying states. Convergence for the lower-lying states can be improved, if necessary, by assuring that their eigenvalues possess the largest absolute values. This can be brought about by the *ad hoc* application of an energy shift E to the spectrum, i.e. one replaces the Hamiltonian H by $H-E$.

It is quite instructive to plot the calculated eigenvalues against the dimension n of the tri-diagonal matrix. It turns out that only a small fraction of the full calculation in the complete model space is needed for a description of the lowest few eigenstates. Typically one needs of the order of one hundred iterations to reach sufficient convergence for, say, the lowest ten states in sd-shell nuclei [Cole, Watt and Whitehead (1975)].

As can be seen from the convergence curves in fig. 18.1, it is difficult to give *a priori* infallible criteria to decide whether convergence has been reached or not. This is a consequence of the treacherous phenomenon that eigenvalues may change very little over several iterations and then suddenly may jump downwards. The almost constant value before the jump corresponds to a genuine eigenvalue. Thus premature termination of the iteration procedure may mean that one misses at least one eigenvalue from the spectrum. Calculation of the expectation values of J^2 and T^2 may often be helpful, since nonintegral (even-A nuclei) or nonhalfintegral (odd-A nuclei) values of J or T indicate incomplete convergence. Since it suffices to diagonalize an $n \times n$ matrix ($n \ll N$) in the upper left corner of H, the Lanczos method offers a natural truncation procedure to a model space spanned by the vectors $v_1, v_2, ..., v_n$.

The eigenvectors of the Hamiltonian are obtained as linear combinations of Lanczos vectors,

$$\Psi = \sum_j c_j v_j \,, \tag{18.16}$$

that can be easily expressed in terms of the original shell-model basis functions

CONVERGENCE WITH THE LANCZOS METHOD

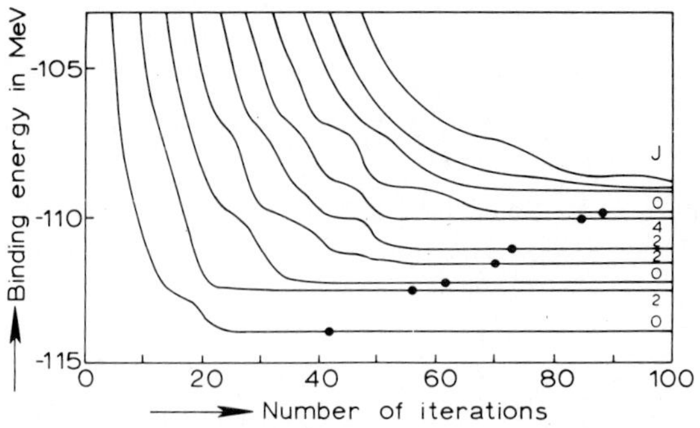

Fig. 18.1 The eigenvalues of the Hamiltonian for ^{26}Mg obtained with the Lanczos method are plotted for J = even as a function of the dimension of the tri-diagonal matrix, i.e. the number of iterations performed. The dots indicate where convergence has been reached [Whitehead, Watt, Cole and Morrison (1977)].

$\Phi_1, ..., \Phi_N$. When the Lanczos vectors are given by

$$v_j = \sum_i a_{ji}\Phi_i \,, \tag{18.17}$$

one finds immediately from eqs. (18.16) and (18.17)

$$\Psi = \sum_{ij} c_j a_{ji}\Phi_i = \sum_i b_i\Phi_i \tag{18.18}$$

with

$$b_i = \sum_j c_j a_{ji} \,. \tag{18.19}$$

A drawback of the Lanczos method is that it depends on the strict orthogonalization of each v_i to all vectors obtained previously [Whitehead, Watt, Cole and Morrison (1977)].

It will be shown that the Lanczos method allows one to perform nuclear shell-model calculations rather efficiently in an uncoupled m-scheme representation, i.e. the rotational symmetries in space and isospace are disregarded. The advantage of this uncoupled representation is that no Racah algebra or c.f.p. enter the calculation. This way one avoids the rather complex evaluation of c.f.p. and also the problems involved in storing large sets of these in a computer.

When the rotational symmetries are ignored, the dimensions of the Hamiltonian matrices necessarily become much larger, since the matrices are no longer divided into submatrices each specified by a given J and T. The Hamiltonian one starts with, however, possesses the proper rotational symmetries, i.e. it commutes with J^2 and T^2. Thus the eigenstates one reaches upon convergence, are characterized by sharp values of J and T.

For a calculation in the m-scheme one may conveniently make use of bit handling when it is performed on a digital computer. Let us illustrate this with a simple example. Consider three neutrons in the orbits $j_a = \frac{1}{2}$ and $j_b = \frac{3}{2}$, e.g. ${}^{31}_{14}\mathrm{Si}_{17}$ with a ${}^{28}\mathrm{Si}$ core and three neutrons in the $2s_{1/2}$ $1d_{3/2}$ subshells. Because of the Pauli exclusion principle only one particle can occupy a state of given angular momentum j and projection m. One of the many possible three-particle states for the orbits $j_a = \frac{1}{2}$ and $j_b = \frac{3}{2}$ may be represented by $j_a = \frac{1}{2}$, $m_a = \frac{1}{2}$, $j_b = \frac{3}{2}$, $m_b = \frac{1}{2}$ and $j_b = \frac{3}{2}$, $m'_b = -\frac{3}{2}$. In second quantization this particular state is given by

$$\Phi(2s_{1/2}\ 1d^2_{3/2}) = a^\dagger_{j_b=\frac{3}{2} m'_b=-\frac{3}{2}}\, a^\dagger_{j_b=\frac{3}{2} m_b=\frac{1}{2}}\, a^\dagger_{j_a=\frac{1}{2} m_a=\frac{1}{2}} |0\rangle \,, \tag{18.20}$$

where $|0\rangle$ denotes the ${}^{28}\mathrm{Si}$ core. The antisymmetry of the three-particle state is guaranteed by the properties of the creation operators $a^\dagger$.

All states with neutrons in the two orbits $j_a = \frac{1}{2}$ and $j_b = \frac{3}{2}$ can be represented by a 6-bit computer word. Denoting with the symbol "1" an occupied state j, m and with "0" an empty state, one may represent the state (18.20) by

$$\begin{array}{lcccccc} i= & 1 & 2 & 3 & 4 & 5 & 6 \\ & \boxed{1} & \boxed{0} & \boxed{0} & \boxed{1} & \boxed{0} & \boxed{1} \\ m= & \frac{1}{2} & -\frac{1}{2} & \frac{3}{2} & \frac{1}{2} & -\frac{1}{2} & -\frac{3}{2} \end{array} \leftrightarrow a^\dagger_{i=6}\, a^\dagger_{i=4}\, a^\dagger_{i=1}|0\rangle\,, \tag{18.21}$$

$$\underbrace{\qquad}_{j_a=\frac{1}{2}} \qquad \underbrace{\qquad\qquad}_{j_b=\frac{3}{2}}$$

where we have introduced for convenience the number $i = 1, 2, ..., 6$ to label the bits of the 6-bit word. The operation of the Hamiltonian on such a state can now be performed quite simply. Therefore we write the Hamiltonian in second-quantization formalism (see eq. (14.39)), as

$$H = H^{(0)} + V = \sum_{i=1}^{6} e_i\, a_i^\dagger a_i + \tfrac{1}{4} \sum_{ijkl} \langle ij|V|kl\rangle\, a_i^\dagger a_j^\dagger a_l a_k \tag{18.22}$$

Operating with a particular two-body term of H, say the term with $i = 5, j = 2, k = 6$ and $l = 4$ on the state (18.21), one obtains

$$a_5^\dagger a_2^\dagger a_4 a_6 \boxed{1\,|\,0\,|\,0\,|\,1\,|\,0\,|\,1} = a_5^\dagger a_2^\dagger \boxed{1\,|\,0\,|\,0\,|\,0\,|\,0\,|\,0} = \boxed{1\,|\,1\,|\,0\,|\,0\,|\,1\,|\,0}\,. \tag{18.23}$$

It should be clear that this method can simply be extended to configurations in which both protons and neutrons occupy states j, m. For example, one can use bits $i = 1, 2, ..., 6$ for neutrons and bits 7, 8, ..., 12 for protons in the orbits $j_a = \frac{1}{2}$ and $j_b = \frac{3}{2}$. For a calculation in the sd shell that involves the proton and neutron orbits $1d_{5/2}$, $2s_{1/2}$ and $1d_{3/2}$ one needs 24-bit words to specify the states. More details about the application of the Lanczos method to shell-model calculations performed in the m-scheme can be found in the literature [Whitehead, Watt, Cole and Morrison (1977)].

Summarizing one may say that the Lanczos tri-diagonalization procedure turns out to be very efficient when one is interested only in the lower eigenvalues and corresponding eigenvectors of matrices with a dimension larger than, say, 500. Moreover, the density of states should not be very high.

It should be remarked that although it is attractive to work in an uncoupled m-scheme, the Lanczos method is also useful for a coupled representation [Sebe and Nachamkin (1969)]. Since one considers in the latter case only states of a given J and T, one obtains of course a lower density of states and hence a faster convergence may result.

18.2. Some truncation methods

One of the main problems of nuclear shell-model calculations concerns the restriction of the configuration space to a manageable size. The orders of the Hamiltonian matrices that must be diagonalized to obtain the wave functions, strongly depend on the number of active particles and active orbits. Moreover, for a given number of particles the orders increase strongly when the j-values of the orbits become larger. This can be observed, for example, from the number of allowed J-values for a configuration j^n, listed in appendix B.2. Thus it is not surprising that for most calculations in which several active particles are involved, only a small number of low-j orbits is taken into account. However, instead of performing a calculation with a very small set of active orbits and without any restriction on their occupation numbers, one may include more orbits, but then the resulting configuration space has to be truncated in some way.

The truncation techniques discussed in this section are all based on the assumption that the residual interaction will not strongly admix high-lying states and low-lying states (see also sect. 3.5). They differ only in the way these low-lying states are selected. It should be mentioned that the discussion given below is not exhaustive and other methods may turn out to be useful as well.

Seniority truncation. It is a well-known fact that the nuclear two-body interaction is strong for zero-coupled pairs (e.g. all even-even nuclei have a $J^\pi = 0^+$ ground state). Therefore one can make the assumption that in a given nucleus the states with a large number of zero-coupled pairs are to be found at low excitation energies. In this connection one can conveniently make use of the seniority quantum number v.

For single-orbit states ρ^n the seniority v is defined as the number of particles that are not coupled in pairs $J^\pi = 0^+$ (see sect. 4.5). Suppose one has a pure, i.e. unmixed, state described by more than one active orbit, e.g.

$$\Phi_{JT} = [(\rho_1^{n_1})_{v_1}(\rho_2^{n_2})_{v_2}(\rho_3^{n_3})_{v_3}]_{JT}\,, \tag{18.24}$$

where the seniority v_i in each of the states $\rho_i^{n_i}$ is well defined. Let v_s denote the sum of the seniorities of the three orbits,

$$v_s = v_1 + v_2 + v_3\,. \tag{18.25}$$

The number v_s can vary between zero or one for even- or odd-A nuclei and the total number of active particles $n_1 + n_2 + n_3$. One can use the number v_s for a truncation of the configuration space by taking into account only those states for which v_s does not exceed a certain limit.

A disadvantage of this method is that one can truncate the space only in rather large steps, in particular when the number of active particles and hence the range of possible values v_s is very small. Moreover, the assumption that seniority v_s increases with excitation energy is not always justified. This is illustrated with an example.

Let a wave function of mixed configurations be given by

$$\Psi_{JT} = \sum_k a_k \Phi_{JT}^{(k)}\,, \tag{18.26}$$

where a_k denotes the amplitude of the basis state $\Phi_{JT}^{(k)}$ of seniority $v_s^{(k)}$. We now define an average seniority $\bar{v}$ by

$$\bar{v} = \sum_k a_k^2 \, v_s^{(k)} . \tag{18.27}$$

Note that $\bar{v}$ does not have to be an integer. From the wave functions of the lower three $J^\pi = 2^+$ states in even Ni isotopes obtained in an unrestricted $2p_{3/2}1f_{5/2}2p_{1/2}$ space [Koops and Glaudemans (1977)], one finds the average seniorities plotted in fig. 18.2. It is seen that the lowest $J^\pi = 2^+$ state in each isotope does satify the assumption of having the lowest possible seniority. The third $J^\pi = 2^+$ state, however, has a considerably lower seniority $\bar{v}$ than the second $J^\pi = 2^+$ state, although the former lies more than 0.5 MeV above the second $J^\pi = 2^+$ state. Note that for ^{58}Ni, which in this model is described by only two active neutrons outside the closed-shell core $^{56}_{28}\mathrm{Ni}_{28}$, the states with $J \neq 0$ can only be formed with $v = 2$.

Single-particle energy truncation (SPET). Once an inert core has been chosen, one has to investigate to which extent active orbits $\rho_1, \rho_2, \rho_3, \ldots$ should be taken into account for the particles outside the core. Let us consider the expression for the binding energy of a state Φ_{JT} with a particle distribution $[\rho_1^{n_2}, \rho_2^{n_2}, \rho_3^{n_3}, \ldots]$. One then obtains for the binding energy with respect to the core, ignoring Coulomb effects, the result (cf. eq. (3.34)),

$$E_{JT}^{\mathrm{b}} = n_1 e_{\rho_1} + n_2 e_{\rho_2} + n_3 e_{\rho_3} + \ldots + E_{JT}^{(1)} (\rho_1^{n_1}, \rho_2^{n_2}, \rho_3^{n_3}, \ldots) . \tag{18.28}$$

Because of its simplicity it is a very common procedure to truncate the model space according to the total single-particle energy of the basis states, i.e. $\Sigma_i n_i e_{\rho_i}$. All configurations for which this quantity exceeds a certain preset value are omitted from the model space. Thus in this truncation it is assumed that the location of each

SENIORITY IN Ni ISOTOPES

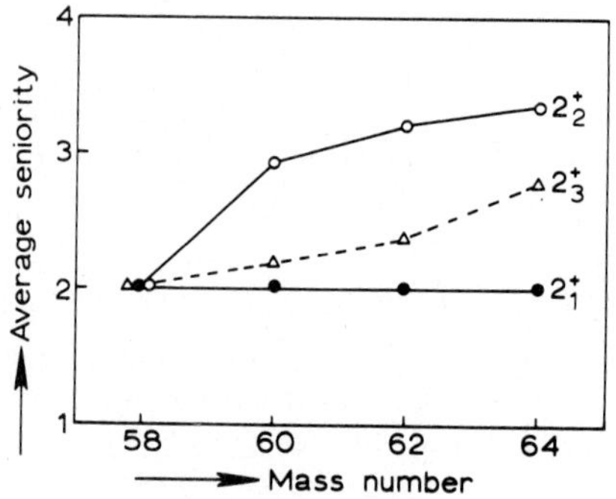

Fig. 18.2. The average seniority $\bar{v}$ for the lowest three $J^\pi = 2^+$ states in the even-mass Ni isotopes; the third state $J^\pi = 2_3^+$ is seen to possess lower seniority $\bar{v}$ than the second one.

state is mainly determined by the single-particle energies e_{ρ_i}. A disadvantage of this method is that one ignores completely the effect of the term $E^{(1)}_{JT}$ in eq. (18.28) for an estimate of the location of the states Φ_{JT}.

Diagonal energy truncation (DET). Rather than use the truncation method SPET, discussed above, one should include the term $E^{(1)}_{JT}$ in eq. (18.28). This complicates the truncation procedure considerably, since one must calculate the contribution $E^{(1)}_{JT}$ from the residual two-body force for a possibly very large set of basis states Φ_{JT}. One should realize, however, that eq. (18.28) represents the diagonal matrix elements of the Hamiltonian matrix *H*. For their evaluation only a very small fraction of the computer time and memory is needed compared to the requirements for a complete diagonalization of *H*.

It turns out that a consecutive combination of the SPET and DET procedures may be quite efficient. This is illustrated in fig. 18.3, where a plot is shown of the level density of $J^\pi = 2^+$ states in ^{26}Mg calculated for configurations $(1d_{5/2})^{n_1}$

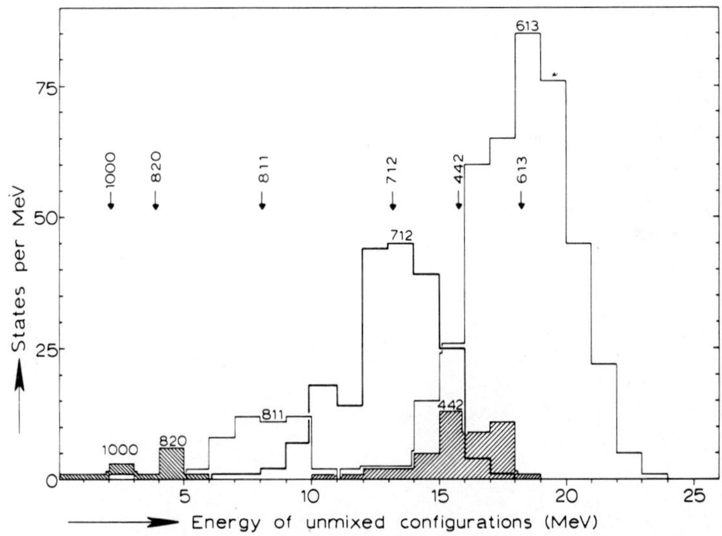

Fig. 18.3. The density of unmixed configurations with $J^\pi = 2^+$ in ^{26}Mg for different particle distributions as a function of their energy. The energy is determined with respect to the lowest-lying configuration. The energies have been calculated with a modified surface delta two-body interaction ($A_0 = A_1 = 1.0$ MeV) and with single-particle energies taken from the experimental spectrum of ^{17}O. The particle distributions are denoted by $n_1n_2n_3$, i.e. the number of particles in the $1d_{5/2}$, $2s_{1/2}$ and $1d_{3/2}$ subshell, respectively. The arrows indicate the single-particle excitation, $n_2(e_2 - e_1) + n_3(e_3 - e_1)$, for the different distributions, where e_1, e_2 and e_3 are the single-particle energies of the orbits given above. [Meurders, Glaudemans, Van Hienen and Timmer (1976)].

$(2s_{1/2})^{n_2}(1d_{3/2})^{n_3}$ with the MSDI matrix elements. It is seen that states with a given particle distribution $[n_1n_2n_3]$ form rather narrow clusters. Each distribution shows a relatively long tail on the low-energy side. This tail contains the basis states Φ_{JT} that are strongly favoured by the two-body interaction. In other words, some states expected to have a high excitation energy because of the single-particle energy contribution, may be found at a considerably lower excitation energy due to the residual interaction. Hence, these low-lying states should be included in the model space.

It is seen from fig. 18.3 that in this calculation the spacings between different distributions $[n_1n_2n_3]$ are determined mainly by the single-particle energy differences. The width of each group turns out not to depend strongly on the particle distribution $[n_1n_2n_3]$. Hence one does not have to calculate the term $E_{JT}^{(1)}$ for the states of very high total single-particle energy. The procedure is then as follows. (i) Calculate the diagonal matrix elements of the Hamiltonian, i.e. the energies of the pure states Φ_{JT}. (ii) Rearrange these states such that they are ordered according to increasing excitation energy as derived from eq. (19.28). (iii) Select the N lowest-lying states Φ_{JT}. Now one can perform a complete diagonalization to derive the wave functions in this N-dimensional model space, where the number N is usually dictated by the computer capacity.

A comparison of the three procedures discussed above is given in fig. 18.4 for a $2p_{3/2}1f_{5/2}2p_{1/2}$ configuration space. Here the nontruncated wave functions Ψ for ^{63}Cu are compared with the functions Ψ_{tr}, obtained from various truncation procedures. The wave function fraction has been plotted *versus* the dimension fraction,

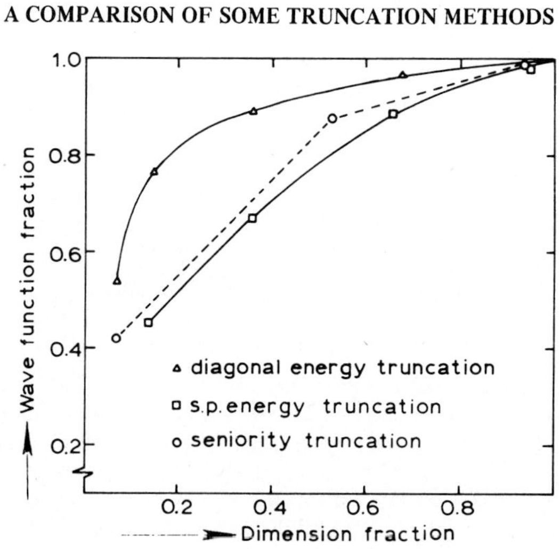

Fig. 18.4. Fractions of wave functions and dimensions averaged over the first two eigenvectors of the $J = \frac{1}{2}, \frac{3}{2}, \frac{5}{2}$ states in ^{63}Cu for three truncation techniques.

i.e. the ratio of the number of components in Ψ_{tr} and Ψ. The latter represents the summed intensities of those configurations in Ψ that are not rejected by the truncation. It is clearly seen that in this example the DET procedure gives the largest similarity between Ψ_{tr} and Ψ for a given reduction in dimension. Hence the DET procedure may be superior to the other methods mentioned above. A disadvantage of all three methods is that one ignores completely the possible effects of admixtures from rejected high-lying states. Only by using the proper effective one- and two-body matrix elements can one hope to simulate the influence of states removed from the configuration space.

18.3. Coulomb energies

The total binding energy of a ground state or an excited state derives not only from the nuclear interaction, but the Coulomb interaction of the protons yields a substantial contribution as well. For most shell-model calculations an inert core of closed shells is assumed. The active particles outside the core then are supposed not to affect the total binding energy of the core (i.e. with the inclusion of the Coulomb energy).

The Coulomb energy that is contributed by the protons outside the core depends on the interaction of the active protons with the core protons as well as on their mutual Coulomb interaction. This approach is in close analogy with the treatment of the nuclear part of the interaction.

Experimentally one can determine only Coulomb displacement energies, which represent the difference in binding energy between analogue states in isobaric mass multiplets. These analogue states, having similar intrinsic structure, should have nearly the same total binding energy if the Coulomb interaction between protons were switched off and the proton-neutron mass difference is taken into account. The charge dependence of nuclear forces and the total contribution of several other effects [Auerbach, Hüfner, Kerman and Shakin (1972)] probably have a relatively small influence and are ignored here.

For the investigation of analogue states most theoretical attention has been paid to the calculation of the Coulomb displacement energies, rather than of the total Coulomb energies. The latter cannot be measured anyway. In our present approach we make rather crude approximations for a numerical evaluation of Coulomb energies. The resulting uncertainties in the Coulomb energies should be acceptable, however, if one takes into account the inaccuracy of the nuclear part of the Hamiltonians in use.

We will not try to give an elaborate discussion of the various methods that can be used to estimate Coulomb energies. For a survey of several procedures the reader is referred to the literature (see e.g. [Jänecke (1969)]).

Let us distinguish three different approaches to obtain an estimate of the Coulomb energy. In all of these it is assumed that the active particles do not affect the Coulomb energy of the core.

In the first approach the Coulomb interaction is added to the nuclear Hamiltonian and the total binding energy is determined by the subsequent diagonalization of the total Hamiltonian. This method, although in principle the most appealing one, has not obtained much attention so far. It is difficult to evaluate the single-particle Coulomb energies accurately, i.e. the interaction of each outer-core proton with the core. This difficulty is also due to the Thomas-Ehrman shift (Thomas (1952); Ehrman (1951)], i.e. the critical dependence of the single-particle Coulomb energy on the depth of the single-particle potential.

Secondly one can estimate the Coulomb energy as the expectation value of the Coulomb energy operator for existing wave functions. Since the nuclear part of the interaction is considerably stronger than the Coulomb part, the latter should not affect the wave functions strongly. Assuming, moreover, that the Coulomb energy does not depend strongly on the details of the wave function one could use rather simple model wave functions.

As an example we discuss an expression [DeShalit and Talmi (1963)] derived for protons occupying a single orbit and coupled to lowest seniority. This approximation is found to work very well for sd-shell nuclei [Glaudemans, Wiechers and Brussaard (1967); Halbert, McGrory, Wildenthal and Pandya (1971)]. In this approach the Coulomb energy E_{C} for Z' protons in a given orbit outside closed shells is obtained as the expression

$$E_{\mathrm{C}}(Z') = CZ' + \tfrac{1}{2}Z'(Z'-1)a + [\tfrac{1}{2}Z']b\,, \tag{18.29}$$

where C, a and b are parameters that depend on the orbit in which the protons move and $[\frac{1}{2}Z']$ stands for the largest integer not exceeding $\frac{1}{2}Z'$. The term CZ' describes the interaction of the outer particles with the core; the parameter C is analogous to e_ρ in eq. (3.18) for the nuclear part. The term $\frac{1}{2}Z'(Z'-1)a$ describes the mutual interaction between the Z' active protons as it counts the number of interacting proton pairs; it is assumed that the interaction strength a is independent of the total spin of the two interacting protons. The last term in eq. (18.29) represents a pairing term, since it is associated with the dependence of the Coulomb interaction on the number of $J = 0$ coupled proton pairs. It should be noted that eq. (18.29) is derived for protons in one shell-model orbit. It turns out that the values of the parameters C, a and b are orbit dependent.

From the assumption of charge independent nuclear forces it follows that the binding energy differences between corresponding states in isobaric mass multiplets, such as mirror nuclei, derive mainly from the differences in Coulomb energy and the proton-neutron mass difference. For the Coulomb energy difference of the mirror nuclei ${}_ZA_N$ and ${}_{Z+1}A_{N-1}$ one obtains from eq. (18.29) the result

$$\Delta_1(Z') = E_{\mathrm{C}}(Z'+1) - E_{\mathrm{C}}(Z') = C + Z'a + \tfrac{1}{2}\{1-(-1)^{Z'}\}b\,, \tag{18.30}$$

where the Z' protons outside the core are assumed to occupy one specific orbit. For pairs of nuclei two charge units apart and given by ${}_ZA_N$ and ${}_{Z+2}A_{N-2}$ one obtains for the Coulomb energy difference from eq. (18.29)

$$\Delta_2(Z') = E_C(Z'+2) - E_C(Z') = 2C + (2Z'+1)a + b\,. \tag{18.31}$$

The contribution from the proton-neutron mass difference can be absorbed in the parameter C, since the coefficient of $(M_n - M_p)$ is equal to the number of protons changed into neutrons or *vice versa* and thus it equals the coefficient of C in eqs. (18.30) and (18.31).

The values of the parameters C, a and b can thus be determined from a fit of the binding energy differences of the nuclei ${}_ZA_N - {}_{Z+1}A_{N-1}$ and ${}_ZA_N - {}_{Z+2}A_{N-2}$. An example of such a fit for nuclei in the mass region $A = 17 - 27$ for a $(1d_{5/2})^n$ configuration is given in table 18.1. It is seen that the differences in the binding energies for the members of an isobaric multiplet after correction for Coulomb energies and the proton-neutron mass difference are generally quite small. The average deviation for the ten low-lying states compared is approximately 25 keV. For an extension of this method see [Harchol, Jaffe, Miron, Unna and Zioni (1967)].

The third approach is applicable when the binding energies of analogue states with zero and one active protons can be compared. For example, let us consider isotopes of ${}_{28}$Ni and ${}_{29}$Cu and assume a ${}^{56}_{28}\text{Ni}_{28}$ core. Since the active particles in Ni isotopes are neutrons, the Coulomb energies in Cu isotopes – due to the active protons –

Table 18.1
Coulomb energies for some low-lying states in $A = 17 - 27$ nuclei

Nuclei		J^π	Binding energy difference in MeV	
			experiment [a]	Coulomb energy corrected [b]
${}^{17}_{8}\text{O}_9$	$-\,{}^{17}_{9}\text{F}_8$	$\frac{5}{2}^+$	−3.541	+0.027
${}^{18}_{8}\text{O}_{10}$	$-\,{}^{18}_{10}\text{Ne}_8$	0^+	−7.667	+0.015
${}^{19}_{9}\text{F}_{10}$	$-\,{}^{19}_{10}\text{Ne}_9$	$\frac{5}{2}^+$	−4.021	+0.063
${}^{21}_{10}\text{Ne}_{11}$	$-\,{}^{21}_{11}\text{Na}_{10}$	$\frac{5}{2}^+$	−4.313	+0.009
${}^{22}_{10}\text{Ne}_{12}$	$-\,{}^{22}_{12}\text{Mg}_{10}$	0^+	−9.207	−0.047
${}^{23}_{11}\text{Na}_{12}$	$-\,{}^{23}_{12}\text{Mg}_{11}$	$\frac{5}{2}^+$	−4.850	−0.012
${}^{24}_{11}\text{Na}_{13}$	$-\,{}^{24}_{13}\text{Al}_{11}$	4^+	−9.933	−0.019
${}^{25}_{12}\text{Mg}_{13}$	$-\,{}^{25}_{13}\text{Al}_{12}$	$\frac{5}{2}^+$	−5.062	+0.014
${}^{26}_{12}\text{Mg}_{14}$	$-\,{}^{26}_{14}\text{Si}_{12}$	0^+	−10.632	+0.036
${}^{27}_{13}\text{Al}_{14}$	$-\,{}^{27}_{14}\text{Si}_{13}$	$\frac{5}{2}^+$	−5.591	+0.001

a) For the lowest state of a given J^π taken from the compilation [Wapstra and Gove (1971)]. Only the cases with an error $\leqslant 0.010$ MeV are given.
b) The Coulomb energy differences have been calculated with eqs. (18.30) and (18.31) with $C = -3.568$ MeV, $a = -0.377$ MeV and $b = -0.139$ MeV.

follow directly from the displacement energies of $T = \frac{1}{2}(A - 56)$ analogue states in the Ni and Cu isotopes.

18.4. Spurious states

A nucleus of mass number A should be described by a translation-invariant Hamiltonian

$$H = \sum_{i=1}^{A} T(i) + \sum_{1=i<j}^{A} W(\boldsymbol{r}(i) - \boldsymbol{r}(j); \boldsymbol{\mathfrak{v}}(i) - \boldsymbol{\mathfrak{v}}(j)) \tag{18.32}$$

with $T(i) = p^2(i)/2M$ representing the kinetic energy of a nucleon with mass M. The potential W, describing the nucleon-nucleon interaction, may show in the general case a velocity dependence but must be Galilean invariant, i.e. may depend on the velocity differences $\boldsymbol{\mathfrak{v}}(i) - \boldsymbol{\mathfrak{v}}(j)$ only.

The general many-body problem

$$H\Psi(\boldsymbol{r}(1), ..., \boldsymbol{r}(A)) = E\Psi(\boldsymbol{r}(1), ..., \boldsymbol{r}(A)) \tag{18.33}$$

is insoluble in exact form. In the shell-model approach the interparticle potential W is replaced by a sum of central, single-particle potentials, $\Sigma_i u(\boldsymbol{r}(i))$, that are fixed in space and a residual interaction. Thus the resulting shell-model Hamiltonian is no longer invariant with respect to translations. As a consequence the wave functions that one calculates may contain unphysical components, which are called *spurious*. The latter describe excitations of the centre-of-mass (c.m.) motion of the nucleus that are introduced with the single-particle potentials in the laboratory system. These excitations are of no physical interest and one wishes to know the *intrinsic* excitations of the nuclear system only. A description of the many-particle wave functions in terms of relative coordinates turns out to be unfeasible because of the antisymmetrization requirements of the Pauli exclusion principle.

Let us consider now the single-particle Hamiltonian for the harmonic-oscillator potential

$$H_{\text{s.p.}} = \frac{1}{2M} \sum_{i=1}^{A} \boldsymbol{p}^2(i) + \tfrac{1}{2}M\omega^2 \sum_{i=1}^{A} \boldsymbol{r}^2(i)$$

$$= \frac{1}{2M} \sum_{i=1}^{A} \left(\boldsymbol{p}(i) - \frac{\boldsymbol{P}}{A}\right)^2 + \frac{\boldsymbol{P}^2}{2\mathcal{M}} + \tfrac{1}{2}M\omega^2 \sum_{i=1}^{A} (\boldsymbol{r}(i) - \boldsymbol{R})^2 + \tfrac{1}{2}\mathcal{M}\omega^2 \boldsymbol{R}^2 , \tag{18.34}$$

where M and $\mathcal{M} = AM$ denote the masses of the nucleon and the nucleus, respectively. The vectors

$$\boldsymbol{R} = \frac{1}{A} \sum_{i=1}^{A} \boldsymbol{r}(i) \qquad \text{and} \qquad \boldsymbol{P} = \sum_{i=1}^{A} \boldsymbol{p}(i) \tag{18.35}$$

represent the c.m. position coordinate and momentum, respectively. It is seen that the shell-model Hamiltonian (18.34) consists of two commuting partial Hamiltonians, i.e. a Galilean invariant part

$$H_{\text{rel}} = \frac{1}{2M} \sum_{i=1}^{A} \left(p(i) - \frac{P}{A}\right)^2 + \tfrac{1}{2}M\omega^2 \sum_{i=1}^{A} (r(i) - R)^2 \qquad (18.36)$$

and a purely c.m. part

$$H_{\text{c.m.}} = \frac{P^2}{2\mathcal{M}} + \tfrac{1}{2}\mathcal{M}\omega^2 R^2 \,. \qquad (18.37)$$

The first part, H_{rel}, depends on $3(A-1)$ independent position coordinates and describes the internal degrees of freedom, the excitations of which are of physical interest.

An eigenfunction of the single-particle Hamiltonian

$$H_{\text{s.p.}}\Psi_N = E_N\Psi_N = (N + \tfrac{3}{2}A)\hbar\omega\Psi_N \qquad (18.38)$$

can be expanded in the complete set of product wave functions $\Phi_{\mathcal{N}}(R)\,\phi_{N'}(1, ..., A-1)$ with

$$\mathcal{N} + N' = N \,. \qquad (18.39)$$

Here $\mathcal{N}$ denotes the number of c.m. oscillator quanta and N' the number of intrinsic oscillator quanta, i.e.

$$H_{\text{c.m.}}\Phi_{\mathcal{N}}(R) = (\mathcal{N} + \tfrac{3}{2})\hbar\omega\Phi_{\mathcal{N}}(R) \qquad (18.40)$$

and

$$H_{\text{rel}}\phi_{N'}(1,2,..., A-1) = \{N' + \tfrac{3}{2}(A-1)\}\hbar\omega\phi_{N'}(1,2,..., A-1) \,. \qquad (18.41)$$

This implies that generally a function $\Psi_N(r(1), ..., r(A))$ is a superposition of states of different intrinsic excitation and c.m. energy. For instance, a state of $2\hbar\omega$ excitation ($N = 2$) may contain components (i) of purely $2\hbar\omega$ intrinsic excitation ($\mathcal{N} = 0$), (ii) of $1\hbar\omega$ intrinsic excitation combined with $1\hbar\omega$ spurious motion ($\mathcal{N} = 1$) and (iii) of purely $2\hbar\omega$ spurious excitation ($\mathcal{N} = 2$). Thus the violation of the translational invariance of the Hamiltonian may lead to spurious c.m. motion in the shell-model wave functions. The states Ψ_N with $\mathcal{N} \neq 0$ are referred to as spurious states. Only the intrinsic excitation corresponds to the genuine excitations of the physical system that are observed.

One can try to project the shell-model wave functions onto the space of non-spurious motion. In principle this can be achieved by generating purely spurious states and then by projecting off and renormalizing the wave function. In practice, however, this approach has rather limited applicability because most of the calculations are done in a truncated configuration space, which in general is too small to accommodate the generated spurious states. As a result only the projections of the spurious states onto the model space are obtained. Since the two operations of projecting off the spurious states and projecting onto the model space do not commute, it is not clear how the spurious states must be disposed of.

It is remarked here that the harmonic-oscillator potential is the only potential that permits the partition into a c.m. Hamiltonian and a Hamiltonian for the relative motion. For any other potential, such as e.g. the Saxon-Woods potential, the problem of the removal of spurious c.m. motion is not even well-defined.

For harmonic-oscillator wave functions it can be shown ([Elliott and Skyrme (1955)] that all wave functions with the lowest energy allowed by the Pauli exclusion principle are completely nonspurious. Excitation of one or more particles into higher orbits may then introduce spuriosity.

The harmonic-oscillator Hamiltonian for a particle with mass M can be rewritten in the second-quantization formalism as [Messiah (1965) ch. 12]

$$H = \frac{\boldsymbol{p}^2}{2M} + \tfrac{1}{2}M\omega^2\boldsymbol{r}^2 = \hbar\omega(\boldsymbol{a}^\dagger \cdot \boldsymbol{a} + \tfrac{3}{2}) \tag{18.42}$$

with

$$\boldsymbol{a}^\dagger = \sqrt{\frac{M\omega}{2\hbar}}\,\boldsymbol{r} - \frac{\mathrm{i}}{\sqrt{2M\hbar\omega}}\,\boldsymbol{p}\,, \tag{18.43}$$

$$\boldsymbol{a} = \sqrt{\frac{M\omega}{2\hbar}}\,\boldsymbol{r} + \frac{\mathrm{i}}{\sqrt{2M\hbar\omega}}\,\boldsymbol{p} \tag{18.44}$$

representing the creation and annihilation operators of the oscillator quanta, respectively. The operator to generate $1\hbar\omega$ c.m. excitations for an A-particle system is given by

$$\boldsymbol{A}^\dagger = \sqrt{\frac{\mathcal{M}\omega}{2\hbar}}\,\boldsymbol{R} - \frac{\mathrm{i}}{\sqrt{2\mathcal{M}\hbar\omega}}\,\boldsymbol{P} = \frac{1}{\sqrt{A}}\sum_{k=1}^{A} \boldsymbol{a}^\dagger(k)\,, \tag{18.45}$$

where $\boldsymbol{R}$ and $\boldsymbol{P}$ represent the c.m. coordinate and momentum, respectively. This operator is obviously a vector operator.

Let $|0\hbar\omega; JMTT_z\rangle$ denote a state without any spurious components, then a set of spurious states with $1\hbar\omega$ c.m. energy is given by [Baranger and Lee (1961)]

$$|1\hbar\omega; J'M'TT_z\rangle = \sum_{Mm} \langle JM1m|J'M'\rangle\, A_m^\dagger\, |0\hbar\omega; JMTT_z\rangle \tag{18.46}$$

with m denoting the spherical components of the vector operator $\boldsymbol{A}^\dagger$. Repeated application of the operator $\boldsymbol{A}^\dagger$ leads to spurious states of higher c.m. excitation, i.e. $2\hbar\omega$, etc.

If a state is to be free of spurious excitations it has to yield zero result when acted upon by the annihilation operator $\boldsymbol{A} \equiv (\boldsymbol{A}^\dagger)^\dagger$. Hence a shell-model state $\Psi_{N,JMTT_z}$ of excitation energy $N\hbar\omega$ is completely nonspurious if the equation

$$\boldsymbol{A}|\Psi_{N,JMTT_z}\rangle = 0 \tag{18.47}$$

is satisfied.

Since the operator A transfers a particle to a lower oscillator shell, i.e. $N \rightarrow N-1$, one sees that eq. (18.47) is fulfilled if all harmonic-oscillator single-particle states of lower energy are occupied. The same result was reached by Elliott and Skyme (see above).

It thus follows that, if all active particles outside a closed-shell core are confined to one major shell, no spurious components are present. Examples of such cases are calculations in the 1d2s shell with a closed ^{16}O core or in the 1f2p shell with a closed ^{40}Ca core.

Not all states with one or more particles excited out of a major shell are necessarily spurious. For example, it is seen that none of the $1f_{7/2}(1d_{3/2})^{-1}$ one-particle, one-hole states in ^{40}Ca can be spurious. The vector operator A cannot lower the $1f_{7/2}$ particle to the $1d_{3/2}$ orbit for reasons of angular-momentum conservation, since the angular momenta $\frac{7}{2}$, $\frac{3}{2}$ and 1 cannot form a triangle. The spurious states are to be sought among, e.g., the $1f_{7/2}(1d_{5/2})^{-1}$ and $1f_{5/2}(1d_{3/2})^{-1}$ states of spin $J^{\pi} = 1^{-}$ and isospin $T = 0$, i.e. states generated by the operator $A^{\dagger}$ acting on the nonspurious doubly closed-shell state of ^{40}Ca.

Another example of nonspurious states is given by configurations like $(1d_{3/2})^m$ $(1f_{7/2})^n$ with a closed ^{32}S core or $(2s_{1/2})^l\,(1d_{3/2})^n\,(1f_{7/2})^m$ with ^{28}Si core. Here also the spin of a $1f_{7/2}$ particle has to change by more than one unit in order to be lowered to an avalaible lower oscillator shell.

It is remarked here that when eq. (18.47) is satisfied not only spurious motion of energy $1\hbar\omega$ is absent, but also of energy $2\hbar\omega$ etc.

The spin and isospin of possibly spurious states can be found by application of the operator $A^{\dagger}$ (and $(A^{\dagger})^n$) on all nonspurious states of a nucleus. As in most cases the latter may possess several values of J_0^{π} and T_0, one is usually led to many sets of J^{π}, T values for states with possibly spurious components.

Several methods have been devised to treat the problem of the removal of spurious states, but except for a full 1 $\hbar\omega$ space [French, Halbert, McGrory and Wong (1969)] none of them has been very successful.

18.5. The particle-vibrator model

In this section we briefly discuss the particle-vibrator model, which combines the single-particle and the vibrational model. Most of the methods and techniques discussed in the previous chapters can be applied also to this model.

The particle-vibrator model is useful in particular in the rare-earth region (just below $A \cong 150$) and in the neighbourhood of ^{208}Pb, where the doubly even nuclei show the characteristics of vibrational spectra. Such vibrations are in fact density fluctuations that can be interpreted microscopically as many-particle, many-hole excitations. For a straightforward description in terms of the shell model too many active orbits should be taken into account, however. The description in terms of the particle-vibrator model is based upon an analogy with the classical vibration of a liquid drop.

The shape of a liquid drop can be given by its radial coordinate $R(\theta, \phi)$, defined by the position where the constant density drops off to zero, as a function of the angle coordinates θ, ϕ. It is convenient to use the multipole expansion

$$R(\theta, \phi) = R_0 \{1 + \sum_{LM} \overset{*}{\alpha}_{LM} Y_{LM}(\theta, \phi)\} + O(\alpha^2) , \tag{18.48}$$

where the complex deformation parameters α_{LM} describe quantitatively the deviation from spherical symmetry. Vibrations of the surface imply that the parameters α_{LM} are time dependent. The spherical equilibrium shape of the liquid drop is given by the radius R_0. Since the radial coordinate $R(\theta, \phi)$ is real, the expansion coefficients obey the relation $\overset{*}{\alpha}_{LM} = (-1)^M \alpha_{L-M}$.

Unlike a liquid drop a nucleus does not possess a well defined surface, however, since the nuclear density drops off gradually with increasing distance from the center. Let us assume that eq. (18.48) can be used to describe the nuclear density oscillations, where $R(\theta, \phi)$ denotes a surface of constant density, for example 90% of the density at the center. The nuclear vibrations represent a collective motion in which many nucleons participate coherently. In the unified model [Bohr and Mottelson (1952); Bohr (1953)] the collective motion of the vibrating core is coupled with the independent-particle motion of one or more extra nucleons or holes. The equipotential surfaces for the single particles in the field caused by the vibrating core are supposed to follow the density vibrations adiabatically, i.e. they should be described also by eq. (18.48). Thus the potential for the vibrating field, $\mathcal{U}$, at the position r, θ, ϕ is given by the value that the potential for the spherical equilibrium shape, U, assumes at the radius $r/\{1 + \Sigma_{LM} \overset{*}{\alpha}_{LM} Y_{LM}(\theta, \phi)\}$. This leads to the expansion

$$\mathcal{U}(r, \theta, \phi) = U\left(\frac{r}{1 + \sum_{LM} \overset{*}{\alpha}_{LM} Y_{LM}(\theta, \phi)}\right)$$

$$= U(r) - r\,\frac{\mathrm{d}U(r)}{\mathrm{d}r} \sum_{LM} \overset{*}{\alpha}_{LM} Y_{LM}(\theta, \phi) + O(\alpha^2) . \tag{18.49}$$

From this equation it is seen that an extra term enters the single-particle potential. This term, denoted by H_{int}, describes the particle-vibration interaction. Thus one has

$$H_{\mathrm{int}} = -k(r) \sum_{LM} \overset{*}{\alpha}_{LM} Y_{LM}(\theta, \phi) \tag{18.50}$$

with

$$k(r) = r\,\frac{\mathrm{d}U(r)}{\mathrm{d}r} , \tag{18.51}$$

if quadratic and higher-order terms in α_{LM} are neglected.

We shall consider here the case of weak and intermediate coupling where H_{int} can be treated as a perturbation in a basis that is diagonal in the single-particle motion with Hamiltonian $H_{\text{s.p.}}$ as well as in the collective motion described by the Hamiltonian H_{coll}. The total Hamiltonian then is written as

$$H = H_{\text{s.p.}} + H_{\text{coll}} + H_{\text{int}} \,. \tag{18.52}$$

The single-particle motion of the particle outside the vibrating core is described by

$$H_{\text{s.p.}} = \frac{p^2}{2M} + U(r) \,, \tag{18.53}$$

where $U(r)$ denotes the shell-model potential.

For the construction of the collective Hamiltonian, H_{coll}, the deformation parameters α_{LM} and their time derivatives $\dot{\alpha}_{LM}$ are considered as dynamical variables. The former play the role of position coordinates and the latter the role of velocities. Thus the small-amplitude vibrations of the collective oscillations of the core are associated with a potential energy

$$V = \tfrac{1}{2} \sum_{LM} C_L |\alpha_{LM}|^2 \tag{18.54}$$

and a kinetic energy

$$T = \tfrac{1}{2} \sum_{LM} B_L |\dot{\alpha}_{LM}|^2 \,. \tag{18.55}$$

The constants B_L and C_L represent the inertial parameter of the collective mass transport and the stiffness parameter for the nuclear surface, respectively.

Quantization of the vibrational motion is achieved by introducing the momentum coordinates [Bohr and Mottelson (1975) ch. 6; Eisenberg and Greiner (1970) vol. 1 ch. 3]

$$\pi_{LM} = \frac{\partial T}{\partial \dot{\alpha}_{LM}} = B_L \dot{\alpha}^{\dagger}_{LM} \,, \tag{18.56}$$

that must obey the commutation relations

$$[\alpha_{LM}, \alpha_{L'M'}] = 0 \,, \qquad [\pi_{LM}, \pi_{L'M'}] = 0 \,,$$

$$[\alpha_{LM}, \pi_{L'M'}] = i\hbar \delta_{LL'} \delta_{MM'} \,. \tag{18.57}$$

The collective Hamiltonian of the nuclear surface now, assumes the form

$$H_{\text{coll}} = T + V = \sum_{LM} \left\{ \frac{1}{2B_L} |\pi_{LM}|^2 + \tfrac{1}{2} C_L |\alpha_{LM}|^2 \right\} \,, \tag{18.58}$$

which represents a set of harmonic oscillators with frequencies

$$\omega_L = \sqrt{\frac{C_L}{B_L}} . \tag{18.59}$$

Defining the boson creation and annihilation operators

$$b^\dagger_{LM} = \sqrt{\frac{C_L}{2\hbar\omega_L}} \left\{ \alpha_{LM} - \frac{\mathrm{i}\omega_L}{C_L} (-1)^M \pi_{L-M} \right\} , \tag{18.60a}$$

$$b_{LM} = \sqrt{\frac{C_L}{2\hbar\omega_L}} \left\{ (-1)^M \alpha_{L-M} + \frac{\mathrm{i}\omega_L}{C_L} \pi_{LM} \right\} , \tag{18.60b}$$

one can rewrite the Hamiltonian (18.58) as

$$H_{\text{coll}} = \sum_{LM} \hbar\omega_L \{ b^\dagger_{LM} b_{LM} + \tfrac{1}{2} \} . \tag{18.61}$$

One can verify with eqs. (18.57) and (18.60) that the operators $b^\dagger_{LM}$ and b_{LM} obey boson commutation relations

$$[b^\dagger_{LM}, b^\dagger_{L'M'}] = 0 , \qquad [b_{LM}, b_{L'M'}] = 0 ,$$

$$[b_{LM}, b^\dagger_{L'M'}] = \delta_{LL'} \delta_{MM'} . \tag{18.62}$$

It then follows that for the commutation relations with the Hamiltonian one has

$$[H_{\text{coll}}, b^\dagger_{LM}] = \hbar\omega_L b^\dagger_{LM} , \tag{18.63}$$

$$[H_{\text{coll}}, b_{LM}] = -\hbar\omega_L b_{LM} . \tag{18.64}$$

Let N_L denote the number of bosons of multipolarity 2^L, then the collective ground state can be denoted by $|N = 0\rangle$ with $N = \Sigma_L N_L$. This state obeys the equation

$$b_{LM} |N = 0\rangle = 0 \qquad \text{for all } L, M . \tag{18.65}$$

Hence one finds from eq. (18.61) the relation

$$H_{\text{coll}} |N = 0\rangle = \tfrac{1}{2} \sum_L \hbar\omega_L (2L + 1) |N = 0\rangle = E_0 |N = 0\rangle . \tag{18.66}$$

The quantity $E_0 = \frac{1}{2} \Sigma_L \hbar\omega_L (2L + 1)$ on the right-hand side of eq. (18.66) represents the zero-point energy of the harmonic oscillator. By the use of the creation operators $b^\dagger_{LM}$ one can now construct states of one or more phonons, i.e. oscillator quanta,

$$H_{\text{coll}}\, b^\dagger_{LM} |N = 0\rangle = b^\dagger_{LM} H_{\text{coll}} |N = 0\rangle + [H_{\text{coll}}, b^\dagger_{LM}]\, |N = 0\rangle$$

$$= (E_0 + \hbar\omega_L)\, b^\dagger_{LM} |N = 0\rangle . \tag{18.67}$$

Similarly one can construct more-phonon states by successive applications of operators $b_{LM}^\dagger$. As each phonon is characterized by its angular momentum L, one can construct many-phonon states of well-defined total angular momentum with the use of Clebsch-Gordan coefficients. For example, for two quadrupole phonons one obtains (the factor $\sqrt{\frac{1}{2}}$ is a normalization factor)

$$|N_2 = 2; L, M\rangle = \sqrt{\tfrac{1}{2}} \sum_{M'M''} \langle 2\,M'2\,M''|LM\rangle\, b_{2M'}^\dagger\, b_{2M''}^\dagger |N=0\rangle\,. \tag{18.68}$$

As the phonons are bosons the states must be completely symmetric. This requirement will rule out certain total angular momenta, as can be seen in fig. 18.5 where the lower end of the spectrum for quadrupole and octopole phonons is shown. For $N_2 = 2$ the nonappearance of states with L = odd follows immediately from the symmetry properties of the Clebsch-Gordan coefficients. For $N_2 \geqslant 3$ it is more complicated to derive the allowed L values [Hecht (1964)]. The symmetric N_L-phonon states can be constructed by the aid of boson coefficients of fractional parentage [Bayman and Lande (1966)].

The interaction term given in eq. (18.50) can also be expressed in terms of the operators $b_{LM}^\dagger$ and b_{LM} as

$$H_{\text{int}} = -\sum_{LM} \sqrt{\frac{\hbar\omega_L}{2C_L}}\; k(r)\; \{(-1)^M b_{L-M}^\dagger + b_{LM}\}\; Y_{LM}(\theta,\phi)\,. \tag{18.69}$$

For a determination of the eigenfunctions and eigenvalues of the total Hamiltonian, given in eq. (18.52), the interaction H_{int} is considered as a perturbation in the weak- and intermediate-coupling schemes. The calculation is performed in a basis of unperturbed wave functions that are eigenfunctions of $H_{\text{s.p.}} + H_{\text{coll}}$. For the calculation one needs the matrix elements of H_{int} between the unperturbed states.

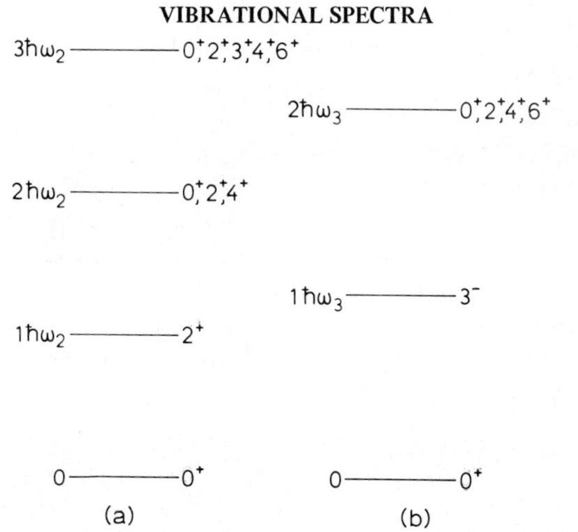

Fig. 18.5. Spectra for quadrupole (a) and octopole (b) vibrations.

Let us consider the case of one odd nucleon outside a vibrating even-even core. The wave functions then are expanded in the basis

$$|j, NR; IM\rangle = \sum_{m_j M_R} \langle j m_j R M_R | IM\rangle | j m_j\rangle | R M_R\rangle\,, \tag{18.70}$$

where the single-particle state of angular momentum j is coupled with the N-phonon state of the core with total angular momentum R to give a total angular momentum I and projection M along the z-axis. The matrix elements of H_{int} in this basis contain radial integrals of $k(r)$ between single-particle states $|jm_j\rangle$. Rather than evaluate all these radial integrals, we shall use one radial average

$$k = \langle k(r)\rangle \tag{18.71}$$

that is considered as a parameter to be fitted to the experimental data.

Eq. (18.69) can be rewritten as

$$H_{\text{int}} = -\sum_{LM} \sqrt{\frac{\pi}{2L+1}}\; \xi_L \hbar\omega_L \{(-1)^M b^\dagger_{L-M} + b_{LM}\}\, Y_{LM}(\theta, \phi)\,, \tag{18.72}$$

where the dimensionless parameters

$$\xi_L = k \sqrt{\frac{2L+1}{2\pi\hbar\omega_L C_L}} \tag{18.73}$$

describe the interaction strengths.

In general the quadrupole vibrations, i.e. $L = 2$, are the most important. (The dipole vibration, i.e. $L = 1$, is equivalent in lowest order to a displacement of the centre of gravity and hence does not represent an intrinsic excitation of the nucleus.) We shall restrict ourselves to the case of quadrupole phonons only; the extension to include higher multipolarities, e.g. octopole phonons, is straightforward.

Since the parameter ξ_2 measures the order of magnitude of the ratio of the interaction energy and the phonon energy, i.e. ξ_2 = order $[\langle H_{\text{int}}\rangle/\hbar\omega_2]$, it is worthwhile to evaluate eq. (18.73) for $L = 2$. For a harmonic-oscillator potential $U(r)$ one can make the estimate (cf. eq. (18.51)) $\langle k(r)\rangle = 2\langle U(r)\rangle \approx 40$ MeV. For a Saxon-Woods potential one finds in the mass region $A \approx 130$ an average $\langle k(r)\rangle \approx 50$ MeV [Vanden Berghe and Heyde (1971)]. Substituting the empirical values $\hbar\omega_2 \approx 1$ MeV and $C_2 \approx 100$–1000 MeV (for nuclei near major-shell closures larger values of C_2 apply), one finds for the coupling parameter the estimate $\xi_2 \gtrsim 1$, which indicates that weak or intermediate coupling applies. The calculations will give fitted values $1 \lesssim \xi_2 \lesssim 4$. The only off-diagonal matrix elements (i.e. in j, N and R) of the total Hamiltonian (18.52) in the representation (18.70) derive from the interaction part H_{int} (cf. eqs. (A.3.d7) and (A.3.e5),

$$\langle j', N_2'R'; IM|H_{\text{int}}|j, N_2R; IM\rangle = -\tfrac{1}{2}\xi_2\hbar\omega_2(-1)^{I+1/2}\sqrt{(2j+1)(2j'+1)}$$

$$\times \begin{Bmatrix} j & R & I \\ R' & j' & 2 \end{Bmatrix} \begin{pmatrix} j' & 2 & j \\ -\frac{1}{2} & 0 & \frac{1}{2} \end{pmatrix} \{(-1)^{R'}\langle N'R'\|b_2^\dagger\|NR\rangle + (-1)^R\langle NR\|b_2^\dagger\|N'R'\rangle\}\, \delta^{\text{even}}_{l+l'}\,. \tag{18.74}$$

The reduced matrix elements of the creation operator $b^\dagger_{LM}$ are defined according to the customary Wigner-Eckart theorem (eq. (A.3.a15). They can be regarded as boson coefficients of fractional parentage. Numerical values for up to three quadrupole phonons are given in table 18.2. It should be noted that other phase conventions and normalization for these matrix elements can be found in the literature. As soon as four or more quadrupole bosons are involved the total angular momentum R is no longer sufficient to specify the many-boson state uniquely [Jahn (1951); Bayman and Lande (1966)]. The collective and single-particle parts of the total Hamiltonian yield the matrix elements

$$\langle j', N_2'R'; IM|H_{\text{s.p.}} + H_{\text{coll}}|j, N_2R; IM\rangle = \hbar\omega_2\left\{\frac{e_j}{\hbar\omega_2} + N_2 + \tfrac{5}{2}\right\}\delta_{N_2'N_2}\,\delta_{R'R}\,\delta_{j'j}\,,$$

where e_j represents the single-particle energy of the odd nucleon. (18.75)

Diagonalization and fitting procedure. Expanding for odd-A nuclei the eigenfunction at an energy $E^{(\alpha)}$ as

$$|E^{(\alpha)}; IM\rangle = \sum_{jNR} C_\alpha(j, N_2R; I)|j, N_2R; IM\rangle\,, \tag{18.76}$$

one can write the Schrödinger equation $H|E^{(\alpha)}; IM\rangle = E^{(\alpha)}|E^{(\alpha)}; IM\rangle$ as

$$\sum_{jNR} \langle j', N_2'R'; IM|H|j, N_2R; IM\rangle\, C_\alpha(j, N_2R; I) = E^{(\alpha)} C_\alpha(j', N_2'R'; I)\,. \tag{18.77}$$

Table 18.2

Numerical values of the reduced matrix elements $\langle N_2'R' \| b_2^\dagger \| N_2R\rangle$ of the boson creation operator $b^\dagger_{2M}$. Phases and normalization are taken according to the Wigner-Eckart theorem, defined in eq. (A.3.a15).

		$N_2 = 0$, $R = 0$
$N_2' = 1$	$R' = 2$	$\sqrt{5}$

		$N_2 = 1$, $R = 2$
$N_2' = 1$	$R' = 0$	$\sqrt{2}$
	2	$\sqrt{10}$
	4	$\sqrt{18}$

		$N_2 = 2$: $R=0$	2	4
$N_2' = 3$	$R' = 0$		$\sqrt{3}$	
	2	$\sqrt{7}$	$\sqrt{\frac{20}{7}}$	$\sqrt{\frac{36}{7}}$
	3		$\sqrt{15}$	$-\sqrt{6}$
	4		$\sqrt{\frac{99}{7}}$	$\sqrt{\frac{90}{7}}$
	6			$\sqrt{39}$

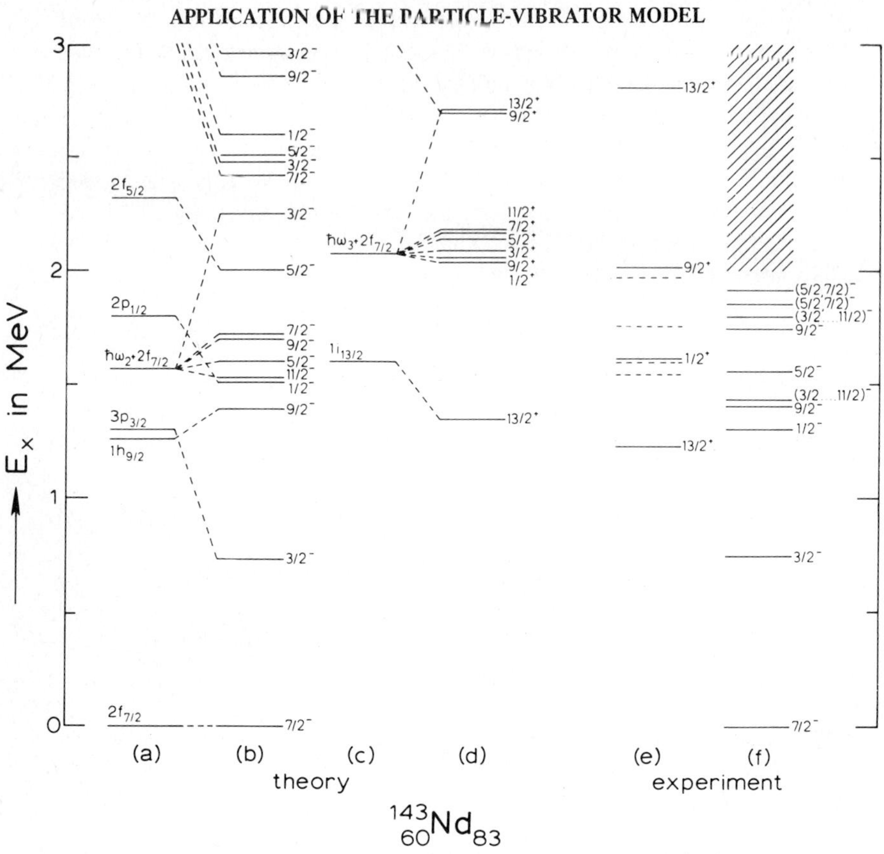

Fig. 18.6. Calculated and experimental spectra of $^{143}_{60}Nd_{83}$. The single-particle motion of a neutron ($2f_{7/2}$, $1h_{9/2}$, $3p_{3/2}$, $2p_{1/2}$, $2f_{5/2}$ orbits) is coupled with quadrupole ($N_2 \leqslant 3$) and octopole ($N_3 \leqslant 2$) vibrations of the ^{142}Nd core. In columns (a) and (c) the unperturbed energies are given, whereas columns (b) and (d) represent the results with the residual interaction taken into account. The parameters are given by: $\xi_2 = 1.40, \hbar\omega_2 = 1.57$ MeV, $\xi_3 = 1.40$ and $\hbar\omega_3 = 2.08$ MeV. The single-particle energies can be read off from the figure [Heyde (1976)]. The experimental data are taken from [Veefkind, Spaargaren, Blok and Heyde (1975)]. The dashed levels of positive parity, which are observed in (d,t) reactions, represent hole states in the $N = 82$ core and thus are not reproduced in the model under consideration.

With the use of eqs. (18.74) and (18.75) all matrix elements of eq. (18.77) can be expressed in terms of the quantities $\xi_2, \hbar\omega_2$ and $e_j/\hbar\omega_2$, which are to be determined by the requirement that the eigenvalues $E^{(\alpha)}$ be a best fit to the experimental spectra, i.e. the level spacings of each nucleus. Again this best fit can be reached with an iterative least-squares procedure. The zeroth-order value of the parameter $\hbar\omega_2$ that is required to start the iteration procedure for an odd-A nucleus can be obtained from the vibrational spectrum of the neighbouring doubly even nuclei. In general it turns out that the final best value of $\hbar\omega_2$ is in between the values of the two neighbouring doubly even nuclei. For a determination of the spectrum of a nucleus it suffices to know the relative single-particle energies, i.e. the differences

$$\Delta_{jj'} \equiv e_j/\hbar\omega_2 - e_{j'}/\hbar\omega_2 \,, \tag{18.78}$$

which implies that the use of n single-particle states in the model space requires the use of $n-1$ parameters $\Delta_{jj'}$.

In fig. 18.6 the results of a calculation on ^{143}Nd are presented. For this calculation quadrupole and octopole vibrations are taken into account.

Doubly odd nuclei. The extension of this model to doubly odd nuclei is straightforward. The description of the interaction of the two odd nucleons with the vibrating core now requires two strength parameters ($\xi_{2\mathrm{p}}$ for the extra proton and $\xi_{2\mathrm{n}}$ for the extra neutron)

$$H_{\mathrm{int}} = -\sqrt{\frac{\pi}{5}}\,\hbar\omega_2 \sum_{\substack{M\\ i=\mathrm{p,n}}} \xi_{2i}\{b_{2M} + (-1)^M b^\dagger_{2-M}\}\, Y_{2M}(\theta(i), \phi(i)) \,. \tag{18.79}$$

Expanding the wave functions as

$$|E^{(\alpha)}; IM\rangle = \sum_{\substack{j_\mathrm{p} j_\mathrm{n} J\\ N_2 R}} C_\alpha((j_\mathrm{p} j_\mathrm{n})J, N_2 R; I)\, |(j_\mathrm{p} j_\mathrm{n})J, N_2 R; IM\rangle \tag{18.80}$$

with

$$|(j_\mathrm{p} j_\mathrm{n})J, N_2 R; IM\rangle = \sum_{\substack{M_J M_R\\ m_\mathrm{p} m_\mathrm{n}}} \langle JM_J RM_R|IM\rangle \langle j_\mathrm{p} m_\mathrm{p} j_\mathrm{n} m_\mathrm{n}|JM_J\rangle\, |j_\mathrm{p} m_\mathrm{p}\rangle |j_\mathrm{n} m_\mathrm{n}\rangle |N_2 R M_R\rangle \,, \tag{18.81}$$

one obtains for the interaction matrix elements

$$\begin{aligned}
&\langle (j'_\mathrm{p} j'_\mathrm{n})J', N'_2 R'; IM|H_{\mathrm{int}}|(j_\mathrm{p} j_\mathrm{n})J, N_2 R; IM\rangle \\
&= -\tfrac{1}{2}(-1)^I \sqrt{(2J'+1)(2J+1)} \begin{Bmatrix} I & R' & J' \\ 2 & J & R \end{Bmatrix} \\
&\times \Bigg\{ \xi_\mathrm{p}(-1)^{j'_\mathrm{p}+j_\mathrm{p}+j_\mathrm{n}-1/2} \begin{Bmatrix} j'_\mathrm{p} & j_\mathrm{p} & 2 \\ J & J' & j_\mathrm{n} \end{Bmatrix} \sqrt{(2j'_\mathrm{p}+1)(2j_\mathrm{p}+1)} \begin{pmatrix} j'_\mathrm{p} & 2 & j_\mathrm{p} \\ -\frac{1}{2} & 0 & \frac{1}{2} \end{pmatrix} \delta^{\mathrm{even}}_{l'_\mathrm{p}+l_\mathrm{p}}\, \delta_{j'_\mathrm{n} j_\mathrm{n}} \\
&+ \xi_\mathrm{n}(-1)^{J'+J+j_\mathrm{p}+1/2} \begin{Bmatrix} j'_\mathrm{n} & j_\mathrm{n} & 2 \\ J & J' & j_\mathrm{p} \end{Bmatrix} \sqrt{(2j'_\mathrm{n}+1)(2j_\mathrm{n}+1)} \begin{pmatrix} j'_\mathrm{n} & 2 & j_\mathrm{n} \\ -\frac{1}{2} & 0 & \frac{1}{2} \end{pmatrix} \delta^{\mathrm{even}}_{l'_\mathrm{n}+l_\mathrm{n}}\, \delta_{j'_\mathrm{p} j_\mathrm{p}} \Bigg\}
\end{aligned}$$

$$\times \{(-1)^R \langle N_2 R \| b_2^\dagger \| N_2' R' \rangle + (-1)^{R'} \langle N_2' R' \| b_2^\dagger \| N_2 R \rangle\} . \tag{18.82}$$

The single-particle part of the total Hamiltonian, given in eq. (18.52), for the present case consists of two shell-model Hamiltonians, i.e. one for the extra proton and one for the extra neutron, and a residual interaction for the two extra nucleons.

It is not immediately clear which effective interaction should be taken for the latter, in particular since for the heavy nuclei the extra proton and the extra neutron may be in single-particle orbits far apart.

One can use a phenomenological interaction, e.g. of Gaussian radial dependence, characterized by range and strength (cf. eq. (6.11)). A particular choice for the exchange mixture can be justified by the agreement of the resulting spectrum with experiment.

Dynamical properties. With the wave functions obtained one can calculate electromagnetic moments and transition rates and spectroscopic factors for a comparison with the experimental data. The operators describing the moments and transition rates for the single-particle components in the particle-vibrator model are the same, of course, as those given in chapters 9 and 10 for the single-particle motion. All one still needs are the operators for the collective core parts.

For a uniform charge density of the oscillating nucleus $\rho_{\mathrm{ch}}(\boldsymbol{r})$ one obtains for the electric 2^L pole operator (cf. eq. (9.32))

$$O(\mathcal{E}LM) = \int \rho_{\mathrm{ch}}(\boldsymbol{r})\, r^L\, Y_{LM}(\hat{\boldsymbol{r}})\, \mathrm{d}\boldsymbol{r}$$

$$= Ze(\tfrac{4}{3}\pi R_0^3)^{-1} \int \mathrm{d}\hat{\boldsymbol{r}} \int_0^{R_0(1+\Sigma_{lm}\alpha_{lm}^* Y_{lm}(\hat{\boldsymbol{r}}))} r^2 \mathrm{d}r\, r^L\, Y_{LM}(\hat{\boldsymbol{r}})$$

$$= \frac{3}{4\pi} ZeR_0^L \alpha_{LM} = \frac{3}{4\pi} ZeR_0^L \sqrt{\frac{\hbar\omega_L}{2C_L}}\, \{b_{LM}^\dagger + (-1)^M b_{L-M}\} , \tag{18.83}$$

where eqs. (18.60) have been used to introduce the phonon annihilation and creation operators. Quantities of second or higher order in the deformation parameter α_{LM} have been neglected. The operators $b_{LM}^\dagger$ and b_{LM} connect states that differ in exactly one phonon. Electric multipole moments are given by the diagonal matrix elements of the operator in eq. (18.83). Thus it is seen that pure N_L-phonon vibrational states do not possess electric multipole moments, which is not unexpected since we have taken the nuclei to oscillate about a *spherical* equilibrium shape. However, as soon as a particular state contains N_L-phonon and (N_L+1)-phonon components, as happens in the particle-vibrator model because of the coupling with the single-particle motion, one can expect contributions from the vibrating core to the electric multipole moments. It is pointed out that for the dipole ($L = 1$) and quadrupole ($L = 2$) cases, the conventional normalization of the operators implies that the expression (18.83) still must be multiplied by a factor $\sqrt{\frac{4}{3}\pi}$ or $\sqrt{\frac{16}{5}\pi}$, respectively (cf. discussion of eqs. (11.13) and (11.21)).

The electric multipole operator for the single-particle contribution is the same as was given in eq. (9.35). Since here one deals with heavier nuclei the c.m. correction that was discussed in sect. 9.3 is even smaller than for nuclei in the sd shell and thus may be safely neglected for electric quadrupole transitions and moments. The use of effective charges is still necessary to account for the processes that are not taken into account explicitly, in particular the polarization of the vibrating core.

The operator for magnetic multipole moments of vibrating nuclei can be derived if one assumes irrotational flow in the nucleus. In analogy with eq. (9.38) one has for the magnetic 2^L pole operator

$$O_R(\mathcal{M}LM) = \frac{e\hbar}{2Mc}\,\frac{2}{L+1}\,g_R \int \mathrm{d}\boldsymbol{r}\,\boldsymbol{R}(\boldsymbol{r})\cdot\nabla r^L Y_{LM}(\hat{r})\,, \tag{18.84}$$

where

$$\boldsymbol{R}(\boldsymbol{r}) = \rho(\boldsymbol{r})\,\boldsymbol{r}\times\boldsymbol{v} \tag{18.85}$$

represents the density of angular momentum of the nuclear motion, and g_R denotes the corresponding g-factor. For irrotational flow ($\nabla\times\boldsymbol{v} = 0$) of the incompressible nuclear fluid ($\nabla\cdot\boldsymbol{v} = 0$), the magnetic 2^L pole operator can be reduced to

$$\begin{aligned} O_R(\mathcal{M}LM) = {} & \frac{e\hbar}{2Mci}\,g_R R_0^{L-1}\sqrt{L(2L+1)(2L-1)/4\pi}\,(L+1)^{-1} \\ & \times \sum_{L'L''} \sqrt{L'(L'+1)}\,(2L'+1)(-1)^{L''}\,[\boldsymbol{\alpha}_{L''}\times\boldsymbol{\pi}^{\dagger}_{L'}]^L_M \\ & \times \langle L',0,L-1,0|L'',0\rangle \begin{Bmatrix} L & L'' & L' \\ L' & 1 & L-1 \end{Bmatrix}. \end{aligned} \tag{18.86}$$

With the use of eqs. (18.60) the operators $\alpha_{L''M''}$ and $\pi^{\dagger}_{L'M'}$ can be expressed in terms of the phonon creation and annihilation operators. The square brackets $[..\times..]^L_M$ denote angular-momentum coupling to L, M. The summation covers the vibrational multipolarities L' and L'' that are taken into account. For the magnetic dipole case ($L = 1$) the operator (18.84) assumes a particularly simple form. Applying eq. (A.2.23) one obtains

$$O_R(\mathcal{M}1M) = \frac{e\hbar}{2Mc}\,g_R R_M\,, \tag{18.87}$$

where the conventional normalization for $\mathcal{M}1$ moments has been used, i.e. an extra factor $\sqrt{\frac{4}{3}\pi}$ added to eq. (18.84).

The magnetic multipole operator for the single-particle contribution is again the same as was given in eq. (9.38). Effective g-factors may be necessary to account for the truncation of the configuration space. For a calculation of $\mathcal{E}2$ and $\mathcal{M}1$ moments and transitions one now has to calculate the matrix elements of the corresponding operators on the basis functions of the particle-vibrator model. Their evaluation requires the standard Racah techniques for angular-momentum recoupling. The somewhat lengthy results are not given here, but the reader is referred to [Heyde and Brussaard (1967); Vanden Berghe and Heyde (1971)] for the explicit expressions for the $\mathcal{E}2$ and $\mathcal{M}1$ cases.

APPENDIX A

A.1. Coupling coefficients

(a) Clebsch-Gordan coefficients and 3-j symbols

Only some frequently used relations for Clebsch-Gordan coefficients and 3-*j* symbols are given here. For an extensive treatment the reader is referred to e.g. [Condon and Shortly (1953); Racah (1942); Edmonds (1957)].

Let $\phi_{j_a m_a}$ be an eigenfunction of the angular-momentum operators $\boldsymbol{j}_a^2$ and j_{az} and similarly $\phi_{j_b m_b}$ that of $\boldsymbol{j}_b^2$ and j_{bz}. It is assumed that the operators $\boldsymbol{j}_a$ and $\boldsymbol{j}_b$ commute, as is the case when they refer to *different* particles or *independent* angular coordinates of the same particle (e.g. orbital angular momentum and intrinsic spin). It then follows that also the sum $\boldsymbol{J} = \boldsymbol{j}_a + \boldsymbol{j}_b$ satisfies the commutation relations of angular momentum and rightly may be called the total angular momentum of the composite system. For the coupling of two spherical harmonics that both depend on the coordinates in one and the same space, the appropriate expressions are given in eqs. (A.2.5) and (A.2.7). For $\Phi_{JM}(j_a j_b)$ being an eigenfunction of $\boldsymbol{J}^2$ and J_z, one may write the expansion

$$\Phi_{JM}(j_a j_b) = \sum_{m_a m_b} \langle j_a m_a j_b m_b | JM \rangle \, \phi_{j_a m_a} \phi_{j_b m_b} \qquad \text{with } m_a + m_b = M . \qquad \text{(A.1.a1)}$$

The amplitudes $\langle j_a m_a j_b m_b | JM \rangle$ are called Clebsch-Gordan coefficients, vector-coupling coefficients or Wigner coefficients.

Important symmetry properties of the Clebsch-Gordan coefficients are given by

$$\begin{aligned} \langle j_a m_a j_b m_b | JM \rangle &= (-1)^{j_a + j_b - J} \langle j_b m_b j_a m_a | JM \rangle \\ &= (-1)^{j_a + j_b - J} \langle j_a - m_a j_b - m_b | J - M \rangle , \end{aligned} \qquad \text{(A.1.a2)}$$

which enable us to change the coupling order of two angular momenta or to change the sign of all three projection quantum numbers. Clebsch-Gordan coefficients are real and satisfy the orthonormality conditions

$$\sum_{JM} \langle j_a m_a j_b m_b | JM \rangle \langle j_a m_a' j_b m_b' | JM \rangle = \delta_{m_a m_a'} \delta_{m_b m_b'} , \qquad \text{(A.1.a3)}$$

$$\sum_{m_a m_b} \langle j_a m_a j_b m_b | JM \rangle \langle j_a m_a j_b m_b | J' M' \rangle = \delta_{JJ'} \delta_{MM'} . \qquad \text{(A.1.a4)}$$

Of course, the coefficient $\langle j_a m_a j_b m_b | JM \rangle$ vanishes unless the three angular momenta involved can form a triangle. This condition can be written formally as $\Delta(j_a j_b J)$, which implies also $m_a + m_b = M$. Using eqs. (A.1.a3) and (A.1.a4) we can invert eq. (A.1.a1)

$$\phi_{j_a m_a} \phi_{j_b m_b} = \sum_{JM} \langle j_a m_a j_b m_b | JM \rangle \, \Phi_{JM}(j_a j_b) \, . \tag{A.1.a5}$$

Instead of the Clebsch-Gordan coefficients, one can also use the Wigner 3-j symbols, which are very symmetric in their labels.

The Clebsch-Gordan coefficients are related to the 3-j symbols by the equation

$$\langle j_a m_a j_b m_b | JM \rangle = (-1)^{j_a - j_b + M} \sqrt{2J+1} \begin{pmatrix} j_a & j_b & J \\ m_a & m_b & -M \end{pmatrix}, \tag{A.1.a6}$$

where the appearance of $-M$ in the 3-j symbol should be noted, i.e. the lower three indices of a 3-j symbol must add up to zero.

The symmetry properties of Clebsch-Gordan coefficients can be derived from those of the 3-j symbols. The latter can be simply summarized by

$$\begin{pmatrix} j_a & j_b & j_c \\ m_a & m_b & m_c \end{pmatrix} = C \begin{pmatrix} j_p & j_q & j_r \\ m_p & m_q & m_r \end{pmatrix}, \tag{A.1.a7}$$

(i) with $C = +1$ when columns p, q, r are an even permutation of columns a, b, c;

(ii) with $C = (-1)^{j_a + j_b + J}$ when columns p, q, r are an odd permutation of columns a, b, c;

(iii) with $C = (-1)^{j_a + j_b + J}$ when all three projection quantum numbers change sign, i.e. $m_p, m_q, m_r = -m_a, -m_b, -m_c$.

The orthogonality of 3-j symbols is expressed by the relations (cf. eqs. (A.1.a3) and (A.1.a4))

$$\sum_{JM} (2J+1) \begin{pmatrix} j_a & j_b & J \\ m_a & m_b & M \end{pmatrix} \begin{pmatrix} j_a & j_b & J \\ m_a' & m_b' & M \end{pmatrix} = \delta_{m_a m_a'} \delta_{m_b m_b'} \, , \tag{A.1.a8}$$

$$\sum_{m_a m_b} \begin{pmatrix} j_a & j_b & J \\ m_a & m_b & M \end{pmatrix} \begin{pmatrix} j_a & j_b & J' \\ m_a & m_b & M' \end{pmatrix} = \frac{1}{2J+1} \delta_{JJ'} \delta_{MM'} \, . \tag{A.1.a9}$$

Some frequently used coefficients are given by the explicit expressions

$$\langle j m j' m' | 00 \rangle = \frac{(-1)^{j-m}}{\sqrt{2j+1}} \, \delta_{jj'} \delta_{m-m'} \, , \tag{A.1.a10}$$

$$\begin{pmatrix} j & 1 & j \\ -m & 0 & m' \end{pmatrix} = (-1)^{j-m} \frac{m}{\sqrt{j(2j+1)(j+1)}} \, \delta_{mm'} \, , \tag{A.1.a11}$$

$$\begin{pmatrix} j & 2 & j \\ -m & 0 & m' \end{pmatrix} = (-1)^{j-m} \frac{3m^2 - j(j+1)}{\sqrt{(2j-1)j(2j+1)(j+1)(2j+3)}} \, \delta_{mm'} \, , \tag{A.1.a12}$$

$$\begin{pmatrix} l \pm \frac{1}{2} & \frac{1}{2} & l \\ -\frac{1}{2} & \frac{1}{2} & 0 \end{pmatrix} = \frac{(-1)^{l+1}}{\sqrt{2(2l+1)}} , \tag{A.1.a13}$$

$$\begin{pmatrix} j + \frac{1}{2} & j & \frac{1}{2} \\ m - \frac{1}{2} & -m & \frac{1}{2} \end{pmatrix} = (-1)^{j-m} \sqrt{\frac{j-m+1}{(2j+2)(2j+1)}} . \tag{A.1.a14}$$

(b) Normalized Racah coefficients and 6-j symbols

For an extensive treatment of Racah coefficients see e.g. [Racah (1942); Biedenharn, Blatt and Rose (1952); Edmonds (1957)]. The normalized Racah coefficients or *U*-coefficients enter when three angular momenta are recoupled. In the pictorial notation used throughout this book the *U*-coefficients are defined by the recoupling relation

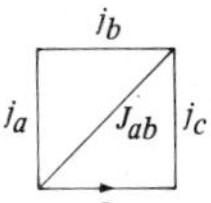

$= \sum_{J_{bc}} U(j_a j_b J j_c ; J_{ab} J_{bc})$

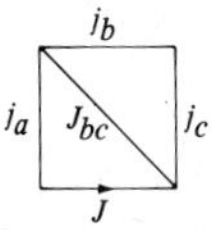

. (A.1.b1)

On the left-hand side the states $\boldsymbol{j}_a$ and $\boldsymbol{j}_b$ are first coupled to $\boldsymbol{J}_{ab}$ and the latter with $\boldsymbol{j}_c$ to the final $\boldsymbol{J}$. On the right-hand side the states $\boldsymbol{j}_b$ and $\boldsymbol{j}_c$ are first coupled to $\boldsymbol{J}_{bc}$ and the latter with $\boldsymbol{j}_a$ to the final $\boldsymbol{J}$, in the order given in eq. (A.1.b1).

The recoupling of three angular momenta involves four Clebsch-Gordan coefficients. It can be shown [Racah (1943)] that the particular combination in which they occur defines a *U*-coefficient by the relation

$$\sum_{m_a m_b M_{bc}} \langle j_a m_a j_b m_b | J_{ab} M_{ab} \rangle \langle J'_{ab} M'_{ab} j_c m_c | JM \rangle \langle j_b m_b j_c m_c | J_{bc} M_{bc} \rangle$$
$$\times \langle j_a m_a J_{bc} M_{bc} | JM \rangle = U(j_a j_b J j_c ; J_{ab} J_{bc}) \, \delta_{J_{ab} J'_{ab}} \delta_{M_{ab} M'_{ab}} . \tag{A.1.b2}$$

Taking $J_{ab} = J'_{ab}$ and $M_{ab} = M'_{ab}$ one finds for the *U*-coefficient the equation

$$U(j_a j_b J j_c ; J_{ab} J_{bc}) = \sum_{m_a m_b} \langle j_a m_a j_b m_b | J_{ab} m_a + m_b \rangle$$
$$\times \langle J_{ab} m_a + m_b j_c M - m_a - m_b | JM \rangle \langle j_b m_b j_c M - m_a - m_b | J_{bc} M - m_a \rangle$$
$$\times \langle j_a m_a J_{bc} M - m_a | JM \rangle . \tag{A.1.b3}$$

The *U*-coefficient vanishes unless certain triangle conditions are satisfied. From the diagrams in eq. (A.1.b1) (and of course from eqs. (A.1.b2) and (A.1.b3)) one finds

$$U(abcd; ef) = 0 \text{ unless } \Delta(abe), \Delta(edc), \Delta(bdf) \text{ and } \Delta(afc) , \tag{A.1.b4}$$

where $\Delta(pqr)$ denotes that the vectors $\boldsymbol{p}, \boldsymbol{q}, \boldsymbol{r}$ can form a triangle. A relation similar to eq. (A.1.b1), but with left- and right-hand side coupling orders interchanged, is given by

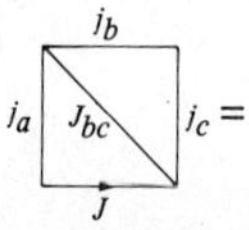 $= \sum_{J_{ab}} U(j_a j_b J j_c; J_{ab} J_{cd})$ 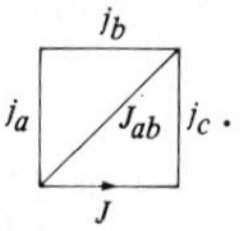 . (A.1.b5)

The orthogonality condition for U-coefficients, relating eqs. (A.1.b1) and (A.1.b5), is given by

$$\sum_{J_{ab}} U(j_a j_b J j_c; J_{ab} J_{bc})\, U(j_a j_b J j_c; J_{ab} J'_{bc}) = \delta_{J_{bc} J'_{bc}} \,. \tag{A.1.b6}$$

The U-coefficients are related to the more symmetric 6-j symbols by

$$U(j_a j_b l_b l_a; j_c l_c) = (-1)^{j_a+j_b+l_a+l_b} \sqrt{(2j_c+1)(2l_c+1)} \begin{Bmatrix} j_a & j_b & j_c \\ l_a & l_b & l_c \end{Bmatrix} . \tag{A.1.b7}$$

The 6-j symbols satisfy the orthogonality relation, (cf. eq. (A.1.b6))

$$\sum_{j_c} (2j_c+1) \begin{Bmatrix} j_a & j_b & j_c \\ l_a & l_b & l_c \end{Bmatrix} \begin{Bmatrix} j_a & j_b & j_c \\ l_a & l_b & l'_c \end{Bmatrix} = \frac{\delta_{l_c l'_c}}{2l_c+1} . \tag{A.1.b8}$$

There are 24 operations on a 6-j symbol that leave its value unaffected. These can be summarized by the relation

$$\begin{Bmatrix} j_a & j_b & j_c \\ j'_a & j'_b & j'_c \end{Bmatrix} = \begin{Bmatrix} j_p & j_q & j_r \\ j'_p & j'_q & j'_r \end{Bmatrix} , \tag{A.1.b9}$$

where (i) columns p, q, r are any permutation of columns a, b, c (6 operations including the identity) or (ii) the right-hand side 6-j symbol is obtained from the left-hand side by a simultaneous interchange of lower and upper arguments in any *two* columns (4 operations including the identity).

When one of the arguments is zero one can simply evaluate the 6-j symbol with the expression

$$\begin{Bmatrix} j_a & j_b & j_c \\ j_b & j_a & 0 \end{Bmatrix} = \frac{(-1)^{j_a+j_b+j_c}}{\sqrt{(2j_a+1)(2j_b+1)}} , \tag{A.1.b10}$$

where the symmetry relation (A.1.b9) can be used to get the zero at the position given.

A useful relation between the 6-j symbol and the 3-j symbols is given by (cf. eq. (A.1.b2))

$$\begin{pmatrix} l_a & l_b & l_c \\ n_a & n_b & n_c \end{pmatrix} \begin{Bmatrix} l_a & l_b & l_c \\ j_a & j_b & j_c \end{Bmatrix}$$

$$= \sum_{m_a m_b m_c} (-1)^{j_a+j_b+j_c+m_a+m_b+m_c} \begin{pmatrix} j_a & j_b & l_c \\ m_a & -m_b & n_c \end{pmatrix} \begin{pmatrix} j_b & j_c & l_a \\ m_b & -m_c & n_a \end{pmatrix} \begin{pmatrix} j_c & j_a & l_b \\ m_c & -m_a & n_b \end{pmatrix}. \tag{A.1.b11}$$

This summation (actually over only one of the indices m_a, m_b or m_c, since n_a, n_b and n_c are fixed) can serve as the starting point to prove many other relations involving 6-j symbols. For instance, application of eq. (A.1.b11) leads to

$$\begin{pmatrix} l_a & l_b & L \\ 0 & 0 & 0 \end{pmatrix} \begin{Bmatrix} l_a & l_b & L \\ j_a & j_b & \frac{1}{2} \end{Bmatrix} = (-1)^{j_a+j_b} \begin{pmatrix} j_a & j_b & L \\ \frac{1}{2} & -\frac{1}{2} & 0 \end{pmatrix} \begin{pmatrix} j_b & \frac{1}{2} & l_a \\ \frac{1}{2} & -\frac{1}{2} & 0 \end{pmatrix} \begin{pmatrix} \frac{1}{2} & j_a & l_b \\ \frac{1}{2} & -\frac{1}{2} & 0 \end{pmatrix}$$

$$+ (-1)^{j_a+j_b-1} \begin{pmatrix} j_a & j_b & L \\ -\frac{1}{2} & \frac{1}{2} & 0 \end{pmatrix} \begin{pmatrix} j_b & \frac{1}{2} & l_a \\ -\frac{1}{2} & \frac{1}{2} & 0 \end{pmatrix} \begin{pmatrix} \frac{1}{2} & j_a & l_b \\ -\frac{1}{2} & \frac{1}{2} & 0 \end{pmatrix}$$

$$= \begin{pmatrix} j_a & j_b & L \\ \frac{1}{2} & -\frac{1}{2} & 0 \end{pmatrix} \frac{-1}{\sqrt{(2l_a+1)(2l_b+1)}} \tfrac{1}{2}\{1 + (-1)^{l_a+L+l_b}\}. \tag{A.1.b12}$$

For the first equality use has been made of the fact that the summation in eq. (A.1.b11) leads to only two terms, i.e. $m_a = m_b = m_c = \frac{1}{2}$ and $m_a = m_b = m_c = -\frac{1}{2}$, and for the second equality the explicit expressions (A.1.a13) for the 3-j symbols have been substituted. The last factor of eq. (A.1.b12) reflects the parity condition satisfied by the 3-j symbol $\left(\begin{smallmatrix} l_a & l_b & L \\ 0 & 0 & 0 \end{smallmatrix}\right)$.

Multiplying the two sides of eq. (A.1.b11) with the 3-j symbol $\left(\begin{smallmatrix} j_a & j_b & l_c \\ m_a' & -m_b' & n_c \end{smallmatrix}\right)$ and summing over l_c and n_c one obtains, applying eq. (A.1.a8), a relation that is useful for the transformation of angular-momentum coupled particle-hole matrix elements of a two-body interaction into particle-particle matrix elements. After a relabelling of the angular momenta one finds, in terms of Clebsch-Gordan coefficients rather than 3-j symbols, the result for half-integral values of $j_a, ..., j_d$

$$\sum_M \langle j_a m_a j_c - m_c | JM \rangle \langle j_d m_d j_b - m_b | JM \rangle (-1)^{j_c - m_c} (-1)^{j_b - m_b}$$

$$= (-1)^{j_a+j_b+j_c+j_d} (2J+1) \sum_{J'M'} \begin{Bmatrix} j_a & j_b & J' \\ j_d & j_c & J \end{Bmatrix} \langle j_b m_b j_a m_a | J'M' \rangle \langle j_c m_c j_d m_d | J'M' \rangle. \tag{A.1.b13}$$

It is noted here that the summations over M and M' involve only one term each.

A special value of a 6-j symbol is given by

$$\begin{Bmatrix} j_a & j_a & 1 \\ j_b & j_b & j_c \end{Bmatrix} = (-1)^{j_a+j_b+j_c+1} \frac{j_a(j_a+1) + j_b(j_b+1) - j_c(j_c+1)}{2\sqrt{j_a(j_a+1)(2j_a+1)\, j_b(j_b+1)(2j_b+1)}}. \tag{A.1.b14}$$

(c) The 9-j symbols

The 9-j symbols are used in the recoupling of four angular momenta and are specified by the relation

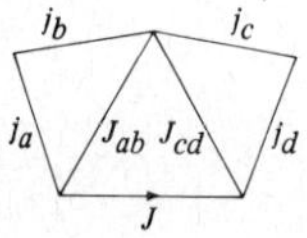

$$= \sum_{J_{ac} J_{bd}} \sqrt{(2J_{ab}+1)(2J_{cd}+1)(2J_{ac}+1)(2J_{bd}+1)} \begin{Bmatrix} j_a & j_b & J_{ab} \\ j_c & j_d & J_{cd} \\ J_{ac} & J_{bd} & J \end{Bmatrix}$$

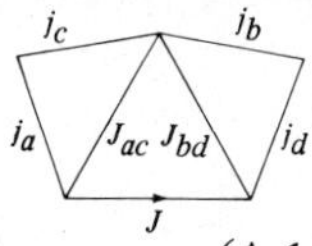

(A.1.c1)

The values of the 9-j symbols are affected neither by an even permutation of rows or columns nor by the interchange of rows and columns. Thus one has for example

$$\begin{Bmatrix} j_a & j_b & J_{ab} \\ j_c & j_d & J_{cd} \\ J_{ac} & J_{bd} & J \end{Bmatrix} = \begin{Bmatrix} j_c & j_d & J_{cd} \\ J_{ac} & J_{bd} & J \\ j_a & j_b & J_{ab} \end{Bmatrix} = \begin{Bmatrix} J_{ac} & J_{bd} & J \\ j_a & j_b & J_{ab} \\ j_c & j_d & J_{cd} \end{Bmatrix} = \begin{Bmatrix} j_a & j_c & J_{ac} \\ j_b & j_d & J_{bd} \\ J_{ab} & J_{cd} & J \end{Bmatrix}. \quad \text{(A.1.c2)}$$

An odd permutation of rows or columns introduces a phase factor $(-1)^P$, where P is equal to the sum of all arguments in the 9-j symbol. Thus one finds for example

$$\begin{Bmatrix} j_a & j_b & J_{ab} \\ j_c & j_d & J_{cd} \\ J_{ac} & J_{bd} & J \end{Bmatrix} = (-1)^{j_a+j_b+J_{ab}+j_c+j_d+J_{cd}+J_{ac}+J_{bd}+J} \begin{Bmatrix} j_c & j_d & J_{cd} \\ j_a & j_b & J_{ab} \\ J_{ac} & J_{bd} & J \end{Bmatrix}. \quad \text{(A.1.c3)}$$

The triangle conditions to be satisfied by the 9-j symbols follow immediately from the diagrams given in eq. (A.1.c1). The 9-j symbol can be expressed as a sum over products of three 6-j symbols or six 3-j symbols. One of these relations reads

$$\begin{Bmatrix} j_a & j_b & J_{ab} \\ j_c & j_d & J_{cd} \\ J_{ac} & J_{bd} & J \end{Bmatrix} = \sum_{J'} (-1)^{2J'}(2J'+1) \begin{Bmatrix} j_a & j_c & J_{ac} \\ J_{bd} & J & J' \end{Bmatrix} \begin{Bmatrix} j_b & j_d & J_{bd} \\ j_c & J' & J_{cd} \end{Bmatrix} \begin{Bmatrix} J_{ab} & J_{cd} & J \\ J' & j_a & j_b \end{Bmatrix}$$

$$= \sum_{\substack{\text{all} \\ m \text{ and } M}} \begin{pmatrix} j_a & j_b & J_{ab} \\ m_a & m_b & M_{ab} \end{pmatrix} \begin{pmatrix} j_c & j_d & J_{cd} \\ m_c & m_b & M_{cd} \end{pmatrix} \begin{pmatrix} J_{ac} & J_{bd} & J \\ M_{ac} & M_{bd} & M \end{pmatrix} \begin{pmatrix} j_a & j_c & J_{ac} \\ m_a & m_c & M_{ac} \end{pmatrix} \begin{pmatrix} j_b & j_d & J_{bd} \\ m_b & m_d & M_{bd} \end{pmatrix} \begin{pmatrix} J_{ab} & J_{cd} & J \\ M_{ab} & M_{cd} & M \end{pmatrix}$$

(A.1.c4)

Some special 9-j symbols are given by

$$\begin{Bmatrix} j_a & j_b & J_{ab} \\ j_a & j_b & J_{ab} \\ 0 & 0 & 0 \end{Bmatrix} = \frac{1}{\sqrt{(2j_a+1)(2j_b+1)(2J_{ab}+1)}}, \quad \text{(A.1.c5)}$$

$$\begin{Bmatrix} j_a & j_b & J_{ab} \\ j_c & j_d & J_{cd} \\ J_{ac} & J_{bd} & 0 \end{Bmatrix} = \begin{Bmatrix} j_a & j_b & J_{ab} \\ j_c & j_d & J_{ab} \\ J_{ac} & J_{ac} & 0 \end{Bmatrix} \delta_{J_{ab}J_{cd}} \delta_{J_{ac}J_{bd}}$$

$$= (-1)^{j_b+j_c+J_{ab}+J_{ac}} \frac{1}{\sqrt{(2J_{ab}+1)(2J_{ac}+1)}} \begin{Bmatrix} j_a & j_c & J_{ac} \\ j_d & j_b & J_{ab} \end{Bmatrix} \delta_{J_{ab}J_{cd}} \delta_{J_{ac}J_{bd}} \,. \qquad \text{(A.1.c6)}$$

Substitution of eq. (A.1.c6) into eq. (A.1.c1) leads us back to the recoupling scheme involved in eq. (A.1.b13).

A.2. Spherical harmonics and spherical components

The angular dependence of wave functions and operators is conveniently described by the spherical harmonics. The spherical harmonics $Y_{LM}(\hat{\boldsymbol{r}})$ are defined as the eigenfunctions of the angular-momentum operators $\boldsymbol{l}^2$ and l_z by

$$\boldsymbol{l}^2 Y_{LM}(\hat{\boldsymbol{r}}) = L(L+1)\, Y_{LM}(\hat{\boldsymbol{r}}) \,, \qquad \text{(A.2.1)}$$

$$l_z Y_{LM}(\hat{\boldsymbol{r}}) = M\, Y_{LM}(\hat{\boldsymbol{r}}) \,, \qquad \text{(A.2.2)}$$

where the unit vector $\hat{\boldsymbol{r}} \equiv \boldsymbol{r}/|\boldsymbol{r}|$ denotes the angular coordinates θ, ϕ.

We shall not present an elaborate discussion of properties of the function $Y_{LM}(\hat{\boldsymbol{r}})$ with derivations. Only some frequently used relations will be given instead. A much more extensive treatment can be found in e.g. [Racah (1942); Edmonds (1957)].

The spherical harmonics form an orthonormal set of functions of the angular variables satisfying the condition

$$\int Y^*_{LM}(\hat{\boldsymbol{r}})\, Y_{L'M'}(\hat{\boldsymbol{r}})\, \mathrm{d}\hat{\boldsymbol{r}} = \int Y^*_{LM}(\theta,\phi)\, Y_{L'M'}(\theta,\phi) \sin\theta \,\mathrm{d}\theta \,\mathrm{d}\phi = \delta_{LL'}\delta_{MM'} \,. \qquad \text{(A.2.3)}$$

A product of two spherical harmonics with the same arguments $\hat{\boldsymbol{r}}$ (or θ, ϕ) can be written as a sum over spherical harmonics

$$Y_{L_aM_a}(\hat{\boldsymbol{r}})\, Y_{L_bM_b}(\hat{\boldsymbol{r}})$$

$$= \sum_{LM} \sqrt{\frac{(2L_a+1)(2L+1)(2L_b+1)}{4\pi}} \begin{pmatrix} L_a & L & L_b \\ M_a & M & M_b \end{pmatrix} \begin{pmatrix} L_a & L & L_b \\ 0 & 0 & 0 \end{pmatrix} Y^*_{LM}(\hat{\boldsymbol{r}}) \,. \qquad \text{(A.2.4)}$$

With Clebsch-Gordan coefficients instead of 3-*j* symbols one has

$$Y_{L_aM_a}(\hat{\boldsymbol{r}})\, Y_{L_bM_b}(\hat{\boldsymbol{r}}) = \sum_{LM} \sqrt{\frac{(2L_a+1)(2L_b+1)}{4\pi(2L+1)}} \langle L_aM_aL_bM_b|LM\rangle \langle L_a0L_b0|L0\rangle\, Y_{LM}(\hat{\boldsymbol{r}}) \,. \qquad \text{(A.2.5)}$$

It should be noticed that the complex conjugate value of Y_{LM} in eq. (A.2.4) does not occur in eq. (A.2.5) due to the property

$$Y_{LM}(\hat{r}) = (-1)^M Y^*_{L-M}(\hat{r}) . \tag{A.2.6}$$

Because of the orthonormality of the Clebsch-Gordan coefficients one obtains from eq. (A.2.5) the inverse relation

$$\sum_{M_aM_b} \langle L_aM_aL_bM_b|LM\rangle Y_{L_aM_a}(\hat{r})\, Y_{L_bM_b}(\hat{r})$$

$$= \sqrt{\frac{(2L_a+1)(2L_b+1)}{4\pi(2L+1)}} \langle L_a0L_b0|L0\rangle Y_{LM}(\hat{r}) . \tag{A.2.7}$$

It is seen that this composition of two spherical harmonics with Clebsch-Gordan coefficients leads to another spherical harmonic, all three with the *same* argument.

As in nuclear physics angular momentum plays such a predominant role, it is not convenient to represent vectors in Cartesian coordinates. It turns out to be more appropriate to use spherical components. The latter are defined by

$$v_{\pm 1} = \sqrt{\tfrac{1}{2}}(\mp v_x - iv_y) , \qquad v_0 = v_z . \tag{A.2.8}$$

The explicit forms of the spherical harmonics Y_{LM} for $L = 0,1$ and 2 both in Cartesian and spherical components are given in table A.2.1. From this table one

Table A.2.1.
Some spherical harmonics

$$Y_{00}(\hat{r}) = \frac{1}{\sqrt{4\pi}}$$

$$Y_{10}(\hat{r}) = \sqrt{\frac{3}{4\pi}} \cos\theta = \sqrt{\frac{3}{4\pi}}\frac{z}{r} = \sqrt{\frac{3}{4\pi}}\frac{r_0}{r}$$

$$Y_{1\pm1}(\hat{r}) = \mp\sqrt{\frac{3}{8\pi}} \sin\theta\, e^{\pm i\phi} = \mp\sqrt{\frac{3}{8\pi}}\frac{x+iy}{r} = \sqrt{\frac{3}{4\pi}}\frac{r_{\pm1}}{r}$$

$$Y_{20}(\hat{r}) = \sqrt{\frac{5}{16\pi}}(2\cos^2\theta - \sin^2\theta) = \sqrt{\frac{5}{16\pi}}\frac{2z^2-x^2-y^2}{r^2} = \sqrt{\frac{5}{4\pi}}\frac{2r_0^2 + r_{+1}r_{-1}}{r^2}$$

$$Y_{2\pm1}(\hat{r}) = \mp\sqrt{\frac{15}{8\pi}} \cos\theta \sin\theta\, e^{\pm i\phi} = \mp\sqrt{\frac{15}{8\pi}}\frac{z(x\pm iy)}{r^2} = \sqrt{\frac{15}{4\pi}}\frac{r_0 r_{\pm1}}{r^2}$$

$$Y_{2\pm2}(\hat{r}) = \sqrt{\frac{15}{32\pi}} \sin^2\theta\, e^{\pm 2i\phi} = \sqrt{\frac{15}{32\pi}}\left(\frac{x\pm iy}{r}\right)^2 = \sqrt{\frac{15}{8\pi}}\left(\frac{r_{\pm1}}{r}\right)^2$$

sees that the spherical components of the vector $\boldsymbol{r}$ can be expressed as

$$r_m = \sqrt{\frac{4\pi}{3}}\, r Y_{1m}(\hat{\boldsymbol{r}}) \qquad \text{with } m = 0, \pm 1 . \tag{A.2.9}$$

This reflects the fact that a vector represents a tensor of rank $L = 1$.

The spherical harmonics form a complete set of functions to describe the angular dependence of a scalar wave function, i.e. for a spin-zero particle. For a spin-one field (the gamma-radiation field of photons) one introduces vector-spherical harmonics. Before we can do so, we must first define the spherical unit vectors by

$$\boldsymbol{e}_{\pm 1} = \sqrt{\tfrac{1}{2}}(\mp\hat{\boldsymbol{x}} - \mathrm{i}\hat{\boldsymbol{y}}) , \qquad \boldsymbol{e}_0 = \hat{\boldsymbol{z}} , \tag{A.2.10}$$

with

$$\hat{\boldsymbol{x}} \equiv \frac{\boldsymbol{x}}{|\boldsymbol{x}|} , \qquad \hat{\boldsymbol{y}} \equiv \frac{\boldsymbol{y}}{|\boldsymbol{y}|} , \qquad \hat{\boldsymbol{z}} \equiv \frac{\boldsymbol{z}}{|\boldsymbol{z}|} \tag{A.2.11}$$

denoting vectors of unit length along the three Cartesian coordinate axes. Combining the orbital part and the spin-one part, one obtains the vector-spherical harmonics

$$\boldsymbol{Y}_{(l)jm}(\boldsymbol{r}) = \sum_{m_l m_s} \langle l\, m_l 1\, m_s | jm \rangle\, Y_{lm_l}(\hat{\boldsymbol{r}})\, \boldsymbol{e}_{m_s} \tag{A.2.12}$$

with the three possibilities $l = j + 1, j$ or $j - 1$ for a given j value. The angular dependence of any vector field can be expressed in terms of vector-spherical harmonics, just as any scalar function can be expressed in terms of spherical harmonics.

From eqs. (A.2.8) and (A.2.10) one easily verifies that the spherical components of a vector can be written as

$$v_m = \boldsymbol{v} \cdot \boldsymbol{e}_m = \boldsymbol{e}_m \cdot \boldsymbol{v} \tag{A.2.13}$$

and that the vector $\boldsymbol{v}$ assumes the form

$$\boldsymbol{v} = \sum_m (-1)^m\, v_{-m}\, \boldsymbol{e}_m = \sum_m v_m^* \boldsymbol{e}_m = \sum_m v_m \boldsymbol{e}_m^* . \tag{A.2.14}$$

Since the unit vectors obey the orthogonality relations

$$\boldsymbol{e}_m^* \cdot \boldsymbol{e}_{m'} = \boldsymbol{e}_m \cdot \boldsymbol{e}_{m'}^* = \delta_{mm'} , \tag{A.2.15}$$

the scalar product of two vectors is given by

$$\boldsymbol{v} \cdot \boldsymbol{w} = \sum_m v_m (-1)^m\, w_{-m} , \tag{A.2.16}$$

as can be verified also directly with eq. (A.2.8).

For the evaluation of the matrix elements of the magnetic multipole operators, one must evaluate matrix elements of the operator $\boldsymbol{v} \cdot \boldsymbol{\nabla} r^L Y_{LM}(\hat{r})$ for any vector $\boldsymbol{v}$. To this purpose one can first write the scalar product $\boldsymbol{v} \cdot \boldsymbol{\nabla}$ in spherical coordinates. The spherical components for the gradient operator $\boldsymbol{\nabla}$ are defined by

$$\nabla_m = e_m \cdot \boldsymbol{\nabla} \tag{A.2.17}$$

and thus one has from eq. (A.2.10)

$$\nabla_{\pm 1} = \sqrt{\tfrac{1}{2}}\left(\mp \frac{\partial}{\partial x} - \mathrm{i}\frac{\partial}{\partial y}\right), \qquad \nabla_0 = \frac{\partial}{\partial z}\,. \tag{A.2.18}$$

The expressions to calculate the action of the gradient operator on any product of a spherical harmonic and a function of the radial distance can be found in [Bethe and Salpeter (1957) eqs. (A.37,38,39) derived with the aid of the preceding expressions and eqs. (A.20,21,22); it should be noted that the definition of spherical harmonics in this reference differs by a factor $(-1)^M$ from ours]. One obtains

$$\begin{aligned}\nabla_m f(r)\, Y_{LM}(\hat{r}) &= \sqrt{\frac{L+1}{2L+3}}\,\langle LM1m|L+1, M+m\rangle\, Y_{L+1,M+m}(\hat{r})\left(\frac{\mathrm{d}f}{\mathrm{d}r} - L\frac{f}{r}\right)\\ &\quad - \sqrt{\frac{L}{2L-1}}\,\langle LM1\,m|L-1, M+m\rangle\, Y_{L-1,\,M+m}(\hat{r})\left(\frac{\mathrm{d}f}{\mathrm{d}r} + (L+1)\frac{f}{r}\right).\end{aligned} \tag{A.2.19}$$

From eqs. (A.2.16) and (A.2.19) one now finds immediately

$$\begin{aligned}\boldsymbol{v}\cdot\boldsymbol{\nabla} f(r)\, Y_{LM}(\hat{r}) &= \sum_m (-1)^m\, v_{-m}\,(\nabla_m f(r)\, Y_{LM}(\hat{r}))\\ &= -\sqrt{\frac{L+1}{2L+1}}\sum_m \langle L+1, M+m, 1, -m|L, M\rangle\, Y_{L+1,M+m}(\hat{r})\, v_{-m}\left(\frac{\mathrm{d}f}{\mathrm{d}r} - L\frac{f}{r}\right)\\ &\quad + \sqrt{\frac{L}{2L+1}}\sum_m \langle L-1, M+m, 1, -m\,|L, M\rangle\, Y_{L-1,M+m}(\hat{r})\, v_{-m}\left(\frac{\mathrm{d}f}{\mathrm{d}r} + (L+1)\frac{f}{r}\right).\end{aligned} \tag{A.2.20}$$

Substitution of $f(r) = r^L$ yields

$$\boldsymbol{v}\cdot\boldsymbol{\nabla} r^L Y_{LM}(\hat{r}) = \sqrt{L(2L+1)}\; r^{L-1}\,[Y_{L-1} \times \boldsymbol{v}]^L_M\,. \tag{A.2.21}$$

Similarly one finds with $f(r) = r^{-L-1}$

$$\boldsymbol{v}\cdot\boldsymbol{\nabla} r^{-L-1} Y_{LM}(\hat{r}) = \sqrt{(L+1)\,(2L+1)}\; r^{-L-2}\,[Y_{L+1} \times \boldsymbol{v}]^L_M\,. \tag{A.2.22}$$

For the frequently used case with $L = 1$ one obtains, inserting the explicit value

$Y_{00} = (4\pi)^{-1/2}$, the relation

$$\boldsymbol{v}\cdot\nabla r Y_{1M}(\hat{r}) = \sqrt{\frac{3}{4\pi}}\, v_M\,, \tag{A.2.23}$$

which follows immediately also from eq. (A.2.9).

A.3. Reduced matrix elements

(a) The Wigner-Eckart theorem

The Wigner-Eckart theorem is very important for the evaluation of matrix elements of spherical tensor operators between states of definite angular momentum. This theorem separates the dependence of the matrix element on the projection quantum numbers (i.e. the dependence on the coordinate frame used) from that on its physical aspects.

Spherical tensor operators are characterized by their transformation properties under rotations. A rotation can be defined in terms of the Euler angles α, β and γ as is illustrated in fig. A.3.1. Let the operator $R(\alpha\beta\gamma)$ represent (i) a rotation of the coordinate frame over an angle α about the original z-axis, followed by (ii) a rotation over an angle β about the y_1 axis in the resulting frame and subsequently followed by (iii) a rotation over an angle γ about the z_2 axis.

It can be shown that the eigenfunctions Φ_{JM} of J^2 and J_z transform as [Edmonds (1957) ch. 4]

$$R(\alpha\beta\gamma)\Phi_{JM} = \sum_{M'} \langle JM'|R(\alpha\beta\gamma)|JM\rangle\Phi_{JM'} \equiv \sum_{M'} D^J_{M'M}(\alpha\beta\gamma)\Phi_{JM'}\,, \tag{A.3.a1}$$

where the Wigner rotation matrix $D^J_{M'M}(\alpha\beta\gamma)$ is introduced. It should be remarked that the elements $D^J_{M'M}(\alpha\beta\gamma)$ are pure numbers and are independent of the coordinates on which the wave functions depend.

THE EULER ANGLES

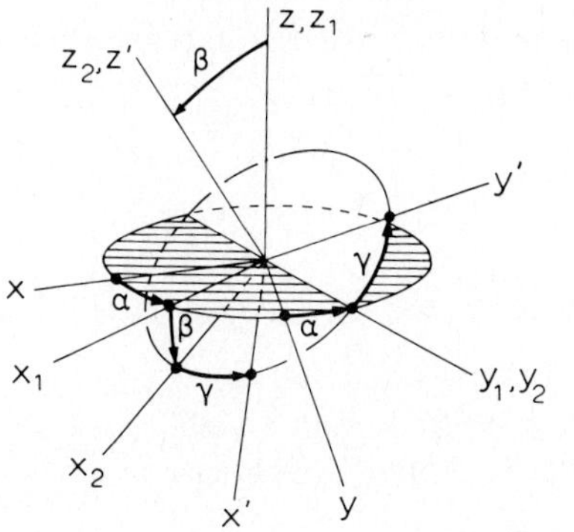

Fig. A.3.1. The Euler angels α, β and γ that define the three successive rotations.

A spherical tensor operator of rank k is defined such that it transforms under rotations $R(\alpha\beta\gamma)$ as

$$R(\alpha\beta\gamma)T_q^k R^{-1}(\alpha\beta\gamma) = \sum_{q'} D^k_{q'q}(\alpha\beta\gamma) T^k_{q'} \,. \tag{A.3.a2}$$

For the definition of the spherical tensor operators of rank k it is essential that the $2k + 1$ components T_q^k (with $q = -k, -k+1, ..., k$) transform among each other under the rotation (A.3. a1). This means that no smaller subset can be found with the same property. It is then said that the tensor is *irreducible.* The term irreducible tensor is more general than spherical tensor in the sense that it applies also to transformation groups other than the rotation group.

The spherical tensor operator $\boldsymbol{T}^k$ acting on the state Φ_{jm} produces a state that can be acted upon by the rotation operator $R(\alpha\beta\gamma)$. Using the shorter notation ω for the set $\{\alpha\beta\gamma\}$ one finds from eqs. (A.3.a1) and (A.3. a2) the result

$$R(\omega)T_q^k\Phi_{jm} = R(\omega)T_q^k R^{-1}(\omega)R(\omega)\Phi_{jm} = \sum_{q'} D^k_{q'q}(\omega)T^k_{q'} \sum_{m'} D^j_{m'm}(\omega)\Phi_{jm'} \,. \tag{A.3.a3}$$

It is seen from this equation that $T_q^k\Phi_{jm}$ is transformed by the product $D^k_{q'q}(\omega) \times D^j_{m'm}(\omega)$. We now derive an expression for the product of D-functions occurring in eq. (A.3.a3).

Let us start with the relation (A.1.a5)

$$\Phi_{j_a m_a}\Phi_{j_b m_b} = \sum_{JM} \langle j_a m_a j_b m_b | JM\rangle \Phi_{JM} \,. \tag{A.3.a4}$$

Applying eq. (A.3.a1) to perform a rotation of axes one finds

$$\sum_{m'_a m'_b} D^{j_a}_{m'_a m_a}(\omega) D^{j_b}_{m'_b m_b}(\omega) \Phi_{j_a m'_a}\Phi_{j_b m'_b} = \sum_{JM'} \langle j_a m_a j_b m_b | JM\rangle D^J_{M'M}(\omega)\Phi_{JM'} \,. \tag{A.3.a5}$$

The right-hand side wave function $\Phi_{JM'}$ can be expanded in terms of product wave functions, which leads to

$$\sum_{m'_a m'_b} D^{j_a}_{m'_a m_a}(\omega) D^{j_b}_{m'_b m_b}(\omega) \Phi_{j_a m'_a}\Phi_{j_b m'_b}$$

$$= \sum_{m''_a m''_b} \sum_{JM'} \langle j_a m''_a j_b m''_b | JM'\rangle \langle j_a m_a j_b m_b | JM\rangle D^J_{M'M}(\omega) \Phi_{j_a m''_a}\Phi_{j_b m''_b} \,. \tag{A.3.a6}$$

Multiplying both sides of this equation with $\Phi^*_{j_a m'''_a}\Phi^*_{j_b m'''_b}$ and integrating over the coordinates of the systems a and b one obtains

$$D^{j_a}_{m'_a m_a}(\omega)\, D^{j_b}_{m'_b m_b}(\omega) = \sum_{JM} \langle j_a m'_a j_b m'_b | JM'\rangle \langle j_a m_a j_b m_b | JM\rangle D^J_{M'M}(\omega) \,. \tag{A.3.a7}$$

It is to be noted here that the right-hand side of eq. (A.3.a6) contains a summation over J. The product function $\Phi_{j_a m_a'}(\boldsymbol{r}(1))\,\Phi_{j_b m_b'}(\boldsymbol{r}(2))$ does not transform according to one angular-momentum J, but it can be decomposed into several parts that are characterized by different values of J. That is, the product $\Phi_{j_a m_a'}(\boldsymbol{r}(1))\,\Phi_{j_b m_b'}(\boldsymbol{r}(2))$ is reducible. Substitution of eq. (A.3.a7) into eq. (A.3.a3) yields after multiplication of both sides with $\langle kq\,jm|JM\rangle$ and summation over q and m, the result

$$R(\omega)\sum_{qm}\langle kq\,jm|JM\rangle T_q^k\Phi_{jm} = \sum_{M'} D^J_{M'M}(\omega)\sum_{q'm'}\langle kq'\,jm'|JM'\rangle T^k_{q'}\Phi_{jm'}\,. \qquad \text{(A.3.a8)}$$

Evidently the coupled product function

$$[T^k\times\phi^j]^J_M \equiv \sum_{qm}\langle kq\,jm|JM\rangle T^k_q\Phi^j_m \qquad \text{(A.3.a9)}$$

transforms as a function with angular-momentum quantum numbers J, M. The two notations Φ_{jm} and Φ^j_m, denoting the same state of angular momentum j and projection m, are used indiscriminately.

The overlap with some function $\phi^{j'}_{m'}$ therefore must be given by

$$\langle\phi^{j'}_{m'}|[T^k\times|\phi^j\rangle]^J_M = A(j'm')\delta_{j'J}\delta_{m'M} \qquad \text{(A.3.a10)}$$

with

$$A(j'm') = \langle\phi^{j'}_{m'}|[T^k\times|\phi^j\rangle]^{j'}_{m'}\,. \qquad \text{(A.3.a11)}$$

The overlaps $A(j'm')$ are independent of m' as can be seen as follows. The overlap $A(j'm'\pm 1)$ can be obtained by the use of the raising and lowering operators $j_\pm = j_x \pm \mathrm{i}j_y$ (cf. eq. (2.69))

$$A(j'\,m'\pm 1) = \langle\phi^{j'}_{m'\pm 1}|[T^k\times|\phi^j\rangle]^{j'}_{m'\pm 1}$$

$$= \langle\phi^{j'}_{m'}|\frac{j_\mp}{\sqrt{(j'\mp m')(j'\pm m'+1)}}\frac{j_\pm}{\sqrt{(j'\mp m')(j'\pm m'+1)}}|[T^k\times|\phi^j\rangle]^{j'}_{m'}$$

$$= \langle\phi^{j'}_{m'}|\frac{j^2-j_z^2\mp j_z}{j'(j'+1)-m'^2\mp m'}|[T^k\times|\phi^j\rangle]^{j'}_{m'}$$

$$= \langle\phi^{j'}_{m'}|[T^k\times|\phi^j\rangle]^{j'}_{m'} = A(j'm')\,. \qquad \text{(A.3.a12)}$$

From eqs. (A.3.a9) and (A.3.a10) we obtain, writing $A(j')$ instead of $A(j'm')$,

$$\langle\phi^{j'}_{m'}|T^k_q|\Phi^j_m\rangle = A(j')\langle kq\,jm|j'm'\rangle\,. \qquad \text{(A.3.a13)}$$

This equation already contains the essentials of the Wigner-Eckart theorem, i.e. that the dependence of the matrix element $\langle \phi^{j'}_{m'} | T^k_q | \Phi^j_m \rangle$ on the projection quantum numbers m', q and m is given by the Clebsch-Gordan coefficient $\langle kq\, jm | j'm' \rangle$. The other factor $A(j')$ is given usually in terms of a *reduced matrix element.*

The *Wigner-Eckart theorem* reads

$$\langle j'm' | T^k_q | jm \rangle = (-1)^{2k} \frac{\langle jm\, kq | j'm' \rangle}{\sqrt{2j'+1}} \langle j' \| \boldsymbol{T}^k \| j \rangle , \tag{A.3.a14}$$

or with a 3-j symbol instead of a Clebsch-Gordan coefficient

$$\langle j'm' | T^k_q | jm \rangle = (-1)^{j'-m'} \begin{pmatrix} j' & k & j \\ -m' & q & m \end{pmatrix} \langle j' \| \boldsymbol{T}^k \| j \rangle . \tag{A.3.a15}$$

From the latter relation one finds the equivalent expression

$$\sum_{m'qm} (-1)^{j'-m'} \begin{pmatrix} j' & k & j \\ -m' & q & m \end{pmatrix} \langle j'm' | T^k_q | jm \rangle$$

$$= \sum_{m'qm} \begin{pmatrix} j' & k & j \\ -m' & q & m \end{pmatrix}^2 \langle j' \| \boldsymbol{T}^k \| j \rangle = \langle j' \| \boldsymbol{T}^k \| j \rangle , \tag{A.3.a16}$$

where the orthonormality of 3-j symbols is used (cf. eq. (A.1.a9)).

The reduced matrix elements, denoted by the double-bar matrix elements in these equations, depend on the physical process described by the operator $\boldsymbol{T}^k$ and on the two states involved. It should be remarked here that in some papers a different normalization or phase is chosen for the reduced matrix element. The phase factor $(-1)^{2k}$ in eq. (A.3.a14) has no effect for tensor operators of integral rank k, but introduces a minus sign for the reduced matrix elements of fermion creation or annihilation operators (except when the reduction takes place in coordinate and isospin space simultaneously, as is discussed below). The convention of eq. (A.3.a14) is that of [Racah (1942); Wigner (1940); Edmonds (1957)].

When the isospin formalism is used, the operators are characterized by a rank in coordinate space as well as a rank in isospace. The Wigner-Eckart theorem can now be formulated as

$$\langle J_a M_a ; T_a T_{az} | T^{L,T}_{M,T_z} | J_b M_b ; T_b T_{bz} \rangle$$

$$= (-1)^{2(L+T)} \frac{\langle J_b M_b LM | J_a M_a \rangle \langle T_b T_{bz} T T_z ; T_a T_{az} \rangle}{\sqrt{(2J_a+1)(2T_a+1)}} \langle J_a T_a \| \boldsymbol{T}^{L,T} \| J_b T_b \rangle \tag{A.3.a17}$$

or with 3-j symbols instead of Clebsch-Gordan coefficients

$$\langle J_a M_a ; T_a T_{az} | T^{L,T}_{M,T_z} | J_b M_b ; T_b T_{bz} \rangle$$

$$= (-1)^{J_a - M_a} (-1)^{T_a - T_{az}} \begin{pmatrix} J_a & L & J_b \\ -M_a & M & M_b \end{pmatrix} \begin{pmatrix} T_a & T & T_b \\ -T_{az} & T_z & T_{bz} \end{pmatrix} \langle J_a T_a \| \boldsymbol{T}^{L,T} \| J_b T_b \rangle , \tag{A.3.a18}$$

where the triple bars indicate the reduction in two spaces.

It is stressed here that the Wigner-Eckart theorem applies to spherical, irreducible tensor operators only, i.e. the transformation properties in coordinate space and in isospace must be given by eq. (A.3.a2). Thus, for instance, the electromagnetic transition operators (see chapter 9) must be written as the sum of an isoscalar and an isovector part before the Wigner-Eckart theorem can be used for the reduction in the two spaces.

(b) A symmetry property of the reduced matrix elements

For many calculations it is convenient to exploit the relation that exists between reduced matrix elements with initial and final states interchanged. The tensor operators of integral rank k have been defined in this book such that their hermitian conjugates are given by

$$(T^k_q)^\dagger = (-1)^q\, T^k_{-q}\,. \tag{A.3.b1}$$

The phases of the wave functions have been taken such that all matrix elements are real. As a result we obtain from the Wigner-Eckart theorem (A.3.1a5)

$$\langle J_a M_a | T^k_q | J_b M_b \rangle = (-1)^{J_a - M_a} \begin{pmatrix} J_a & k & J_b \\ -M_a & q & M_b \end{pmatrix} \langle J_a \| \boldsymbol{T}^k \| J_b \rangle\,. \tag{A.3.b2}$$

Using the hermitian conjugate one can write

$$\langle J_a M_a | T^k_q | J_b M_b \rangle = \langle J_b M_b | (T^k_q)^\dagger | J_a M_a \rangle^*$$

$$= (-1)^q\, \langle J_b M_b | T^k_{-q} | J_a M_a \rangle^* = (-1)^q (-1)^{J_a - M_b} \begin{pmatrix} J_b & k & J_a \\ -M_b & -q & M_a \end{pmatrix} \langle J_b \| \boldsymbol{T}^k \| J_a \rangle^*\,. \tag{A.3.b3}$$

From a comparison of the right-hand members of eqs. (A.3.b2) and (A.3.b3) and application of some symmetry properties of 3-j symbols one deduces for real matrix elements the relation

$$\langle J_a \| \boldsymbol{T}^k \| J_b \rangle = (-1)^{J_a - J_b} \langle J_b \| \boldsymbol{T}^k \| J_a \rangle\,. \tag{A.3.b4}$$

It should be remarked here that instead of eq. (A.3.b1) another phasing of tensor operators is also in use. This then affects relation (A.3.b4).

Analogously one finds for the reduced matrix element of an operator acting both in coordinate space and isospace

$$\langle J_a T_a ||| \boldsymbol{T}^k ||| J_b T_b \rangle = (-1)^{J_a + T_a - J_b - T_b} \langle J_b T_b ||| \boldsymbol{T}^k ||| J_a T_a \rangle^*. \tag{A.3.b5}$$

In chapter 13 the creation operator for single-particle states, $a^\dagger_{jm}$, was seen to be a spherical tensor operator. In eq. (13.53) the operator $\widetilde{a}_{jm}$ was introduced as a spherical tensor operator that describes the process of annihilation. In order to derive a relation between the reduced matrix elements of these two operators, that are not hermitian as T_q^k is in eq. (A.3.b5), we shall apply the Wigner-Eckart theorem twice.

In the first place we have

$$\langle \rho^{n-1}\Gamma M_\Gamma|\widetilde{a}_{\rho m_\rho}|\rho^n\Gamma' M'_\Gamma\rangle = (-1)^{\Gamma - M_\Gamma}\begin{pmatrix} \Gamma & \rho & \Gamma' \\ -M_\Gamma & m_\rho & M'_\Gamma \end{pmatrix}\langle \rho^{n-1}\Gamma|||\widetilde{a}_\rho|||\rho^n\Gamma'\rangle . \tag{A.3.b6}$$

With eq. (13.53) we find also

$$\begin{aligned}
&\langle \rho^{n-1}\Gamma M_\Gamma|\widetilde{a}_{\rho m_\rho}|\rho^n\Gamma' M'_\Gamma\rangle \\
&= (-1)^{\rho + m_\rho}\langle \rho^{n-1}\Gamma M_\Gamma|a_{\rho -m_\rho}|\rho^n\Gamma' M'_\Gamma\rangle \\
&= (-1)^{\rho + m_\rho}\langle \rho^n\Gamma' M'_\Gamma|a^\dagger_{\rho -m_\rho}|\rho^{n-1}\Gamma M_\Gamma\rangle^* \\
&= (-1)^{\rho + m_\rho}(-1)^{\Gamma' - M'_\Gamma}\begin{pmatrix} \Gamma' & \rho & \Gamma \\ -M'_\Gamma & -m_\rho & M_\Gamma \end{pmatrix}\langle \rho^n\Gamma'|||a^\dagger_\rho|||\rho^{n-1}\Gamma\rangle^* .
\end{aligned} \tag{A.3.b7}$$

The asterisk that is introduced to denote that the complex conjugate matrix element should be taken when the transition to the hermitian conjugate operator is made, can be ignored since the matrix elements are real. As the two 3-j symbols in eqs. (A.3.b6) and (A.3.b7) are the same, one obtains the result

$$\langle \rho^{n-1}\Gamma|||\widetilde{a}_\rho|||\rho^n\Gamma'\rangle = (-1)^{\Gamma+\rho-\Gamma'}\langle \rho^n\Gamma'|||a^\dagger_\rho|||\rho^{n-1}\Gamma\rangle . \tag{A.3.b8}$$

A similar relation connects the reduced matrix elements of the state operators Z^Γ and $\widetilde{Z}^\Gamma$ (cf. eqs. (13.43) and (13.59)).

(c) Elementary reduced matrix elements

Let us evaluate first the reduced matrix element of the unit operator. From the Wigner-Eckart theorem (A.3.a16) one derives

$$\begin{aligned}
\langle j\|1\|j'\rangle &= \sum_{mm'}(-1)^{j-m}\begin{pmatrix} j & 0 & j' \\ -m & 0 & m' \end{pmatrix}\langle jm|1|j'm'\rangle \\
&= \sum_m (-1)^{j-m}\begin{pmatrix} j & 0 & j \\ -m & 0 & m \end{pmatrix}\delta_{jj'} = \sqrt{2j+1}\,\delta_{jj'} ,
\end{aligned} \tag{A.3.c1}$$

where for the last step eq. (A.1.a10) is used. Similarly one has for the triple-bar matrix elements with ρ denoting j and t,

$$\langle \rho ||| \mathbf{1} ||| \rho \rangle = \sqrt{2\rho + 1} = \sqrt{(2j+1)(2t+1)}\,. \tag{A.3.c2}$$

The reduced matrix element of the angular-momentum operator can be calculated most conveniently by writing down the Wigner-Eckart theorem for the component j_z

$$m = \langle jm | j_z | jm \rangle = \frac{\langle jm\, 10 | jm \rangle}{\sqrt{2j+1}} \langle j \| \boldsymbol{j} \| j \rangle\,. \tag{A.3.c3}$$

Substitution of the explicit value of the Clebsch-Gordan coefficient

$$\langle jm\, 10 | jm \rangle = \frac{m}{\sqrt{j(j+1)}} \tag{A.3.c4}$$

leads to the result

$$\langle j \| \boldsymbol{j} \| j \rangle = \sqrt{j(j+1)(2j+1)}\,. \tag{A.3.c5}$$

For the spin-$\frac{1}{2}$ operator one derives from eq. (A.3.c5)

$$\langle \tfrac{1}{2} \| \boldsymbol{s} \| \tfrac{1}{2} \rangle = \sqrt{\tfrac{3}{2}} \qquad \text{or} \qquad \langle \tfrac{1}{2} \| \boldsymbol{\sigma} \| \tfrac{1}{2} \rangle = \sqrt{6} \tag{A.3.c6}$$

and also

$$\langle \tfrac{1}{2} \| \boldsymbol{t} \| \tfrac{1}{2} \rangle = \sqrt{\tfrac{3}{2}} \qquad \text{or} \qquad \langle \tfrac{1}{2} \| \boldsymbol{\tau} \| \tfrac{1}{2} \rangle = \sqrt{6}\,. \tag{A.3.c7}$$

From eqs. (A.3.c1), (A.3.c6) and (A.3.c7) one obtains for some common triple-bar matrix elements

$$\langle j, t = \tfrac{1}{2} ||| \boldsymbol{j}\, \mathbf{1} ||| j, t = \tfrac{1}{2} \rangle = \sqrt{2j(j+1)(2j+1)}\,, \tag{A.3.c8}$$

$$\langle j, t = \tfrac{1}{2} ||| \boldsymbol{j}\, \boldsymbol{\tau} ||| j, t = \tfrac{1}{2} \rangle = \sqrt{6j(j+1)(2j+1)}\,. \tag{A.3.c9}$$

(d) Reduced matrix elements of tensor products

Operators acting in different spaces. Consider the tensor product operator

$$[T^p \times U^q]^r_{m_r} = \sum_{m_p m_q} \langle p\, m_p\, q\, m_q | r\, m_r \rangle\, T^p_{m_p} U^q_{m_q}\,, \tag{A.3.d1}$$

where the two tensor operators $\boldsymbol{T}^p$ and $\boldsymbol{U}^q$ act on *different* sets of coordinates and hence commute. For example $\boldsymbol{T}^p$ may act only on the orbital coordinates and $\boldsymbol{U}^q$ on the spin coordinates.

The reduced matrix elements of the tensor product operator (A.3.d1) can be written according to eq. (A.3.a16) as

$$\langle j_a j_b J \| [T^p \times U^q]^r \| j_c j_d J' \rangle$$

$$= \sum_{M m_r M'} (-1)^{J-M} \begin{pmatrix} J & r & J' \\ -M & m_r & M' \end{pmatrix} \langle j_a j_b JM | [T^p \times U^q]^r_{m_r} | j_c j_d J'M' \rangle . \quad \text{(A.3.d2)}$$

We shall show that this reduced matrix element of the product operator in the coupled representation $|j_a j_b J\rangle$ can be expressed in terms of the reduced matrix elements of the individual operators.

Let j_a and j_c refer to the system on which T^p acts and j_b and j_d to the system of U^q. Expressing the right-hand side matrix element in eq. (A.3.d2) in the uncoupled scheme and inserting a complete set of intermediate states, one obtains with eq. (A.3.d1)

$$\langle j_a j_b JM | [T^p \times U^q]^r_{m_r} | j_c j_d J'M' \rangle$$

$$= \sum_{\substack{m_a m_b \\ m_c m_d \\ m_p m_q}} \langle j_a m_a j_b m_b | JM \rangle \langle j_c m_c j_d m_d | J'M' \rangle \langle p m_p q m_q | r m_r \rangle$$

$$\times \langle j_a m_a j_b m_b | T^p_{m_p} | j_c m_c j_b m_b \rangle \langle j_c m_c j_b m_b | U^q_{m_q} | j_c m_c j_d m_d \rangle . \quad \text{(A.3.d3)}$$

It is seen that the complete set of intermediate states is reduced to the terms $|j_c m_c j_b m_b\rangle \langle j_c m_c j_b m_b|$. This follows from the orthogonality of the states $|jm\rangle$, since the operator $T^p_{m_p}$ acts on the parts labelled $j_a m_a$ and $j_c m_c$ only and similarly $U^q_{m_q}$ on the parts $j_b m_b$ and $j_d m_d$.

After substitution of eq. (A.3.d3) into eq. (A.3.d2) and application of the Wigner-Eckart theorem one finds an expression which contains a summation over the product of six 3-j symbols

$$\langle j_a j_b J \| [T^p \times U^q]^r \| j_c j_d J' \rangle$$

$$= \sqrt{(2J+1)(2r+1)(2J'+1)} \sum_{\text{all } m, M} \begin{pmatrix} j_a & j_b & J \\ m_a & m_b & -M \end{pmatrix} \begin{pmatrix} j_c & j_d & J' \\ -m_c & -m_d & M' \end{pmatrix}$$

$$\times \begin{pmatrix} p & q & r \\ -m_p & -m_q & m_r \end{pmatrix} \begin{pmatrix} j_a & j_c & p \\ m_a & -m_c & -m_p \end{pmatrix} \begin{pmatrix} j_b & j_d & q \\ m_b & -m_d & -m_q \end{pmatrix} \begin{pmatrix} J & J' & r \\ -M & M' & m_r \end{pmatrix}$$

$$\times \langle j_a \| T^p \| j_c \rangle \langle j_b \| U^q \| j_d \rangle$$

$$= \sqrt{(2J+1)(2r+1)(2J'+1)} \begin{Bmatrix} j_a & j_b & J \\ j_c & j_d & J' \\ p & q & r \end{Bmatrix} \langle j_a \| T^p \| j_c \rangle \langle j_b \| U^q \| j_d \rangle . \quad \text{(A.3.d4)}$$

Here in the last equality the 9-j symbol results from the summation over the product of six 3-j symbols (see eq. (A.1.c4)). Putting one of the three ranks p, q, or r equal to zero one obtains three special cases of eq. (A.3.d4) that are used very frequently.

After substitution of $r = 0$ (and hence $p = q$) into eq. (A.3.d1) the tensor product assumes the form

$$[T^p \times U^p]^0_0 = \sum_{m_p m_q} \langle p m_p p m_q | 00 \rangle T^p_{m_p} U^p_{m_q}$$

$$= \sum_{m_p} \frac{(-1)^{p-m_p}}{\sqrt{2p+1}} T^p_{m_p} U^p_{-m_p}, \qquad \text{(A.3.d5)}$$

where the explicit value of the Clebsch-Gordan coefficient has been substituted. From the definition of the scalar product of two tensors of the same integral rank p [Edmonds (1957)] one obtains with eq. (A.3.d5) the relation *

$$T^p \cdot U^p \equiv \sum_{m_p} (-1)^{m_p} T^p_{m_p} U^p_{-m_p} = (-1)^p \sqrt{2p+1}\, [T^p \times U^p]^0_0 . \qquad \text{(A.3.d6)}$$

We are now able to derive from eq. (A.3.d4), using eqs. (A.1.c6) and (A.3.d6), the expression for the reduced matrix element of the scalar product of two tensor operators, which is given by

$$\langle j_a j_b J \| T^p \cdot U^p \| j_c j_d J' \rangle = (-1)^{j_b+j_c+J} \sqrt{2J+1} \begin{Bmatrix} j_a & j_b & J \\ j_d & j_c & p \end{Bmatrix} \langle j_a \| T^p \| j_c \rangle \langle j_b \| U^p \| j_d \rangle\, \delta_{JJ'} .$$

(A.3.d7)

Another quite useful specialization of eq. (A.3.d4) is the case with $p = 0$ and hence $q = r$. The operator T^p then reduces to a scalar and therefore does not act on the angular or spin variables. The reduced matrix element of an operator working only on one part in the coupled representation is obtained from eq. (A.3.d4) by taking $T^{p=0} = 1$. Using eqs. (A.1.c6) and (A.3.c2), one obtains

$$\langle j_a j_b J \| U^q \| j_c j_d J' \rangle$$

$$= (-1)^{j_c+j_d+J+q} \sqrt{(2J+1)(2J'+1)} \begin{Bmatrix} j_b & j_d & q \\ J' & J & j_a \end{Bmatrix} \langle j_b \| U^q \| j_d \rangle\, \delta_{j_a j_c} , \qquad \text{(A.3.d8)}$$

where the operator U^q does not act on the states labelled j_a and j_c. Similarly one finds for $U^{q=0} = 1$ the corresponding expression

$$\langle j_a j_b J \| T^p \| j_c j_d J' \rangle$$

$$= (-1)^{j_a+j_b+J'+p} \sqrt{(2J+1)(2J'+1)} \begin{Bmatrix} j_a & j_c & p \\ J' & J & j_d \end{Bmatrix} \langle j_a \| T^p \| j_c \rangle\, \delta_{j_b j_d} , \qquad \text{(A.3.d9)}$$

* It should be noted that the scalar product of two vectors ($p = q = 1$) differs by a factor $-\sqrt{3}$ from the tensor-coupled product ($r = 0$). Similarly one finds from eq. (A.3.d1) that the vector product of two vectors ($p = q = 1$) differs by a factor $-i\sqrt{2}$ from the tensor-coupled product ($r = 1$).

where the operator T^p does not act on the states labelled j_b and j_d.

Operators acting in one space. Consider the tensor product

$$[T^p \times T^q]^r_{m_r} = \sum_{m_p m_q} \langle p m_p q m_q | r m_r \rangle T^p_{m_p} T^q_{m_q} , \tag{A.3.d10}$$

where the two tensor operators T^p and T^q are taken to act in one and the *same* space, e.g. on the orbital coordinates of one particle only or the spin coordinates of one particle only. Then the matrix element of $[T^p \times T^q]^r$ can be expressed in terms of the matrix elements of T^p and T^q by insertion of a complete set of intermediate states $|j_c m_c\rangle$ as follows

$$\langle j_a m_a | [T^p \times T^q]^r_{m_r} | j_b m_b \rangle$$

$$= \sum_{\substack{m_p m_q \\ j_c m_c}} \langle p m_p q m_q | r m_r \rangle \langle j_a m_a | T^p_{m_p} | j_c m_c \rangle \langle j_c m_c | T^q_{m_q} | j_b m_b \rangle . \tag{A.3.d11}$$

Applying the Wigner-Eckart theorem (A.3.a15) to the right-hand side twice and using 3-*j* symbols rather than Clebsch-Gordan coefficients, one can rewrite eq. (A.3.d11) as

$$\langle j_a m_a | [T^p \times T^q]^r_{m_r} | j_b m_b \rangle$$

$$= \sum_{\substack{m_p m_q \\ j_c m_c}} (-1)^{j_a - m_a} \begin{pmatrix} p & q & r \\ m_p & m_q & -m_r \end{pmatrix} \begin{pmatrix} q & j_c & j_b \\ -m_q & m_c & -m_b \end{pmatrix} \begin{pmatrix} j_c & p & j_a \\ -m_c & -m_p & m_a \end{pmatrix}$$

$$\times (-1)^{p+q+j_c+m_p-m_q-m_c} \sqrt{2r+1} \langle j_a \| T^p \| j_c \rangle \langle j_c \| T^q \| j_b \rangle$$

$$= (-1)^{j_a - m_a} \begin{pmatrix} j_b & j_a & r \\ -m_b & m_a & -m_r \end{pmatrix} \sqrt{2r+1} \sum_{j_c} \begin{Bmatrix} j_b & j_a & r \\ p & q & j_c \end{Bmatrix} \langle j_a \| T^p \| j_c \rangle \langle j_c \| T^q \| j_b \rangle . \tag{A.3.d12}$$

For the last equality use has been made of eq. (A.1.b11) to perform the summation over m_p, m_q and m_c.

Applying the Wigner-Eckart theorem to the left-hand side, one sees that eq. (A.3.d12) can be rewritten for reduced matrix elements as

$$\langle j_a \| [T^p \times T^q]^r \| j_b \rangle$$

$$= (-1)^{j_a+r+j_b} \sqrt{2r+1} \sum_{j_c} \begin{Bmatrix} j_b & j_a & r \\ p & q & j_c \end{Bmatrix} \langle j_a \| T^p \| j_c \rangle \langle j_c \| T^q \| j_b \rangle , \tag{A.3.d13}$$

where T^p and T^q both act in one and the same space. Writing the 6-*j* symbol as a *U*-coefficient one finds

$$\langle j_a \| [T^p \times T^q]^r \| j_b \rangle = (-1)^{r-p-q} \sum_{j_c} \frac{1}{\sqrt{2j_c+1}} U(j_b q j_a p; j_c r) \langle j_a \| T^p \| j_c \rangle \langle j_c \| T^q \| j_b \rangle . \tag{A.3.d14}$$

(e) Reduced matrix elements of spherical harmonics

From eq. (A.3.a15) one finds the relation

$$\langle l_a m_a | Y_{LM} | l_b m_b \rangle = (-1)^{l_a - m_a} \begin{pmatrix} l_a & L & l_b \\ -m_a & M & m_b \end{pmatrix} \langle l_a \| Y_L \| l_b \rangle . \tag{A.3.e1}$$

The left-hand side matrix element above is given by the integral over a product of three spherical harmonics. Application of eq. (A.2.4) to this product then leads to

$$\langle l_a m_a | Y_{LM} | l_b m_b \rangle = \int Y^*_{l_a m_a}(\hat{r}) Y_{LM}(\hat{r}) Y_{l_b m_b}(\hat{r}) \mathrm{d}^2 \hat{r}$$

$$= (-1)^{m_a} \sqrt{\frac{(2l_a+1)(2L+1)(2l_b+1)}{4\pi}} \begin{pmatrix} l_a & L & l_b \\ 0 & 0 & 0 \end{pmatrix} \begin{pmatrix} l_a & L & l_b \\ -m_a & M & m_b \end{pmatrix} . \tag{A.3.e2}$$

Comparing these equations one finds immediately

$$\langle l_a \| Y_L \| l_b \rangle = (-1)^{l_a} \sqrt{\frac{(2l_a+1)(2L+1)(2l_b+1)}{4\pi}} \begin{pmatrix} l_a & L & l_b \\ 0 & 0 & 0 \end{pmatrix} . \tag{A.3.e3}$$

Since $\boldsymbol{Y}_L$ acts only on the orbital coordinates one can use eq. (A.3.d9) for the evaluation of the reduced matrix element of a spherical harmonic in the coupled representation $\boldsymbol{l} + \boldsymbol{s} = \boldsymbol{j}$. Using also eq. (A.3.e3) one thus obtains

$$\langle l_a \tfrac{1}{2} j_a \| \boldsymbol{Y}_L \| l_b \tfrac{1}{2} j_b \rangle$$

$$= (-1)^{l_a + \frac{1}{2} + j_b + L} \sqrt{(2j_a+1)(2j_b+1)} \begin{Bmatrix} l_a & j_a & \frac{1}{2} \\ j_b & l_b & L \end{Bmatrix} \langle l_a \| \boldsymbol{Y}_L \| l_b \rangle$$

$$= (-1)^{\frac{1}{2} + j_b + L} \sqrt{\frac{(2j_a+1)(2j_b+1)(2l_a+1)(2l_b+1)(2L+1)}{4\pi}} \begin{pmatrix} l_a & L & l_b \\ 0 & 0 & 0 \end{pmatrix} \begin{Bmatrix} l_a & l & l_b \\ j_b & \frac{1}{2} & j_a \end{Bmatrix} . \tag{A.3.e4}$$

In this expression the product of a 3-j symbol and a 6-j symbol can be reduced further with eq. (A.1.b12) to

$$\langle l_a \tfrac{1}{2} j_a \| \boldsymbol{Y}_L \| l_b \tfrac{1}{2} j_b \rangle$$

$$= (-1)^{j_a + \frac{1}{2}} \sqrt{\frac{(2j_a+1)(2j_b+1)(2L+1)}{4\pi}} \begin{pmatrix} j_a & L & j_b \\ \frac{1}{2} & 0 & -\frac{1}{2} \end{pmatrix} \tfrac{1}{2} \{1 + (-1)^{l_a + L + l_b}\} . \tag{A.3.e5}$$

It is noted here that if a different coupling order is used, i.e. $s + l = j$ instead of $l + s = j$, a different phase factor in eqs. (A.3.e4) and (A.3.e5) results.

A.4. The Landé formula

For the evaluation of matrix elements $\langle JM|V|JM'\rangle$ that are diagonal in the angular momentum J it is often convenient to apply the Landé formula. According to this formula only the components of the vector operator V along J are relevant.

The Landé formula is obtained when a nonvanishing matrix element of the scalar product $V \cdot J$ is rewritten after insertion of a complete set of intermediate states $|JM'\rangle$. Thus one obtains

$$\langle JM|V \cdot J|JM\rangle = \sum_{M'} \langle JM|V|JM'\rangle \cdot \langle JM'|J|JM\rangle \,. \tag{A.4.1}$$

Here no summation over intermediate J-values occurs, since all matrix elements of J are diagonal in J.

From the Wigner-Eckart theorem (A.3.a14) one obtains the relations ($k = 1$)

$$\langle JM|V_m|JM'\rangle = \frac{\langle JM'1m|JM\rangle}{\sqrt{2J+1}} \langle J\|V\|J\rangle \,, \tag{A.4.2}$$

$$\langle JM|J_m|JM'\rangle = \frac{\langle JM'1m|JM\rangle}{\sqrt{2J+1}} \langle J\|J\|J\rangle \,. \tag{A.4.3}$$

Since the Clebsch-Gordan coefficients in eqs. (A.4.2) and (A.4.3) are equal, one finds that the matrix elements of V_m and J_m are related by

$$\langle JM|V_m|JM'\rangle = \frac{\langle J\|V\|J\rangle}{\langle J\|J\|J\rangle} \langle JM|J_m|JM'\rangle \,. \tag{A.4.4}$$

Insertion of eqs. (A.4.4) into eq. (A.4.1) thus yields

$$\langle JM|V \cdot J|JM\rangle = \sum_{M'} \frac{\langle J\|V\|J\rangle}{\langle J\|J\|J\rangle} \langle JM|J|JM'\rangle \cdot \langle JM'|J|JM\rangle$$

$$= \frac{\langle J\|V\|J\rangle}{\langle J\|J\|J\rangle} \langle JM|J^2|JM\rangle = \frac{\langle J\|V\|J\rangle}{\langle J\|J\|J\rangle} J(J+1) \,. \tag{A.4.5}$$

Substitution of the value of $\langle J\|V\|J\rangle/\langle J\|J\|J\rangle$ obtained from eq. (A.4.5) into eq. (A.4.4) leads to the generalized Landé formula

$$\langle JM|V|JM'\rangle = \frac{\langle JM|V \cdot J|JM\rangle}{J(J+1)} \langle JM|J|JM'\rangle \,, \tag{A.4.6}$$

A SEMICLASSICAL INTERPRETATION OF THE LANDÉ FORMULA

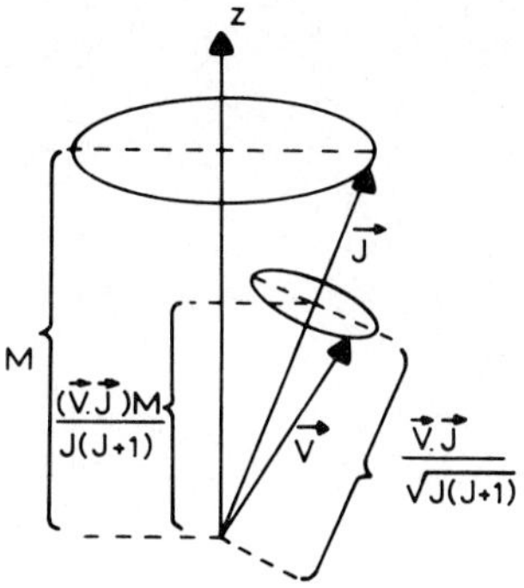

Fig. A.4.1. A semiclassical picture of eq. (A.4.6); the vector V precesses about J and the latter vector about the z-axis.

where it is obvious that this relation can hold only for matrix elements diagonal in J, since $\langle JM|\boldsymbol{J}|JM'\rangle$ is diagonal in J.

In eq. (A.4.6) the operator $\boldsymbol{V}$ in the left-hand member is replaced in the right-hand member by $(\boldsymbol{V}\cdot\boldsymbol{J})\boldsymbol{J}/\{J(J+1)\}$. The interpretation can be given as follows. The unit vector along $\boldsymbol{J}$ is given by

$$\boldsymbol{e}_J = \frac{\boldsymbol{J}}{|\boldsymbol{J}|} = \frac{\boldsymbol{J}}{\sqrt{J(J+1)}} \ . \tag{A.4.7}$$

The projection of $\boldsymbol{V}$ along this unit vector $\boldsymbol{e}_J$ is thus given by

$$(\boldsymbol{V}\cdot\boldsymbol{e}_J)\boldsymbol{e}_J = \frac{(\boldsymbol{V}\cdot\boldsymbol{J})}{\sqrt{J(J+1)}}\frac{\boldsymbol{J}}{\sqrt{J(J+1)}} = \frac{(\boldsymbol{V}\cdot\boldsymbol{J})\boldsymbol{J}}{J(J+1)} \ . \tag{A.4.8}$$

In a semiclassical picture this can be visualized as shown in fig. A.4.1. According to eq. (A.4.8) it is seen that for the expectation value of a vector operator $\boldsymbol{V}$ in a state of sharp angular momentum $\boldsymbol{J}$ the components perpendicular to $\boldsymbol{J}$ average out to zero when $\boldsymbol{V}$ precesses about $\boldsymbol{J}$. Subsequently the component of $\boldsymbol{V}$ along $\boldsymbol{J}$ is projected onto the z-axis to yield the expectation value in the state $|JM\rangle$ with $\boldsymbol{J}$ precessing about the z-axis.

A.5. Some relations for vector operators

For the derivation of expressions for electromagnetic transition operators several manipulations are to be performed with the vector operators $\boldsymbol{\nabla}$ and $\boldsymbol{l} = -i\boldsymbol{r}\times\boldsymbol{\nabla}$. Most of the relevant formulas can be derived with the use of the antisymmetric tensor ϵ_{jkl}, defined by

$$\begin{aligned} \epsilon_{jkl} &= 1 && \text{for } j, k, l = x, y, z \text{ or an even permutation of } x, y, z\ , \\ \epsilon_{jkl} &= -1 && \text{for } j, k, l = \text{an odd permutation of } x, y, z\ , \\ \epsilon_{jkl} &= 0 && \text{otherwise (i.e. for at least two identical subscripts)}\ . \end{aligned} \tag{A.5.1}$$

For instance, the identities

$$\text{div curl } \boldsymbol{v} = 0 \qquad \text{or } \boldsymbol{\nabla}\cdot(\boldsymbol{\nabla}\times\boldsymbol{v}) = 0 \tag{A.5.2}$$

for any vector $\boldsymbol{v}$ and

$$\text{curl grad } \phi = 0 \qquad \text{or } \boldsymbol{\nabla}\times(\boldsymbol{\nabla}\phi) = 0 \tag{A.5.3}$$

for any scalar function ϕ can be proved as follows.

Let us introduce for notational convenience

$$\partial_j \equiv \frac{\partial}{\partial x_j} \qquad \text{for } j = 1, 2, 3 \qquad (x_1 = x, x_2 = y, x_3 = z)\,. \tag{A.5.4}$$

A vector product

$$\boldsymbol{c} = \boldsymbol{a}\times\boldsymbol{b} \tag{A.5.5}$$

can be expressed with the use of the antisymmetric tensor as

$$c_j = \sum_{kl} \epsilon_{jkl}\, a_k b_l\,. \tag{A.5.6}$$

Thus one gets

$$\begin{aligned}\boldsymbol{\nabla}\cdot(\boldsymbol{\nabla}\times\boldsymbol{v}) &= \sum_{jkl}\epsilon_{jkl}\partial_j\partial_k v_l = \sum_{jkl}\epsilon_{jkl}\partial_k\partial_j v_l \\ &= \sum_{jkl}\epsilon_{kjl}\partial_j\partial_k v_l = -\sum_{jkl}\epsilon_{jkl}\partial_j\partial_k v_l = -\boldsymbol{\nabla}\cdot(\boldsymbol{\nabla}\times\boldsymbol{v})\,,\end{aligned} \tag{A.5.7}$$

and hence $\boldsymbol{\nabla}\cdot(\boldsymbol{\nabla}\times\boldsymbol{v}) = 0$ for any vector $\boldsymbol{v}$. For the second equal sign in eq. (A.5.7) the commuting differentations ∂_j and ∂_k are interchanged, for the third equal sign the summation labels j and k are interchanged, and for the fourth equal sign the antisymmetry of ϵ_{jkl} is used.

Similarly one finds for the vector component

$$(\boldsymbol{\nabla}\times(\boldsymbol{\nabla}\phi))_j = \sum_{kl}\epsilon_{jkl}\partial_k\partial_l\phi = 0\,, \tag{A.5.8}$$

which vanishes for the same reasons as above. Hence $\boldsymbol{\nabla}\times(\boldsymbol{\nabla}\phi) = 0$ for any function ϕ.

Next we prove also the relation

$$\boldsymbol{\nabla}\cdot\boldsymbol{l}\phi = 0 \text{ for an arbitrary function } \phi\,. \tag{A.5.9}$$

Employing eqs. (A.5.1) and (A.5.4), one obtains

$$\begin{aligned}\boldsymbol{\nabla}\cdot\boldsymbol{l}\phi &= -\mathrm{i}\,\boldsymbol{\nabla}\cdot(\boldsymbol{r}\times\boldsymbol{\nabla}\phi) = -\mathrm{i}\sum_{jkl}\epsilon_{jkl}\partial_j x_k\partial_l\phi = -\mathrm{i}\sum_{jkl}\epsilon_{jkl}(\delta_{jk} + x_k\partial_j)\partial_l\phi \\ &= -\mathrm{i}\sum_{ikl}\epsilon_{jkl}\delta_{jk}\partial_l\phi - \mathrm{i}\sum_{ikl}\epsilon_{jkl}x_k\partial_j\partial_l\phi\,.\end{aligned} \tag{A.5.10}$$

The first sum in the last member vanishes since one has either $\epsilon_{jkl} = 0$ (for $j = k$) or $\delta_{jk} = 0$ (for $j \neq k$). The second sum vanishes since, with a reasoning as given before, one obtains

$$\sum_{jkl} \epsilon_{jkl} x_k \partial_j \partial_l \phi = -\sum_{jkl} \epsilon_{lkj} x_k \partial_j \partial_l \phi = -\sum_{jkl} \epsilon_{jkl} x_k \partial_l \partial_j \phi = -\sum_{jkl} \epsilon_{jkl} x_k \partial_j \partial_l \phi \,. \qquad \text{(A.5.11)}$$

A rewriting of the vector operator $\mathrm{i}(\boldsymbol{\nabla} \times \boldsymbol{l})\phi$ with ϕ an arbitrary function is somewhat more complicated. For the j-component we may write

$$\mathrm{i}(\boldsymbol{\nabla} \times \boldsymbol{l}\phi)_j = (\boldsymbol{\nabla} \times (\boldsymbol{r} \times \boldsymbol{\nabla} \phi))_j = \sum_{klmn} \epsilon_{jkl} \epsilon_{lmn} \partial_k x_m \partial_n \phi \,. \qquad \text{(A.5.12)}$$

For a further reduction we use the expression

$$\sum_a \epsilon_{abc} \epsilon_{ade} = \delta_{bd} \delta_{ce} - \delta_{be} \delta_{cd} \,, \qquad \text{(A.5.13)}$$

which follows directly from the definition of ϵ_{jkl} in eq. (A.5.1). Thus performing the summation over l in eq. (A.5.12) we obtain

$$\begin{aligned} \mathrm{i}(\boldsymbol{\nabla} \times \boldsymbol{l}\phi)_j &= \sum_{kmn} (\delta_{jm} \delta_{kn} - \delta_{jn} \delta_{km}) \partial_k x_m \partial_n \phi \\ &= \sum_k \partial_k x_j \partial_k \phi - \sum_k \partial_k x_k \partial_j \phi \\ &= \sum_k (x_j \partial_k \partial_k \phi + \delta_{jk} \partial_k \phi) - \sum_k (\partial_j \partial_k x_k \phi - \partial_k \delta_{jk} \phi) \,. \end{aligned} \qquad \text{(A.5.14)}$$

Rewriting the right-hand side further, one obtains

$$\begin{aligned} \mathrm{i}(\boldsymbol{\nabla} \times \boldsymbol{l}\phi)_j &= x_j \boldsymbol{\nabla}^2 \phi + \partial_j \Big(2 - \sum_k \partial_k x_k\Big) \phi \\ &= x_j \boldsymbol{\nabla}^2 \phi + \partial_j \Big(-1 - \sum_k x_k \partial_k\Big) \phi \\ &= x_j \boldsymbol{\nabla}^2 \phi - \partial_j \left(1 + r \frac{\partial}{\partial r}\right) \phi \\ &= x_j \boldsymbol{\nabla}^2 \phi - \partial_j \frac{\partial}{\partial r} r \phi \,. \end{aligned} \qquad \text{(A.5.15)}$$

Summarizing, one finds the relation

$$\mathrm{i}(\boldsymbol{\nabla} \times \boldsymbol{l}\phi) = \boldsymbol{r} \boldsymbol{\nabla}^2 \phi - \boldsymbol{\nabla} \frac{\partial}{\partial r} r \phi \,, \qquad \text{(A.5.16)}$$

where ϕ is an arbitrary function.

With the aid of the antisymmetric tensor ϵ_{jkl} one can also easily rewrite the expression $\boldsymbol{\nabla} \times \boldsymbol{\nabla} \times \boldsymbol{v}$ with $\boldsymbol{v}$ an arbitrary vector. For the j-component one finds, applying eq. (A.5.6) twice,

$$(\nabla \times \nabla \times \boldsymbol{v})_j = \sum_{klmn} \epsilon_{jkl}\epsilon_{lmn}\partial_k\partial_m v_n = \sum_{kmn} (\delta_{jm}\delta_{kn} - \delta_{jn}\delta_{km})\partial_k\partial_m v_n \,, \tag{A.5.17}$$

where eq. (A.5.13) has been used.

After summation, eq. (A.5.17) reduces to

$$(\nabla \times \nabla \times \boldsymbol{v})_j = \sum_k \partial_j\partial_k v_k - \sum_k \partial_k\partial_k v_j \tag{A.5.18}$$

or

$$\nabla \times \nabla \times \boldsymbol{v} = \nabla\nabla\cdot\boldsymbol{v} - \nabla^2\boldsymbol{v}\,. \tag{A.5.19}$$

A.6. Antisymmetry of many-particle wave functions

In eq. (5.4) the order-preserving permutations are introduced. They are used to express a completely antisymmetric two-orbit configuration in terms of configurations that are antisymmetric in the two separate sets of particles only. Each of these permutations $\hat{P}_r$ is multiplied by a phase factor $\hat{\Pi}_r$, where the circumflex indicates that it concerns not only a number of transpositions between the two groups of particles but also a reshuffling within each group to restore the required ascending order of particle labels.

We shall now consider a slightly different way of achieving the full antisymmetrization [Towner and Hardy (1969)]. Let $P^{(t)}$ represent the operator that interchanges $2t$ particles between the two groups under consideration, i.e. $P^{(t)}$ consists of t transpositions. The total number of possible interchanges is given by

$$\sum_{t=0}^{\min(n,m)} \binom{n}{t}\binom{m}{t} = \binom{n+m}{n} = \frac{(n+m)!}{n!\,m!}\,. \tag{A.6.1}$$

As all $(n+m)!/n!\,m!$ resulting states are orthogonal, one obtains for the completely antisymmetric configuration with the proper normalization

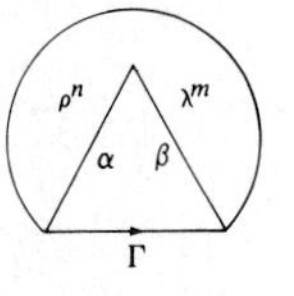

$$= \sqrt{\frac{n!\,m!}{(n+m)!}} \sum_{t=0}^{\min(n,m)} (-1)^t \binom{n}{t}\binom{m}{t} P^{(t)}$$

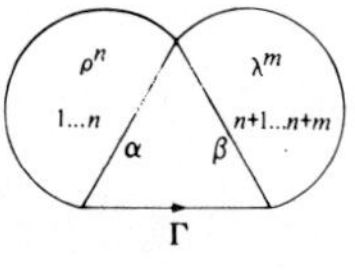

. (A.6.2)

It is seen that for application of this expression there is no need to construct the phases $\hat{\Pi}_r$ for the particular order-preserving permutations $\hat{P}_r$, since for the interchange of $2t$ particles each time any permutation $P^{(t)}$ may be taken as the representative. This permutation $P^{(t)}$ is associated with the phase factor $(-1)^t$.

APPENDIX B

B.1. Numerical values of 3-j and 6-j symbols

The tables include all 3-j and 6-j symbols with arguments j, l, $|m| \leqslant 3$. For more extensive tables see e.g. [Appel (1968); Rotenberg, Bivins, Metropolis and Wooten (1959)].

The entries are ordered according to increasing values of j_1. The 3-j and 6-j symbols listed satisfy the conditions $j_1 \geqslant j_2 \geqslant j_3; j_1 \geqslant l_i$ and $m_i \geqslant 0$. In order to look up 3-j or 6-j symbols not satisfying these conditions one should apply the symmetry relations given in eqs. (A.1.a7) or (A.1.b9).

Values of 3-j symbols $\begin{pmatrix} j_1 & j_2 & j_3 \\ m_1 & m_2 & m_3 \end{pmatrix}$ *for* j_i, $|m_i| \leqslant 3$

The relation between a Clebsch-Gordan coefficient and a 3-j symbol is given in eq. (A.1.a6).

j_1	j_2	j_3	m_1	m_2	m_3	Value	j_1	j_2	j_3	m_1	m_2	m_3	Value
1/2	1/2	0	1/2	-1/2	0	.70711	2	1	1	0	0	0	.36515
1	1/2	1/2	0	-1/2	1/2	.40825	2	1	1	1	-1	0	-.31623
1	1/2	1/2	1	-1/2	-1/2	-.57735	2	1	1	2	-1	-1	.44721
1	1	0	0	0	0	-.57735	2	3/2	1/2	0	-1/2	1/2	-.31623
1	1	0	1	-1	0	.57735	2	3/2	1/2	1	-3/2	1/2	.22361
1	1	1	0	0	0	.00000	2	3/2	1/2	1	-1/2	-1/2	.38730
1	1	1	1	-1	0	.40825	2	3/2	1/2	2	-3/2	-1/2	-.44721
3/2	1	1/2	1/2	-1	1/2	.28868	2	3/2	3/2	0	-3/2	3/2	-.22361
3/2	1	1/2	1/2	0	-1/2	.40825	2	3/2	3/2	0	-1/2	1/2	-.22361
3/2	1	1/2	3/2	-1	-1/2	-.50000	2	3/2	3/2	1	-3/2	1/2	.31623
3/2	3/2	0	1/2	-1/2	0	-.50000	2	3/2	3/2	1	-1/2	-1/2	.00000
3/2	3/2	0	3/2	-3/2	0	.50000	2	3/2	3/2	2	-3/2	-1/2	-.31623
3/2	3/2	1	1/2	-1/2	0	-.12910	2	2	0	0	0	0	.44721
3/2	3/2	1	1/2	1/2	-1	.36515	2	2	0	1	-1	0	-.44721
3/2	3/2	1	3/2	-3/2	0	.38730	2	2	0	2	-2	0	.44721
3/2	3/2	1	3/2	-1/2	-1	-.31623	2	2	1	0	0	0	.00000
2	1	1	0	-1	1	.18257	2	2	1	1	-1	0	-.18257

j_1	j_2	j_3	m_1	m_2	m_3	Value	j_1	j_2	j_3	m_1	m_2	m_3	Value
2	2	1	1	0	-1	.31623	5/2	5/2	2	1/2	-1/2	0	-.19518
2	2	1	2	-2	0	.36515	5/2	5/2	2	1/2	1/2	-1	.00000
2	2	1	2	-1	-1	-.25820	5/2	5/2	2	3/2	-3/2	0	.04880
2	2	2	0	0	0	-.23905	5/2	5/2	2	3/2	-1/2	-1	.16903
2	2	2	1	-1	0	.11952	5/2	5/2	2	3/2	1/2	-2	-.25355
2	2	2	2	-2	0	.23905	5/2	5/2	2	5/2	-5/2	0	.24398
2	2	2	2	-1	-1	-.29277	5/2	5/2	2	5/2	-3/2	-1	-.26726
5/2	3/2	1	1/2	-3/2	1	.12910	5/2	5/2	2	5/2	-1/2	-2	.18898
5/2	3/2	1	1/2	-1/2	0	.31623	3	3/2	3/2	0	-3/2	3/2	.08452
5/2	3/2	1	1/2	1/2	-1	.22361	3	3/2	3/2	0	-1/2	1/2	.25355
5/2	3/2	1	3/2	-3/2	0	-.25820	3	3/2	3/2	1	-3/2	1/2	-.16903
5/2	3/2	1	3/2	-1/2	-1	-.31623	3	3/2	3/2	1	-1/2	-1/2	-.29277
5/2	3/2	1	5/2	-3/2	-1	.40825	3	3/2	3/2	2	-3/2	-1/2	.26726
5/2	2	1/2	1/2	-1	1/2	-.25820	3	3/2	3/2	3	-3/2	-3/2	-.37796
5/2	2	1/2	1/2	0	-1/2	-.31623	3	2	1	0	-1	1	-.16903
5/2	2	1/2	3/2	-2	1/2	.18257	3	2	1	0	0	0	-.29277
5/2	2	1/2	3/2	-1	-1/2	.36515	3	2	1	1	-2	1	.09759
5/2	2	1/2	5/2	-2	-1/2	-.40825	3	2	1	1	-1	0	.27603
5/2	2	3/2	1/2	-2	3/2	-.16903	3	2	1	1	0	-1	.23905
5/2	2	3/2	1/2	-1	1/2	-.24398	3	2	1	2	-2	0	-.21822
5/2	2	3/2	1/2	0	-1/2	.11952	3	2	1	2	-1	-1	-.30861
5/2	2	3/2	1/2	1	-3/2	.25355	3	2	1	3	-2	-1	.37796
5/2	2	3/2	3/2	-2	1/2	.27603	3	2	2	0	-2	2	-.11952
5/2	2	3/2	3/2	-1	-1/2	.06901	3	2	2	0	-1	1	-.23905
5/2	2	3/2	3/2	0	-3/2	-.29277	3	2	2	0	0	0	.00000
5/2	2	3/2	5/2	-2	-1/2	-.30861	3	2	2	1	-2	1	.20702
5/2	2	3/2	5/2	-1	-3/2	.26726	3	2	2	1	-1	0	.16903
5/2	5/2	0	1/2	-1/2	0	.40825	3	2	2	2	-2	0	-.26726
5/2	5/2	0	3/2	-3/2	0	-.40825	3	2	2	2	-1	-1	.00000
5/2	5/2	0	5/2	-5/2	0	.40825	3	2	2	3	-2	-1	.26726
5/2	5/2	1	1/2	-1/2	0	.06901	3	5/2	1/2	0	-1/2	1/2	.26726
5/2	5/2	1	1/2	1/2	-1	-.29277	3	5/2	1/2	1	-3/2	1/2	-.21822
5/2	5/2	1	3/2	-3/2	0	-.20702	3	5/2	1/2	1	-1/2	-1/2	-.30861
5/2	5/2	1	3/2	-1/2	-1	.27603	3	5/2	1/2	2	-5/2	1/2	.15430
5/2	5/2	1	5/2	-5/2	0	.34503	3	5/2	1/2	2	-3/2	-1/2	.34503
5/2	5/2	1	5/2	-3/2	-1	-.21822	3	5/2	1/2	3	-5/2	-1/2	-.37796

j_1	j_2	j_3	m_1	m_2	m_3	Value	j_1	j_2	j_3	m_1	m_2	m_3	Value
3	5/2	3/2	0	-3/2	3/2	.20702	3	3	0	3	-3	0	.37796
3	5/2	3/2	0	-1/2	1/2	.16903	3	3	1	0	0	0	.00000
3	5/2	3/2	1	-5/2	3/2	-.13363	3	3	1	1	-1	0	.10911
3	5/2	3/2	1	-3/2	1/2	-.24152	3	3	1	1	0	-1	-.26726
3	5/2	3/2	1	-1/2	-1/2	.04880	3	3	1	2	-2	0	-.21822
3	5/2	3/2	1	1/2	-3/2	.25355	3	3	1	2	-1	-1	.24398
3	5/2	3/2	2	-5/2	1/2	.24398	3	3	1	3	-3	0	.32733
3	5/2	3/2	2	-3/2	-1/2	.10911	3	3	1	3	-2	-1	-.18898
3	5/2	3/2	2	-1/2	-3/2	-.26726	3	3	2	0	0	0	.19518
3	5/2	3/2	3	-5/2	-1/2	-.29881	3	3	2	1	-1	0	-.14639
3	5/2	3/2	3	-3/2	-3/2	.23146	3	3	2	1	0	-1	-.06901
3	5/2	5/2	0	-5/2	5/2	.14086	3	3	2	1	1	-2	.23905
3	5/2	5/2	0	-3/2	3/2	.19720	3	3	2	2	-2	0	.00000
3	5/2	5/2	0	-1/2	1/2	-.11269	3	3	2	2	-1	-1	.18898
3	5/2	5/2	1	-5/2	3/2	-.21822	3	3	2	2	0	-2	-.21822
3	5/2	5/2	1	-3/2	1/2	-.06901	3	3	2	3	-3	0	.24398
3	5/2	5/2	1	-1/2	-1/2	.19518	3	3	2	3	-2	-1	-.24398
3	5/2	5/2	2	-5/2	1/2	.24398	3	3	2	3	-1	-2	.15430
3	5/2	5/2	2	-3/2	-1/2	-.10911	3	3	3	0	0	0	.00000
3	5/2	5/2	3	-5/2	-1/2	-.19920	3	3	3	1	-1	0	-.15430
3	5/2	5/2	3	-3/2	-3/2	.25198	3	3	3	2	-2	0	.15430
3	3	0	0	0	0	-.37796	3	3	3	2	-1	-1	.00000
3	3	0	1	-1	0	.37796	3	3	3	3	-3	0	.15430
3	3	0	2	-2	0	-.37796	3	3	3	3	-2	-1	-.21822

Values of 6-j symbols $\begin{Bmatrix} j_1 & j_2 & j_3 \\ l_1 & l_2 & l_3 \end{Bmatrix}$ *for* $j, l \leqslant 3$

The relation between a *U*-coefficient and a 6-*j* symbol is given in eq. (A.1.b7).

j_1	j_2	j_3	l_1	l_2	l_3	Value	j_1	j_2	j_3	l_1	l_2	l_3	Value
1/2	1/2	0	0	0	1/2	-.70711	2	3/2	1/2	3/2	1	1	.09129
1/2	1/2	0	1/2	1/2	0	-.50000	2	3/2	1/2	2	3/2	1/2	.05000
1	1/2	1/2	0	1/2	1/2	.50000	2	3/2	3/2	0	3/2	3/2	-.25000
1	1/2	1/2	1	1/2	1/2	.16667	2	3/2	3/2	1/2	1	1	-.20412
1	1	0	0	0	1	.57735	2	3/2	3/2	1	3/2	1/2	-.22361
1	1	0	1/2	1/2	1/2	.40825	2	3/2	3/2	1	3/2	3/2	.05000
1	1	0	1	1	0	.33333	2	3/2	3/2	3/2	1	1	-.16330
1	1	1	1/2	1/2	1/2	-.33333	2	3/2	3/2	2	3/2	1/2	-.10000
1	1	1	1	1	0	-.33333	2	3/2	3/2	2	3/2	3/2	.15000
1	1	1	1	1	1	.16667	2	2	0	0	0	2	.44721
3/2	1	1/2	0	1/2	1	-.40825	2	2	0	1/2	1/2	3/2	.31623
3/2	1	1/2	1/2	1	1/2	-.33333	2	2	0	1	1	1	.25820
3/2	1	1/2	1	1/2	1	-.16667	2	2	0	1	1	2	-.25820
3/2	1	1/2	3/2	1	1/2	-.08333	2	2	0	3/2	3/2	1/2	.22361
3/2	3/2	0	0	0	3/2	-.50000	2	2	0	3/2	3/2	3/2	-.22361
3/2	3/2	0	1/2	1/2	1	-.35355	2	2	0	2	2	0	.20000
3/2	3/2	0	1	1	1/2	-.28868	2	2	1	1/2	1/2	3/2	-.22361
3/2	3/2	0	1	1	3/2	.28868	2	2	1	1	0	2	-.25820
3/2	3/2	0	3/2	3/2	0	-.25000	2	2	1	1	1	1	-.22361
3/2	3/2	1	1/2	1/2	1	.26352	2	2	1	1	1	2	.07454
3/2	3/2	1	1	0	3/2	.28868	2	2	1	3/2	1/2	3/2	-.15811
3/2	3/2	1	1	1	1/2	.26352	2	2	1	3/2	3/2	1/2	-.21213
3/2	3/2	1	1	1	3/2	-.10541	2	2	1	3/2	3/2	3/2	.14142
3/2	3/2	1	3/2	1/2	1	.16667	2	2	1	2	1	1	-.10000
3/2	3/2	1	3/2	3/2	0	.25000	2	2	1	2	2	0	-.20000
3/2	3/2	1	3/2	3/2	1	-.18333	2	2	1	2	2	1	.16667
2	1	1	0	1	1	.33333	2	2	2	1	1	1	.15275
2	1	1	1	1	1	.16667	2	2	2	3/2	3/2	1/2	.18708
2	1	1	2	1	1	.03333	2	2	2	3/2	3/2	3/2	.00000
2	3/2	1/2	0	1/2	3/2	.35355	2	2	2	2	1	1	.15275
2	3/2	1/2	1/2	1	1	.28868	2	2	2	2	2	0	.20000
2	3/2	1/2	1	1/2	3/2	.15811	2	2	2	2	2	1	-.10000
2	3/2	1/2	1	3/2	1/2	.25000	2	2	2	2	2	2	-.04286

j_1	j_2	j_3	l_1	l_2	l_3	Value
5/2	3/2	1	0	1	3/2	-.28868
5/2	3/2	1	1/2	3/2	1	-.25000
5/2	3/2	1	1	1	3/2	-.15811
5/2	3/2	1	3/2	3/2	1	-.10000
5/2	3/2	1	2	1	3/2	-.04082
5/2	3/2	1	5/2	3/2	1	-.01667
5/2	2	1/2	0	1/2	2	-.31623
5/2	2	1/2	1/2	1	3/2	-.25820
5/2	2	1/2	1	1/2	2	-.14907
5/2	2	1/2	1	3/2	1	-.22361
5/2	2	1/2	1	3/2	2	.19720
5/2	2	1/2	3/2	1	3/2	-.09129
5/2	2	1/2	3/2	2	1/2	-.20000
5/2	2	1/2	2	3/2	1	-.05774
5/2	2	1/2	2	3/2	2	.10000
5/2	2	1/2	5/2	2	1/2	-.03333
5/2	2	3/2	0	3/2	2	.22361
5/2	2	3/2	1/2	1	3/2	.17078
5/2	2	3/2	1/2	2	3/2	.15000
5/2	2	3/2	1	1/2	2	.19720
5/2	2	3/2	1	3/2	1	.18708
5/2	2	3/2	1	3/2	2	-.02357
5/2	2	3/2	3/2	1	3/2	.15275
5/2	2	3/2	3/2	2	1/2	.18708
5/2	2	3/2	3/2	2	3/2	-.10000
5/2	2	3/2	2	1/2	2	.10000
5/2	2	3/2	2	3/2	1	.10801
5/2	2	3/2	2	3/2	2	-.13363
5/2	2	3/2	5/2	1	3/2	.05000
5/2	2	3/2	5/2	2	1/2	.06667
5/2	2	3/2	5/2	2	3/2	-.11190
5/2	5/2	0	0	0	5/2	-.40825
5/2	5/2	0	1/2	1/2	2	-.28868
5/2	5/2	0	1	1	3/2	-.23570
5/2	5/2	0	1	1	5/2	.23570
5/2	5/2	0	3/2	3/2	1	-.20412

j_1	j_2	j_3	l_1	l_2	l_3	Value
5/2	5/2	0	3/2	3/2	2	.20412
5/2	5/2	0	2	2	1/2	-.18257
5/2	5/2	0	2	2	3/2	.18257
5/2	5/2	0	2	2	5/2	-.18257
5/2	5/2	0	5/2	5/2	0	-.16667
5/2	5/2	1	1/2	1/2	2	.19720
5/2	5/2	1	1	0	5/2	.23570
5/2	5/2	1	1	1	3/2	.19720
5/2	5/2	1	1	1	5/2	-.05634
5/2	5/2	1	3/2	1/2	2	.14907
5/2	5/2	1	3/2	3/2	1	.18708
5/2	5/2	1	3/2	3/2	2	-.11581
5/2	5/2	1	2	1	3/2	.10000
5/2	5/2	1	2	1	5/2	-.14254
5/2	5/2	1	2	2	1/2	.17638
5/2	5/2	1	2	2	3/2	-.13859
5/2	5/2	1	2	2	5/2	.07559
5/2	5/2	1	5/2	3/2	1	.06667
5/2	5/2	1	5/2	5/2	0	.16667
5/2	5/2	1	5/2	5/2	1	-.14762
5/2	5/2	2	1	1	3/2	-.12472
5/2	5/2	2	1	1	5/2	-.14254
5/2	5/2	2	3/2	1/2	2	-.16330
5/2	5/2	2	3/2	3/2	1	-.15275
5/2	5/2	2	3/2	3/2	2	-.02182
5/2	5/2	2	2	0	5/2	-.18257
5/2	5/2	2	2	1	3/2	-.14142
5/2	5/2	2	2	1	5/2	.07559
5/2	5/2	2	2	2	1/2	-.16330
5/2	5/2	2	2	2	3/2	.05832
5/2	5/2	2	2	2	5/2	.05832
5/2	5/2	2	5/2	1/2	2	-.10000
5/2	5/2	2	5/2	3/2	1	-.10690
5/2	5/2	2	5/2	3/2	2	.11429
5/2	5/2	2	5/2	5/2	0	-.16667
5/2	5/2	2	5/2	5/2	1	.10952

j_1	j_2	j_3	l_1	l_2	l_3	Value	j_1	j_2	j_3	l_1	l_2	l_3	Value
5/2	5/2	2	5/2	5/2	2	-.01667	3	5/2	1/2	5/2	2	2	-.06901
3	3/2	3/2	0	3/2	3/2	.25000	3	5/2	1/2	3	5/2	1/2	.02381
3	3/2	3/2	1	3/2	3/2	.15000	3	5/2	3/2	0	3/2	5/2	-.20412
3	3/2	3/2	2	3/2	3/2	.05000	3	5/2	3/2	1/2	1	2	-.14907
3	3/2	3/2	3	3/2	3/2	.00714	3	5/2	3/2	1/2	2	2	-.14142
3	2	1	0	1	2	.25820	3	5/2	3/2	1	1/2	5/2	-.17817
3	2	1	1/2	3/2	3/2	.22361	3	5/2	3/2	1	3/2	3/2	-.16330
3	2	1	1	1	2	.14907	3	5/2	3/2	1	3/2	5/2	.00891
3	2	1	1	2	1	.20000	3	5/2	3/2	1	5/2	3/2	-.10000
3	2	1	3/2	3/2	3/2	.10000	3	5/2	3/2	3/2	1	2	-.14254
3	2	1	2	1	2	.04364	3	5/2	3/2	3/2	2	1	-.16330
3	2	1	2	2	1	.06667	3	5/2	3/2	3/2	2	2	.07559
3	2	1	5/2	3/2	3/2	.02182	3	5/2	3/2	2	1/2	5/2	-.09759
3	2	1	3	2	1	.00952	3	5/2	3/2	2	3/2	3/2	-.10690
3	2	2	0	2	2	-.20000	3	5/2	3/2	2	3/2	5/2	.12002
3	2	2	1/2	3/2	3/2	-.14142	3	5/2	3/2	2	5/2	1/2	-.15936
3	2	2	1	2	1	-.16330	3	5/2	3/2	2	5/2	3/2	.10952
3	2	2	1	2	2	.00000	3	5/2	3/2	5/2	1	2	-.05345
3	2	2	3/2	3/2	3/2	-.14142	3	5/2	3/2	5/2	2	1	-.07619
3	2	2	2	2	1	-.10690	3	5/2	3/2	5/2	2	2	.10722
3	2	2	2	2	2	.11429	3	5/2	3/2	3	3/2	3/2	-.02857
3	2	2	5/2	3/2	3/2	-.06061	3	5/2	3/2	3	5/2	1/2	-.04762
3	2	2	3	2	1	-.02857	3	5/2	3/2	3	5/2	3/2	.08452
3	2	2	3	2	2	.07143	3	5/2	5/2	0	5/2	5/2	.16667
3	5/2	1/2	0	1/2	5/2	.28868	3	5/2	5/2	1/2	2	2	.14142
3	5/2	1/2	1/2	1	2	.23570	3	5/2	5/2	1	3/2	3/2	.10000
3	5/2	1/2	1	1/2	5/2	.14086	3	5/2	5/2	1	5/2	3/2	.13093
3	5/2	1/2	1	3/2	3/2	.20412	3	5/2	5/2	1	5/2	5/2	-.05238
3	5/2	1/2	1	3/2	5/2	-.17817	3	5/2	5/2	3/2	2	1	.13093
3	5/2	1/2	3/2	1	2	.08909	3	5/2	5/2	3/2	2	2	.04041
3	5/2	1/2	3/2	2	1	.18257	3	5/2	5/2	2	3/2	3/2	.12857
3	5/2	1/2	3/2	2	2	-.16903	3	5/2	5/2	2	5/2	1/2	.14639
3	5/2	1/2	2	3/2	3/2	.05976	3	5/2	5/2	2	5/2	3/2	-.03499
3	5/2	1/2	2	3/2	5/2	-.09759	3	5/2	5/2	2	5/2	5/2	-.06905
3	5/2	1/2	2	5/2	1/2	.16667	3	5/2	5/2	5/2	2	1	.10498
3	5/2	1/2	5/2	2	1	.03984	3	5/2	5/2	5/2	2	2	-.09091

j_1	j_2	j_3	l_1	l_2	l_3	Value
3	5/2	5/2	3	3/2	3/2	.06429
3	5/2	5/2	3	5/2	1/2	.07143
3	5/2	5/2	3	5/2	3/2	-.10000
3	5/2	5/2	3	5/2	5/2	.06270
3	3	0	0	0	3	.37796
3	3	0	1/2	1/2	5/2	.26726
3	3	0	1	1	2	.21822
3	3	0	1	1	3	-.21822
3	3	0	3/2	3/2	3/2	.18898
3	3	0	3/2	3/2	5/2	-.18898
3	3	0	2	2	1	.16903
3	3	0	2	2	2	-.16903
3	3	0	2	2	3	.16903
3	3	0	5/2	5/2	1/2	.15430
3	3	0	5/2	5/2	3/2	-.15430
3	3	0	5/2	5/2	5/2	.15430
3	3	0	3	3	0	.14286
3	3	1	1/2	1/2	5/2	-.17817
3	3	1	1	0	3	-.21822
3	3	1	1	1	2	-.17817
3	3	1	1	1	3	.04454
3	3	1	3/2	1/2	5/2	-.14086
3	3	1	3/2	3/2	3/2	-.16903
3	3	1	3/2	3/2	5/2	.09860
3	3	1	2	1	2	-.09759
3	3	1	2	1	3	.13363
3	3	1	2	2	1	-.15936
3	3	1	2	2	2	.11952
3	3	1	2	2	3	-.05976
3	3	1	5/2	3/2	3/2	-.06901
3	3	1	5/2	3/2	5/2	.10351
3	3	1	5/2	5/2	1/2	-.15058
3	3	1	5/2	5/2	3/2	.12800
3	3	1	5/2	5/2	5/2	-.09035
3	3	1	3	2	1	-.04762
3	3	1	3	3	0	-.14286
3	3	1	3	3	1	.13095
3	3	2	1	1	2	.10690
3	3	2	1	1	3	.13363
3	3	2	3/2	1/2	5/2	.14639
3	3	2	3/2	3/2	3/2	.13093
3	3	2	3/2	3/2	5/2	.03273
3	3	2	2	0	3	.16903
3	3	2	2	1	2	.13093
3	3	2	2	1	3	-.05976
3	3	2	2	2	1	.13997
3	3	2	2	2	2	-.03499
3	3	2	2	2	3	-.06415
3	3	2	5/2	1/2	5/2	.09759
3	3	2	5/2	3/2	3/2	.10498
3	3	2	5/2	3/2	5/2	-.09915
3	3	2	5/2	5/2	1/2	.14286
3	3	2	5/2	5/2	3/2	-.07857
3	3	2	5/2	5/2	5/2	-.00476
3	3	2	3	1	2	.05714
3	3	2	3	2	1	.07825
3	3	2	3	2	2	-.10000
3	3	2	3	3	0	.14286
3	3	2	3	3	1	-.10714
3	3	2	3	3	2	.04524
3	3	3	3/2	3/2	3/2	-.07825
3	3	3	2	2	1	-.11066
3	3	3	2	2	2	-.05533
3	3	3	5/2	3/2	3/2	-.11737
3	3	3	5/2	5/2	1/2	-.13041
3	3	3	5/2	5/2	3/2	.01304
3	3	3	5/2	5/2	5/2	.07390
3	3	3	3	2	1	-.10102
3	3	3	3	2	2	.07377
3	3	3	3	3	0	-.14286
3	3	3	3	3	1	.07143
3	3	3	3	3	2	.02381
3	3	3	3	3	3	-.07143

B.2. Quantum numbers of single-shell states

The quantum numbers of the single-shell states $(j)^n_{JTvt}$ with n denoting the number of particles or holes, J the total spin, T the total isospin, v the seniority and t the reduced isospin are listed for all states with $j \leqslant \frac{5}{2}$ [Flowers (1952)].

n	T	(v,t)	J		n	T	(v,t)	J
0	0	(0,0)	0	$j=\frac{1}{2}$	2	0	(2,0)	1
1	$\frac{1}{2}$	$(1,\frac{1}{2})$	$\frac{1}{2}$		2	1	(0,0)	0
0	0	(0,0)	0	$j=\frac{3}{2}$	4	0	(0,0)	0
1	$\frac{1}{2}$	$(1,\frac{1}{2})$	$\frac{3}{2}$				(2,1)	2
2	0	(2,0)	1 3				(4,0)	2 4
2	1	(0,0)	0		4	1	(2,0)	1 3
		(2,1)	2				(2,1)	2
3	$\frac{1}{2}$	$(1,\frac{1}{2})$	$\frac{3}{2}$		4	2	(0,0)	0
		$(3,\frac{1}{2})$	$\frac{1}{2}$ $\frac{5}{2}$ $\frac{7}{2}$					
3	$\frac{3}{2}$	$(1,\frac{1}{2})$	$\frac{3}{2}$					
0	0	(0,0)	0	$j=\frac{5}{2}$	5	$\frac{1}{2}$	$(1,\frac{1}{2})$	$\frac{5}{2}$
1	$\frac{1}{2}$	$(1,\frac{1}{2})$	$\frac{5}{2}$				$(3,\frac{1}{2})$	$\frac{1}{2}$ $\frac{3}{2}$ $\frac{5}{2}$ $(\frac{7}{2})^2$ $\frac{9}{2}$ $\frac{11}{2}$ $\frac{13}{2}$
2	0	(2,0)	1 3 5				$(3,\frac{3}{2})$	$\frac{3}{2}$ $\frac{9}{2}$
2	1	(0,0)	0				$(5,\frac{1}{2})$	$\frac{1}{2}$ $\frac{3}{2}$ $(\frac{5}{2})^2$ $(\frac{7}{2})^2$ $(\frac{9}{2})^2$ $(\frac{11}{2})^2$ $\frac{13}{2}$ $\frac{15}{2}$ $\frac{17}{2}$
		(2,1)	2 4		5	$\frac{3}{2}$	$(1,\frac{1}{2})$	$\frac{5}{2}$
3	$\frac{1}{2}$	$(1,\frac{1}{2})$	$\frac{5}{2}$				$(3,\frac{1}{2})$	$\frac{1}{2}$ $\frac{3}{2}$ $\frac{5}{2}$ $(\frac{7}{2})^2$ $\frac{9}{2}$ $\frac{11}{2}$ $\frac{13}{2}$
		$(3,\frac{1}{2})$	$\frac{1}{2}$ $\frac{3}{2}$ $\frac{5}{2}$ $(\frac{7}{2})^2$ $\frac{9}{2}$ $\frac{11}{2}$ $\frac{13}{2}$				$(3,\frac{3}{2})$	$\frac{3}{2}$ $\frac{9}{2}$
3	$\frac{3}{2}$	$(1,\frac{1}{2})$	$\frac{5}{2}$		5	$\frac{5}{2}$	$(1,\frac{1}{2})$	$\frac{5}{2}$
		$(3,\frac{3}{2})$	$\frac{3}{2}$ $\frac{9}{2}$		6	0	(2,0)	1 3 5
4	0	(0,0)	0				(4,1)	1 2 3^2 4 5 6 7
		(2,1)	2 4				(6,0)	1 3^2 4 5 6 7 9
		(4,0)	0 2^2 3 4^2 5 6^2 8		6	1	(0,0)	0
4	1	(2,0)	1 3 5				(2,1)	2^2 4^2
		(2,1)	2 4				(4,0)	0 2^2 3 4^2 5 6^2 8
		(4,1)	1 2 3^2 4 5 6 7				(4,1)	1 2 3^2 4 5 6 7
4	2	(0,0)	0		6	2	(2,0)	1 3 5
		(2,1)	2 4				(2,1)	2 4
					6	3	(0,0)	0

B.3. Coefficients of fractional parentage

The coefficients of fractional parentage $\langle j^n JTvt | \} j^{n-1} J'T'v't' \rangle$ for $j = \frac{1}{2}, \frac{3}{2}$ and $\frac{5}{2}$ with $n \leqslant 3$ are given below. The state j^n is characterized by the quantum numbers J (total spin), T (total isospin), v (seniority) and t (reduced isospin). The phase convention corresponds to that of the Oak Ridge-Rochester shell-model code [French, Halbert, McGrory and Wong (1969); McGrory (1967)].

$n = 1$ or 2; for all j-values $\quad \langle j^n JTvt | \} j^{n-1} J'T'v't' \rangle = +1$

$n = 3; j = \frac{1}{2}$ $\quad \langle (\frac{1}{2})^3 \frac{1}{2} \frac{1}{2} 1 \frac{1}{2} | \} (\frac{1}{2})^2\, 0\, 1\, 0\, 0 \rangle = -0.7071 \quad \langle (\frac{1}{2})^3 \frac{1}{2} \frac{1}{2} 1 \frac{1}{2} | \} (\frac{1}{2})^2\, 1\, 0\, 2\, 0 \rangle = +0.7071$

$n = 3; j = \frac{3}{2}$

$(\frac{3}{2})^3$ \ $(\frac{3}{2})^2$ $(JTvt)$; $(J'T'v't')$	(0100)	(1020)	(2121)	(3020)
$(\frac{1}{2}\ \frac{1}{2}\ 3\ \frac{1}{2})$	0	−0.7071	−0.7071	0
$(\frac{3}{2}\ \frac{1}{2}\ 1\ \frac{1}{2})$	−0.6455	+0.3873	−0.2887	+0.5916
$(\frac{3}{2}\ \frac{3}{2}\ 1\ \frac{1}{2})$	+0.4082	0	−0.9129	0
$(\frac{5}{2}\ \frac{1}{2}\ 3\ \frac{1}{2})$	0	+0.4830	−0.7071	−0.5164
$(\frac{7}{2}\ \frac{1}{2}\ 3\ \frac{1}{2})$	0	0	−0.7071	+0.7071

$n = 3; j = \frac{5}{2}$

$(\frac{5}{2})^3$ \ $(\frac{5}{2})^2$ $(JTvt)$; $(J'T'v't')$	(0100)	(1020)	(2121)	(3020)	(4121)	(5020)
$(\frac{1}{2}\ \frac{1}{2}\ 3\ \frac{1}{2})$	0	0	−0.7071	+0.7071	0	0
$(\frac{3}{2}\ \frac{1}{2}\ 3\ \frac{1}{2})$	0	−0.6325	−0.3779	−0.3162	−0.5976	0
$(\frac{3}{2}\ \frac{3}{2}\ 3\ \frac{3}{2})$	0	0	−0.8452	0	+0.5345	0
$(\frac{5}{2}\ \frac{1}{2}\ 1\ \frac{1}{2})$	−0.6236	+0.2673	−0.1992	+0.4082	−0.2673	+0.5118
$(\frac{5}{2}\ \frac{1}{2}\ 3\ \frac{1}{2})$	0	+0.3381	−0.5669	−0.5594	+0.4226	+0.2697
$(\frac{5}{2}\ \frac{3}{2}\ 1\ \frac{1}{2})$	+0.4714	0	−0.5270	0	−0.7071	0
$(\frac{7}{2}\ \frac{1}{2}\ 3\ \frac{1}{2})$ [a]	0	+0.2474	−0.7071	+0.3563	0	−0.5584
$(\frac{7}{2}\ \frac{1}{2}\ 3\ \frac{1}{2})$ [a]	0	+0.4738	0	−0.5118	−0.7071	−0.1166
$(\frac{9}{2}\ \frac{1}{2}\ 3\ \frac{1}{2})$	0	0	−0.6268	+0.3727	−0.3273	+0.6009
$(\frac{9}{2}\ \frac{3}{2}\ 3\ \frac{3}{2})$	0	0	+0.4629	0	−0.8864	0
$(\frac{11}{2}\ \frac{1}{2}\ 3\ \frac{1}{2})$	0	0	0	+0.4907	−0.7071	−0.5092
$(\frac{13}{2}\ \frac{1}{2}\ 3\ \frac{1}{2})$	0	0	0	0	−0.7071	+0.7071

[a] Since there are two independent states $(\frac{5}{2})^3$ with identical quantum numbers $J' = \frac{7}{2}$, $T' = \frac{1}{2}$, $v' = 3$ and $t' = \frac{1}{2}$, one must introduce an extra label, say $x = 1$ and $x = 2$, to distinguish the two states from each other.

B.4. Values of MSDI two-body matrix elements

The values of the two-body matrix elements are calculated with the MSDI (see chapter 6) for the orbits $j = \frac{5}{2}, \frac{3}{2}$ and $\frac{1}{2}$. The values listed are derived with the strength parameters (see eqs. (6.44), (6.47) and (6.49)) given by $A_0 = A_1 = 1$ MeV, $B = C = 0$.

The phases correspond to the orbits $1f_{5/2}$, $2p_{3/2}$ and $2p_{1/2}$, the coupling order $j = l + s$ and radial wave functions that are positive near the origin. The listed values are also applicable to the $1d_{5/2}$, $1d_{3/2}$ and $2s_{1/2}$ orbits. Since, however, the n, l values for the 1f2p shell differ from those of the 1d2s shell, the phase factor $(-1)^{n_a+n_b+n_c+n_d}$ (cf. eq. (6.44)) should be corrected for in the latter case. The phase factor associated with a different coupling order of the orbits can be obtained from eq. (5.14).

Orbits [a)]

a	*b*	*c*	*d*	*J*	*T*	$\langle ab\|V\|cd\rangle$ [b)]	*a*	*b*	*c*	*d*	*J*	*T*	$\langle ab\|V\|cd\rangle$ [b)]
f5	f5	f5	f5	0	1	−3.0000	f5	p3	p3	p3	1	0	0.5657
f5	f5	f5	f5	1	0	−1.6286	f5	p3	p3	p3	2	1	0.3703
f5	f5	f5	f5	2	1	−0.6857	f5	p3	p3	p3	3	0	−0.3959
f5	f5	f5	f5	3	0	−0.9143	f5	p3	p3	p1	1	0	0.8944
f5	f5	f5	f5	4	1	−0.2857	f5	p3	p3	p1	1	1	0.0000
f5	f5	f5	f5	5	0	−1.4286	f5	p3	p3	p1	2	0	−1.3093
f5	f5	f5	p3	1	0	−1.8142	f5	p3	p3	p1	2	1	0.5237
f5	f5	f5	p3	2	1	0.4849	f5	p3	p1	p1	1	0	−1.7889
f5	f5	f5	p3	3	0	−0.5938	f5	p1	f5	p1	2	0	−0.8000
f5	f5	f5	p3	4	1	0.5714	f5	p1	f5	p1	2	1	−1.2000
f5	f5	f5	p1	2	1	−0.9071	f5	p1	f5	p1	3	0	−2.0000
f5	f5	f5	p1	3	0	−1.3279	f5	p1	f5	p1	3	1	0.0000
f5	f5	p3	p3	0	1	−2.4495	f5	p1	p3	p3	2	1	−0.6928
f5	f5	p3	p3	1	0	1.1759	f5	p1	p3	p3	3	0	0.2213
f5	f5	p3	p3	2	1	−0.5237	f5	p1	p3	p1	2	0	0.9798
f5	f5	p3	p3	3	0	0.3429	f5	p1	p3	p1	2	1	−0.9798
f5	f5	p3	p1	1	0	−0.6761	p3	p3	p3	p3	0	1	−2.0000
f5	f5	p3	p1	2	1	−0.7407	p3	p3	p3	p3	1	0	−1.2000
f5	f5	p1	p1	0	1	−1.7321	p3	p3	p3	p3	2	1	−0.4000
f5	f5	p1	p1	1	0	−1.1832	p3	p3	p3	p3	3	0	−1.2000
f5	p3	f5	p3	1	0	−3.6000	p3	p3	p3	p1	1	0	1.2649
f5	p3	f5	p3	1	1	0.0000	p3	p3	p3	p1	2	1	−0.5657
f5	p3	f5	p3	2	0	−1.4286	p3	p3	p1	p1	0	1	−1.4142
f5	p3	f5	p3	2	1	−0.3429	p3	p3	p1	p1	1	0	0.6325
f5	p3	f5	p3	3	0	−0.7429	p3	p1	p3	p1	1	0	−2.0000
f5	p3	f5	p3	3	1	0.0000	p3	p1	p3	p1	1	1	0.0000
f5	p3	f5	p3	4	0	−1.4286	p3	p1	p3	p1	2	0	−1.2000
f5	p3	f5	p3	4	1	−1.1429	p3	p1	p3	p1	2	1	−0.8000
f5	p3	f5	p1	2	0	1.0690	p3	p1	p1	p1	1	0	0.0000
f5	p3	f5	p1	2	1	0.6414	p1	p1	p1	p1	0	1	−1.0000
f5	p3	f5	p1	3	0	−1.0222	p1	p1	p1	p1	1	0	−1.0000
f5	p3	f5	p1	3	1	0.0000							

[a)] The symbols f5, p3 and p1 denote the orbits $1f_{5/2}$, $2p_{3/2}$ and $2p_{1/2}$, respectively.
[b)] Values in MeV.

B.5. Harmonic-oscillator radial matrix elements

The radial matrix elements $\langle nl|r^L|n'l'\rangle$, defined in eq. (10.46), are calculated for the lower shell-model orbits n, l and $L \leqslant 4$ with harmonic-oscillator radial wave functions $R_{nl}(r)$ that are positive near the origin. The values listed below are given for the harmonic-oscillator size parameter $b = 1$ fm. Because of the relation between the size parameter and the mass number, the dependence on the latter follows from the relation $\langle nl|r^L|n'l'\rangle_b = A^{L/6}\langle nl|r^L|n'l'\rangle_{b=1\,\mathrm{fm}}$ (see eq. (10.49)).

Values of $\langle nl|r^L|n'l'\rangle_{b=1\,\mathrm{fm}}$ in fm^L

n	l	n'	l'	$L = 0$	$L = 1$	$L = 2$	$L = 3$	$L = 4$
1	0	1	0	1.000	1.128	1.500	2.257	3.750
1	0	1	1	0.921	1.225	1.843	3.062	5.528
1	0	1	2	0.775	1.165	1.936	3.496	6.778
1	0	1	3	0.623	1.035	1.869	3.623	7.475
1	1	1	0	0.921	1.225	1.843	3.062	5.528
1	1	1	1	1.000	1.505	2.500	4.514	8.750
1	1	1	2	0.952	1.581	2.855	5.534	11.418
1	1	1	3	0.845	1.526	2.958	6.103	13.311
1	2	1	0	0.775	1.165	1.936	3.496	6.778
1	2	1	1	0.952	1.581	2.855	5.534	11.418
1	2	1	2	1.000	1.805	3.500	7.222	15.750
1	2	1	3	0.965	1.871	3.860	8.419	19.301
1	3	1	0	0.623	1.035	1.869	3.623	7.475
1	3	1	1	0.845	1.526	2.958	6.103	13.311
1	3	1	2	0.965	1.871	3.860	8.419	19.301
1	3	1	3	1.000	2.063	4.500	10.317	24.750
2	0	1	0	0.000	−0.461	−1.225	− 2.764	− 6.124
2	0	1	1	−0.376	−1.000	−2.257	− 5.000	−11.284
2	0	1	2	−0.632	−1.427	−3.162	− 7.136	−16.602
2	0	1	3	−0.763	−1.690	−3.815	− 8.874	−21.362
2	0	2	0	1.000	1.693	3.500	7.899	18.750
2	0	2	1	0.833	1.581	3.568	8.696	22.123
2	1	1	0	0.291	0.000	−0.583	− 1.936	− 5.244
2	1	1	1	0.000	−0.476	−1.581	− 4.282	−11.068
2	1	1	2	−0.301	−1.000	−2.708	− 7.000	−18.054
2	1	1	3	−0.535	−1.448	−3.742	− 9.650	−25.256
2	1	2	0	0.833	1.581	3.568	8.696	22.123
2	1	2	1	1.000	1.956	4.500	11.284	29.750

B.6. Reduced single-particle matrix elements

The reduced single-particle matrix elements $\langle n_f l_f j_f \| O(\bar{\omega}L) \| n_i l_i j_i \rangle$ for $\mathcal{E}L$ and $\mathcal{M}L$ transitions defined in eqs. (10.55) and (10.73) can be calculated from the functions $f_I^{(\mathcal{E}L)}(l_f j_f; l_i j_i)$ and $f_I^{(\mathcal{M}L)}(l_f j_f; l_i j_i)$ listed below and the radial matrix elements $\langle n_f l_f | r^L | n_i l_i \rangle$ given in appendix B.5. The index I labels the isoscalar ($I = 0$) and isovector ($I = 1$) matrix elements. The interchange of left- and right-hand side quantum numbers nlj introduces the phase factor $(-1)^{j_f - j_i}$ (cf. eq. (10.57)). For the calculation of the functions $f_I^{(L)}$ the coupling order $\boldsymbol{j} = \boldsymbol{l} + \boldsymbol{s}$ has been used.

Values of the functions $f_I^{\bar{\omega}L}(l_f j_f; l_i j_i)$

l_f	j_f	l_i	j_i	I	$\mathcal{M}1$	$\mathcal{M}2$	$\mathcal{M}3$	$\mathcal{E}1$	$\mathcal{E}2$	$\mathcal{E}3$	$\mathcal{E}4$
0	$\frac{1}{2}$	0	$\frac{1}{2}$	0	0.744	0	0	0	0	0	0
				1	6.898	0	0	0	0	0	0
0	$\frac{1}{2}$	1	$\frac{1}{2}$	0	0	0	0	−0.282	0	0	0
				1	0	0	0	−0.489	0	0	0
0	$\frac{1}{2}$	1	$\frac{3}{2}$	0	0	− 1.755	0	−0.399	0	0	0
				1	0	−16.259	0	−0.691	0	0	0
0	$\frac{1}{2}$	2	$\frac{3}{2}$	0	0	0	0	0	0.399	0	0
				1	0	0	0	0	0.691	0	0
0	$\frac{1}{2}$	2	$\frac{5}{2}$	0	0	0	3.009	0	0.489	0	0
				1	0	0	27.878	0	0.846	0	0
0	$\frac{1}{2}$	3	$\frac{5}{2}$	0	0	0	0	0	0	−0.489	0
				1	0	0	0	0	0	−0.846	0
0	$\frac{1}{2}$	3	$\frac{7}{2}$	0	0	0	0	0	0	−0.564	0
				1	0	0	0	0	0	−0.977	0
1	$\frac{1}{2}$	1	$\frac{1}{2}$	0	0.316	0	0	0	0	0	0
				1	− 1.322	0	0	0	0	0	0
1	$\frac{1}{2}$	1	$\frac{3}{2}$	0	0.303	0	0	0	0.399	0	0
				1	5.813	0	0	0	0.691	0	0
1	$\frac{1}{2}$	2	$\frac{3}{2}$	0	0	− 0.447	0	−0.399	0	0	0
				1	0	1.870	0	−0.691	0	0	0
1	$\frac{1}{2}$	2	$\frac{5}{2}$	0	0	− 1.068	0	0	0	−0.489	0
				1	0	−14.802	0	0	0	−0.846	0
1	$\frac{1}{2}$	3	$\frac{5}{2}$	0	0	0	0.547	0	0.489	0	0
				1	0	0	− 2.290	0	0.846	0	0
1	$\frac{1}{2}$	3	$\frac{7}{2}$	0	0	0	2.132	0	0	0	0.564
				1	0	0	26.127	0	0	0	0.977
1	$\frac{3}{2}$	1	$\frac{3}{2}$	0	1.677	0	− 3.296	0	−0.399	0	0
				1	8.816	0	−30.539	0	−0.691	0	0
1	$\frac{3}{2}$	2	$\frac{3}{2}$	0	0	− 0.096	0	−0.178	0	0.535	0
				1	0	5.122	0	−0.309	0	0.927	0

Table (continued)

l_f	j_f	l_i	j_i	I	$\mathcal{M}1$	$\mathcal{M}2$	$\mathcal{M}3$	$\mathcal{E}1$	$\mathcal{E}2$	$\mathcal{E}3$	$\mathcal{E}4$
1	$\frac{3}{2}$	2	$\frac{5}{2}$	0	0	− 2.827	0	−0.535	0	0.437	0
				1	0	−17.013	0	−0.927	0	0.757	0
1	$\frac{3}{2}$	3	$\frac{5}{2}$	0	0	0	0.324	0	0.261	0	−0.640
				1	0	0	− 5.232	0	0.452	0	−1.108
1	$\frac{3}{2}$	3	$\frac{7}{2}$	0	0	0	4.045	0	0.640	0	−0.477
				1	0	0	26.435	0	1.108	0	−0.826
2	$\frac{3}{2}$	2	$\frac{3}{2}$	0	1.135	0	− 0.600	0	−0.399	0	0
				1	− 1.582	0	2.509	0	−0.691	0	0
2	$\frac{3}{2}$	2	$\frac{5}{2}$	0	0.406	0	− 0.227	0	0.261	0	−0.640
				1	7.798	0	−11.978	0	0.452	0	−1.108
2	$\frac{3}{2}$	3	$\frac{5}{2}$	0	0	− 1.400	0	−0.535	0	0.437	0
				1	0	2.768	0	−0.927	0	0.757	0
2	$\frac{3}{2}$	3	$\frac{7}{2}$	0	0	− 1.398	0	0	0	−0.326	0
				1	0	−19.380	0	0	0	−0.564	0
2	$\frac{5}{2}$	2	$\frac{5}{2}$	0	2.884	0	− 4.431	0	−0.522	0	0.452
				1	11.631	0	−28.958	0	−0.905	0	0.784
2	$\frac{5}{2}$	3	$\frac{5}{2}$	0	0	− 0.126	0	−0.143	0	0.357	0
				1	0	6.706	0	−0.248	0	0.618	0
2	$\frac{5}{2}$	3	$\frac{7}{2}$	0	0	− 4.247	0	−0.640	0	0.564	0
				1	0	−20.076	0	−1.108	0	0.977	0
3	$\frac{5}{2}$	3	$\frac{5}{2}$	0	2.232	0	− 1.734	0	−0.522	0	0.452
				1	− 0.875	0	4.090	0	−0.905	0	0.784
3	$\frac{5}{2}$	3	$\frac{7}{2}$	0	0.486	0	− 0.293	0	0.213	0	−0.431
				1	9.321	0	−15.463	0	0.369	0	−0.747
3	$\frac{7}{2}$	3	$\frac{7}{2}$	0	4.299	0	− 6.092	0	−0.616	0	0.579
				1	14.789	0	−32.031	0	−1.066	0	1.002

B.7. Numerical results for the $A = 57 - 59$ isotopes of Ni and Cu

The results presented here may serve as a check for shell-model calculations on the relatively simple systems of one, two and three active nucleons in a three-orbit configuration space. All numerical values needed for the calculation can be found in the preceding appendices, i.e. the c.f.p., the two-body matrix elements and the single-particle transition matrix elements.

The calculations are performed for the lowest states in the $A = 57-59$ isotopes of Ni and Cu for the active orbits $1f_{5/2}$, $2p_{3/2}$ and $2p_{1/2}$ with a ${}^{56}_{28}Ni_{28}$ closed core.

The MSDI parameters used to calculate the two-body matrix elements (see appendix B.4) and the single-particle energies are given in table B.7.1. The resulting energies of the lowest three states (see fig. B.7.1) and those of the next higher states with the same J^π, T values are given in table B.7.2. The corresponding wave functions are listed in table B.7.3. The spectroscopic factors for single-particle transfer reactions are listed in table B.7.4. The $\mathcal{M}1$ and $\mathcal{E}2$ transition rates are shown in table B.7.5, and the multipole moments in table B.7.6. In some cases the available experimental data are given also for comparison.

Table B.7.1
Strength parameters of the MSDI and single-particle energies [a)] (in MeV)

A_0	A_1	B	C	$e_{2p_{3/2}}$	$e_{1f_{5/2}}$	$e_{2p_{1/2}}$
+0.2818	+0.5293	+0.3754	+0.0711	−10.2549	−9.4356	−9.1562

a) These parameter values are obtained from a least-squares fit to the energies of 95 states in $A = 57-68$ isotopes of Ni and Cu [Koops and Glaudemans (1977)].

LOW-LYING STATES IN SOME Ni AND Cu ISOTOPES

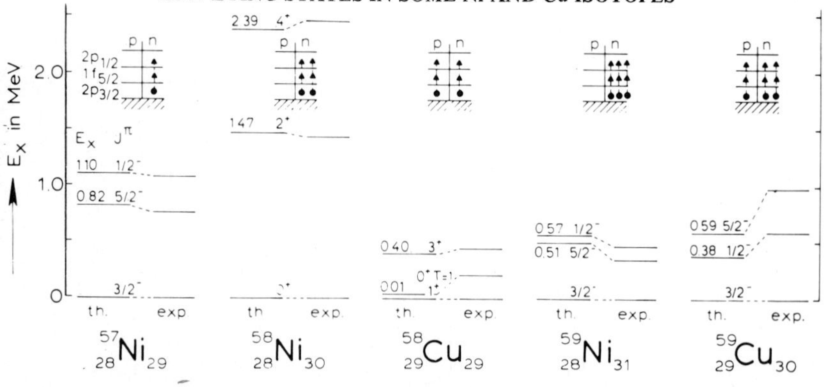

Fig. B.7.1. A comparison between theory and experiment for the excitation energies of the lowest three states in the $A = 57-59$ isotopes of Ni and Cu. The calculations are performed in a $2p_{3/2}1f_{5/2}2p_{1/2}$ configuration space with the MSDI two-body matrix elements. The parameter values used are given in table B.7.1.

Table B.7.2
Binding energies with respect to the ^{56}Ni core (in MeV), see also fig. B.7.1

Nucleus	J^π	T	Binding energy a) theory	experiment b)
^{57}Ni	$\frac{3}{2}^-$	$\frac{1}{2}$	−10.25	−10.27
	$\frac{5}{2}^-$	$\frac{1}{2}$	− 9.44	− 9.51
	$\frac{1}{2}^-$	$\frac{1}{2}$	− 9.16	− 9.16
^{58}Ni	0^+	1	−22.31 (−19.25)	−22.47 (−19.53)
	2^+	1	−20.84 (−19.72)	−21.02 (−19.69)
	4^+	1	−19.92 (−18.51)	−20.01 (−18.85)
^{59}Ni	$\frac{3}{2}^-$	$\frac{3}{2}$	−31.54 (−30.46)	−31.47 (−30.59)
	$\frac{5}{2}^-$	$\frac{3}{2}$	−31.03 (−30.03)	−31.13 (−30.28)
	$\frac{1}{2}^-$	$\frac{3}{2}$	−30.97 (−30.34)	−31.00 (−30.16)
^{57}Cu	$\frac{3}{2}^-$	$\frac{1}{2}$	−10.25	
	$\frac{5}{2}^-$	$\frac{1}{2}$	− 9.44	
	$\frac{1}{2}^-$	$\frac{1}{2}$	− 9.16	
^{58}Cu	1^+	0	−22.32 (−21.91)	−22.67
	0^+	1	−22.31 (−19.25)	−22.47 (−19.53)
	3^+	0	−21.92 (−21.14)	−22.23
^{59}Cu	$\frac{3}{2}^-$	$\frac{1}{2}$	−35.31 (−32.89)	−35.37
	$\frac{1}{2}^-$	$\frac{1}{2}$	−34.93 (−32.77)	−34.88
	$\frac{5}{2}^-$	$\frac{1}{2}$	−34.72 (−32.89)	−34.46 (−33.41)

a) The values between brackets refer to the second state with the same $J^\pi T$.
b) The Coulomb energy due to the active proton in Cu has been subtracted.

Table B.7.3
Wave functions [a] for the A = 58 and 59 isotopes of Ni and Cu

J^π		1f$_{5/2}$					2p$_{3/2}$					coupled		2p$_{1/2}$					amplitudes	
	no.	n_1	$2J_1$	$2T_1$	v_1	$2t_1$	n_2	$2J_2$	$2T_2$	v_2	$2t_2$	$2J_{12}$	$2T_{12}$	n_3	$2J_3$	$2T_3$	v_3	$2t_3$	k = 1	k = 2
A = 58, T = 1																				
0^+	1	0	0	0	0	0	0	0	0	0	0	0	0	2	0	2	0	0	−0.2799	0.2561
	2	0	0	0	0	0	2	0	2	0	0	0	2	0	0	0	0	0	−0.7836	−0.6178
	3	2	0	2	0	0	0	0	0	0	0	0	2	0	0	0	0	0	−0.5546	0.7435
2^+	1	0	0	0	0	0	1	3	1	1	1	3	1	1	1	1	1	1	−0.4166	0.4393
	2	0	0	0	0	0	2	4	2	2	2	4	2	0	0	0	0	0	−0.7128	−0.6901
	3	1	5	1	1	1	0	0	0	0	0	5	1	1	1	1	1	1	−0.3549	0.2585
	4	1	5	1	1	1	1	3	1	1	1	4	2	0	0	0	0	0	0.3206	−0.4556
	5	2	4	2	2	2	0	0	0	0	0	4	2	0	0	0	0	0	−0.2994	0.2375
4^+	1	1	5	1	1	1	1	3	1	1	1	8	2	0	0	0	0	0	0.9755	0.2200
	2	2	8	2	2	2	0	0	0	0	0	8	2	0	0	0	0	0	−0.2200	0.9755
A = 58, T = 0																				
1^+	1	0	0	0	0	0	0	0	0	0	0	0	0	2	2	0	2	0	0.2024	−0.1106
	2	0	0	0	0	0	1	3	1	1	1	3	1	1	1	1	1	1	0.1139	0.4215
	3	0	0	0	0	0	2	2	0	2	0	2	0	0	0	0	0	0	−0.6764	−0.6021
	4	1	5	1	1	1	1	3	1	1	1	2	0	0	0	0	0	0	0.6187	−0.6660
	5	2	2	0	2	0	0	0	0	0	0	2	0	0	0	0	0	0	0.3252	−0.0640
3^+	1	0	0	0	0	0	2	6	0	2	0	6	0	0	0	0	0	0	0.9935	0.0543
	2	1	5	1	1	1	0	0	0	0	0	5	1	1	1	1	1	1	−0.0316	−0.3959
	3	1	5	1	1	1	1	3	1	1	1	6	0	0	0	0	0	0	0.0962	−0.8622
	4	2	6	0	2	0	0	0	0	0	0	6	0	0	0	0	0	0	−0.0528	−0.3112
A = 59, T = $\frac{3}{2}$																				
$\frac{1}{2}^-$	1	0	0	0	0	0	2	0	2	0	0	0	2	1	1	1	1	1	0.7895	0.2894
	2	1	5	1	1	1	1	3	1	1	1	2	2	1	1	1	1	1	0.3204	−0.4387
	3	1	5	1	1	1	2	4	2	2	2	1	3	0	0	0	0	0	0.3317	−0.5067
	4	2	0	2	0	0	0	0	0	0	0	0	2	1	1	1	1	1	0.3075	0.5759
	5	2	4	2	2	2	1	3	1	1	1	1	3	0	0	0	0	0	−0.2634	0.3679
$\frac{3}{2}^-$	1	0	0	0	0	0	1	3	1	1	1	3	1	2	0	2	0	0	−0.2537	−0.2416
	2	0	0	0	0	0	2	4	2	2	2	4	2	1	1	1	1	1	0.1056	−0.2926
	3	0	0	0	0	0	3	3	3	1	1	3	3	0	0	0	0	0	−0.7715	0.1995
	4	1	5	1	1	1	1	3	1	1	1	2	2	1	1	1	1	1	−0.0601	0.2330
	5	1	5	1	1	1	1	3	1	1	1	4	2	1	1	1	1	1	−0.1460	0.4600
	6	1	5	1	1	1	2	4	2	2	2	3	3	0	0	0	0	0	−0.0883	0.3965
	7	2	4	2	2	2	0	0	0	0	0	4	2	1	1	1	1	1	−0.0152	0.1732
	8	2	0	2	0	0	1	3	1	1	1	3	3	0	0	0	0	0	−0.5350	−0.5090
	9	2	4	2	2	2	1	3	1	1	1	3	3	0	0	0	0	0	0.0954	−0.2467
	10	3	3	3	3	3	0	0	0	0	0	3	3	0	0	0	0	0	−0.0313	0.2079
$\frac{5}{2}^-$	1	0	0	0	0	0	2	4	2	2	2	4	2	1	1	1	1	1	0.1095	0.7512
	2	1	5	1	1	1	0	0	0	0	0	5	1	2	0	2	0	0	0.2589	−0.1657
	3	1	5	1	1	1	1	3	1	1	1	4	2	1	1	1	1	1	0.0254	0.0626
	4	1	5	1	1	1	1	3	1	1	1	6	2	1	1	1	1	1	0.0730	0.3761
	5	1	5	1	1	1	2	0	2	0	0	5	3	0	0	0	0	0	0.8544	−0.0164
	6	1	5	1	1	1	2	4	2	2	2	5	3	0	0	0	0	0	0.0604	−0.0373
	7	2	4	2	2	2	0	0	0	0	0	4	2	1	1	1	1	1	0.0005	0.0751
	8	2	4	2	2	2	1	3	1	1	1	5	3	0	0	0	0	0	−0.0616	−0.4651
	9	2	8	2	2	2	1	3	1	1	1	5	3	0	0	0	0	0	−0.0501	−0.0262
	10	3	5	3	1	1	0	0	0	0	0	5	3	0	0	0	0	0	0.4184	−0.1962

Table B.7.3 (continued)

J^π		$1f_{5/2}$					$2p_{3/2}$					coupled		$2p_{1/2}$					amplitudes	
	no.	n_1	$2J_1$	$2T_1$	v_1	$2t_1$	n_2	$2J_2$	$2T_2$	v_2	$2t_2$	$2J_{12}$	$2T_{12}$	n_3	$2J_3$	$2T_3$	v_3	$2t_3$	$k = 1$	$k = 2$
$A = 59, T = \frac{1}{2}$																				
$\frac{1}{2}-$	1	0	0	0	0	0	0	0	0	0	0	0	0	3	1	1	1	1	−0.2466	−0.1325
	2	0	0	0	0	0	1	3	1	1	1	3	1	2	2	0	2	0	−0.0010	0.0912
	3	0	0	0	0	0	2	0	2	0	0	0	2	1	1	1	1	1	0.5320	0.1937
	4	0	0	0	0	0	2	2	0	2	0	2	0	1	1	1	1	1	0.1937	−0.2861
	5	0	0	0	0	0	3	1	1	3	1	1	1	0	0	0	0	0	−0.2794	0.7980
	6	1	5	1	1	1	1	3	1	1	1	2	0	1	1	1	1	1	−0.3988	0.0760
	7	1	5	1	1	1	1	3	1	1	1	2	2	1	1	1	1	1	0.0115	−0.1728
	8	1	5	1	1	1	2	4	2	2	2	1	1	0	0	0	0	0	−0.2785	−0.2113
	9	1	5	1	1	1	2	6	0	2	0	1	1	0	0	0	0	0	−0.0651	−0.0981
	10	2	0	2	0	0	0	0	0	0	0	0	2	1	1	1	1	1	0.4075	0.2882
	11	2	2	0	2	0	0	0	0	0	0	2	0	1	1	1	1	1	−0.2000	−0.0689
	12	2	2	0	2	0	1	3	1	1	1	1	1	0	0	0	0	0	−0.0938	0.1337
	13	2	4	2	2	2	1	3	1	1	1	1	1	0	0	0	0	0	0.2367	−0.1100
	14	3	1	1	3	1	0	0	0	0	0	1	1	0	0	0	0	0	−0.1695	−0.1013
$\frac{3}{2}-$	1	0	0	0	0	0	1	3	1	1	1	3	1	2	0	2	0	0	−0.2868	−0.0174
	2	0	0	0	0	0	1	3	1	1	1	3	1	2	2	0	2	0	−0.0776	−0.1691
	3	0	0	0	0	0	2	2	0	2	0	2	0	1	1	1	1	1	−0.1312	−0.3582
	4	0	0	0	0	0	2	4	2	2	2	4	2	1	1	1	1	1	−0.1268	−0.2325
	5	0	0	0	0	0	3	3	1	1	1	3	1	0	0	0	0	0	−0.6895	0.4282
	6	1	5	1	1	1	0	0	0	0	0	5	1	2	2	0	2	0	−0.1164	−0.2313
	7	1	5	1	1	1	1	3	1	1	1	2	0	1	1	1	1	1	−0.0682	−0.1289
	8	1	5	1	1	1	1	3	1	1	1	2	2	1	1	1	1	1	0.0018	0.0380
	9	1	5	1	1	1	1	3	1	1	1	4	0	1	1	1	1	1	−0.1315	−0.2935
	10	1	5	1	1	1	1	3	1	1	1	4	2	1	1	1	1	1	0.0905	0.1934
	11	1	5	1	1	1	2	2	0	2	0	3	1	0	0	0	0	0	0.0641	0.1853
	12	1	5	1	1	1	2	4	2	2	2	3	1	0	0	0	0	0	−0.0987	−0.2480
	13	1	5	1	1	1	2	6	0	2	0	3	1	0	0	0	0	0	−0.0764	−0.2602
	14	2	2	0	2	0	0	0	0	0	0	2	0	1	1	1	1	1	0.0395	0.0717
	15	2	4	2	2	2	0	0	0	0	0	4	2	1	1	1	1	1	−0.0957	−0.1565
	16	2	0	2	0	0	1	3	1	1	1	3	1	0	0	0	0	0	0.5263	−0.1256
	17	2	2	0	2	0	1	3	1	1	1	3	1	0	0	0	0	0	0.1307	0.2244
	18	2	4	2	2	2	1	3	1	1	1	3	1	0	0	0	0	0	0.1442	0.3355
	19	2	6	0	2	0	1	3	1	1	1	3	1	0	0	0	0	0	0.0601	0.0907
	20	3	3	1	3	1	0	0	0	0	0	3	1	0	0	0	0	0	0.1022	0.1736
$\frac{5}{2}-$	1	0	0	0	0	0	1	3	1	1	1	3	1	2	2	0	2	0	−0.1703	−0.0741
	2	0	0	0	0	0	2	4	2	2	2	4	2	1	1	1	1	1	−0.1695	−0.1325
	3	0	0	0	0	0	2	6	0	2	0	6	0	1	1	1	1	1	−0.0401	−0.0675
	4	0	0	0	0	0	3	5	1	3	1	5	1	0	0	0	0	0	0.1386	0.8041
	5	1	5	1	1	1	0	0	0	0	0	5	1	2	0	2	0	0	0.2591	−0.0710
	6	1	5	1	1	1	0	0	0	0	0	5	1	2	2	0	2	0	−0.1184	−0.0216
	7	1	5	1	1	1	1	3	1	1	1	4	0	1	1	1	1	1	0.1127	0.0682
	8	1	5	1	1	1	1	3	1	1	1	4	2	1	1	1	1	1	0.1121	−0.0536
	9	1	5	1	1	1	1	3	1	1	1	6	0	1	1	1	1	1	0.1351	0.2031
	10	1	5	1	1	1	1	3	1	1	1	6	2	1	1	1	1	1	−0.0051	−0.1192
	11	1	5	1	1	1	2	0	2	0	0	5	1	0	0	0	0	0	0.6156	−0.1934
	12	1	5	1	1	1	2	2	0	2	0	5	1	0	0	0	0	0	0.1856	−0.1262
	13	1	5	1	1	1	2	4	2	2	2	5	1	0	0	0	0	0	0.2156	0.0035
	14	1	5	1	1	1	2	6	0	2	0	5	1	0	0	0	0	0	0.1043	0.2881
	15	2	4	2	2	2	0	0	0	0	0	4	2	1	1	1	1	1	−0.1253	−0.0167
	16	2	6	0	2	0	0	0	0	0	0	6	0	1	1	1	1	1	0.1267	0.0072
	17	2	2	0	2	0	1	3	1	1	1	5	1	0	0	0	0	0	−0.1718	−0.1086
	18	2	4	2	2	2	1	3	1	1	1	5	1	0	0	0	0	0	−0.1027	−0.2586
	19	2	6	0	2	0	1	3	1	1	1	5	1	0	0	0	0	0	−0.0774	0.0099
	20	2	8	2	2	2	1	3	1	1	1	5	1	0	0	0	0	0	−0.1457	0.0119

Table B.7.3. (continued)

J^π	$1f_{5/2}$					$2p_{3/2}$					coupled		$2p_{1/2}$					amplitudes	
no.	n_1	$2J_1$	$2T_1$	v_1	$2t_1$	n_2	$2J_2$	$2T_2$	v_2	$2t_2$	$2J_{12}$	$2T_{12}$	n_3	$2J_3$	$2T_3$	v_3	$2t_3$	$k = 1$	$k = 2$
21	3	5	1	1	1	0	0	0	0	0	5	1	0	0	0	0	0	0.4708	−0.2024
22	3	5	1	3	1	0	0	0	0	0	5	1	0	0	0	0	0	0.0722	−0.0269

a) The components of the wave functions are denoted as

$$\{[(1f_{5/2})^{n_1}_{J_1T_1v_1t_1}\,(2p_{3/2})^{n_2}_{J_2T_2v_2t_2}]_{J_{12}T_{12}}\,(2p_{1/2})^{n_3}_{J_3T_3v_3t_3}\}_{JT}\,.$$

The single-shell states for each of the three orbits $\rho = 1f_{5/2}, 2p_{3/2}$ or $2p_{1/2}$ are specified by the quantum numbers $\rho^{n_i}_{2J_i2T_iv_i2t_i}$ with n_i = the number of particles; $2J_i$ = twice the total spin; $2T_i$ = twice the total isospin; v_i = the seniority; $2t_i$ = twice the reduced isospin. The last columns labelled $k = 1$ and 2 give the amplitudes of the corresponding components for the lowest two states of given J and T.

Table B.7.4
Spectroscopic factors for single-particle stripping and pick-up on ^{58}Ni

Nucleus $J^\pi T$						Transferred nucleon	S-factor a)	
initial			final				theory	experiment b)
^{58}Ni	0^+	1	^{57}Ni	$\frac{3}{2}^-$	$\frac{1}{2}$	$2p_{3/2}$	1.23	0.93
				$\frac{5}{2}^-$	$\frac{1}{2}$	$1f_{5/2}$	0.62	0.63
				$\frac{1}{2}^-$	$\frac{1}{2}$	$2p_{1/2}$	0.16	0.20
^{58}Ni	0^+	1	^{59}Ni	$\frac{3}{2}^-$	$\frac{3}{2}$	$2p_{3/2}$	0.63 (0.06)	0.68 (0.07)
				$\frac{5}{2}^-$	$\frac{3}{2}$	$1f_{5/2}$	0.87 (0.02)	0.70
				$\frac{1}{2}^-$	$\frac{3}{2}$	$2p_{1/2}$	0.62 (0.30)	0.62 (0.27)
^{58}Ni	0^+	1	^{59}Cu	$\frac{3}{2}^-$	$\frac{1}{2}$	$2p_{3/2}$	0.95 (0.19)	0.57
				$\frac{1}{2}^-$	$\frac{1}{2}$	$2p_{1/2}$	0.53 (0.13)	0.60
				$\frac{5}{2}^-$	$\frac{1}{2}$	$1f_{5/2}$	0.70 (0.09)	0.72

a) For the lowest three states (see fig. B.7.1). For the second state of a particular $J^\pi T$ value the S-factor is given in parentheses.

b) From the compilation [Koops and Glaudemans (1977)].

Table B.7.5
Calculated [a] magnetic dipole and electric quadrupole strengths (in W.u.) for the lowest three states in the $A = 57–59$ isotopes of Ni and Cu (see fig. B.7.1)

Nucleus	$J_i^\pi T_i \to J_f^\pi T_f$	$M_W^2(\mathcal{M}1)$	$M_W^2(\mathcal{E}2)$ [b]	
			$\Delta e = 0$	$\Delta e = 1.7e$
^{57}Ni	$\frac{5}{2}^- \frac{1}{2} \to \frac{3}{2}^- \frac{1}{2}$	0	0	1.0
	$\frac{1}{2}^- \frac{1}{2} \to \frac{3}{2}^- \frac{1}{2}$	1.30	0	10.6
	$\frac{1}{2}^- \frac{1}{2} \to \frac{5}{2}^- \frac{1}{2}$		0	11.0
^{58}Ni	$2^+ 1 \to 0^+ 1$		0	8.8
	$4^+ 1 \to 2^+ 1$		0	7.0
^{59}Ni	$\frac{5}{2}^- \frac{3}{2} \to \frac{3}{2}^- \frac{3}{2}$	<0.01	0	0.2
	$\frac{1}{2}^- \frac{3}{2} \to \frac{3}{2}^- \frac{3}{2}$	0.81	0	1.2
	$\frac{1}{2}^- \frac{3}{2} \to \frac{5}{2}^- \frac{3}{2}$		0	19.7
^{57}Cu	$\frac{5}{2}^- \frac{1}{2} \to \frac{3}{2}^- \frac{1}{2}$	0	0.4	2.6
	$\frac{1}{2}^- \frac{1}{2} \to \frac{3}{2}^- \frac{1}{2}$	1.87	3.7	26.7
	$\frac{1}{2}^- \frac{1}{2} \to \frac{5}{2}^- \frac{1}{2}$		3.8	27.7
^{58}Cu	$0^+ 1 \to 1^+ 0$	2.77		
	$3^+ 0 \to 1^+ 0$		0.1	2.6
^{59}Cu	$\frac{1}{2}^- \frac{1}{2} \to \frac{3}{2}^- \frac{1}{2}$	1.14	1.6	49.4
	$\frac{5}{2}^- \frac{1}{2} \to \frac{3}{2}^- \frac{1}{2}$	<0.01	0.2	6.9
	$\frac{5}{2}^- \frac{1}{2} \to \frac{1}{2}^- \frac{1}{2}$		0.7	23.5

[a] See eqs. (9.106), (10.8b) and (10.9a).
[b] The values are given for bare-nucleon charges ($\Delta e = 0$) and for $e_p = 2.7\,e$, $e_n = 1.7\,e$.

Table B.7.6
Calculated [a] magnetic dipole and electric quadrupole moments of the lower states in the $A = 57–59$ isotopes of Ni and Cu (see fig. B.7.1)

Nucleus	$J^\pi T$	μ(n.m.)	$Q(e \cdot \text{fm}^2)$		Nucleus	$J^\pi T$	μ(n.m.)	$Q(e \cdot \text{fm}^2)$	
			$\Delta e = 0$	$\Delta e = 1.7e$				$\Delta e = 0$	$\Delta e = 1.7e$
^{57}Ni	$\frac{3}{2}^- \frac{1}{2}$	−1.91	0	−11.8	^{57}Cu	$\frac{3}{2}^- \frac{1}{2}$	+3.79	−6.9	−18.7
	$\frac{5}{2}^- \frac{1}{2}$	+1.37	0	−16.8		$\frac{5}{2}^- \frac{1}{2}$	+0.86	−9.9	−26.7
^{58}Ni	$2^+ 1$	−0.52	0	−17.4	^{58}Cu	$1^+ 0$	+0.51	+2.0	+ 8.6
^{59}Ni	$\frac{3}{2}^- \frac{1}{2}$	−1.55	0	+ 8.8	^{59}Cu	$\frac{3}{2}^- \frac{1}{2}$	+2.65	−5.1	−26.9
	$\frac{5}{2}^- \frac{1}{2}$	+1.26	0	−16.8		$\frac{1}{2}^- \frac{1}{2}$	−0.44		

[a] See eq. (11.75).

REFERENCES

Ajzenberg-Selove F., Nucl. Phys. A166 (1971) 1.
Ajzenberg-Selove F., Nucl. Phys. A190 (1972) 1.
Appel H., Landolt-Börnstein, New Series, Group I, vol. 3 (Springer, 1968).
Arvieu R. and S.A. Moszkowski, Phys. Rev. 145 (1966) 830.
Auerbach N., J. Hüfner, A.K. Kerman and C.M. Shakin, Rev. Mod. Phys. 44 (1972) 48.
Baranger E. and C.W. Lee, Nucl. Phys. 22 (1961) 157.
Baranger M., Proc. Int. School of Physics Enrico Fermi, course 40, ed. M. Jean and R.A. Ricci (Academic Press, 1969).
Barrett B.R. and M.W. Kirson, Adv. Nucl. Phys. 6 (1973) 219.
Barrett B.R., ed., Effective interactions and operators in nuclei, Lecture notes in Physics 40 (Springer, 1975).
Bassel R.H., Phys. Rev. 149 (1966) 791.
Bayman B.F. and A. Lande, Nucl. Phys. 77 (1966) 1.
Bertsch G.F., Nucl. Phys. 74 (1965) 234.
Bethe H.A. and E.E. Salpeter, Encyclopedia of physics, vol. 35 (Springer, 1957) p. 88.
Biedenharn L.C., J.M. Blatt and M.E. Rose, Rev. Mod. Phys. 24 (1952) 249.
Biedenharn L.C. and M.E. Rose, Rev. Mod. Phys. 25 (1953) 729.
Blatt J.M. and V.F. Weisskopf, Theoretical nuclear physics (Wiley, New York, 1952).
Bohr A., Mat. Fys. Medd. Dan. Vid. Selsk. 26 (1952) no. 14.
Bohr A. and B.R. Mottelson, Mat. Fys. Medd. Dan. Vid. Selsk. 27 (1953) no. 16.
Bohr A. and B.R. Mottelson, Nuclear structure, vol. 1 (Benjamin, New York, 1969).
Bohr A. and B.R. Mottelson, Nuclear structure, vol. 2 (Benjamin, Reading, 1975).
Bohr N., Phil. Mag. 26 (1913) 1, 476, 857.
Brandow B.H., Rev. Mod. Phys. 39 (1967) 771.
Brown B.A., D.B. Fossan, J.M. McDonald and K.A. Snover, Phys. Rev. C9 (1974) 1033.
Chaloupka V. et al., Phys. Letters 50B (1974) 1.
Chung W., Thesis, Michigan State University (1976).
Cohen S. and D. Kurath, Nucl. Phys. 73 (1965) 1.
Cole B.J., A. Watt and R.R. Whitehead, J. of Phys. G1 (1975) 935.
Condon E.U. and G.H. Shortley, The theory of atomic spectra (Cambridge University Press, 1953).
Day B.D., Rev. Mod. Phys. 39 (1967) 719.
DeShalit A. and I. Talmi, Nuclear shell theory (Academic Press, New York, 1963).
DeShalit A. and H. Feshbach, Theoretical nuclear physics, vol. 1 (Wiley, New York, 1974).
De Voigt M.J.A., P.W.M. Glaudemans, J. de Boer and B.H. Wildenthal, Nucl. Phys. A186 (1972) 365.
Dieperink A.E.L. and P.J. Brussaard, Nucl. Phys. A129 (1969) 33.
Edmonds A.R., Angular momentum in quantum mechanics (Princeton University Press, 1957).
Ehrman J.B., Phys. Rev. 81 (1951) 412.
Eisenberg J.M. and W. Greiner, Nuclear theory, vol. 1, 2 (North-Holland, Amsterdam, 1970).
Eisenberg J.M. and W. Greiner, Nuclear theory, vol. 3 (North-Holland, Amsterdam, 1972).
Elliott J.P. and T.H.R. Skyrme, Proc. Roy. Soc. A232 (1955) 561.
Elliott J.P., A.D. Jackson, H.A. Mavromatis, E.A. Sanderson and B. Singh, Nucl. Phys. A121 (1968) 241.
Ellis P.J. and H.A. Mavromatis, Nucl. Phys. A175 (1971) 309.
Endt P.M. and C. van der Leun, Nucl. Phys. A214 (1973) 1.
Endt P.M. and C. van der Leun, Atomic data and nuclear data tables 13 (1974a) 68.

Endt P.M. and C. van der Leun, Nucl. Phys. A235 (1974b) 27.
Endt P.M., Atomic data and nuclear data tables 19 (1977) 23.
Faessler A. and A. Plastino, Nuovo Cimento 47B (1967) 297.
Ferguson A.J., Angular correlation methods in gamma-ray spectroscopy (North-Holland, Amsterdam, 1965).
Fermi E., Z. Phys. 88 (1934) 161.
Flowers B.H., Proc. Roy. Soc. A212 (1952) 248.
French J.B. and M.H. Macfarlane, Nucl. Phys. 26 (1961) 168.
French J.B., E.C. Halbert, J.B. McGrory and S.S.M. Wong, Adv. in Nucl. Phys. 3 (1969) 193.
Fulmer R.H., A.L. McCarthy, B.L. Cohen and R. Middleton, Phys. Rev. 133 (1964) B955.
Gartenhaus S. and C. Schwartz, Phys. Rev. 108 (1957) 482.
Glaudemans P.W.M., G. Wiechers and P.J. Brussaard, Nucl. Phys. 56 (1964) 529, 548.
Glaudemans P.W.M., P.J. Brussaard and B.H. Wildenthal, Nucl. Phys. A102 (1967) 593.
Glaudemans P.W.M. and C. van der Leun, Phys. Letters 34B (1971) 41.
Glaudemans P.W.M., J.E. Koops, F. Meurders and B.J. Cole, Proc. Int. Conf. on nuclear structure and spectroscopy, vol. 2, ed. H.P. Blok and A.E.L. Dieperink (Scholar's Press, Amsterdam, 1974).
Halbert E.C., J.B. McGrory, B.H. Wildenthal and S.P. Pandya, Adv. in Nucl. Phys. 4 (1971) 315.
Hardy J.C. and I.S. Towner, Nucl. Phys. A254 (1975) 221.
Haxel O., J.H.D. Jensen and H.E. Suess, Phys. Rev. 75 (1949) 1766.
Hecht K.T., Selected topics in nuclear spectroscopy, ed. B.J. Verhaar (North-Holland, Amsterdam, 1964) p. 51.
Heisenberg W., Z. Phys. 77 (1932) 1.
Heyde K. and P.J. Brussaard, Nucl. Phys. A104 (1967) 81.
Heyde K., private communication, 1976.
Hinterberger F., G. Mairle, U. Schmidt-Rohr, P. Turek and G.J. Wagner, Z. Phys. 202 (1968) 236.
Horoshko R.N., D. Cline and P.M. Lesser, Nucl. Phys. A149 (1970) 562.
Jackson J.D., Classical electrodynamics (Wiley, New York, 1962).
Jahn H.A., Proc. Roy. Soc. A205 (1951) 192.
Jänecke J., Isospin in nuclear physics, ed. D.H. Wilkinson (North-Holland, Amsterdam, 1969) p. 297.
Jardine L.J., S.G. Prussin and J.M. Hollander, Nucl. Phys. A190 (1972) 261.
Klein O., J. de Phys. et le Radium 9 (1938) 1.
Koops J.E. and P.W.M. Glaudemans, Z. Phys. A280 (1977) 181.
Kuo T.T.S. and G.E. Brown, Nucl. Phys. 85 (1966) 40.
Kuo T.T.S., Nucl. Phys. A103 (1967) 71.
Kuo T.T.S. and G.E. Brown, Nucl. Phys. A114 (1968) 241.
Kuo T.T.S., Annual Review of Nuclear Science 24 (1974) 101.
Lawson R.D., M.H. Macfarlane and T.T.S. Kuo, Phys. Letters 22 (1966) 168.
Lederer C.M., J.M. Hollander and I. Perlman, Table of isotopes (Wiley, New York, 1968).
Lee Jr. L.L., J.P. Schiffer, B. Zeidman, G.R. Satchler, R.M. Drisko and R.H. Bassel, Phys. Rev. 136 (1964) B971.
Litherland A.E. and A.J. Ferguson, Can. J. of Phys. 39 (1961) 788.
Macfarlane M.H. and J.B. French, Rev. Mod. Phys. 32 (1960) 567.
Magnus W., F. Oberhettinger and R.P. Soni, Formulas and theorems for the special functions of mathematical physics (Springer, 1966).
March N.H., W.H. Young and S. Sampanthar, The many-body problem in quantum mechanics (Cambridge University Press, 1967).
Mayer M.G., Phys. Rev. 75 (1949) 1969.
McCarthy I.E., Introduction to nuclear theory (Wiley, New York, 1968)
McGrory J.B., private communication, 1967.
Messiah A., Quantum mechanics, vol. 1 (North-Holland, Amsterdam, 1965).
Meurders F. and A. van der Steld, Nucl. Phys. A230 (1974) 317.

Meurders F., P.W.M. Glaudemans, J.F.A. van Hienen and G.A. Timmer, Z. Phys. A276 (1976) 113.
Molinari A., M.B. Johnson, H.A. Bethe and W.M. Alberico, Nucl. Phys. A239 (1975) 45.
Morse P.M. and H. Feshbach, Methods of theoretical physics (McGraw-Hill, New York, 1953).
Motz H.T., E.T. Jurney, E.B. Shera and R.K. Sheline, Phys. Rev. Letters 26 (1971) 854.
O'Brien B.J., W.E. Dorenbusch, T.A. Belote and J. Rapaport, Nucl. Phys. A104 (1967) 609.
Olin A., O. Häusser, T.K. Alexander, A.J. Ferguson and W. Witthuhn, Nucl. Phys. A221 (1974) 555.
Pauli W., Encyclopedia of physics, vol. 5/1 (Springer, 1958) p. 1.
Plastino A., R. Arvieu and S.A. Moszkowski, Phys. Rev. 145 (1966) 837.
Poletti A.R. and K. Warburton, Phys. Rev. 137 (1965) B595.
Racah G., Phys. Rev. 62 (1942) 438.
Racah G., Phys. Rev. 63 (1943) 367.
Raman S., T.A. Walkiewicz and H. Behrens, Atomic data and nuclear data tables 16 (1975) 451.
Rose H.J. and D.M. Brink, Rev. Mod. Phys. 39 (1967) 306.
Rotenberg M., R. Bivins, M. Metropolis and J.K. Wooten Jr., The 3-*j* and 6-*j* symbols (Technology Press MIT, Cambridge, 1959).
Rowe D.J., Nuclear collective motion (Methuen, London, 1970).
Roy R.R. and B.P. Nigam, Nuclear physics (Wiley, New York, 1967).
Saayman R., P.R. de Kock and J.H. van der Merwe, Z. Phys. 265 (1973) 69.
Satchler G.R., Nucl. Phys. 55 (1964) 1.
Schiffer J.P., Ann. of Phys. 66 (1971) 798.
Schucan T.H. and H.A. Weidenmüller, Ann. of Phys. 76 (1973) 483.
Schwalm D., Habilitationsschrift, Max-Planck-Institut, Heidelberg (1973).
Sebe T. and M. Harvey, AECL Report 3007, Chalk River (1968).
Sebe T. and J. Nachamkin, Ann. of Phys. 51 (1969) 100.
Shirley V.S. and C.M. Lederer, Hyperfine interactions studied in nuclear reactions and decay, ed. E. Karlsson and R. Wäppling (Almqvist & Wiksell, Stockholm, 1975).
Siegert A.J.F., Phys. Rev. 52 (1937) 787.
Smith P.B., Nuclear reactions, vol. 2, ed. P.M. Endt and P.B. Smith (North-Holland, Amsterdam, 1962) p. 248.
Sprung D.W., Adv. in Nucl. Phys. 5 (1972) 225.
Starkand Y. and M.W. Kirson, Nucl. Phys. A261 (1976) 453.
Stock R., R. Bock, P. David, H.H. Duhm and T. Tamura, Nucl. Phys. A104 (1967) 136.
Thomas R.G., Phys. Rev. 88 (1952) 1109.
Towner I.S. and J.C. Hardy, Adv. in Phys. 18 (1969) 401.
Vanden Berghe G. and K. Heyde, Nucl. Phys. A163 (1971) 478.
Van Hienen J.F.A. and P.W.M. Glaudemans, Phys. Letters 42B (1972) 301.
Van Hienen J.F.A., P.W.M. Glaudemans and J. van Lidth de Jeude, Nucl. Phys. A225 (1974) 119.
Van Hienen J.F.A., Thesis, Utrecht University (1975).
Veefkind J.C., D. Spaargaren, J. Blok and K. Heyde, Z. Phys. A275 (1975) 55.
Wapstra A.H., G.J. Nijgh and R. van Lieshout, Nuclear spectroscopy tables (North-Holland, Amsterdam, 1959).
Wapstra A.H. and N.B. Gove, Nucl. Data Tables 9 (1971) 265.
Weidenmüller H.A., Effective interactions and operators in nuclei, Lecture notes in physics 40, ed. B.R. Barrett (Springer, 1975) p. 152.
Whitehead R.R., A. Watt, B.J. Cole and I. Morrison, Adv. in Nucl. Phys. 9 (1977) 123.
Wigner E.P., On the matrices which reduce the Kronecker products of representation of S.R. groups (1940), reprinted in L.C. Biedenharn and H. van Dam, Quantum theory of angular momentum (Academic Press, 1965) p. 87.
Wildenthal B.H. and P.W.M. Glaudemans, Nucl. Phys. A108 (1968) 49.
Wildenthal B.H., J.B. McGrory and P.W.M. Glaudemans, Phys. Rev. Letters 26 (1971) 96.
Wildenthal B.H., E.C. Halbert, J.B. McGrory and T.T.S. Kuo, Phys. Rev. C4 (1971) 1266.
Wildenthal B.H., J.B. McGrory, E.C. Halbert and H.D. Graber, Phys. Rev. C4 (1971) 1708.

Wildenthal B.H. and J.B. McGrory, Phys. Rev. C7 (1973) 714.
Wilkinson D.H., Isospin in nuclear physics, ed. D.H. Wilkinson (North-Holland, Amsterdam, 1969) p. 3.
Wilkinson D.H., Nucl. Phys. A209 (1973) 470.
Wilkinson D.H. and B.E.F. Macefield, Nucl. Phys. A232 (1974) 58.
Wilkinson J.H., The algebraic eigenvalue problem (Clarendon Press, Oxford, 1965).
Wu C.S. and S.A. Moszkowski, Beta decay (Interscience, New York, 1966).
Yukawa H., Proc. Phys. Math. Soc. 17 (1935) 48.

SUBJECT INDEX

A-dependence of
  MSDI 116
  nuclear radius 17
  size parameter b 17
Additivity relation 256ff
Adjoint state operator 289
Allowed beta decay (*see* Beta decay)
Analogue states 24, 268, 383
Angular momentum 10ff
Annihilation operators
  bosons 390
  fermions 275ff
Anticommutation relations 279
Antisymmetry
  definition 4
  many-particle states 79ff, 424
  two-particle states 30ff, 84
Average number of nucleons 166ff

$B(\bar{\omega}L; J_i \to J_f)$ 189, 198
Bartlett exchange operator 104
Bessel function, spherical 179
Beta decay, allowed 259ff
  and magnetic moments 273ff
  and magnetic transitions 268ff
  Fermi matrix elements 262, 264
  Gamow–Teller matrix elements 262, 264ff
  log ft value 266ff
  selection rules 262ff
Bethe–Goldstone equation 341
Binding energy 37, 115
Branching ratio 191
Brillouin–Wigner expansion 332
Brueckner theory 340

Central potential 10
Centre-of-mass corrections 184ff
Charge
  density 182
  effective 207ff, 348ff
  exchange operator 104
  independence 25
  operator 26
  symmetry 23
Clebsch–Gordan coefficients (*see* Three-j symbols)
Closed shells and
  electromagnetic transition rates 228
  energies 37, 42ff
  spectroscopic factors 153, 164
Coefficients of fractional parentage (c.f.p.)
  bosons 393
  fermions 64ff, 71ff, 299ff, 324ff
  tables 76, 433
Collective motion
  and multipole operators 396, 397
  and single-particle motion 387ff
Commutation relations of
  angular momentum 11, 26
  annihilation–creation operators 276, 390
Compound nucleus 144
Condon–Shortley phase convention 190
Configuration
  definition 52
  dimensions 8
  mixing 45, 52ff, 155ff, 231ff
  space 8, 119, 129ff, 160ff
Continuity equation 177
Contraction of operators 358ff
Core, hard 340
Core polarization 352
Correlated wave function 340
Coulomb
  energies 381ff
  interaction 29
Coupling rules 79ff
Creation operators
  bosons 390
  fermions 275ff

D-matrices 409
Defect wave function 340
Deformation parameter 388
Diagonal correlation matrix (DCM) 140

Diagonalization of matrices 55ff, 371ff
Diagrams
  Feynman 333ff
  French 79ff
Dimension of configuration space 8
Dipole moment, magnetic (*see* Magnetic dipole moment)
Dipole radiation
  electric (*see* Electric multipole)
  magnetic (*see* Magnetic multipole)
Direct reactions (*see* Transfer reactions)
Distorted-wave Born approximation (DWBA) 145
Double-parentage coefficients (d.p.c.) 71ff, 324ff

Effective
  charges 207, 225, 348ff, 350
  interactions 100ff, 330ff, 343ff
  single-particle m.e. 233ff
  transition operators 346ff
Effective operators 9, 327ff
Electric multipole
  collective operator 396
  moments 237ff
  parity 188
  radial integrals 214, 435
  single-particle m.e. 213ff, 436
Electric quadrupole moment
  intrinsic and spectroscopic 247ff
  sd-shell nuclei 253
  single-particle value 249
Electromagnetic transition
  isoscalar–isovector contributions 196ff, 204ff
  operators 176ff
  rates 199ff
  selection rules 187ff
Empirical matrix elements 76ff, 100ff, 132ff
Energy
  binding 37ff, 115
  excitation 37ff
  j^n configuration 68ff
  two-orbit system 79ff
  two-particle states 42ff
Energy shell 342
Energy, vibration 391
Exchange potentials 103ff
Euler angles 409

Fermi matrix elements (*see* Beta decay)
Fermi surface 338
Feynman diagrams 333ff, 362ff
Flow, irrotational 397
Folded diagrams 333
Fractional parentage (*see* Coefficients of fractional parentage)
French diagrams 79ff
ft values (*see* Beta decay)

g-factor
  collective 397
  isoscalar-isovector 253ff
  neutron 219
  proton 219
  single-particle 251
G matrix 339ff
Gamma radiation (*see* Electromagnetic transition)
Gamow-Teller matrix elements (*see* Beta decay)
Gauge 178
Generalized Pauli principle 30
Gradient operator 408
Ground-state energy (*see* Binding energy)

Half life 203, 266
Hamiltonian
  first quantization 34ff
  second quantization 305ff
Hansen solutions 179
Hard-core potential 340
Harmonic oscillator 13ff
Harmonics, spherical 405ff
Hartree–Fock method 5, 337ff, 360ff
Healing property 340
Heisenberg exchange operator 104
Helmholtz equation 178ff
Hole states 286, 366ff

Impulse approximation 183
Independent-particle motion 4
Interactions
  effective 100ff, 327ff, 343ff
  empirical 76ff, 100ff, 132ff
  plots of matrix elements 123ff
  realistic 102
  residual 5, 35, 361
  schematic 102, 106ff
Internal-conversion ratio 195
Intrinsic quadrupole moment 247ff
Irreducible tensor operators 410
Irrotational flow 397

Isobaric analogue states 24, 268, 383
Isoscalar contributions 197, 204ff
Isospin 22ff
  Clebsch–Gordan coefficients 149
  reduced 75
  selection rules 198
Isospinor 25, 48
Isovector contributions 197, 204ff
Iteration procedure 132ff

j-j coupling 13
j^2 configurations 30ff
j^n configurations 62ff
  energies 68ff
  gamma transitions 221ff
  J, T values 73ff, 432
  spectroscopic factors 149ff

Kinetic energy 3, 34, 360
Kuo–Brown matrix elements 102, 121, 344ff

l-forbiddenness 353
L-S coupling 13, 85
Ladder diagram 341
Lanczos method 371ff
Landé formula 420ff
Least-squares fitting procedure 132ff
Lepton number 259
Level densities 58
Levels, single-particle 19
Lifetime 189, 203, 266
Linked diagrams 333
Long-wavelength approximation 180

m-scheme 73ff, 375
Magic numbers 3
Magnetic charge density 242
Magnetic dipole moment
  additivity relation 256ff
  isoscalar, isovector contributions 254ff
  Schmidt values 251
Magnetic multipole
  collective operator 397
  moments 241ff
  parity 188
  radial integrals 221, 435
  single-particle m.e. 216ff, 436
Magneton, nuclear 200
Majorana exchange operator 104
Maxwell equations 177
Mean lifetime 189, 203, 266
Mean square radius 17
Mesonic effects 183
Mirror nuclei 22
Mixing ratio 189ff, 202
Modified surface delta interaction (MSDI) 113ff, 434
Moments
  electric multipole 237ff
  magnetic multipole 241ff
Multishell
  matrix elements 294ff
  operators 291ff

Neutron–proton formalism 47ff
Nine-*j* symbols 404
Normal product 358
Nuclear magneton 200
Number operator 280

Occupation number formalism (*see* Second quantization)
Operators, effective 9, 327ff

Pairing 20
Pandya relation 368
Parametrization 132ff, 234
Parentage (*see* Coefficients of fractional parentage)
Parity 15, 187
Particle–hole configurations 366ff
Particle–hole conjugation 286ff
Particle–vibrator model 387ff
Pauli
  exclusion principle 2, 30
  operator 341
Permutation operators 64, 80, 424
Perturbation expansion
  Brillouin–Wigner 332
  Rayleigh–Schrödinger 333
Phases
  c.f.p. 433
  Condon–Shortley 190
  coupling order $\boldsymbol{l} + \boldsymbol{s}$ 143
  hole states 287
  mixing ratios 190
  MSDI m.e. 434
  two-body m.e. 142
Phenomenological interaction (*see* Interactions)
Pick-up reactions 157ff, 321ff
Poisson's equation 238

Polarization, core 352
Potential, nuclear (*see* Interactions)
Potential, scalar–vector 176
Projection operators 329
Proton–neutron formalism 47ff

Quadrupole moment, electric (*see* Electric quadrupole moment)
Quadrupole transition (*see* Electromagnetic transition)
Quasiparticles 357

Racah coefficients (*see* Six-j symbols)
Racah unit tensor 299
Radial matrix elements 435
Radiation field 176
Radius, nuclear 17
Random-phase approximation (RPA) 370
Rayleigh–Schrödinger expansion 333
Reaction matrix 340
Realistic and effective operators 327ff
Recoil corrections 184ff
Reduced isospin 75
Reduced matrix elements 409ff
Reduced transition probability 189
Residual interaction 5, 35, 308ff
Root mean square (RMS) deviation 137
Rotation matrix 409

Saxon–Woods potential 17, 103
Schiffer plots 123ff
Schmidt value 251
Second quantization 275ff
  angular-momentum coupled states 283ff
  comparison with first quantization 312ff
  matrix elements 294ff
  operators 280ff, 305ff, 318ff
Selection rules
  beta decay 262ff
  gamma decay 187ff, 198, 226
  moments 246
Selfconsistent potential 339
Seniority 74
Siegert's theorem 184
Single-orbit configurations (*see* j^n configurations)
Single-particle moments 249ff
Single-particle states 13ff
  energies 35, 41
  potential 34
  radial wave function 14
Single-particle transfer reactions 144ff, 321ff
Single-particle transitions
  matrix elements ($\mathcal{E}L$) 213ff, ($\mathcal{M}L$) 216ff
  operators in second quantization 280ff
  Weisskopf estimates 191ff, 199ff, 203
Single-shell matrix elements (s.s.m.e.) 295, 301ff
Single-shell states, JT values 432
Six-j symbols
  properties 401ff
  tables 428ff
Slater determinants 5, 276
Spectroscopic amplitude 168ff, 324ff
Spectroscopic factor 144ff, 321ff
Spherical Bessel function 179
Spherical components 405ff
Spherical harmonics 405ff
Spherical tensor operators 410
Spin exchange operator 104
Spinor 12, 25
Spin–orbit coupling 18
Spurious states 384ff
Standard-form expansion 292
Starting energy 342, 349
State operator 285, 289ff
Stripping reactions 148ff, 321ff
Surface-delta interaction (SDI) 106ff
  adjusted (ASDI) 140
  matrix elements 113
  modified (MSDI) 113ff
  numerical values 434
  phases 434

Tamm–Dancoff approximation (TDA) 369
Tensor operators 409ff
Three-j symbols
  properties 12, 399ff
  tables 425ff
Transfer reactions
  cross section 145, 148, 158
  single-particle 144ff, 321ff
  sum rules 162ff, 321ff
  two-particle 168ff, 324ff
Transition rates
  beta decay 259ff
  gamma decay 188ff
Triple-bar matrix elements 197
Truncation methods 376ff

Two-particle configurations 30ff, 62, 283ff
matrix elements (*see* Interactions)
transfer reactions 168ff, 324ff

U-coefficients (*see* Six-*j* symbols)
Unified model 388
Unit tensor 299

Vacuum
expectation value 279, 358
state 276, 357
Vector-coupling coefficients (*see* Three-*j* symbols)
Vector operators 410ff, 421ff
Vector potential 176
Vibrations, nuclear 388

Wave equation 178
Wave number 178
Weisskopf estimates 191ff, 199ff, 203
Wick's theorem 357ff
Width 189, 201
Wigner
coefficients (*see* Three-*j* symbols)
D-matrices 409
force 103
Wigner–Eckart theorem 409ff